ANNUAL REVIEW OF EARTH AND PLANETARY SCIENCES

ANNUAL REVIEW OF EARTH AND PLANETARY SCIENCES

VOLUME 10, 1982

GEORGE W. WETHERILL, *Editor*
Carnegie Institution of Washington

ARDEN L. ALBEE, *Associate Editor*
California Institute of Technology

FRANCIS G. STEHLI, *Associate Editor*
Case Western Reserve University

ANNUAL REVIEWS INC. 4139 EL CAMINO WAY PALO ALTO, CALIFORNIA 94306 USA

ANNUAL REVIEWS INC.
Palo Alto, California, USA

International Standard Serial Number: 0084-6597
International Standard Book Number: 0-8243-2010-7
Library of Congress Catalog Card Number: 72-82137

PRINTED AND BOUND IN THE UNITED STATES OF AMERICA

Annual Review of Earth and Planetary Sciences
Volume 10, 1982

CONTENTS

SOME RELATED ARTICLES IN OTHER *ANNUAL REVIEWS*

From the *Annual Review of Astronomy and Astrophysics,* Volume 19 (1981):

On the Theory of Coronal Heating Mechanisms, Max Kuperus, James A. Ionson, and Daniel S. Spicer

Abundances in Stellar Populations and the Interstellar Medium in Galaxies, B. E. J. Pagel and M. G. Edmunds

The Present Status of Dynamo Theory, T. G. Cowling

Accretion Discs in Astrophysics, J. E. Pringle

From the *Annual Review of Ecology and Systematics,* Volume 12 (1981):

Late Cenozoic Freshwater Fishes of North America, Gerald R. Smith

Significance of Fossils in Determining Evolutionary Relationships, Colin Patterson

From the *Annual Review of Fluid Mechanics,* Volume 14 (1982):

Vilhelm Bjerknes and His Students, Arnt Eliassen

Sediment Ripples and Dunes, Frank Engelund and Jørgen Fredsøe

Dynamics of Glaciers and Large Ice Masses, Kolumban Hutter

The Mathematical Theory of Frontogenesis, B. J. Hoskins

Dynamics of Lakes, Reservoirs, and Cooling Ponds, Jörg Imberger and Paul F. Hamblin

Gravity Currents in the Laboratory, Atmosphere, and Ocean, John E. Simpson

ANNUAL REVIEWS INC. is a nonprofit scientific publisher established to promote the advancement of the sciences. Beginning in 1932 with the *Annual Review of Biochemistry*, the Company has pursued as its principal function the publication of high quality, reasonably priced *Annual Review* volumes. The volumes are organized by Editors and Editorial Committees who invite qualified authors to contribute critical articles reviewing significant developments within each major discipline. Annual Reviews Inc. is administered by a Board of Directors, whose members serve without compensation.

1982 Board of Directors, Annual Reviews Inc.

Management of Annual Reviews Inc.

Publications

J. Tuzo Wilson.

Ann. Rev. Earth Planet. Sci. 1982. 10:1-14

EARLY DAYS IN UNIVERSITY GEOPHYSICS

J. Tuzo Wilson

Ontario Science Centre, Don Mills, Ontario M3C 1T3

The editors of this series have decided that in the introductory chapter to each volume some earth scientist should have the opportunity to describe factors which influenced his or her career. This is not easy. Few of us plan our lives. We are carried along, seizing some opportunities, missing others, making great efforts on some occasions and at other times wasting chances in abysmally stupid ways. Afterwards it is hard enough to reconstruct what happened, even more difficult to judge why.

Probably ones genes provide the dominant control. I believe I was born energetic, restless, independent and contrary-minded, sociable, yet inclined to get bored and to dash off as a loner in search of novelty. Certainly my early life reinforced these natural inclinations.

I was the eldest of three children of parents who were older than most newly married couples. They had settled in Ottawa where my father had found a job, but where they knew no one. The job soon vanished and for a time they were badly off, but they founded a happy family and soon made many friends; indeed we seemed to meet many of the most interesting people to come to Ottawa, characters as varied as Queen Victoria's youngest son, the Duke of Connaught (whom I vividly remember talking to at a children's fancy-dress party at Government House given when he was Governor General during World War I), Mrs. Emmeline Pankhurst, the suffragette leader whom my mother admired, and Vilhjalmur Stefansson, whose expeditions my father helped organize. Ottawa was then a very small city, but with splendid environs which provided an invigorating place in which to grow up.

Before describing life there I should mention my relations. I had few in Canada, but many in Britain and several times during my youth my grandmother enabled mother to bring her family or to send me alone to see them.

0084-6597/82/0515-0001$02.00

By a coincidence, the forebears of three of my four grandparents had come from the land to make money in Dundee, Edinburgh, and London during the Industrial Revolution and the expansion of trade and wealth which followed. My many elderly relatives had been brought up as members of the merchant and professional class and they led conventional and rather dull lives in comfort. Accustomed to affluence, they ineffectually frittered away their inheritance and their lives, or looked back to a happier past when they still had money and prospects.

It was fascinating to visit them, whether we stayed in large houses or shared genteel poverty, but I envied none of them. I preferred our moderate means but greater independence from convention, which weighed heavily upon the English. The lesson that I learned was that although the accumulation of wealth and power is a stimulating activity, the extent of wealth, once acquired, bears little relationship to happiness. At any rate, in my own life I sought excitement rather than fortune.

As a boy of four I well remember visiting my grandmother in Surrey during the summer of 1913. We travelled by train and steamer, saw whales and sailing ships on the Atlantic, and rode to and from the stations in horse-drawn carriages. My grandmother had a large house, garden, and woods outside of London, looked after by plenty of servants who were poorly paid by present standards, but who were nevertheless devoted and well trained.

Except when we went on a shopping expedition or to the zoo, Sundays provided the principal excitement of each week. After a long walk to church and back, a contingent of my many great-aunts and uncles arrived by the London train. The ladies wore silk dresses that swept the ground and the men, cutaway morning coats and silk top hats. Like characters from John Galsworthy's novels, they whiled away the pleasant afternoon chatting or strolling in the garden until it was time for tea and the 5:15 train back to town. A few had exciting tales to tell. Several of my grandmother's brothers had served in India and Africa as soldiers, merchants, or administrators. My Scottish grandmother could recall sailing to the Baltic Sea where my grandfather's ships had traded. Because of that, he was an Honourary Consul of the Czar in Dundee and the couple had visited the court at St. Petersburg on state occasions, such as coronations.

All was not quite as rosy as it then appeared to my young childish eyes. Both my grandfathers were long since dead and my Scottish grandmother had lost her money when her husband died. It occurred to no one that within five years the old Victorian Raj would be swept away forever and that most of the sons of those I met would be killed. Nevertheless, prewar London was a splendid sight for a boy to see with its panoply and grandeur, its confusion of horse-drawn traffic, its red-coated soldiers with bands playing, and its steam engineshissing and tooting every few minutes over the great city viaducts or through the rolling countryside.

My parents, profiting by what they had experienced and seen, grew up to take a stern and realistic view of life, which I suppose they imposed on me. I enjoyed holidaying in Europe, but preferred to live in Canada. This involvement with North America was greatly heightened by the small amount I ever learned about my other grandfather's North American lineage. It epitomized the romance and excitement that a new world made possible for those who dared. His family were descendents of Angevin Huguenots who had migrated to Virginia in the seventeenth century. I believe that their name was originally Touselle or Touzelle, later corrupted to Tuzo. They prospered, but after the American Revolution left for Bermuda taking some of their slaves with them and thence moved to Quebec City where my grandfather grew up. More adventurous than most in 1853, he joined the Hudson Bay Company as a doctor upon graduating in medicine from McGill. That summer he crossed the continent with Sir George Simpson travelling by canoe to Manitoba, on horseback to the mountains and down the Columbia River by longboat. On the prairies the party avoided hostile Indians and shot buffalo from horseback. After many adventures, he settled in Fort Vancouver, then still part of the Hudson Bay Company's territory, although now in the state of Washington.

After twenty years he visited England, married, and went back to British Columbia where my mother was born. Soon afterwards, by a mysterious transformation he became a bank manager in New York and retired to Surrey where he built the house I remember, and then died young. My mother was forced to leave medical school and wait upon her selfish mother. It was not until she was 34 and attending the first camp of the Alpine Club of Canada that she met my father and escaped. That camp was held at Moraine Lake in the Valley of the Ten Peaks, a famous beauty spot near Banff. She and others made the first ascents of the peaks then numbered one to ten. Years later the authorities changed the names of the peaks from numbers to the surnames of those who had first climbed them. Thus it is that Mount Tuzo can be seen as the conspicuous peak in the engraving on the back of the Canadian twenty dollar bill.

An odd chain of circumstances also brought my father to Banff that summer. When he was sixteen, my grandfather had died, forcing my father to learn engineering as an apprentice. He took a job in India until malaria caused him to look for work in a colder climate, and this he found in Alberta.

This background has had a considerable influence upon my outlook. Although our family never had much money, mother in particular behaved exactly as though we did and, indeed, we enjoyed many of the benefits of wealth without its debilitating effects. Thus I grew up expecting to travel, taking a good education for granted, and being used to meeting people and having lots of books. We lived in a large old house on the outskirts of Ottawa surrounded by two acres of woods and a garden in which the family grew much of its food. From an early age I hoed and weeded vegetables, tended chickens, and picked fruit. We were also expected to study hard, and to walk four miles a day to get to school and back. On weekends we swam, paddled, or skied. Later, this upbringing made geological field work seem natural and not a labor.

Since both my parents had had their own education cut short, they were determined that their children should fare better and as a consequence in 1913 mother brought back a friend from England who acted as a governess to myself and my sister. I have always felt that this early start was of great benefit to me although scarcely in the manner intended. As the youngest and smallest in my class, I sailed through school at its head. This did not make me popular. Because I was out of my own age group, I was forced at the private school to play games with older and larger boys. Thus I came to dislike all team sports and this has since saved me a great deal of time. Although naturally gregarious I became accustomed to following my own path. I learned early to distrust orthodoxy and whenever possible quietly to find a different way from the accepted.

So far from feeling that I suffered, I am grateful that I was not held back. Apart from a few sad moments as a child my life has been enormously enriched by the encouragement my upbringing gave to originality. I can well imagine that if one lives a routine existence without much travel, that clubs, lodges, and the like can greatly enrich ones life; but if one has an occupation that is varied and rewarding, one has little time for such activities.

Another advantage of the hard upbringing that my parents imposed was that when I was fifteen they dispatched me to the woods for the summer. At seventeen I had the good fortune to become a field assistant to Noel Odell, a charming man and natural leader, who had just returned from his triumphs on Mount Everest. He showed me the wonders of field geology. At ninety, he is still hale and travelling about the world from the University of Cambridge.

As a result of his inspiration, I found, after I had successfully completed my first year in honors math and physics at the University of Toronto, that I preferred field geology to laboratory physics. Much as I admired the elegance of physical theories, theories which at that time geology wholly lacked, I preferred a life in the woods to one in the laboratory. This decision caused great consternation. My professor in physics was shocked that a promising student should abandon physics, then in its heyday, in favor of geology which Ernest Rutherford had likened to postage stamp collecting. My geology professor was equally unreceptive and said that I must repeat my first year because I had not taken any elementary courses in geology and biology.

Fortunately an elderly classical physicist, Professor Lachlan Gilchrist, rescued me. He had recognized early the potential of geophysical prospecting and he was able to arrange that I could take a double major in physics and geology. Thus I became, more by accident than intent, the first student in Canada to graduate with a degree in geophysics, although men trained in physics and engineering had been making geophysical measurements in Canada two centuries before.

University life really suited me and on graduating I won a scholarship to Cambridge. I had no clear idea of what I wanted to do, but someone made the logical suggestion that I should study geophysics under Harold Jeffreys. He is a remarkable and charming man, but he was still a bachelor then and about as unworldly as a great English eccentric can be. Teddy Bullard who knew him well and who was certainly one of the brightest geophysicists of our generation once remarked to me that the only time he ever felt in the presence of genius was when he went to see Harold.

Jeffreys is courteous and affable, but aloof. A few years ago at 85, he astonished my wife on a main street in Cambridge by lifting his hat and bowing to her over the handlebars of his bicycle as he pedalled past. Jeffreys is primarily a mathematician, which I am not. He worked alone, hardly ever said anything, and had no idea of teaching. It is said that he only ever had one true graduate student, another brilliant mathematician, Keith Bullen. I took his course of lectures, but failed to understand them and spent my first year rowing, learning to fly, and travelling around Europe. My tutor was James Wordie, a canny Scottish geographer famous for having spent a winter in the Antarctic, living on nearly raw seal meat under an overturned lifeboat during one of the less successful of Shackleton's expeditions. I am indebted to him for giving me an interest in the polar regions, the idea of collecting travel books, and for introducing me to many interesting people, among them Louis S. B. Leakey, then an unknown young anthropologist working in St. John's College. If this appears to be a vague way to do graduate work, it was, but graduate study was not well organized then and the concept of having a Department of Geophysics at Cambridge was not agreed upon until after I had been at the university for a year. Even after I had left, there was still no building for geophysics or any regular courses apart from Jeffreys' and some surveying classes. Later Teddy Bullard returned from East Africa where he had been doing his Ph.D field work to establish what was to become a great department. During my stay at Cambridge, I took miscellaneous courses in geology and physics and another B.A. degree.

I returned more sophisticated but no clearer upon what to do in life and spent the next year in Ottawa working on Sudbury with Dr. W. H. Collins, then Director of the Geological Survey. From that experience I gained an affection for Collins, but I reached the conclusion that none of the theories that he or anyone else had advanced to explain the origin of the Sudbury Basin could possibly be correct. However, I couldn't think of a better one. This was part of a more general philosophical problem. My courses in physics and chemistry showed me that science could and indeed should have precise theories, but at that time geology lacked them and all right-minded geologists scoffed at the search for any. They said that this was armchair geology and that more maps were both the aim and the method of geology. So sterile a concept baffled me, but I was too stupid to accept, until I was fifty, the explanation which Frank Taylor and Alfred Wegener had advanced in the year I was born.

In my youth scarcely anyone mentioned Wegener's ideas of a mobile earth and moving continents. Only in middle age was I converted and understood why it was impossible to theorize successfully about the earth as a static body if in reality it was a mobile one. The great impediment was that geologists only studied that one quarter of the earth's surface not covered by ice or water; at that time no one had any means for exploring the great interior or the ocean floors.

Collins sensed that geophysics might be useful to geology, if only in prospecting, but he could get no money to employ a geophysicist. He recommended me to get a Ph.D. degree in geology and to return when the depression was over.

I accordingly wrote to Harvard, M.I.T., and Princeton and was accepted by all. I chose Princeton both because it offered the most money and because Professor R. M. Field said that he hoped to start teaching geophysics there. In the same year he also recruited George Woollard, an engineer from Georgia Tech, and Kelly Skeels, a mathematician from Montana who had won a Rhodes Scholarship and studied geology at Oxford, but he failed to bring anyone to Princeton to teach us geophysics.

Field had conceived the idea, at the time considered eccentric, that it might be feasible to study the ocean floor. To do this he had pursuaded the US Coast and Geodetic Survey to give a research grant of $2000 to Maurice Ewing, then a physics instructor at Lehigh University, to start this vast investigation by applying seismic methods of prospecting first to the New Jersey coastal plain and thence out to sea. He had picked the key idea and the right man, but at the time few appreciated his perception.

As a result George and I on a few weekends drove over to Bethlehem to help Ewing and learn what we could. He later said that he regarded us as his first honorary graduate students. Harry Hess arrived at Princeton as a lecturer at the same time that we did, but his interests then lay in mineralogy and petrology. What little geophysics we learned we taught ourselves with primitive magnetometers and a Geiger counter connected to a backpack loaded with 100 pounds of electric batteries.

After the first winter Professor Taylor Thom gave Skeels and me $180 each and told us to buy ourselves cars and spend the summer mapping structural geology in Montana. By buying cars for about $50 each and camping out, this proved possible. In theory Taylor supervised our work, but since he was occupied with establishing a geology summer camp at Red Lodge, 150 miles away by gravel road, Kelly and I were essentially on our own, the more so because my thesis area ranged across 50 miles of mountains varying in elevation from 4500 to 12,100 feet and his area was much the same.

The highest point of my area, Mount Hague, in the Beartooth Mountains, was rather inaccessible, but I reached it by walking, climbing, and running for the best part of three days and sleeping at night by a fire. I was rewarded by finding that the top of Mount Hague was a flat area. This I found surprising, and the discovery later influenced my ideas that North America had overridden and been uplifted by the East Pacific Rise. I had been taught that mountains were usually pointed, and that flat areas were only produced by prolonged erosion down to sea level, and hence I thought that Mount Hague must have fairly recently been uplifted 12,000 feet. The top was also completely undisturbed which supported the view of the local dude ranchers that the peak had never been climbed before. One of them was so pleased when I arrived back at his ranch dripping wet from swimming across the Stillwater River that he arranged for me to visit a remote but excellent fishing camp of a friend. To do this I had to learn to ride. This was accomplished in the simplest possible way by mounting me one morning at 7 o'clock on a docile mare with instructions to follow a trail for 25 miles and to remember to get off and pull the horse over a 9000 foot pass. In spite of a snow flurry, I managed to pick up the trail on the other side and I believe I enjoyed the trip more than the horse and was in better shape at the end of it.

After one more winter, I completed my formal education having been one of the first students in geophysics at three great universities. By today's standards my studies were extremely casual, but I had learned to work hard, taking courses which it turned out were often irrelevant, old-fashioned, and frequently wrong. Nevertheless, the very casualness encouraged independence in thought and action. I am grateful to all the fine people who helped me.

Dr. Collins kept his promise and I joined the Geological Survey of Canada for four summers of strenuous reconnaissance mapping in Nova Scotia, Quebec, and the Northwest Territories. Since I had already spent ten summers in the "bush" the work was familiar, but challenging and exciting. I was in turn frightened by rapids, exhausted by portages, and thrilled to walk out of the woods onto the Arctic "barren ground" or tundra. On some of the portages we found ancient Indian birch-bark canoes rotting and several times we paddled up to moose and caribou swimming in large lakes. I jumped out of the canoe on to one moose's back and killed another by hitting it on the head with an axe when we were short of food. Caribou are more dangerous than moose because they have sharper horns, are more lively, and when cornered they are inclined to try to climb into a canoe.

Intellectually it was also stimulating. We had some of the first air photographs and used them to pick the best routes and to extend our ground observations. The older geologists regarded this as a form of cheating, but large features such as great faults, the bedding of stratified rocks, and glacial deposits could be expeditiously mapped from aerial photos. The experience enabled some of us later to produce, largely with the aid of photographs, the first maps of the tectonic features and glacial deposits for all of Canada.

The winters were delightful too, and I had the good fortune to become engaged and happily married. For a time World War II disrupted our early married life. In 1939, I joined the Canadian Army and spent four years overseas, chiefly in technical work. I can recall two benefits. Enforced practice with reports taught me to write quickly and the end of the war provided a great opportunity.

Secretly during the war, the Canadian forces had accumulated much new equipment designed for Arctic operations. To make full use of it, in the winter of 1945–46 after the war was over, some of us organized the first and still most extensive motorized expedition ever to cross the Canadian Arctic. Forty men in ten fast, tracked-vehicles travelled 3400 miles north from railhead at Churchill, Manitoba, on Hudson Bay, across still unmapped wastes to reach the north magnetic pole on the nearest Arctic Islands, thence west over the sea ice to Coppermine, inland to Great Bear Lake, and back to railhead again near Edmonton. I travelled part of the way and spent one night in an igloo on the sea ice with some of the last Eskimos who still led traditional lives. For supper, we enjoyed seal meat stewed over stone lamps. In the evening we watched them drum-dance and slept at night in caribou-fur robes.

Many flights over the Arctic followed, searching for the last islands to be discovered outside of Antarctica. I flew as an observer on the first United States Air Force flight to the North Pole. These adventures stirred my interest in exporing remote places and nourished the broad outlook that I already possessed.

In 1946 I had to choose whether to remain in the army engineers, where I had reached the rank of colonel, return to the Survey where I was promised that I could soon be Director, enter industry, or succeed Gilchrist as Professor of Geophysics at Toronto. I sought the advice of C. J. Mackenzie, then the wise President of the National Research Council of Canada. He is the third man (with Odell and Jeffreys) who greatly influenced my career and also is still alive at the age of ninety. He advised me to go back to the university and to take no administrative job for twenty years for he predicted that I could be successful in research. I accepted his advice and he rewarded me with ample opportunities to travel and to organize projects.

The next twenty years were the most exciting in the history of the earth sciences. During that time new methods and adequate support led to great discoveries about the earth's interior and ocean floors, culminating in the scientific revolution in the earth sciences marked by the acceptance of plate tectonics. The same period saw the rapid introduction of air travel which in those days had for the geologist the great advantages that it was cheap and by propellor-driven aircraft. Although slow, rough, and noisy, those planes flew close to the ground and stopped often. Because of this, in 1950 I took four and a half days to reach Johannesburg by flying boat from London, stopping at seven places on the Mediterranean, the Nile, and the Great African lakes en route. On other trips I visited islands not often seen today, including Iceland, the Azores in the Atlantic, Wake and Canton Islands in the Pacific, and Seychelles and Cocos Islands in the Indian Ocean. In those years and subsequently, nine trips around the world and scores of other journeys have given me a glimpse, if only a superficial one, of all the continents and indeed most major regions of the earth. More valuable still have been the insights given me by men and women explaining their own discoveries. At Little America, Lloyd Berkner told me about Byrd's first expedition of which he was a member. In Moscow, Shatsky, and on the steppes north of the Caspian Sea, a party chief, explained Shatsky's great discovery of aulacogens. On the Great Barrier Reef, local biologists told me its history. In South Africa, Mrs. Plumstead, Nel, and King, all students of du Toit, showed me the geology of that country. In South America, I spent three weeks on reconnaissance flights over the Peruvian Andes which gave me a great appreciation of those mountains. During 1971 in China, I tried to explain plate tectonics to eighty sceptical Chinese geologists through the help of C.-Y. Fu, who had studied at McGill at the same time that I was a student at Toronto. Many such experiences have certainly enriched my life.

Many of these trips were made with the object of attending some international meeting or other, meetings which were necessary to bring together the results of new discoveries and which the advent of air travel greatly facilitated. The peak of activity was reached during the International Geophysical Year and this led to my most unusual journey.

It happened that the largest meeting of geophysicists during the IGY was held in Toronto. At that meeting, both of the two parts of China expressed an interest in participating officially. This was impossible. Neither would cooperate with the other, and worse still, if the matter came to a vote the United States and the USSR representatives were bound to support different governments. Inasmuch as everyone considered that their cooperation was essential, especially in the exchange of data from satellites which both the USSR and the

US were about to launch, a solution had to be found. Berkner, the leading American, and Beloussov, the senior Russian, discussed the matter amiably and, realizing that scientists could not resolve a difference which was of a political nature, agreed to temporize. They would send a committee to both parts of China to study who in fact had control of geophysics and thus to delay matters at least until a report had been submitted.

Since I was host and had just been elected president of the largest international union involved, and above all because I had no connections with nor much knowledge of China, I was appointed to be the one-man committee. I crossed Asia by the Trans-Siberian Railway, toured much of China, passed through Hong Kong, and visited Taiwan. Both sides knew of this, but treated me royally. I duly reported that the Academia Sinica in Peking controlled geophysics on the mainland and that a separate Academia Sinica in Taipei controlled activities in Taiwan and that neither had any influence or control over the other, no matter what the politicians might say. I also wrote two books in which I described the two parts of my mission, one in each book, without making any comparisons. This was a fortunate introduction to a fascinating country at a time, twenty-three years ago, when no Americans and few Westerners could visit most of it. This prestigious introduction and my own documentation of my views made me known to some Chinese. It has stood me in good stead since, and I have returned to Peking on three other occasions.

During that time and indeed throughout the twenty-eight years I spent at the University of Toronto, my research interests ranged widely.

In 1946 I again took up the study of the great faults I had seen in the field before the war. Using some of them as boundaries and combining radiometric ages of rocks then available, I outlined the major divisions of the Canadian Shield. Quite independently, Professor J. E. Gill at McGill University did the same thing simultaneously and we both arrived at similar divisions. Soon afterwards when graduate students had begun to produce more ages and when I had travelled more widely, R. D. Russell, R. M. Farquhar, and I first showed that every shield has similar major divisions and we indicated the special features which distinguish the older Archean rocks from the young Proterozoic rocks. With the help of Arthur Holmes, who provided samples, and Harry Shillibeer, we first established the existence of Archean rocks in Scotland.

Mapping large faults from aerial photographs disclosed how many ore deposits lay near intersections. I wrote a paper about the application of this to the Canadian Archean but missed concluding that important deposits should be found near Timmins, Ontario, and Thompson, Manitoba, as they have been.

I also looked at the Sudbury area again. Two undergraduate physicists who were helping me, Anita Evans and Mary James, discovered that the bedding of the sedimentary rocks within the Sudbury Basin could be traced on air photographs into the so-called granite or micropegmatite part of the Sudbury intrusion. This showed that the micropegmatite was not really part of the intrusion at all, but its baked upper cover. Unfortunately, we never published this, but the results strengthened my view that much of the Canadian Shield was made of cooked sediments. Although unorthodox at the time, it was, I realized, a return to an earlier view.

These two very capable students and several others did a remarkable job of examining the air photographs of about a million square miles of Canada. When combined with the work of others this resulted in the first glacial map of Canada, which the Geological Association of Canada published for the International Geophysical Year in 1957. This provided a splendid picture of the previously unknown effects of the ice age over vast areas. Again I failed to publish the interpretation which the work deserved.

The map showed clearly for the first time that the great ice sheets flowed away from linear divides, which corresponded to watersheds, and not as had been previously believed, from point centers. It showed how most of the central ice flowed south out of Hudson Bay across Ontario to melt in the northern United States, rather than out through Hudson Strait. It demonstrated that over the whole interior of Canada, moraines are scarce. This was unexpected because in the southern regions that had been mapped they are abundant. This distribution makes sense because moraines are dumps of debris left where the ice melts, but they should not form in regions in which the ice is actively moving. The map also showed that the carrying power of ice, like that of water, appears to increase with the velocity of motion. The marginal areas where the surface of the ground dips most steeply away from the raised Canadian Shield have been denuded of soil more than other areas where the ice motion would not have been as fast. This offered an explanation for the superb exposures around the north shores of many large Canadian lakes, such as Great Slave Lake or Lake Huron, and how it was that those pavements of rock are in such contrast to the soil-covered barrens and swamps of much of the interior of the Shield. Much else could be seen, but overall the results showed that to understand the earth one had to assemble a grand view of the earth. Individual little maps might be accurate, but they were hard to interpret.

The activities of the IGY led me away from these efforts, and when I got back to research in about 1960 I recalled the remote ocean islands I had seen and started to compile their geology. This was not easy because most of them had only been examined on chance expeditions and the results of many of these expeditions were published in obscure places. Fortunately I discovered a clue to locating them. I found by good fortune that the standard bibliographical work which anyone would use for references was inconsistent in dealing with small islands, and frequently listed different references to one island under several headings. Thus it might list different references to one island, such as Santa Maria, under these headings: Santa Maria, Azores, Portuguese Colonies, and Atlantic Ocean. If one only looked under one heading, one would miss many important references. With this knowledge, I made a better compilation of what was known about the islands. This information, combined with the work that Harry Hess and H. W. Menard were producing, provided a basis upon which to support Hess's concepts of seafloor spreading and my own ideas upon the hot-spot origin of many of these islands.

Hess's ideas, built upon a discovery by Ewing and Heezen that the rifts in the mid-ocean ridges provided sharp loci for the places where separation and parting took place, led me to think of transform faults. Once I had that idea it became obvious that the stability of the Canadian Shield (which had so long been an impediment to my acceptance of continental drift) could be understood if a few great faults had broken the surface of the earth into rigid plates. Then movements and earthquakes would be largely confined to their sharp boundaries. Menard's views also helped me to visualize the uplift of continents where they have overridden hot spots and mid-ocean ridges.

Later Kevin Burke and Bill Kidd were kind enough to include me in their more extensive investigations of hot spots. I believe that hot spots are long lived and relatively stationary and that their locations determine the lines along which continents break up. Since hot spots only move slowly relative to one another, they provide a reasonably good frame of reference to the absolute motion of continents over the interior of the earth.

By that time it was 1967, and the excitement of the recognition of the role of great faults and of the existence of plates and their relative motions (which others were working upon) had reached its peak. I considered myself fortunate to play even a small part and I could not see anything else that I could obviously do. It was an appropriate time to move on, and by chance, Claude Bissell invited me to build a new campus, Erindale, of the University of Toronto. I was doubtful about making a move, but when my wife and I went to see the 300 rolling acres with one handsome mansion beside a river she was delighted and I agreed. The twenty years of scientific research which C. J. Mackenzie had suggested and which I had enjoyed was up. I was glad to try something fresh and I realized that unless senior academics took their turn at administrative jobs, universities would suffer.

We moved into the house, where Isabel entertained 10,000 people in the next seven years. By good fortune Peter Robinson was among the very few staff already recruited and he became the Dean. Like many chemists, he was an excellent adminstrator and he had looked after all the details. We both regarded the project of designing a campus and buildings, and of recruiting 3,000 students and the staff to teach them, if not as scientific, at least as a research enterprise of another sort. We certainly tackled the problems like research projects. I also believe that in directing staff and students and in negotiating with higher authorities, the experience that I had gained from chairing large international gatherings was valuable. In both circumstances, persuasion and goodwill are the only routes to consensus.

So far from having any regrets, my wife and I found Erindale to be a delightful experience, one much more interesting to me than continuing to get deeper into the same ruts in research. One achievement which pleased me was that by recruiting the help of a psychiatrist, I was able to persuade the authorities to throw out $100,000 worth of architectural drawings and to start again with a simpler concept.

In 1974 when I had reached 65, the university regulations required that I cease to be in charge of any administration. Oddly enough the Premier of Ontario offered me the job of directing the Ontario Science Centre, which I still do.

This has been most rewarding, for the Ontario Science Centre is a novel, perhaps unique, institution. There are several small science centers in the world and many science museums, large and small. Some of the latter have some aspects of centers, but no other institution is so large and so fully a science center as this one. This requires explanation, because most people are quite confused about the differences between science museums and science centers.

A museum deals with history, and its original collections are all-important. Copies of original artifacts are of little value. In the whole field of the arts nothing can be said about the future of the arts and there are no precise mathematical principles. Thus, there are no other related institutions. In science, the situation is different. One can make a great many precise forecasts, such as times of sunrises, eclipses, or seasons, and one can state the precise principles upon which these depend and relate them to such mathematical laws as those of mechanics, gravity, and optics.

No artifacts to illustrate these principles and physical laws can be collected, but models can be built to illustrate all of them, and these, rather than collections of ancient artifacts, are the stock-in-trade of science centers. Thus, besides science museums, which hold stocks of artifacts, there are science centers which show manufactured models. Everyone knows that the best way to teach science is by doing experiments. Science centers are in effect public science laboratories and they are exceedingly popular. To point out this difference upsets many curators, but the solution lies in their own hands. Many, if not most, institutions are a mixture. It is perfectly reasonable to display what artifacts one can alongside participatory exhibits that enable the public to try scientific experiments with their own hands.

In directing such a center, a wide experience is useful. Among the staff of 250 are a wide diversity of skilled people representing more than 20 countries. Some, like teachers and craftsmen, are conservative. Others, like scientists and designers, tend to be more radical. Some, such as bookkeepers and security guards follow the rules very carefully while others, like public relations officers and writers, seek the new and the unusual. Visitors and callers come from all over the world. A few among the million and a half visitors a year get themselves and the Centre into unexpected predicaments.

Nor is a science center a static affair. Under my predecessors and myself, the Centre has staged many temporary exhibitions on all manner of subjects. The latest one, which we have agreed to hold during the summer of 1982, will illustrate with the help of many Chinese demonstrators the achievements of Chinese science and technology through 3,000 years. My past visits to China and my friends there have proved to be invaluable in arranging it. By interchanges of visits, the Chinese designers and ours are studying how best to combine the Chinese knowledge of their history and their great artifacts with a science center's desire for active demonstration and public participation.

The Centre has many other activities and opportunities. It has dispatched travelling exhibitions to hundreds of places. It produces and gives away over 50,000 copies each month of its small newspaper. It has organized the industrial manufacture of copies of its exhibits, has started a day school on the premises, and launched a society to popularize science. Its successful operation requires imagination and a good background in science, but not the intense application of original research.

I appreciate that I am extremely fortunate to enjoy so varied and interesting a life, and in concluding I wish to thank innumerable people all over the world for their help and friendship. Most have been in Canada and the United States where my colleagues have been exceedingly generous, but nearly as many are in Britain and Australia where I have also worked extensively. I hope this account illustrates how delightful and rewarding a life in earth sciences can be. I cannot help noticing that while some scientists have achieved great success by staying with the same field of research throughout their lives, others have also succeeded in changing fields and in so doing transferring ideas obtained in one situation to other quite different circumstances. Certainly my own life has been and continues at age 73 to be varied and full of excitement and happiness.

Ann. Rev. Earth Planet. Sci. 1982. 10:15-38

POLEWARD HEAT TRANSPORT BY THE OCEAN: Observations and Models[1]

Kirk Bryan

Geophysical Fluid Dynamics Laboratory/NOAA, Princeton University, Princeton, New Jersey 08540

INTRODUCTION

The role of the ocean is one of the most poorly understood elements of climate. Progress in quantitative modeling of climate can only proceed in a systematic way, when the knowledge of the oceanic general circulation is gradually raised to that of the atmospheric general circulation. Meteorologists have found that systematic studies of the heat, momentum, and vorticity budgets of the atmosphere are extremely helpful in interpreting global atmospheric data. Although oceanographers have much more meager data to work with, they have recognized the validity of this approach and have started to pursue it vigorously.

The earth surface receives most solar energy in equatorial and subtropical latitudes. Long wave radiation into space, on the other hand, is relatively uniform over the globe. A large poleward transport of heat by the earth's fluid envelope is required to maintain a steady state balance. This includes a poleward flux in the atmosphere, in the oceans, and in drifting sea ice. Long a neglected subject, poleward heat transport equatorward by ocean currents is now being given widespread attention by oceanographers. Plans are being considered for direct measurements of heat transport. In one sense, the time is not ripe to review such an active field, but the intense interest in the subject appears to call for a careful examination of previous research before embarking on new, large-scale measurements.

Much of what has been said about the global heat budget applies equally well to the global water budget. Evaporation greatly exceeds precipitation in certain latitude zones. The atmosphere carries water away from these dry zones, and the oceans are the return branch of the hydrologic cycle. Much can be learned by considering heat and water balance together. While the emphasis of this review is on the role of the oceans in the global heat balance, parallel studies of poleward water flux are included whenever possible.

OBSERVATIONS

Surface Heat and Water Balance Estimates

Empirical formulas have been developed and tested over the years to calculate the net vertical heat flux in or out of the ocean from historical weather ship data. Water flux, the difference between precipitation and evaporation, can also be estimated. In the case of water, considerable uncertainty is caused by the poor quality of precipitation measurements over the ocean. Pioneering work along these lines was conducted by Albrecht (1960), Budyko (1956, 1963), and Sverdrup (1957). Slightly higher resolution maps calculated from the raw data have been provided recently by Bunker (1976), Hastenrath & Lamb (1977), and Wyrtki (1965). Once local heat or water sources and sinks are calculated, the poleward flux can be estimated by integrating over an entire polar cap extending from the pole to a fixed latitude. Since random errors tend to cancel out in an integration over large areas, the principle uncertainty is caused by systematic errors in the balance calculations. Systematic errors are particularly troublesome in the tropics where the net heat uptake by the ocean is a small difference between net radiative heating and cooling by evaporation.

Early estimates of ocean heat transport using the surface heat balance method were made by Sverdrup (1957), Bryan (1962), Sellers (1965), and Emig (1967). Transport curves based on more recent heat and water balance estimates are shown in Figure 1. In Figure 1, the Pacific and Indian Oceans have been combined because recent work by Godfrey & Golding (1981) suggests that the flow of surface waters between the Pacific and Indian Oceans, and the area north of Australia, may be much larger than previously estimated.

As pointed out by Stommel (1980) and Hastenrath (1980), a northward heat transport in the South Atlantic is anomalous since the earth's fluid envelope as a whole must transport heat away from the equator toward the poles. Although the Hastenrath (1980) and Bunker (1976) results for poleward heat transport are qualitatively alike, there is a considerable difference in magnitude. The radiation balance in Hastenrath's (1980) results is partly calibrated with the satellite flux used by Vonder Haar & Oort (1973), while Bunker's (1976) radiation estimate is derived independently.

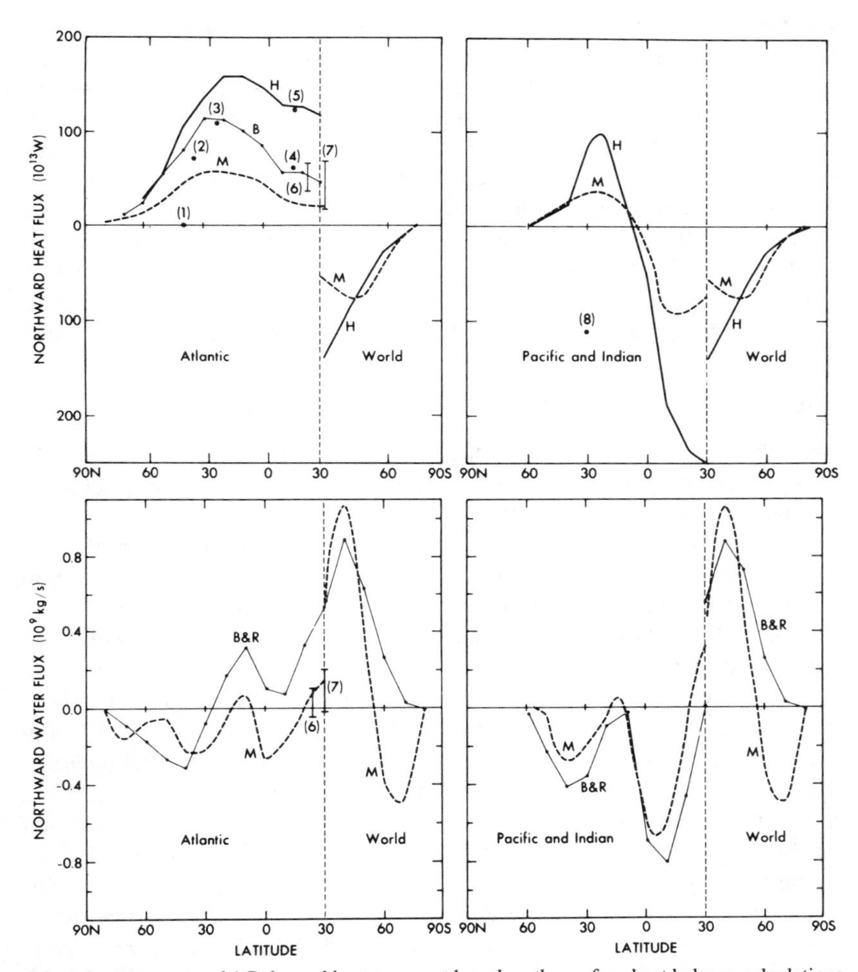

Figure 1 (*Upper panels*) Poleward heat transport based on the surface heat balance calculations of Hastenrath (1980), denoted by *H*, and Bunker (1976), denoted by *B*. Dashed line is the heat transport computed from the Bryan & Lewis (1979) model. The numbers in parentheses refer to entries in Table 1. (*Lower panels*) Poleward water transport based on the Baumgartner & Reichel (1975) atlas (*B&R*), *M* denotes the Bryan & Lewis (1979) model.

Hastenrath's (1980) heat transport curve for the Pacific is partly based on some earlier work of Wyrtki (1965) for the North Pacific. According to Hastenrath (1980), the combined Pacific and Indian Ocean export into the southern ocean is 2.5 PW (PW = petawatt = 10^{15}W) of which approximately 1.0 PW flows northward into the Atlantic. This result, which was anticipated in an earlier study by Albrecht (1960), is generally consistent with the interpretation of water-mass properties of the ocean. As shown by Reid & Lynn (1971), the North Atlantic is the site of extensive deep water formation. This deep water can be traced by its relatively high salinity as it flows at depth into the southern ocean. Once in the southern ocean it turns eastward and flows into the Indian and Pacific Oceans, gradually losing its distinctive water mass properties. The outflow of cold deep water must be compensated by an inflow. Assume for the moment that the inflow takes place near the surface in water 10°C warmer than the deep water outflow. The production of deep water in the North Atlantic is estimated by Worthington (1976) to be approximately 10 megatons/s (10^{10}kg/s). The heat capacity of water is about 4000 J/kg°C. Therefore, the implied heat gain by the Atlantic at the latitude of the Cape of Good Hope is

$$10^{10}\ \text{kg/s} \times 10^\circ\text{C} \times 4000\ \text{J/kg}^\circ\text{C} = 0.4\ \text{PW}.$$

Since there is no way to assign the difference in temperature between the incoming and outgoing water with confidence, this calculation only serves to illustrate the magnitudes involved.

Except along the rim of the Arctic Ocean, the poleward transport of water by rivers is relatively inconsequential. The atmosphere tends to transport moisture away from dry subtropical areas both toward the equator and toward the poles. The return flow required for a steady state is largely within the ocean, since the largest rivers of the world, the Amazon and the Congo, flow in an east-west direction. The surface water balance of the globe has been studied by Drozdov (1964) at the Central Geophysical Observatory in Leningrad. Similar calculations have been compiled into an atlas by Baumgartner & Reichel (1975) at the University of Munich. The Munich results are shown as water transport curves in Figure 1. As pointed out previously, a major source of uncertainty is the estimation of precipitation over the oceans. Precipitation measurement from ships in a strong wind is extremely difficult. The results from the Baumgartner & Reichel (1975) atlas indicate an equatorward flow of fresh water in the ocean in both the North Atlantic and North Pacific. Equatorward flow is also indicated in the southern ocean poleward of 30°S. The Congo and the Amazon both flow into the equatorial Atlantic, but the Pacific and Indian Oceans have a combined equatorial area of excess precipitation much greater than the Atlantic. An equatorial input of excess water is therefore greatest in the Pacific and Indian Ocean. Baumgartner & Reichel (1975) indicate net water transport from the northern to the southern hemisphere. This is reasonable from a climatic standpoint, since the intertropical convergence areas in the atmosphere lie north of the equator. Low-level winds in the atmosphere tend to transport moisture from the southern hemisphere into the intertropical convergence regions. The ocean acts as a return branch for the fresh water flow southward across the equator.

Poleward Flux Estimates Based on Hydrographic Data

Poleward heat flux across an east-west vertical section extending across an entire ocean basin is (Bennett 1978)

$$\mathrm{HT} = \int_{\lambda_2}^{\lambda_1} \int_{-H(\lambda)}^{0} \rho c_p v \theta \, \mathrm{d}z \, a \cos\phi \, \mathrm{d}\lambda, \tag{1}$$

where v is the meridional velocity and θ is the potential temperature, ϕ is the latitude, and a is the radius of the earth. λ is longitude and H is the total depth. If the abundant velocity and temperature measurements available for the atmosphere were also available for the oceans, the evaluation of the right hand side of (1) would be straightforward. The advantage of a direct approach based on (1) over the heat balance method is obvious, since it allows an examination of the actual mechanisms of heat transport in the ocean and provides a much more complete guide in constructing models of ocean circulation. Field experiments are in the planning stage to make extensive measurements across sections that will allow a reliable evaluation of HT. All attempts to use existing data to evaluate (1) must rest on the implicit assumption that most of the variability of the thermocline in extratropical areas is due to mesoscale eddies and still smaller scale features. The large-scale structure is assumed to be sufficiently steady so that single sections taken over a short period of time are representative of the time-averaged state. Comparisons of hydrographic sections taken by the METEOR (Wüst & Defant 1936) with more recent data provide some support for this assumption.

A pioneering calculation of heat transport using hydrographic data was carried out by Jung (1955). In a later study by Bryan (1962) the method was worked out in more detail to avoid an arbitrary choice of geostrophic reference level. Assuming hydrostatic balance, the pressure may be expressed as a function of surface elevation and the density structure as

$$p(z) = g\rho_s\eta + \int_{z}^{0} \rho g \, \mathrm{d}z \tag{2}$$

where η is the surface elevation and ρ_s is the density at the surface. The linearized steady-state equation of horizontal motion is

$$2\Omega \sin\phi \, \mathbf{k} \times \mathbf{v}\rho_0 = -g\nabla\left(\eta\rho_s + \int_{z}^{0} \rho \, \mathrm{d}z\right) + \partial_z \boldsymbol{\tau}^z \tag{3}$$

where $\mathbf{v}$ is the horizontal velocity vector, Ω is the rotation of the earth and

$$\boldsymbol{\tau}^z = \mathbf{i}\, \tau^{\lambda z} + \mathbf{j}\tau^{\phi z}$$

is the stress due to the vertical transfer of momentum in the planetary boundary layer by turbulence. On the basis of (3), the meridional component of velocity may be written as three components:

$$v = v_1 + v_2 + v_3, \tag{4}$$

$$v_1 = c_1 (\lambda, \phi), \tag{5}$$

$$v_2 = \frac{g}{2\Omega \sin \phi \cos \phi \rho_0 a} \partial_\lambda \int_z^0 \rho \, dz + c_2(\lambda, \phi), \tag{6}$$

$$v_3 = -\frac{1}{2\Omega \sin \phi \, \rho_0} \partial_z \, \tau^{\lambda z} + c_3(\lambda, \phi). \tag{7}$$

If the constants c_2 and c_3 are chosen so that

$$\int_{-H}^0 \rho_0(v_2, v_3) \, dz = 0, \tag{8}$$

all the information on the total mass transport in the meridional direction is carried in c_1 in (5).

Let ($\bar{\ }$) denote a vertical average and ($\hat{\ }$) the departure, so that

$$v = \bar{v} + \hat{v}, \tag{9}$$

$$\theta = \bar{\theta} + \hat{\theta}. \tag{10}$$

The integral (1) may be written as

$$\mathrm{HT} = \int_{\lambda_2}^{\lambda_1} \int_{-H(\lambda)}^0 \rho c_p (\bar{v}\bar{\theta} + \hat{v}\hat{\theta}) \, dz \cos \theta \, a \, d\lambda. \tag{11}$$

Hydrographic data provide a basis for determining $\bar{\theta}$ and $\hat{\theta}$. The problem is to determine the corresponding velocity components. Assuming that (2) is a reasonable approximation, $\hat{v}$ can be evaluated from (6) and (7) with the assumption that the wind-drift velocity component is confined to the upper mixed layer. The estimation of $\bar{v}$ is a classical problem in observational oceanography and there is no universally accepted method of determining it except by direct in situ measurements of velocity.

An indirect approach to estimating $\bar{v}$ is to vertically integrate (3) and apply the curl$_z$ operator. If bottom friction and the effect of pressure forces on bottom topography are neglected

$$\bar{v} = \frac{a}{2\Omega \cos \phi \, H \, \rho_0} \mathbf{k} \cdot \nabla \times \tau^z \big|_{z=0}, \tag{12}$$

which is the classic Sverdrup (1947) transport formula. Bryan (1962) and Bennett (1978) use (12) to estimate $\bar{v}$ along east-west sections for which good hydrographic data are available. Transport in the western boundary current obeys a much more complicated dynamics. In a basin closed on the northern or southern end the net flow through an entire east-west section is approximately zero. Bryan (1962) and Bennett (1978) assume that all the Sverdrup transport over the ocean interior is balanced in the western boundary current. A certain arbitrariness enters into the choice of width of the western boundary current. Bennett (1978) makes separate poleward heat flux computations for a reasonable range of western boundary current widths. If the width of the boundary current is very narrow, the current may be confined to shallow water and the $\bar{\theta}$ assigned to the western boundary current will be correspondingly large. On the other hand, if the western boundary current is wide and extends to deep water, $\bar{\theta}$ is apt to be close to its normal mid-ocean value. In that case, the contribution of $\bar{v}\bar{\theta}$ over the whole section will be small.

Heat transport values calculated by Bryan (1962) and Bennett (1978) may be identified in Figure 1 by the key in Table 1. Their calculations were based on the METEOR (Wüst & Defant 1936) and the IGY (Fuglister 1960) sections, and various wind-stress estimates. Bryden & Hall (1980) recently made a similar poleward heat flux calculation, but with a unique advantage due to the special geometry of the Atlantic at 24°N. Niiler & Richardson (1973) monitored the transport of the Florida Current and found it to be equal to the total Sverdrup transport across the entire 24°N section (Leetmaa et al 1977). The Florida Current runs in a confined channel less than 1500 meters deep, so a value of $\bar{\theta}$ can be assigned to it with reasonable confidence. In the remainder of the section at 24°N, the ocean is quite deep with a nearly uniform vertically averaged temperature. Thus at 24°N in the North Atlantic the contribution of the $\bar{v}\bar{\theta}$ term in the heat transport integral (11) is approximately equal to the transport of the Florida Current times the difference in $\bar{\theta}$ between the deep ocean and the channel between Florida and the Bahamas. With some of the uncertainty in the $\bar{v}\bar{\theta}$ term eliminated, the major source of error in heat transport at 24°N must then be assigned to the $\hat{v}\hat{\theta}$ term. Since this term is calculated from a single hydrographic section, $\hat{v}\hat{\theta}$ may or may not be representative of time-averaged conditions.

Table 1 Estimates of heat transport made on the basis of direct calculations from hydrographic sections

	Author	Latitude	Ocean	Data source	Northward heat flux (10^{15} W)
1[a]	Bryan (1962)	40°N	A	IGY 10/57	0.0
2	Bryan (1962)	36°N	A	IGY 5/59	0.7
3	Bryden & Hall (1980)	24°N	A	IGY 10/57	1.1
4	Bryan (1962)	16°S	A	Meteor 5/26	0.6
5	Bryan (1962)	16°S	A	IGY 4/57	1.2
6	Bennett (1978)	24°S	A	IGY 10/58	0.3–0.6
7	Bennett (1978)	32°S	A	IGY 5/59	0.2–0.7
8	Bryan (1962)	32°N	P	NORPAC 8/55	−1.1

[a]Indices in the first column identify points in Figure 1.

As mentioned previously, one of the key advantages of direct in situ calculations of poleward heat transport is that they allow some insight into the mechanisms involved. All of the studies using the geostrophic method agree that the main contribution to poleward heat transport is made by overturning in the meridional-vertical plane. Zonally averaged Ekman flux and the thermohaline circulation are both important. Except at high latitudes, the temperature contrast between surface and deep water is much greater than horizontal differences along a typical east-west section. Therefore a meridional overturning is much more effective in transporting heat than a horizontal gyre of similar strength.

Examining the poleward heat flux calculations denoted by points 1–7 in Figure 1, we see a good deal of scatter. A measurement at 40°N based on an October section shows no heat flux at all, while measurements at 16°S show a factor of two difference between METEOR and IGY data taken in different seasons of the year. Bennett's (1978) measurements denoted by 6 and 7 show a considerable spread based on a range of widths for the western boundary current needed to balance the Sverdrup interior flow. A major source of uncertainty is the contribution of mesoscale eddies. The IGY and METEOR sections do not have enough spatial resolution to resolve mesoscale eddies, and even if the resolution was good enough a single synoptic section could not be expected to provide a statistically reliable measure of the eddy transport. Large amplitude mesoscale eddies are concentrated near major features like the Gulf Stream, Kuroshio, and the Antarctic Circumpolar Currents. While mesoscale eddies could play an important role in heat transport at 40°N in the North Atlantic, Bryden & Hall (1980) indicate that eddies are a negligible contributor to heat transport at 24°N.

Note that the direct calculations all show northward heat transport in the South Atlantic. With the exception of point 5 in Figure 1, there is a better agreement with Bunker's (1976) transport curve than Hastenrath's. However, the errors involved in both methods are such that this apparent agreement is probably not significant. In the Pacific the single measurement by Bryan (1962) indicates a paradoxical southward transport at 30°N. In this case mesoscale eddies along the Kuroshio may play an important role in compensating the heat transport by the large-scale circulation, but judgement must be reserved until additional data are available.

The physical interpretation of salt and net water transport requires some explanation. In a steady state the salinity field of the ocean has no significant sources or sinks. In a closed basin the total transport of salt would therefore be approximately zero. Let $\{\ \}$ denote an average across an entire λ-z section, and $(\ )^+$ denote a departure for the average over the section. Then

$$v = \{v\} + v^+ \quad \text{and} \quad s = \{s\} + s^+ \tag{13}$$

where s denotes the salinity. The total poleward flux of salt through a section is then proportional to $\{vs\}$, where

$$\{vs\} = \{v\}\{s\} + \{v^+s^+\}. \tag{14}$$

In a steady state, the net poleward salinity transport is nearly zero in a closed basin, so that

$$\{v\} = -\{v^+s^+\} / \{s\}. \tag{15}$$

The net transport of water through a section is therefore proportional to minus the "apparent" salt transport divided by the mean salinity.

Bennett (1978) estimated water flux and his results are shown in Figure 1. In the South Atlantic, Bennett's (1978) results show a significantly lower influx of water into the Atlantic from the southern ocean than the Baumgartner & Reichel (1975) atlas indicates.

Bennett (1978) calculated an apparent salt flux for the South Pacific and Indian Ocean as well. His results for sections in the vicinity of 30°S are shown in Table 2. He carried out calculations for the SCORPIO 28°S section (Reid 1973) and two sections taken during the Indian Ocean Expedition at 32°S. Bennett's (1978) flux calculations indicate a large spread due to uncertainty of the choice of western boundary current width. In the Indian Ocean, Bennett's (1978) results in Table 2 seem to show a heat and water flux nearly opposite to that determined by surface-balance calculations. Meteorological data indicate that the Indian Ocean as a whole is a region of strong surface heating and high evaporation, and yet Bennett's (1978) calculation suggests an import rather than export of heat for the Indian Ocean, and a net outflow of water rather than an inflow. Furthermore, there is a tendency for Bennett's (1978) transport results for the South Pacific and Indian Ocean to cancel when summed. Bennett (1978) noted the difficulty of interpreting his results and suggested two factors; (*a*) seasonal variations may make his sections taken

Table 2 Fluxes at 30°S

Author	Indian	Pacific	Atlantic	Total
	Northward Heat Transport (10^{15}W)			
Hastenrath (1980)	−0.49	−1.92	1.15	−1.26
Bennett (1978)	−0.46, 1.74	−1.16, −0.17	0.16, 0.68	—
Model[a]	−0.67	−0.07	0.18	−0.55
	Northward Water Transport (10^9kg/s)			
Baumgartner & Reichel (1975)	0.5	−0.5	0.6	0.6
Bennett (1978)	−0.5, 0.1	0.2, 0.5	0, 0.2	—
Model	0.1	0.3	0.2	0.5

[a]Model refers to case III of Bryan & Lewis (1979).

during the Austral autumn and winter unrepresentative, and (*b*) mesoscale eddies may be important enough at 32°S to seriously affect the heat and water transport. Recent work by Godfrey & Golding (1981) suggests another important factor. Based on a study of the dynamical topography of the Indian Ocean, they inferred that the net transport from the Pacific to the Indian Ocean north of Australia is an order of magnitude larger than previously estimated. If this is true, the assumption of closed basins on which Bennett's (1978) calculations for the Pacific and Indian Oceans depend may no longer apply.

A recent development has been the application of inverse theory to the heat transport problem. Again the poleward heat flux is calculated from hydrographic sections using geostrophy and wind-stress estimates to calculate the $\hat{v}\hat{\theta}$ component in the poleward heat flux integral (11). The difference lies in the way in which $\bar{v}$ is determined along the east-west section. The method rests on the assumption that water mass properties in the main thermocline are conserved along trajectories and the thermocline is in equilibrium. Consider a large volume of thermocline bounded by two surfaces of constant temperature or salinity. Conservation of heat and salinity requires that

$$\oint \int_{z}^{z+\Delta z} \mathbf{n} \cdot (\bar{\mathbf{v}} + \hat{\mathbf{v}})\, \mathrm{d}z\, \mathrm{d}l = 0 \tag{16}$$

if no mixing through the isothermal or isohaline surfaces takes place. In (16), z and $z + \Delta z$ are the vertical coordinates of the isothermal or isohaline surfaces and $\mathbf{n}$ is the normal vector to the lateral boundary of the volume.

If the path of integration coincides with a line of hydrographic stations, (16) may be written in discrete form as

$$\sum_{i=1}^{I} \mathbf{n} \cdot (\bar{\mathbf{v}}_i + \hat{\mathbf{v}}_i)\, \Delta z_i\, \Delta l_i = 0.$$

The index i refers to consecutive pairs of hydrographic stations. If we consider other volumes above and below, we obtain the series of equations

$$\sum_{k}^{K} \sum_{i}^{I} \mathbf{n} \cdot (\bar{\mathbf{v}}_i + \hat{\mathbf{v}}_{ik})\, \Delta z_{i,k}\, \Delta l_i = 0,$$

where $\hat{\mathbf{v}}_{ik}$ can be determined at each level for each station pair, and $\Delta z_{i,k}$ depends on the distribution of water-mass properties. The size of K depends on how small the increments of temperature and salinity are chosen to be. In general, making K large does not introduce more independent information since adjacent layers will behave in a nearly parallel manner. In most cases $K << I$; that is, the number of independent water-mass properties to be conserved will be less than the number of pairs of hydrographic stations surrounding the volume. Thus, $\bar{\mathbf{v}}_i$ will be underdetermined. Inverse theory (Wunsch 1978) is a formal procedure for dealing with underdetermined systems.

The equations are satisfied by a large number of solutions. Inverse theory provides a method for selecting a particular solution which satisfies reasonable constraints, such as smoothness, and proximity to a "first-guess" solution.

Results based on inverse theory are shown in Figure 2 for the North and South Atlantic. The NA-1A solution is one in which the bottom velocity is set to zero, and the total solution is similar but includes the effect of Ekman drift. At 24°N the total transport of 30×10^9kg/s measured by Niiler & Richardson (1973) was used by Roemmich (1980) as an additional constraint. In that case the method is closely parallel to that used by Bryden & Hall (1980). The poleward heat flux estimate is essentially the same. Figure 2 shows that poleward heat transport in the North Atlantic agrees with the heat balance results in mid-latitudes, but indicates a precipitous drop at high latitudes. In the light of observations that show the Norwegian Current transports warm water to very high latitudes, this feature does not look realistic.

Results for the South Atlantic computed by Fu (1981) from the IGY and METEOR data are generally consistent with the heat balance results of Bryan (1962) and Bennett (1978). Northward heat flux is indicated throughout the entire Atlantic.

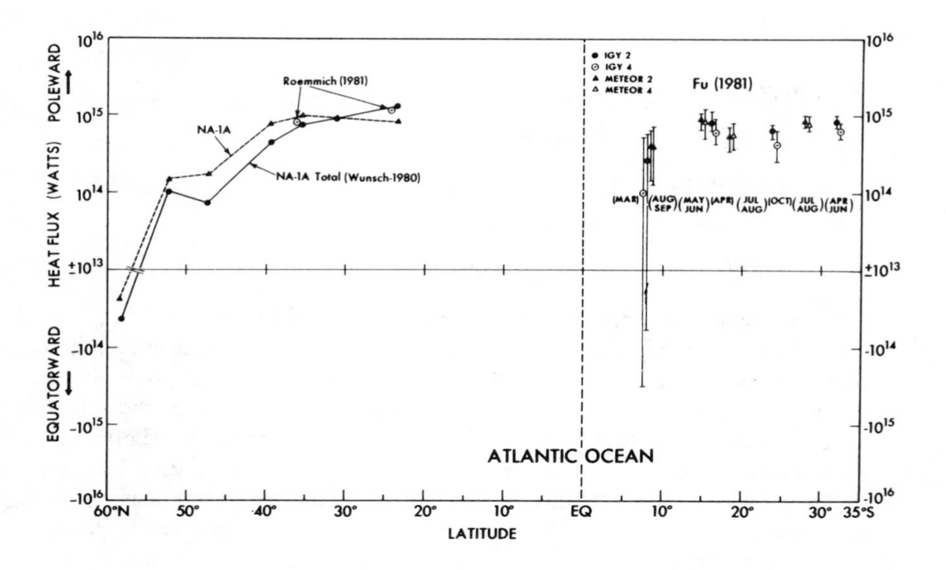

Figure 2 Poleward heat transport computed from hydrographic sections for the Atlantic Ocean using the inverse method. On the right IGY 2 and IGY 4 refer to a first-guess level of a meridional motion of 2000 and 4000 db, respectively. Redrawn from Wunsch (1980) and Fu (1981).

THE COMPONENTS OF POLEWARD HEAT BALANCE

Consider a basin closed at one end so that the net flow through an east-west section is small enough to be neglected. Exchanging the order of integration in (1), the poleward heat transport is

$$\mathrm{HT} = \int_{-H}^{0} \int_{\lambda_1(z)}^{\lambda_2(z)} \rho_0 c_p \, v\theta \cos \phi a \, \mathrm{d}\lambda \, \mathrm{d}z \,, \tag{17}$$

where v and θ are the meridional velocity and the potential temperature of sea water, respectively. H is the depth of the basin, and λ_1 and λ_2 are the western and eastern boundaries, which are functions of depth. The integral becomes slightly more complicated when the bottom is split into several smaller basins.

Let $(\bar{\ })$ be a time average over a year and $(\ )'$ the deviation from this average. Let $[\ ]$ be the zonal average at any depth and $(\ )^*$ the deviation from this average. We can express v and θ as

$$v = [\bar{v} + v'] + (\bar{v} + v')^*, \tag{18}$$

$$\theta = [\bar{\theta} + \theta'] + (\bar{\theta} + \theta')^*. \tag{19}$$

The time average of the poleward heat transport is simply

$$\overline{\mathrm{HT}} = \int_{-H}^{0} \rho_0 c_p \, \overline{[v\theta]} \, (\lambda_2 - \lambda_1) \cos \phi a \, \mathrm{d}z \,. \tag{20}$$

The components of $\overline{[v\theta]}$ are

$$\begin{aligned} \overline{[v\theta]} &= [\bar{v}][\bar{\theta}] && \text{(overturning)} \\ &+ [\bar{v}^*\bar{\theta}^*] && \text{(gyre effect)} \\ &+ \overline{[v'][\theta']} && \text{(``seasonal overturning'')} \\ &+ \overline{[v^{*\prime}\theta^{*\prime}]} && \text{(transient eddies).} \end{aligned} \tag{21}$$

Let us consider the individual components on the right-hand side of (21) in turn. The first term represents the overturning in the meridional plane averaged over one year. For example, a northward heat transport can take place due to the northward movement of warm surface waters compensated by the southward movement of cold deep water. The second term represents the effect of horizontal correlations between velocity and temperature in standing features of the ocean circulation. As an example, a warm Gulf Stream compensated by a cold eastern boundary current would give a positive contribution to this term.

The third term is like the first in that it represents the effect of meridional overturning. In this case it is not the time-averaged overturning of the permanent circulation, but fluctuations that are correlated with large-scale changes in ocean surface temperature. Since such large-scale temperature and velocity fluctuations are apt to be of low frequency, the term has been tentatively labeled "seasonal." The final term represents the effect of correlations between deviations from both zonal and time-means. This term has been identified with transient eddies.

The most reliable in situ measurements of heat transport are those at 24°N in the Atlantic where the transport of the western boundary current can be measured directly. Synoptic measurements, however, do not provide definite information on the relative contribution of time-averaged components of velocity to heat transport. The measurements of Bryden & Hall (1980) and Roemmich (1980) both suggest that large-scale overturning is the dominant mechanism, and that mesoscale eddies are unimportant at this particular latitude. Until additional data are available, more insight can be gained by examining the predictions of models. The breakdown of poleward heat transport in a water-mass model is shown in the final section.

MODELS OF OCEAN CIRCULATIONS

The Role of Ekman Transport and Simplified Models

The key to formulating a simple model is to isolate essential factors and exclude peripheral phenomena. In the case of ocean heat transport, both surface wind drift and deep ocean circulation are involved. The problem of constructing a simple model of ocean heat transport is essentially the same as finding a simple model of the ocean circulation. Experience has shown, however, that it is not easy to formulate mathematical models of ocean circulation that can be solved without resorting to numerical methods.

In the previous section, overturning in the meridional plane was identified as a mode of poleward heat transport of the time-averaged ocean circulation and it appears to be a dominant mechanism at low latitudes. The overturning circulation has two components: one associated with the Ekman transport and the other a geostrophically balanced component. The total wind-driven overturning can be determined by integrating with respect to depth and longitude. Let ET be the total northward Ekman transport across an ocean basin, then

$$\mathrm{ET} = -\int_{\lambda_1}^{\lambda_2} \left.\frac{\tau^{\lambda z}}{2\Omega \sin \phi}\right|_{z=0} a \cos \phi \, d\lambda . \tag{22}$$

The Ekman transport is confined to the planetary boundary layer. It will be effective in transporting heat if warm surface waters carried poleward are compensated by a return flow of colder deep water. The amount of heat that could be transported in this way depends on the precise temperature of the return flow. A maximum estimate of poleward heat flux due to meridional overturning by wind may be obtained by assuming that the return flow takes place in the cold deep water below the main thermocline.

To illustrate this point, the zonally averaged surface temperature of the globe (Sellers 1965) minus a representative temperature of the ocean deep water is shown in Figure 3(*a*). Meridional Ekman transport for the entire globe is shown in Figure 3(*b*) from some recent stress calculations by S. Hellerman

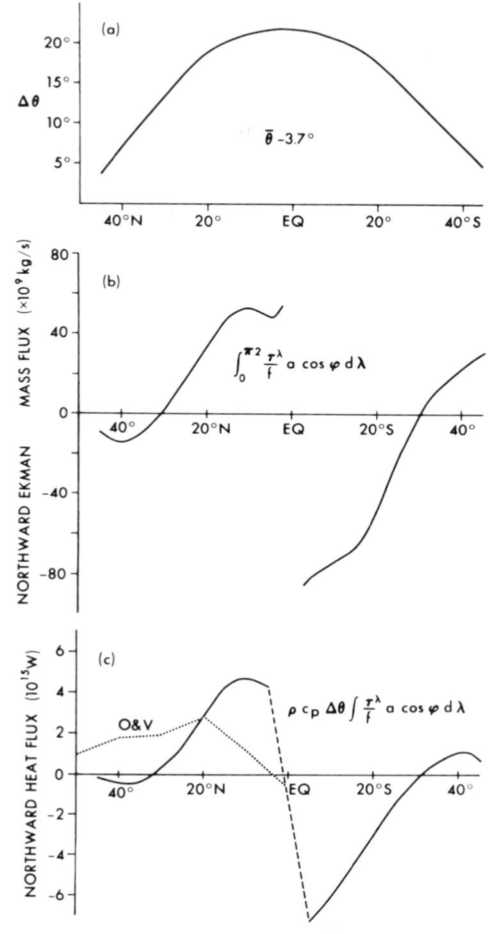

Figure 3 A schematic diagram illustrating heat transport by meridional Ekman transport. (*a*) Zonally averaged surface temperature for the globe minus 3.7°C (*b*) Northward Ekman transport in the World Ocean. (*c*) The product $\rho c_p \Delta\theta \times$ ET. *O & V* refers to an estimate of northward heat transport in the oceans by Oort & Vonder Haar (1976). The ordinate in (*b*) and (*c*) is minus the integral shown in the figure.

(in preparation). In the trade wind region an Ekman transport of over 40 megatons/s (40×10^9kg/s) is indicated. If we assume that this meridional transport is compensated by deep return flow, the computed heat transport will be very large and poleward at low latitudes. A smaller equatorward component exists at higher latitudes under the westerlies.

The heat transport curve in Figure 3(*c*) corresponds to a simple model in which all the upwelled water at the equator originates directly from the deep water. A model of this kind has been proposed by Broecker et al (1978) to explain observations of bomb-produced ^{14}C in surface waters. Dividing the divergence of heat indicated by Figure 3(*c*) by the total area of the ocean between 5°N and 5°S, an average surface-heating rate of 300 W/m^2 would be required. Since the solar constant is approximately 1375 W/m^2, this simple model would imply that a very large fraction of incident radiative energy was being directly absorbed by the ocean. On the other hand, Bunker's (1976) heat balance maps show that surface heating of the tropical only exceeds 100 W/m^2 in a few places of intense upwelling. Except where surface temperature is low due to upwelling, the ocean is a rather poor solar collector due to cooling by evaporation. Over wide areas of the equatorial, ocean surface heating calculated by standard formulas is less than 50 W/m^2. On this basis we cannot pin down the precise depth from which the upwelled water comes, but we can reject as unlikely the idea that it all comes from below the thermocline.

Simplified models of the ocean have been developed by Webster & Lau (1977), Lau (1978), and Bye (1979) to study heat transport. These models are able to incorporate an essentially linear mechanism like Ekman transport, but have difficulty incorporating the effects of the subtropical gyres and the thermohaline circulation.

Three-Dimensional Models

While progress has been slow in formulating simple analytic solutions for the ocean circulation, some success has been achieved by numerical methods. The numerical models are analogous to the general circulation models developed for the atmosphere. The entire volume of the ocean or a single basin is subdivided into cells typically 100–200 km on a side and a few hundred meters in depth. If an attempt is made to resolve the mesoscale eddies, the horizontal dimensions of the cells must be much less. Conservation equations for momentum, heat, and salinity are applied to each cell. The velocity and water-mass properties of each cell change because of fluxes from the surface, horizontal, and vertical advection, and because of internal mixing. The parameterization of small-scale mixing and convection are important aspects of the model. Ideally, the design of the parameterization of mixing should be simple and in accord with observations in the ocean itself.

Let $\mathbf{v}$ be the horizontal velocity vector and w be the vertical velocity. Let

$$(\dot{\ }) = \partial_t (\ ) + \mathbf{v}\nabla (\ ) + w\, \partial_z ,$$

where ∇ is the horizontal gradient vector.

The equations of motion in the horizontal plane may be written

$$\dot{\mathbf{v}} + \mathbf{k}\, 2\Omega \sin \phi \times \mathbf{v} + \rho_0^{-1} \nabla p = \mathbf{F}, \tag{23}$$

where $\mathbf{F}$ represents Reynolds' stresses due to motions unresolved by the model. Temperature and salinity are the other predicted quantities and

$$\begin{Bmatrix} \dot{\theta} \\ \dot{s} \end{Bmatrix} = \begin{Bmatrix} Q \\ \sigma \end{Bmatrix} \tag{24}$$

where Q and σ represent the mixing of heat and salinity by smaller scales in analogy with $\mathbf{F}$. The remaining governing equations are diagnostic relations needed to relate w and p from the predicted variables:

$$\rho g + \partial_z p = 0 \tag{25}$$

$$\nabla \cdot \mathbf{v} + \partial_z w = 0 \tag{26}$$

$$\rho - G(\theta, s, p) = 0, \tag{27}$$

where (25) is the hydrostatic approximation and (26) and (27) are the continuity equation and the equation of state for seawater respectively.

It is well known that transient cyclones dominate heat transport in the atmosphere. It is natural to ask if mesoscale eddies do not play a similar role with respect to poleward heat transport by ocean currents. Very few long-term measurements exist which would allow a direct answer to this question. The calculation by Semtner & Mintz (1977) is one of the few model studies that can provide some theoretical guidance.

The Semtner & Mintz (1977) model is a mid-latitude ocean driven by wind and differential heating with governing equations essentially similar to (23)–(27). The spatial resolution of the numerical computation is fine enough to allow the formation of a realistic western boundary current and mesoscale eddies.

As shown by Mintz (1979), the Semtner & Mintz (1977) calculations indicate that mesoscale eddies may not be important everywhere, but they can be very important in the vicinity of sharp temperature discontinuities. It is difficult for mesoscale eddies to play as large a role in poleward heat flux as cyclones do in the atmosphere because of their relatively small size. However, this does not imply that eddies may not play a very large indirect role by their dynamical effects on large-scale, steady circulations (Holland 1977).

There are now several model studies of the World Ocean circulation, including pioneering studies by Takano (1975), Cox (1975), and Andreyev et al

(1976). A review of these studies is given in Bryan (1979). To study many aspects of the ocean circulation it is not necessary to treat heat and salinity separately. Frequently the effects of heat and salinity are lumped together in a single variable which is a measure of buoyancy. For a climate model, however, this treatment is not satisfactory. Salinity has an approximate 30% contribution to buoyancy in low latitudes, and it is the dominant factor in polar regions. Its separate role in large-scale air-sea interaction is an important, if often neglected, factor. A model by Bryan & Lewis (1979) is almost unique in that it was designed with the climate problem in mind. Temperature and salinity are treated separately and the model provides a crude simulation of the formation of the major water masses of the World Ocean.

In the Bryan & Lewis (1979) model a simple closure scheme is used to represent small scale mixing. **F** in (23) and Q in (24) are specified as

$$\mathbf{F} = A_{\mathrm{HM}}(\nabla^2\mathbf{V} + \ldots) + A_{\mathrm{VM}}\,\partial_z\partial_z\,\mathbf{V} \tag{28}$$

$$Q = A_{\mathrm{HH}}\,\nabla^2\theta + \partial_z\,A_{\mathrm{VH}}\,\partial_z\theta \tag{29}$$

and σ is specified in the same way as Q. Several terms in (28) that are only important at high latitudes are not written out explicitly. Values of the closure parameters are given in Table 3 along with information about the lateral and vertical resolution. The vertical diffusion values in Table 3 are for stable stratification only. In the case of unstable stratification a simple convective adjustment procedure restores neutral stratification while conserving heat and salinity. The finite-difference model is similar to that of Semtner & Mintz (1977), but the resolution is much coarser. In the final stages of the integration the horizontal resolution is about $2\frac{1}{2}^\circ \times 2\frac{1}{2}^\circ$ of latitude and longitude. The high resolution calculations are referred to as case III. The model has 12 levels that are placed to resolve the upper thermocline in some detail with only a minimum of levels in the deep water.

Table 3 Parameter[a]

Name	Symbol	Low resolution (m^2s^{-1})	High resolution (m^2s^{-1})
E-W spacing	$\Delta\lambda$	$\pi/32$	$\pi/64$
N-S spacing	$\Delta\phi$	$\pi/38$	$\pi/76$
Lateral diffusion coefficient of heat	A_{HH}(upper)	2.5×10^3	10^3
and salt	A_{HH}(lower)	0.5×10^3	0.5×10^3
Lateral viscosity	A_{HM}	8.0×10^5	10^5
Vertical diffusion coefficient of heat	A_{VH}(upper)	0.3×10^{-4}	0.3×10^{-4}
and salt	A_{VH}(lower)	1.3×10^{-4}	1.3×10^{-4}

[a]Important constants used in a global ocean model by Bryan & Lewis (1979). Where upper and lower values are indicated, a smooth analytical function of depth connects values in the upper thermocline with those indicated for deep water. The vertical viscosity, A_{VM}, has a uniform value of $10^{-2}m^2/s$.

The heat flux at the upper boundary is chosen so that the upper layer is forced toward a reference temperature based on historical data. The relaxation time is 20 days (Haney 1974). The reference temperature and the wind stress are taken to be functions of season, while the reference surface salinity does not include a seasonal variation.

The average of January and July poleward heat fluxes calculated from the Bryan & Lewis (1979) model are shown in Figure 1 by the curves marked *M*. In the Atlantic the shape of the curve predicted by the model is in good agreement with heat balance results, but the amplitude is much less. It is about one half of Bunker's (1976) curve and about one third of Hastenrath's (1980). The thermohaline circulation of the model was only 10 megatons/s (10×10^9kg/s) in the North Atlantic, while Roemmich (1980) estimates a value of 18 megatons/s from IGY data and the inverse method. The relative weakness of the thermohaline circulation in the model is associated with a lower meridional heat flux.

In the Pacific and Indian Ocean sectors the model also shows a smaller amplitude than the heat balance results, but in the Southern Hemisphere there is a qualitative difference as well. A maximum heat transport is shown at about 10°S and another maximum in the southern ocean at 50°S. After the Antarctic Circumpolar Current goes through the Drake Passage it turns sharply equatorward. The secondary maximum in the southern ocean is associated with a strong heat gain at high latitudes in the Atlantic sector.

In the model the salinity field is calculated exactly the same way as the temperature field. A salinity flux at the surface is proportional to the difference between the first-level salinity and a reference value. No special allowance is made for subsurface inputs due to rivers or features like the Straits of Gibraltar. The water transport curves predicted by the model shown in Figure 1 generally agree with the water balance atlas of Baumgartner & Reichel (1975) except in the Equatorial and South Atlantic. The water balance atlas shows a net loss of 0.4 megaton/s of water for the entire Atlantic basin, which is compensated by an inflow from the World Ocean. The model shows a much smaller water loss of only 0.1 megaton/s. Bennett's (1978) calculations also show a much smaller inflow of water into the Atlantic Basin.

The marked discrepancy in the water transport near the Antarctic Continent predicted by the model and the surface water balance method can be easily explained. The freezing and melting of sea ice has an appreciable effect on the water balance. The Baumgartner & Reichel (1975) atlas treats the ocean and sea ice as a single system, while the model considers only the ocean. In the Austral winter, ice forms near the continent and then spreads equatorward and melts. The southward transport of water indicated by the model balances the equatorward transport of water by sea ice.

GLOBAL POLEWARD HEAT TRANSPORT

An ingenious method was developed by Vonder Haar & Oort (1973) for determining the contribution of the ocean to the global meridional heat transport. Measurements from meteorological satellites of albedo and net long-wave radiation to space provide a measure of local heating. In a steady state the total radiative heating must be balanced by a divergence of heat within the atmosphere and ocean. At high latitudes the movement of sea ice must be included as well. Vonder Haar & Oort (1973) subtracted out the divergence of atmospheric heat transport using data from the northern hemisphere upper air radiosonde network. The contribution of the ocean is then a residual term. In a later study, Oort & Vonder Haar (1976) attempted to include seasonal effects by including the seasonal heat storage in the air and water column. The annual mean ocean heat transport based on this later study is shown in Figure 4. The major source of error is believed to be systematic biases in the satellite data of about 5 W/m^2. Trenberth (1979) estimated ocean heat transport in the southern hemisphere in the same way, but the sparser radiosonde network south of the equator makes the estimate less reliable.

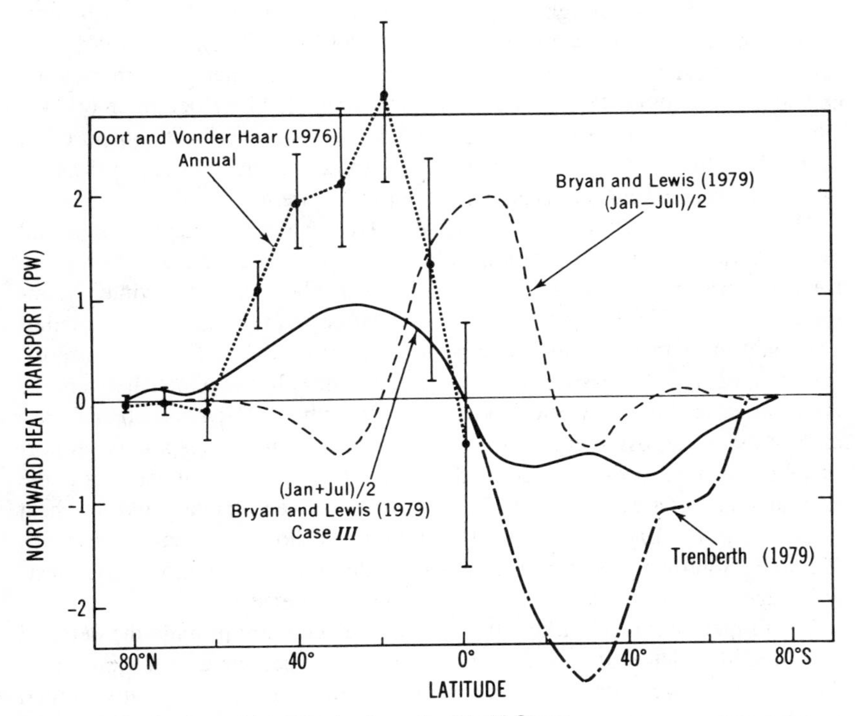

Figure 4 Total poleward heat flux by the entire World Ocean.

The Vonder Haar & Oort method has the great advantage of being entirely independent of the empirical formulas needed to determine surface heat balance from ship data. A major conclusion based on the new method was that the role of the ocean in poleward heat transport may have been seriously underestimated using the surface heat balance method. For example, Sellers (1965) estimated heat transport by the ocean from Budyko's (1963) heat atlas, and found a maximum heat transport of only 1.5 PW (1.5×10^{15}W) in each hemisphere. Hastenrath's (1980) surface heat balance estimate of poleward heat transport in individual ocean basins is shown in Figure 1. When Hastenrath's estimates are combined for the global ocean, the total heat flux for the northern hemisphere oceans is comparable to that of Vonder Haar & Oort (1973) while in the southern hemisphere Hastenrath's estimate is less than Seller's (1965).

The poleward heat flux from the Bryan & Lewis (1979) water-mass model is also shown in Figure 4. A sensitivity study made by Bryan and Lewis showed that the only parameter that had a very large effect on heat transport was the amplitude of the wind stress. Since the wind stress is fairly well known from observations, the results for case III shown here and in Figure 1 for individual oceans are roughly representative of the model. As noted before, the rate of formation of deep water in the model North Atlantic is weak, only about 10 megatons/s (10×10^9kg/s) compared to an estimate of a meridional cell strength of about 18 megatons/s at 24°N estimated by Roemmich (1980). Obviously a stronger meridional cell would allow a stronger heat transport, but even when this is considered it is hard to explain the differences in the heat flux of the model and observations shown in Figure 4.

The estimates of Oort & Vonder Haar (1976), which included the seasonal cycle, showed a large fluctuation in heat transport in the equatorial region. Heat was transported out of the summer hemisphere into the winter hemisphere. Lau (1978) demonstrated the same effect with a very simple model. The main mechanism seems to be a variation of poleward Ekman transport, shown in (22), with seasonal changes in the winds. In the winter hemisphere both the easterlies and westerlies tend to strengthen. The wind changes are antisymmetric across the equator, but since the Ekman transport is proportional to the wind stress divided by the Coriolis force, seasonal changes in the Ekman transport are symmetric. The difference between January and July heat transports of the Bryan & Lewis (1979) model is shown as a dashed curve in Figure 4. Southward heat transport is indicated under the atmospheric westerlies and northward transport in the region of the easterlies.

In situ measurements of heat transport will eventually provide the detailed data needed to determine the actual mechanisms of poleward heat transport in the oceans. As yet, however, the in situ measurements provide only limited information for single, synoptic sections at a few latitudes. All we have at present are the predictions of models to be verified or discarded as more detailed measurements become available. A detailed breakdown of the poleward heat transport of the Bryan & Lewis (1979) model is shown in Figure 5. Following the notation developed for (18)–(21), let [ ] denote a zonal average, and ( )* denote a departure from the zonal average. Let Γ be proportional to poleward heat transport in the model.

$$\Gamma = [v][\theta] + [v^*\theta^*] + A_{\mathrm{HH}}\, \partial_\phi\, [\theta]/a. \tag{30}$$

The first two terms may be interpreted as a measure of the heat transport due to meridional overturning and horizontal gyres. The final term is associated with the parameterization of mesoscale eddies that cannot be resolved explicitly by the approximate 200-km mesh size of the model.

As indicated by the in situ measurements discussed in the section on poleward flux estimates based on hydrographic data, meridional overturning dominates the heat transport at low latitudes. The meridional overturning transport term in Figure 4 has the same shape near the equator as the Ekman component shown in Figure 3, but the amplitude is much less, since equatorial upwelling brings water up from intermediate levels, not from below the thermocline. In the model, the heat transport due to meridional overturning reverses sign in the southern hemisphere. In the zone of the southern hemisphere westerlies, "the

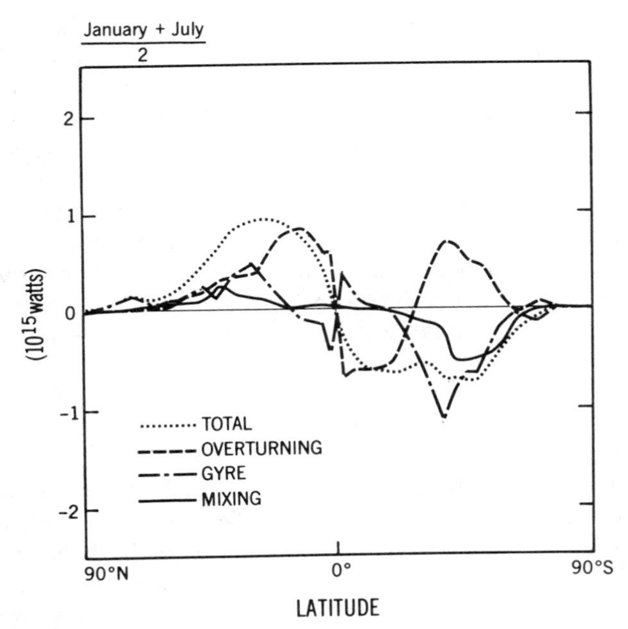

Figure 5 Components of model poleward heat transport (from Bryan & Lewis 1979).

roaring forties," very strong Ekman transport carries heat equatorward. The Ekman transport effect is compensated by strong down-gradient mixing across the Antarctic Circumpolar front, and a strong gyre term. The gyre term is associated with the fact that over most of the southern ocean the Circumpolar Current flows southeastward, carrying warmer surface water toward the pole. Only east of the Drake Passage does it turn abruptly equatorward as the cold Falkland (Malvinas) Current. Strong mixing across the circumpolar thermal front is consistent with recent measurements of mesoscale heat transport in the Drake Passage by Bryden (1978).

In the northern hemisphere the thermohaline circulation of the model is weaker than estimated from observations, but still strong enough to overcome the effect of equatorward Ekman transport under the westerlies. Thus the meridional overturning component of the heat transport decreases without changing sign. Since the total width of the ocean is smaller and the thermal gradients are not as well defined, the transport due to down-gradient mixing in the northern hemisphere is much less than in the southern ocean. Nevertheless, there is a distinct maximum at the latitude of the Atlantic eastward drift and the Kuroshio extension.

OUTLOOK

Attempts to explain short time-scale climatic fluctuations in historical data and longer time-scale changes in the geologic record have met with indifferent success, simply because the fundamentals of the Earth's climate are stilll poorly understood. One of the most unknown elements of climate is the role of the oceans in redistributing heat within the Earth's fluid envelope. It is not known how poleward heat transport is partitioned between the ocean and atmosphere. It appears that the atmosphere dominates poleward heat flux at middle and higher latitudes, but no real explanation has been offered. Heat balance calculations at the sea surface, heat balance calculations using satellite and radiosonde data, and in situ flux calculations based on hydrographic data all have inherent large errors. As pointed out by Wunsch (1980), the errors are so large that there is no statistically significant difference between the heat transport estimates of the different approaches. This unsatisfactory state of affairs should be rectified as new data from field studies specifically designed to examine the role of the ocean become available.

As oceanographers gain the same familiarity with numerical methods as atmospheric scientists, steady progress can be expected in building mathematical models relevant to large-scale heat transfer in the ocean. Models will benefit from new information of heat flux and the transport of geochemical tracers. The design of observational experiments will be improved in turn through insight gained by ocean circulation models.

ACKNOWLEDGMENTS

The author is extremely grateful to Mrs. Elizabeth Williams and Miss Martha Jackson for their help in preparing the manuscript for this review, and to Mr. Philip Tunison and his staff for completion of the drawings.

Literature Cited

Albrecht, F. 1960. Jahreskarten des Warme- and Wasserhaushaltes der Ozeane. *Ber. Dtsch. Wetterdienstes,* 66, Bd 9:1–191

Andreyev, O. A., Kagan, B. A., Oganesyan, L. A. 1976. On the global circulation in a two-layer model. *Oceanology* 16:1–5

Baumgartner, A., Reichel, E. 1975. *The World Water Balance*. Munich: Oldenbourge Verlag. 179 pp.

Bennett, A. F. 1978. Poleward heat fluxes in southern hemisphere oceans. *J. Phys. Oceanogr*. 8:785–98

Broecker, W. S., Peng, T.-H., Stuiver, M. 1978. An estimate of the upwelling rate in the equatorial Atlantic based on the distribution of bomb radiocarbon. *J. Geophys. Res.* 83:6179–86

Bryan, K. 1962. Measurements of meridional heat transport by ocean currents. *J. Geophys. Res.* 67(9):3403–14

Bryan, K. 1979. Models of the World Ocean. *Dyn. Atmos. Ocean* 3:327–38

Bryan, K., Lewis, L. J. 1979. A water mass model of the world ocean. *J. Geophys. Res.* 84(C5):2503–17

Bryden, H. L. 1978. Poleward heat flux and conversion of potential energy in the Drake Passage. *J. Mar. Res.* 37:1–22

Bryden, H. L., Hall, M. M. 1980. Heat transport by ocean currents across 25°N latitude in the Atlantic. *Science* 207:884–86

Budyko, M. I. 1956. *Heat Balance of the Earth's Surface*. Leningrad: Gidrometeor. 254 pp.

Budyko, M. I. 1963. *Guide to the Atlas of the Heat Balance of the Earth*. Gidrometeor, Moscow, 69 pp.

Bunker, A. 1976. Computations of surface energy flux and annual air-sea interaction cycles of the North Atlantic Ocean. *Mon. Weather Rev.* 104(9):1122–40

Bye, J.A.T. 1979. A one-dimensional model of meridional oceanic heat transport. *J. Mar. Res.* 37(3):493–514

Cox, M. D. 1975. A baroclinic model of the World Ocean: preliminary results. *Numerical Models of Ocean Circulation, Proc. Natl. Acad. Sci. USA,* pp. 107–20

Drozdov, A. A. 1964. Precipitation Charts in *The Physical Geographical World Atlas*. Moscow: USSR Acad. Sci. 298 pp.

Emig, M. 1967. Heat transport by ocean currents. *J. Geophys. Res.* 72(10):2519–29

Fu, L-L. 1981. The general circulation and meridional heat transport of the subtropical South Atlantic determined by inverse methods. *J. Phys. Ocean.* In press

Fuglister, F. C. 1960. *Atlantic Ocean Atlas*. Woods Hole, Mass: Woods Hole Oceanogr. Inst. 209 pp.

Godfrey, J. S., Golding, T. J. 1981. The Sverdrup relation in the Indian Ocean, and the effect of the Pacific Indian Ocean through-flow on Indian Ocean circulation and on the East Australian Current. *J. Phys. Oceanogr.* 11(6):771–79

Haney, R. 1974. A numerical study of the response of an idealized ocean to large scale surface heat and momentum flux. *J. Phys. Oceanogr.* 4:145–67

Hastenrath, S. 1980. Heat budget of tropical ocean and atmosphere. *J. Phys. Oceanogr.* 10:159–70

Hastenrath, S., Lamb, P. 1977. *Climatic Atlas of the Tropical Atlantic and Eastern Pacific Oceans*. Madison: Univ. Wis. Press. 105 pp.

Holland, W. R. 1977. *Oceanic general circulation models in The Sea, VI, Marine Modeling*. New York: John Wiley, pp. 3–45

Jung, G. H. 1955. *Heat transport in the Atlantic Ocean. Rep. 55-34T,* Oceanogr. Dept., Texas A & M Univ. 41 pp.

Lau, K.M.W. 1978. Experiment with a simple ocean-atmosphere climate model: The role of the ocean in global climate. *J. Phys. Oceanogr.* 35:1144–63

Leetmaa, A., Niiler, P., Stommel, H. 1977. Does the Sverdrup relation account for the mid-Atlantic circulation? *J. Mar. Res.* 35:1–10

Mintz, Y. 1979. *On the simulation of the oceanic general circulation in Vol. II, Performance, Intercomparison and Sensitivity Studies,* Global Atmos. Res. Prog. Publ. 22, Geneva, 1037 pp.

Niiler, P. P., Richardson, W. S. 1973. Seasonal variability of the Florida Current. *J. Mar. Res.* 31:144–67

Oort, A. H., Vonder Haar, T. H. 1976. On the observed annual cycle in the ocean-atmosphere heat balance over the northern hemisphere. *J. Phys. Oceanogr.* 6(6):781–800

Reid, J. L. 1973. Transpacific hydrographic sections at latitudes 42°S and 28°S; the SCORPIO Expedition. *Deep-Sea Res.* 20:39–49

Reid, J. L., Lynn, R. J. 1971. On the influence of the Norwegian-Greenland and Weddell seas upon the bottom water of the Indian and Pacific Oceans. *Deep-Sea Res.* 18:1963–88

Roemmich, D. 1980. Estimation of meridional heat flux in the North Atlantic by inverse methods. *J. Phys. Oceanogr.* 10:1972–83

Sellers, W. D. 1965. *Physical Climatology.* Univ. Chicago Press. 272 pp.

Semtner, A. J., Mintz, Y. 1977. Numerical simulation of the Gulf Stream and mid-ocean eddies. *J. Phys. Oceanogr.* 7:208–30

Stommel, H. 1980. Asymmetry of interoceanic fresh-water and heat fluxes. *Proc. Natl. Acad. Sci. USA* 77(5):2377–81

Sverdrup, H. U. 1947. Wind-driven currents in a baroclinic ocean: with application to the equatorial currents of the eastern Pacific. *Proc. Natl. Acad. Sci. USA* 33:318–26

Sverdrup, H. U. 1957. *Oceanography in Handbuch der Physik, 48,* pp. 630–38. Berlin: Springer-Verlag.

Takano, K. 1975. A numerical simulation of the World Ocean circulation: preliminary results. In *Numerical Models of Ocean Circulation,* pp. 121–29. Washington, D.C.: Natl. Acad. Sci.

Trenberth, K. E. 1979. Mean annual poleward energy transports by the oceans in the southern hemisphere. *Dyn. Atmos. Oceans* 4: 57–64

Vonder Haar, T. H., Oort, A. H. 1973. New estimate of annual poleward energy transport by northern hemisphere oceans. *J. Phys. Oceanogr.* 3(2):169–72

Webster, P. J., Lau, K. M. 1977. A simple large-scale ocean-atmosphere interaction model. *J. Atmos. Sci.* 34:1063–84

Worthington, L. V. 1976. *On the North Atlantic Circulation.* Johns Hopkins Univ. Press. 110 pp.

Wunsch, C. 1978. The North Atlantic general circulation west of 50°W determined by inverse methods. *Rev. Geophys. Space Phys.* 16(4):583–620

Wunsch, C. 1980. Meridional heat flux of the North Atlantic Ocean. *Proc. Natl. Acad. Sci. USA* 77(9):5043–47

Wüst, G., Defant, A. 1936. *Meteor 1925–1927. Wissenschaftliche Ergebnisse, Bd. 6 - Atlas (103 pls).* W. de Gruyter, Co: Berlin.

Wyrtki, K. 1965. The average annual heat balance of the North Pacific Ocean and its relation to ocean circulation. *J. Geophys. Res.* 70:4547–59

Ann. Rev. Earth Planet. Sci. 1982. 10:39-60

THE GEOLOGICAL CONTEXT OF HUMAN EVOLUTION[1]

A. K. Behrensmeyer

Department of Paleobiology, Smithsonian Institution, Washington D.C. 20560

INTRODUCTION

Geological processes and changes during the last 15 million years helped to shape the course of human evolution, in the same way that environments influenced the adaptation or extinction of all organisms. This is obvious in a broad sense, but just how geology influenced our emergence as a unique species is not obvious. With the recent increase in understanding of global tectonic and climatic patterns for the later Cenozoic and the recovery of an ever-increasing fossil and contextual record for human evolution, we are beginning to see how geological processes and the evolution of *Homo sapiens* may fit together.

This paper focuses on the fossil and paleoenvironmental record for the larger hominoids over the period between 15 and 1 m.y. B.P. This time interval encompasses the major evolutionary changes that transformed one of the many primitive apelike primates that existed before 15 m.y. B.P. into the unmistakable *Homo* of 1 m.y. B.P. *Hominoid* refers to the superfamily Hominoidea, which includes the Hylobatidae (gibbons), Pliopithecidae (small fossil apes), Pongidae (apes), and Hominidae (humans and their closest fossil relatives) (65, 80). In this paper *hominoid* is used as the inclusive term for the larger-bodied fossil Pondigae and Hominidae, which are of most interest to the evolutionary history of *Homo sapiens*. Familiar genera included under this label are *Homo, Australopithecus, Sivapithecus, Ramapithecus, Gigantopithecus, Pongo, Dryopithecus*, and *Proconsul*. *Gorilla* and *Pan* also belong with the larger hominoids, although they have no fossil record and are not discussed in this paper. For a review of the evolutionary relationships of the larger hominoids, readers are referred to papers by Pilbeam (65, 66).

When hominoid fossils were rare, stratigraphic and paleoenvironmental information sparse, and dating techniques less reliable than at present, ideas about human evolution were based on behavioral and anatomical similarities and differences between modern apes and humans (66). The standard reconstruction that the Hominidae evolved from a forest-dwelling, apelike ancestor in Africa was based originally on such reasoning and still has a strong influence on current thinking. The study of the geological context of fossil evidence contributed a time framework for human evolution, allowing it to be aligned with the timing of important Cenozoic tectonic and climatic events. Reconstruction of the paleoenvironments and faunal and floral communities associated with the hominoids provides the first independent tests of the anatomically-based African forest-origin hypothesis.

Because of the interest in the human evolutionary story, the hominoid fossil record is probably the best-documented, in terms of geochronologic and sedimentological information, for land vertebrates of any age. Research in human origins has become a large-scale multidisciplinary effort, and progress has been accompanied by advances in radiometric dating, paleomagnetic reversal stratigraphy in nonmarine sediments, environmental reconstruction of nonmarine paleoenvironments, and paleontological sampling of vertebrate fossil assemblages.

Focal questions that are guiding present multidisciplinary research include

1. What habitat and dietary shifts accompanied the major morphological changes in the emergence of bipedal and (later) large-brained hominoids?
2. How many different species of hominoids coexisted at a given time, and what adaptive characters permitted coexistence?
3. Did hominoids at any point begin to demonstrate independence from environmental constraints, relative to other species in their community?
4. Is there correspondence implying cause and effect between global climate changes and periods of evolutionary change in hominoid lineages?

In this review I summarize the fossil and geological evidence bearing on these questions and others, and show how this evidence is being used to test previous hypotheses or to create new ones.

THE EVIDENCE

Fossils and Trace Fossils

The number of hominoid fossils now known for the period between 1 and 15 m.y. B.P. is estimated to be around 2000. Many of these are single teeth and most are fragmentary; still, there are enough specimens for paleoanthropologists to be in moderate agreement regarding the meaningful species groupings and lineages. In addition to the fossil bones and teeth, two other kinds of evidence are of prime importance to the human evolutionary story: archeological materials and footprints, which in a geological sense can be regarded as "trace fossils."

These three forms of direct evidence for hominoid morphology, diet, and behavior are found in varying abundance at the localities listed in Table 1. There are approximately 50 hominoid-producing localities stretching from Spain across southern Europe, western and southern Asia, China, and down into northern, eastern, and southern Africa (Figure 1). Localities vary greatly in quality and quantity of both fossil and contextual information, ranging from a small patch of outcrop with an isolated tooth to richly fossiliferous sequences covering hundreds of square kilometers. About a third of the localities listed in Table 1 include significant stratigraphic sequences where evolutionary and environmental change through time can be directly documented. The value of these sequences in continental deposits, where there is always an element of uncertainty in reconstructing the time relationships of isolated small localities, cannot be overemphasized. The long-sequence localities that have been studied in detail up to now are East Lake Turkana, Omo, and Olduvai in Africa; and Haritalyanger-Lehri, Hasnot, and Khaur in southern Asia. These provide the current geochronological framework to which other hominoid-producing localities in Asia and Africa are correlated.

Important contextual evidence that occurs along with hominoid fossils at the localities includes the associated faunal and floral remains, sedimentary units and structures, and their spatial relationships, all of which allow reconstruction of the taphonomic history of the hominoid fossils. Most hominoid fossils are not found by digging in excavations, but occur on outcrop surfaces, where they have weathered out of the sedimentary rocks. Thus it may not be possible to determine their exact provenance, although the source stratum is often obvious from matrix on the specimen. Most of the fossils regarded as "associated" with the hominoids occur on the surface as well, and this leads to problems in interpreting exactly what "association" means, both in terms of the buried death-assemblage and the once-living community of plants and animals. The problems of association are critical to paleoecological interpretations.

After discovery, hominoid fossils are usually removed immediately from the field to the comparative safety of the laboratory, where they are cleaned, reconstructed and anatomically studied. The fossils are eventually interpreted on the basis of taxonomy, function, and diet, and placed on the hominoid family tree. However, archeological sites, footprints, and the taphonomic and sedimentary context are studied initially in the field, where it is possible to put together a highly integrated reconstruction of the paleoenvironmental setting before proceeding to laboratory analysis.

Table 1 Hominoid localities between 1.0 and 15.0 m.y. B.P.

	Locality[a]	Place	Age[b] (m.y. B.P.)	Sedimentary[c] environment	Reference[d]
	Africa				
1.	Chemeron	West Kenya	(1.5–2.5)	Lake margin	53
2.	Chesowanja	West Kenya	2.0–0.7	Lake margin	14, 36
3.	East Lake Turkana*	North Kenya	3.0–1.2	Delta margin, floodplain, channel	51
4.	Fort Ternan*	West Kenya	14.0	Volcanic uplands	74, 86
5.	Gadeb	Central Ethiopia	1.5–0.7	Fluvial	29
6.	Hadar*	Northeast Ethiopia	3.0–4.0	Lake margin, floodplain	44
7.	Kanam	West Kenya	(2.0–4.0)	Fluvial, lake margin	36
8.	Kanapoi	Northwest Kenya	4.0	Lake margin	10, 61
9.	Kromdrai*	Northern South Africa	(1.5)	Cave	37, 89
10.	Laetoli*	North Tanzania	3.6–3.8	Volcanic uplands	49, 50
11.	Lothagam	Northwest Kenya	(5.0–6.0)	Fluvial	10, 60
12.	Lukeino	West Kenya	6.5	Fluvial to lake margin	63
13.	Maboko	West Kenya	15	Wet floodplain	4
14.	Makapansgat*	Northeastern South Africa	(2.8–3.2)	Cave	20, 37, 59
15.	Melka Kunture	Central Ethiopia	(1.0)	Fluvial, paleosol	27
16.	Ngorora	West Kenya	9–12	Lake margin, (paleosol)	64
17.	Olduvai*	North Tanzania	1.8–0.3	Lake margin	47, 48
18.	Omo*	South Ethiopia	2.9–1.0	Fluvial	39
19.	Peninj	North Tanzania	(1.0–1.5)	Deltaic, fluvial	41, 42
20.	Sahabi	Northeast Libya	7–4	Deltaic	16, 17
21.	Sterkfontein*	Northern South Africa	(2.8–3.0, 1.5)	Cave	37, 58, 89
22.	Swartkrans*	Northern South Africa	(1.7–1.9)	Cave	21, 37, 89
23.	Taung	Northern South Africa	(1.0–2.5)	Cave	37, 82

[a] Localities with more than one specimen are marked with *.
[b] Age is given only for hominoid- or artifact-producing strata. Ages in parentheses are based on indirect methods such as faunal correlation, those without parentheses on direct radiometric or paleomagnetic determinations.
[c] Sedimentary environment only for hominoid-bearing portion of the local section.
[d] References chosen to give easiest access to the literature, not on the basis of principal workers at the localities.

Table 1 (*continued*)

Locality[a]	Place	Age[b] (m.y. B.P.)	Sedimentary[c] Environment	Reference[d]
Southern Europe, Western Asia				
24. Ad Dabiteyah*	Arabia	(15–17)	Fluvial	3
25. Candir	North Central Turkey	(12–14)	Fluvial, lacustrine	81
26. Klein Haders Dorf*	Austria	(12–14)	Fluvial	92
27. La Grive	Central France	(12–14)	—	77
28. Neudorf	Czechoslovakia	(12–14)	—	77
29. Pasalar*	Northwest Turkey	(15–16)	Fluvial	5
30. Pyrgos	Greece	(8–9)	—	88
31. Rudabanya*	Northeast Hungary	(10–12)	Lake margin, coal swamp	46
32. Swabia Jura	Germany	(9–10)	—	77
33. St. Stefan	South Austria	(11–12)	Lignites	77
34. St. Gaudens*	France	(12–13)	—	67
35. Udabno*	Georgia, U.S.S.R.	(10–12)	—	80
36. Vallès Penedes* (Catalana)	Northeast Spain	(10–12)	Fluvial, lacustrine	30
37. Vathylakkos* (Ravin de la Pluie)	Greece	(10–12)	Fluvial, lacustrine	18
38. Yassarien	Central Turkey	(10–12)	—	57
China and Southern Asia				
39. Bama	South China	(1.0–2.0)	—	62
40. Chinji*	North Pakistan	(11–14)	Fluvial	9
41. Djetis-Trinil*	East Java	(0.7–1.9)	Lacustrine, fluvial	43, 56
42. Haritalyangar-Lehri*	North India	(6–9)	Fluvial	76, 77
43. Hasnot*	North Pakistan	9–11	Fluvial	9
44. Jian Shi*	Central China	(1.0–2.0)	Cave	26, 68
45. Khaur*	North Pakistan	7.6–9.4	Fluvial	8, 9, 65
46. Keiyuan	South China	(10–13)	Coal swamp	26, 68, 90
47. Lufeng*	South China	(8–10)	Fluvial-lacustrine with lignite	26, 71, 72
48. Ramnagar*	North India	(11–13)	Fluvial	77
49. Sethi Nagri*	North Pakistan	9–10	Fluvial	9, 65
50. Xin-She-Chong*	South China	(1.6–?3.0)	Cave	28, 68
51. Yuanmou* (H. erectus)	South China	1.5–2.0	Fluvial-lacustrine	40, 68

Figure 1 Map of southern Eurasia and Africa showing the distribution of hominoid localities for the period between 15.0 and 1.0 m.y. B.P.

The Time Framework

The time framework for the fossils and archeology must also be studied initially in the field. Accurate dating of the fossiliferous sediments may be relatively straightforward if there are interstratified volcanic tuffs or lavas (as there often are in East Africa), but age determination is usually extremely complex, involving faunal correlations (sometimes from the continental to the marine record) and extensive paleomagnetic sampling. As can be seen from Table 1, most ages are relative and based on faunal correlations, rather than direct radiometric dating or paleomagnetic stratigraphy. They can provide absolute age estimates, however, because they are ultimately tied into sections with radiometric dates. In mammalian faunas, biostratigraphic markers such as immigrations, extinctions, size trends, and even morphological stages of evolution do not necessarily provide reliable isochrons on a continental scale. The appearance of *Hipparion* in Europe, for example, was regarded as an isochronous event for Eurasia (24, 83, 79), but it is now clear that *Hipparion* appears at least 1 m.y. later in Pakistan (9) than in Europe. For some of the South African cave localities, short paleomagnetic columns make it possible to assign the fossil-bearing units to blocks of normal or reversed polarity (54), but the decision as to which paleomagnetic epoch these represent is based primarily on the mammalian faunas. The uncertainty inherent in faunal correlations contributes to the broad range of some age estimates shown in parentheses in Table 1.

Although ages based on faunal correlations must be regarded with some caution, the absolute geochronology for much of the fossil record of human evolution is, on the whole, as secure as any time framework based on radiometric dating methods. In East Africa, repeated K-Ar age determinations of the basal lava and interstratified tuffs at Olduvai Gorge make this locality the accepted standard for African faunal correlations as well as the original type area for the Olduvai Event in the Matuyama Reversed Epoch (31), which marks the base of the Pleistocene. Because of a controversy over the age of the KBS Tuff in the East Lake Turkana deposits (11), the methodology of dating reworked tuffs using Argon 40– Argon 39 and Potassium-Argon techniques has been reanalyzed and compared with Fission Track determinations on the same units. Moreover, repeated age determinations have been made on the same samples by independent laboratories. Because of the intense interest generated by human evolution, absolute dating of hominoid-bearing localities is among the most cautious and rigorously tested work in late Cenozoic geochronology.

The array of localities on the time scale in Figure 2 shows that there are clusters of localities in the earlier and later portions of the 15 to 1 m.y. B.P. period and a gap in the middle. The distribution of localities is patchy in space as well as time, with the earlier ones being primarily in Eurasia and the later in Africa. This pattern is due to both preservation bias and paleoecology and is discussed later.

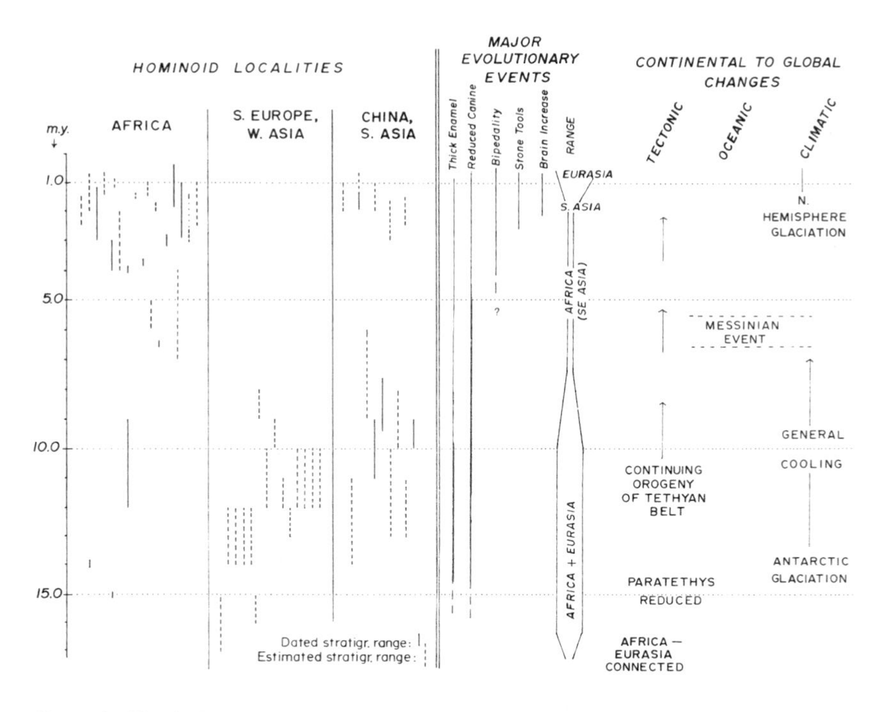

Figure 2 Hominoid locality distribution through time for the period from 15.0 to 1.0 m.y. B.P.; major evolutionary and paleogeographic changes documented by using fossil and contextual evidence from these localities; and climatic and tectonic events of continental to global scale which may have affected hominoid evolution. Stratigraphic range shown is the range of possible dates for hominoid remains.

HOW THE EVIDENCE IS USED FOR PALEOECOLOGICAL RECONSTRUCTION

It is important to understand what lies behind such statements as ". . .a change in habitat (for hominoids) is inferred, from forest to woodland, along with a shift in feeding behavior. . .", (65) which are typical of recent publications on human evolution. Such inferences shape what we think concerning the adaptive changes that led to *Homo*. There is a strong desire among paleoanthropologists to determine the ecological niche, especially the preferred vegetational habitat and diet, of the progression of hominoid species. They base their inferences on comparative functional anatomy of the fossils and on contextual information (Figure 3). In order for readers to comprehend what lies behind interpretations presented in the following sections, the lines of reasoning, derived from geological and paleontological contextual information, that are used in hominoid paleoecology must be examined.

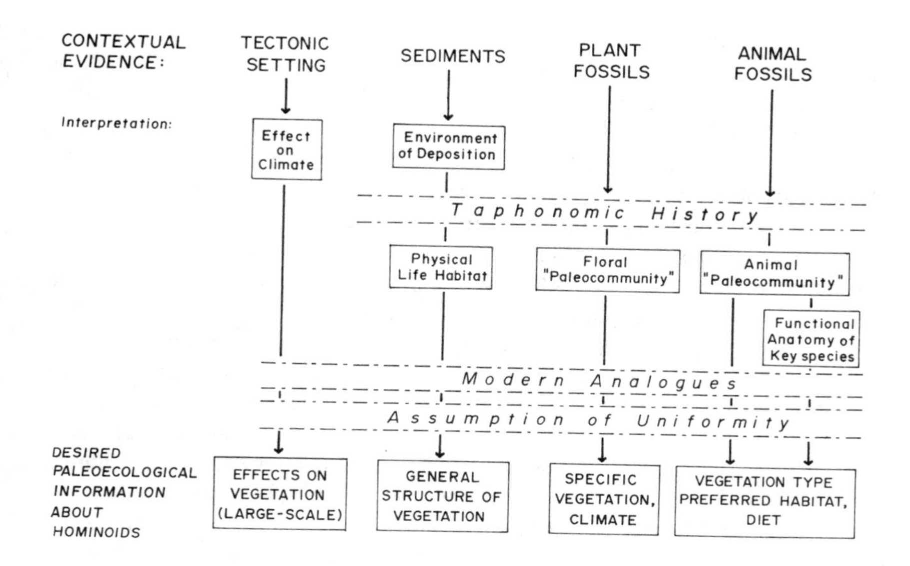

Figure 3 Lines of reasoning used in deriving paleoecological interpretations from contextual evidence associated with fossil hominoids. Items in solid boxes represent the various levels of interpretation, and those enclosed by dashed lines represent assumptions or information that is needed in order to proceed to the next interpretative level.

The large-scale paleogeographic and tectonic setting of hominoid localities is used to infer general conditions of temperature and rainfall. For example, the elevation of East Africa in the early Miocene, prior to major rifting, influenced the breaking up of the lowland equatorial forest belt and helped initiate more open, woodland-to-savanna habitats (6). The rising mountain ranges from the Alpine belt to the Himalaya and the accompanying demise of most of the Tethyan and Parathethyan seaways can be used as a basis for inferring progressively drier and more seasonal continental conditions through the Miocene in Eurasia (24, 75). Such paleoecological interpretations provide an overall framework for reconstructing conditions at hominoid localities, but undoubtedly are oversimplified with respect to smaller-scale features of the local habitats that were probably of more proximal importance to the hominoids.

Evidence for paleoecological features of the local hominoid habitats is derived from associated sediments and fossils (Figure 3). The environment of deposition and some indicators of local climate can be reconstructed from sedimentary units and structures; for instance, paleosols with $CaCO_3$ precipitates are evidence for seasonally dry soil conditions and fluctuations in oxygen isotope ratios for aridity trends (25). Environments such as fluvial channels and floodplains, lake margins, or coal swamps represent the burial context of the hominoid and other fossils, and provide information about the nature of their physical habitat. This is, however, of limited value to the paleoanthropologist, whose goal is reconstruction of the vegetation and subhabitats where the hominoids actually lived.

In extending the evidence from the physical environment of burial to the life habitat of the hominoid, the first critical step is to establish the taphonomic history of the hominoid remains in relation to the environment of deposition and the associated fossils. Skeletal parts of terrestrial mammals found in channel deposits, for example, came originally from various upstream sources, and the goal of taphonomic study is to determine how the processes of transport and preservation have altered the original life-associations among plant and animal remains and environments. If primate fossils are found with tree trunks in a channel deposit, there is some probability that these were associated in life, but also a probability that they were not. Taphonomic study allows paleoecologists to assess these probabilities. Interpretations of hominoid ecology based on contextual evidence therefore always bear an element of uncertainty. This uncertainty may be considerable for localities where the context of the hominoid remains has not been studied taphonomically.

Having crossed the taphonomic hurdle and established with some certainty that a physical environment was the habitat of the living hominoid, a paleoecologist can expand the reconstruction to indicate plant communities through the use of modern analogy. For instance, in a fluvial environment with channel, levee, and floodplain facies, it might be assumed on the basis of modern analogues that the densest vegetation (e.g. forest) grew along the levees (8). This is an example of a typical uniformitarian hypothesis. Fossil root structures and characters of paleosols are used as additional evidence and may lead to modification of the original hypothesis. The interpretation of the vegetation based on sedimentary evidence alone is, however, only as good as the assumption of uniformity. There is little doubt that the modern world provides a very limited model for past vegetation associations, thereby restricting our view of this aspect of hominoid paleoecology.

Fossil plants and pollen are direct evidence for vegetation, but most hominoid localities lack such remains. Pollen spectra recovered from sedimentary deposits associated (in a broad sense) with hominoids are used to reconstruct the overall nature of the flora (e.g. forest, semiarid bush) (19). Only in rare instances has plant evidence been found in close association with hominoid fossils (1) or archeological sites (87). Otherwise, there is always uncertainty in relating the flora documented at one level in a stratigraphic sequence with hominoid fossils found at another. In reconstructing a specific vegetation type (e.g. an evergreen woodland) and drawing inferences about climate from this, the paleobotanist is also constrained by modern analogues and the assumption of uniformity, i.e. that physiological processes and basic biological responses were similar in the past to what they are now.

Hominoid fossils typically occur with remains of other vertebrates, and occasionally with invertebrates and trace fossils. The associated fauna is thus the most used source of paleoecological information about hominoids. The chain of reasoning, as shown in Figure 3, is more complex than for the other forms of contextual evidence, but if the assumptions are acceptable, it can lead to relatively detailed interpretations of hominoid paleoecology. Many associations between hominoid remains and other fossils are fairly loose, because the fauna has been recovered from the same formation or area of outcrop, but not necessarily the same unit, as the hominoids. Taphonomic study allowing the reconstruction of probable life-associations between hominoids and other species has been done at only a few localities. For most sites, it is simply assumed that the fauna and the hominoids were members of the same paleocommunity, at least in a broad sense. Beyond this, several methods are currently employed to infer vegetational habitat from the fauna: functional anatomy of key species (e.g. teeth adapted for browsing indicate soft leafy vegetation), preferred habitat of key species (based on similarity to modern relatives), and habitat "spectra" based on characteristic morphological features (e.g. mode of locomotion, body size, mode of feeding) of vertebrate faunas in specific modern ecosystems (2, 85, 55). For instance, if a particular fauna is dominated by browsing species and includes obviously arboreal forms, this indicates a forest or dense woodland habitat, and perhaps a diet of fruit as well, for the associated hominoids.

For any given locality, the assumptions and lines of reasoning used in paleoecological interpretation can be questioned and the end result may be only a set of alternative hypotheses rather than one clear-cut hypothesis. Broader interpretations, based on converging lines of evidence from many localities, provide much stronger support for a particular hypothesis. Recurring faunas associated with hominoids in a number of localities is much stronger evidence for their characteristic paleocommunity than information from a single locality.

There is a tendency for paleoecological statements about hominoids to extend far beyond what can be justified given the evidence and assumptions at hand. Readers should be aware that many interpretations about hominid habits are speculative and must be treated with caution. The desire for such knowledge may be ahead of what is possible at present, but methods are being developed to use the contextual evidence in more logical and scientifically valid ways. These methods will undoubtedly contribute to the human evolutionary story.

PALEOGEOGRAPHIC PATTERNS

The broadest-scale and, in some respects, most interesting evidence for human origins is contained in the temporal and spatial distribution of fossil localities

(Figure 1). This can be used to show the pattern of interaction of the paleocommunities that include hominoids with large-scale geological processes linked to global climate change and the collision of the African and Indian continents with the Eurasian block.

The pattern of locality distribution must first be examined to determine whether it represents the actual paleogeographic distribution of hominoid species. Molasse deposition from the rising mountain belts in southern Eurasia helped to preserve a relatively good fossil record for land organisms from the Miocene through the Pleistocene. The pattern of spatial distribution of fossil hominoids along the southern Eurasian regions thus is partly a consequence of tectonically favorable conditions for preservation. North of this belt, fossiliferous localities within the 15 to 1 m.y. B.P. period lack hominoids, which suggests an original northern limit to their distribution. The disappearance of European hominoids in the later Miocene appears to be a true extinction event, documented by a number of fossil localities that preserve other members of their characteristic paleocommunity but lack hominoids after 7–8 m.y. B.P. (75). In Pakistan, a continuous sedimentary and faunal record from 11–2 m.y. B.P. documents the disappearance of hominoids at 7.5 m.y. B.P. accompanied by other extinctions, but there is no major faunal turnover at that time (9). In Asia the presence of the living orangutan is best explained by the continued persistence of some of the Miocene hominoids; the lack of a fossil record for them until the Pleistocene indicates that they survived in areas not sampled by the fossil record.

The locality distribution in Africa is restricted compared to that of Eurasia, and this can be seen as a consequence of the overall tectonic stability of the continent. Only in a few marginal basins, in areas of active rifting, and in the limestone plateaus of South Africa is there a vertebrate fossil record for the later Cenozoic. There is little doubt that this provides a poor sample of the original distribution pattern of the hominoids. Even within the rift system, the fossil record is "good" only for the early Miocene and the last 4 m.y. B.P. The scarcity of evidence for hominoids prior to 4 m.y. B.P. can be attributed to geological processes affecting fossil availability, rather than to original ecological or paleogeographic factors.

The paleogeographic pattern for hominoids shows that shortly after their initial emigration from Africa between 16 and 18 m.y. B.P. (86) they were widespread across Eurasia, at least along the southern margins of the rising mountain belts, and even experienced a period of species diversification (66). They were members of a mammalian paleocommunity that had genera in common from Spain to China, despite regional variations (13), for the period between about 12 and 8 m.y. B.P. It is believed that in the middle to late Miocene this paleocommunity coincided from Europe to western Asia with a more or less continuous vegetation termed the "sclerophyllous evergreen woodland" (7). There is considerable direct evidence in fossil pollen spectra and lignite deposits to support this (33, 34). Although there is a gap between Turkey and Pakistan in the locality record for hominoids, similarity of the faunas and hominoid morphologies between the western and eastern regions indicates that there was faunal exchange. The evergreen woodland may have extended into the Indian subcontinent in the middle to late Miocene, although Prasad reconstructs a more forested vegetation for the middle Miocene of India (70) and Ferguson shows the typical woodland genera extending to China north of the Himalaya, but not along the southern Himalaya through India (34). In the late Miocene the European woodland biome broke up due to increasingly seasonal continental climates and general cooling of global temperatures (7). There is evidence that between 10 and 8 m.y. B.P. the distribution of hominoids became restricted in southern Europe; one of the richest Cenozoic fossil localities on the Greek island of Samos, dated radiometrically at about 8.5 m.y. B.P., lacks hominoids but includes a great diversity of typical late Miocene species (78). The absence of hominoids in the Maragheh fossiliferous sequence in Iran, which spans the period between 9.5 and 7.0 m.y. B.P. (23), indicates that by then there was no longer any contact between the European and southeast Asia hominoid populations, although continuity for many of their faunal associates persisted.

In East Africa, the existing evidence for hominoids between 15 and 8 m.y. B.P. indicates that they were associated with woodland-to-wooded savanna habitats. Depending on how one reconstructs the structure and density of the Eurasian evergreen woodland as opposed to the African woodland, this could indicate that either the habitats of middle Miocene hominoids were similar in the two major regions or that the evolution to more open habitats first occurred in East Africa. By the late Miocene the total range of hominoids was greatly reduced; apparently they were not able to adapt to environmental changes in much of Eurasia and became extinct except in southeast Asia and Africa. The reason may be as simple as a drop in temperature or an increase in seasonality. Whatever habitat change eliminated the hominoids seems to have had less dramatic effects on other members of their paleocommunity, and careful reexamination of environments and of patterns of extinction, immigration, and evolution for other mammals across the 9 to 7 m.y. B.P. period might provide some clues to the nature of this change.

In Africa the development of more open savanna habitats and their faunas is thought to have proceeded throughout the middle to late Miocene (85). This assumption is based on extrapolation from the evidence at either end of this time period because of the scarcity of fossil localities within it. A faunal community of modern aspect began to emerge between 8 and 10 m.y. B.P. (64) and became the typical Plio-Pleistocene savanna paleocommunity in East Africa. The hominoids were apparently present throughout this period and by about 4 m.y. B.P. one group was fully bipedal and associated with the savanna community.

The period of late Miocene through Pliocene range restriction for the hominoids ended around 1.5–2.0 m.y. B.P. when *Homo erectus* or its immediate ancestor immigrated to southeast Asia. The immigration route must have been through Arabia or the Mideast and then across southern Asia, but Pleistocene sediments in these areas have not yet produced hominoid fossils. The early Pleistocene of Europe also lacks clear evidence for hominoids, although shortly after the 1.0 m.y. B.P. milestone, archeological sites and some skeletal remains occur in Europe. In southeast Asia, in addition to records of *Homo* in the period before 1.0 m.y. B.P., there are fossil remains of both *Gigantopithecus* and *Pongo* in southern China. This indicates that the ancestral orangutan and its cousin were widespread and successful members of the Plio-Pleistocene fauna in southeast Asia when the hominoids from Africa first appeared there.

The overall pattern of hominoid paleogeography through the last 15 m.y. can be summarized as follows: initial expansion and diversification; extinction and range contraction; evolution of a few surviving groups in Africa and southeast Asia; followed finally by a second phase of range expansion from Africa by the genus *Homo*. This pattern is seen from the perspective of our present fossil evidence. New information, particularly for the period between 7 and 4 m.y. B.P., might change it drastically, for example, if a hominoid is found that originated in Asia and migrated into Africa during this time interval (24). There is enough to the present pattern, however, to enable us to examine it in the context of global climates and continental-scale tectonics.

GEOLOGICAL CHANGES AND HOMINOID EVOLUTION

Major environmental changes for the 15 to 1 m.y. B.P. time period are shown in Figure 2 in relation to the hominoid localities and major events in hominoid evolution. Prior to 15 m.y. B.P. global climates were relatively warm (45, 91) and subtropical floras were present in southern Eurasia (7, 69). A significant cooling trend, associated with the formation of a permanent Antarctic ice cap, began around 15 to 14 m.y. B.P. (45, 91). This reached its present extent by 11–12 m.y. B.P., and global cooling continued into the Pleistocene. Superimposed upon this trend was the Messinian event between 6.5 and 5.5 m.y. B.P. when the Antarctic ice cap suddenly expanded; sea level dropped, and the Mediterranean Sea became a closed evaporitic basin (84). After a return to an open Mediterranean in the early Pliocene, glaciation began in the northern hemisphere 2.5–3.0 m.y. B.P. and full glacial conditions were reached by about 1.8 m.y. B.P. The effects of the glacial cycles on low latitude climates are not well understood, but there is evidence for generally dry conditions in East Africa with shorter periods of increased moisture (19, 25, 52).

Major tectonic changes in Eurasia and Africa over the past 15 m.y. involve the collision of the African and Indian continental blocks with Eurasia and the full development of the East African and Red Sea rift systems (32, 73, 79). The northward drift of Africa established the land bridge with Eurasia between 18 and 16 m.y. B.P., a time when many endemic African mammals, including hominoids, emigrated to Eurasia (83, 86). The draining of the Tethys and Paratethys seaways, along with the uplift of multiple mountain belts in southern Eurasia, changed this region from oceanic to continental climatic regimes. Increased seasonality and drier conditions overall can be attributed to the tectonic evolution of region, although the global cooling trend is probably also reflected in the floral and faunal changes of the late Miocene. The effects of the Messinian event on the floras and faunas are not well understood, although documentation exists for faunal exchange between Africa and Europe across the Betic strait in the western Mediterranean (38).

Within Africa, the uplift of the Kenyan and Ethiopian domes during early and middle Miocene was accompanied by vulcanism and later by rifting, creating a varied mosaic of habitats with sharp topographic boundaries where formerly (in the early Miocene) there had been a more uniform tropical rain forest (6, 86). Changes to more open conditions and the evolution of the savanna-mosaic flora and fauna can be explained by a combination of the regional tectonic processes and the overall global cooling. However, the diversity of local rainfall and temperature conditions, which was undoubtedly represented in the past as it is today in East Africa, is the unique result of the rift valley setting.

From a 15 m.y. perspective, the timing of the important events in hominoid evolution (Figure 2) appears to correspond to periods of more rapid global climate change, with dentition evolution occurring during the onset of the middle Miocene cooling trend and increased brain size and stone tool manufacture accompanying the beginning of northern hemisphere glaciation. On this basis we might predict that the fossil evidence, when it is found, will show that bipedality emerged out of the environmental pressures of the Messinian event. However, many of the important evolutionary changes leading to *Homo*, such as speech and the development of complex social behavior, cannot be placed within this time-climate framework. Moreover, the beginning of tool manufacture and use may be inaccurately represented, since we can only document those tools made from stone or bone. There are indications about how global-scale changes affected the course of human evolution, but to conclude that megaprocesses were the major driving force is premature.

The paleogeographic pattern of the hominoids through time is more easily linked to tectonic changes and their climatic consequences than to the general trend of global cooling. The Eurasian evergreen woodland and subtropical forest habitats that existed when the hominoids first emerged from Africa were gradually eliminated as continental climates accompanying the emergence of the mountain belts became dominant. The hominoid radiation that was in its initial phase during the middle Miocene terminated. We can only speculate as to how many new forms might have evolved, given a few more million years of stable habitats in Eurasia. Hominoids continued to survive in both southeast Asia and Africa, but apparently only Africa produced a lineage of bipedal forms with expanded crania and cultural ability. Perhaps both survival and the course of hominoid evolution in Africa were related to the productivity and diversity of habitats that characterized the rift valley setting, possibly providing a regional buffering of global scale events such as the Messinian.

RECONSTRUCTING HOMINOID PALEOECOLOGY

Within the large geographical regions inhabited by hominoids during the 15 to 1 m.y. B.P. period, there were many physical environments and vegetational provinces containing a wide variety of smaller-scale habitats. Geological reconstruction and taphonomic analysis of fossil localities, both with and without hominoid remains, is being used in attempts to show which of these habitats were preferred by the different hominoid genera.

Analysis of the sediments and faunas associated with hominoid remains in the middle Miocene sites of Maboko and Fort Ternan in East Africa indicates a densely wooded floodplain for the former and a mixed forest-woodland savanna for the latter (55). The existence of patches of more open habitat at Fort Ternan is inferred from the presence of ostriches and artiodactyls with dentition indicative of mixed grass and browse diets. At Fort Ternan there is taphonomic evidence that the forest elements in the fauna, including *Proconsul*, were transported to the burial site, while the remains of *Ramapithecus* and the more open country forms were locally available for burial (74). The interpretation that *Ramapithecus* was adapting to more open habitats in Africa at about 14 m.y. B.P. is based on the contextual evidence from Fort Ternan, and also on the differences in dentition, which suggest a major change in diet relative to other hominoids of that time.

Middle Miocene hominoid localities in southern Europe and western Asia have not been studied in comparable detail. The presence of lignites at a number of localities documents the existence of coal-forming swamps or wet forests, and the presence of hominoid remains in the lignitic sediments indicates that they inhabited this environment. Hominoids are also preserved in fluvial and lacustrine deposits lacking coals, however, and in association with mammals that represent a variety of habitats from forest to grassland. The combined contextual evidence suggests that the hominoids preferred the more densely vegetated habitats or portions of habitat mosaics that offered a spectrum from forest to savanna.

Paleoecological study of late Miocene hominoid localities in northern Pakistan (Khaur, Sethi Nagri; Table 1) allows reconstruction of their life habitat as a broad, well-drained alluvial plain with meandering-to-braided rivers and a variety of soil types, indicating a vegetation mosaic. Because most of the fossil remains occur in channel deposits and were transported from different parts of this mosaic, it is not possible to resolve the preferred habitat of the hominoids (8). Judging from modern analogues for alluvial plains and the mixture of feeding and locomotor types in the associated mammalian fauna, forest, woodland, and grassland habitats were all available (8). There does not appear to have been any sudden change in this pattern across the time interval (7–8 m.y. B.P.) when the hominoids became locally extinct.

Thorough faunal analysis and study of sedimentologic and taphonomic context at two important late Miocene localities that lack hominoids [Samos in Greece (78) and Maragheh in Iran (23)] show that in both cases open-country, woodland-to-savanna mammal communities are strongly represented. This offers evidence that the hominoids occupied more densely vegetated habitats (23) up to the time when they virtually disappeared from the Eurasian paleocommunity.

The Plio-Pleistocene record in Africa provides many opportunities for contextual studies of hominoid localities, and a number have been done in South and East Africa. The Pliocene localities of Laetoli and Hadar show strong contrast between the habitats occupied by *Australopithecus*, with Laetoli consisting of dry volcanic slopes with open bush-to-grassland (50) while Hadar was characterized by low-lying lake margins and floodplains (44). At Laetoli, the hominoid footprints associated with those of other savanna mammals provide the best possible fossil evidence for their life-association with this community (49). There is little doubt that by the middle Pliocene, hominoids were capable of ranging over a variety of habitats. Which, if any, they preferred cannot yet be determined.

Study of the context of hominoid fossils (*Homo* and *Australopithecus*) and archeological materials between 3.0 and 1.0 m.y. B.P. in East and South Africa documents a persistent association with the savanna-mosaic mammal community (85), which includes species adapted to habitats ranging from riverine forest to open grassland to semiarid bush. There is supporting paleobotanical evidence for this spectrum in East Africa (19), along with indications that conditions became drier during the early Pleistocene. There is some evidence that the more robust species of *Australopithecus*, which appears in the record about 2.5 m.y. B.P., preferred more vegetated habitats than did *Homo* (12, 15, 89), but overall there is no particular pattern of habitat association within the available sample for the Plio-Pleistocene hominoids. The sedimentary contexts listed for localities in Table 1 represent only those that provided favorable conditions for fossil preservation, a small portion of the habitats that were actually available to the hominoids.

Archeological sites are also distributed across the spectrum of sedimentary environments, although there is a distinct pattern of preference at East Lake Turkana for fluvial rather than lake margin occupation (35). In one case, geological reconstruction and pollen show that habitation occurred on the bank of a shallow, probably seasonal river, with some gallery woodland along the banks and semiarid bush vegetation on the adjacent floodplain (22).

The hominid branch of the hominoids had produced forms that were adapted to drier, more open savanna habitats by the middle Pliocene, if not earlier. Other African hominoids, presumably the ancestors to *Pan* and *Gorilla*, left no associated fossil record and were probably excluded from such habitats. Important ecological factors in selecting for the characteristic attributes of *Homo* probably included the increasingly fluctuating, arid and seasonal conditions of the Plio-Pleistocene. The occurrence of hominid remains and traces in a wide spectrum of Plio-Pleistocene contexts suggests that one of the earlier hominid adaptations was ecological opportunism, perhaps in response to fluctuating resources.

CONCLUSION

Studies of geological context in hominoid evolution have modified the concepts originally derived from comparative anatomy and behavior of apes and humans. The idea of a forest origin remains, but we see it now as only an initial step that occurred over 15 m.y. ago along with a few morphological changes that accompanied the emergence of some of the hominoids into a more open woodland habitat. The ecological significance of this transition is that the more open tree canopy of the woodland encourages more terrestrial locomotion, and a different dietary strategy is necessary because of seasonal resources. Once adapted to woodland habitats, the hominoids apparently remained in these for a long period of time and did not produce more open savanna forms until the late Miocene to Pliocene in Africa.

This interpretation of the evidence rests heavily upon the lines of reasoning described earlier, and represents only one of the likely hypotheses. It does show, however, how the contextual evidence has contributed a new perspective on hominoid evolution, one with many intriguing implications for how we perceive our ancestral story. Among these implications is the possibility that our similarities to modern apes are based on a common woodland ancestor rather than (or in addition to) a forest one.

The juxtaposition of the evolutionary story of global climates and continental tectonics and the patterns of change in the hominoids leads to many possible hypotheses concerning cause and effect. We need to know more about smaller-scale environmental patterns, however, before concluding that human evolution responded to megageological processes. There are many different scales of process, in time and space, that could have provided the critical selective pressures for important thresholds in human evolution. The idea that these processes may have been at times in phase with the global changes, thus linking them directly to hominoid evolution, is possible and intriguing. With further study of the geological context of hominoid evolution, we will undoubtedly be able to say more about this in the future.

ACKNOWLEDGMENTS

The ideas in this paper have grown out of discussions with many colleagues and thus represent far more than I could have achieved independently. I thank all of them, but accept full responsibility for the viewpoints presented. I thank David Pilbeam, John Barry, and Catherine Badgley, in particular, for discussions and help in compiling the background information. I also thank Hu Chang Kang and Li Youheng for help with Chinese paleoanthropology. The initial impetus for the paper came from a symposium organized for the Geological Society of America's annual meeting in 1979 by Léo F. Laporte.

Literature Cited

1. Andrews, P. 1981. Hominoid habitats of the Miocene. *Nature* 289:749
2. Andrews, P., Evans, E. M. N. 1979. The Environment of *Ramapithecus* in Africa. *Paleobiology* 5:22–30
3. Andrews, P., Hamilton, W. R., Whybrow, P. J. 1978. Dryopithecines from the Miocene of Saudi Arabia. *Nature* 274:249–51
4. Andrews, P., Meyer, G. E., Pilbeam, D. R., Van Couvering, J. A., Van Couvering, J. A. H. 1981. The Miocene fossil beds of Maboko Island, Kenya: Geology, age, taphonomy, and paleontology. *J. Hum. Evol.* 10:35–48
5. Andrews, P., Tobien, H. 1977. New Miocene locality in Turkey with evidence on the origin of *Ramapithecus* and *Sivapithecus*. *Nature* 268:699–701
6. Andrews, P., Van Couvering, J. A. H. 1975. Paleoenvironments in the East African Miocene. In *Approaches to Primate Paleobiology*, ed. F. Szalay, pp. 62–103. Basel: Karger
7. Axelrod, D. I. 1975. Evolution and biogeography of Madrean-Tethyan Sclerophyll vegetation. *Ann. Missouri Bot. Gard.* 62:280–334
8. Badgley, C. E., Behrensmeyer, A. K. 1980. Paleoecology of middle Siwalik sediments and faunas, northern Pakistan. *Palaeogeogr. Palaeoclimatol. Palaeoecol.* 30:133–55
9. Barry, J. C., Lindsay, E. H., Jacobs, L. L. 1982. A biostratigraphic zonation of the middle and upper Siwaliks of the Potwar Plateau of northern Pakistan. *Palaeogeogr. Palaeoclimatatol. Palaeoecol.* In press
10. Behrensmeyer, A. K. 1976. Lothagam Hill, Kanapoi, and Ekora: a general summary of stratigraphy and faunas. In *Earliest Man and Environments in the Lake Rudolf Basin*, ed. Y. Coppens, F. C. Howell, G. L. Isaac, R. E. Leakey, pp. 163–70. Chicago: Univ. Chicago Press. 609 pp.
11. Behrensmeyer, A. K. 1978a. Correlation of Plio-Pleistocene sequences in the northern Lake Turkana Basin: a summary of evidence and issues. In *Geological Background to Fossil Man*, ed. W. W. Bishop, pp. 421–40. Edinburgh: Scottish Acad. 585 pp.
12. Behrensmeyer, A. K. 1978b. The habitat of Plio-Pleistocene hominids in East Africa: taphonomic and micro-stratigraphic evidence. In *Early Hominids of Africa*, ed. C. Jolly, pp. 165–90. London: Duckworth. 598 pp.

13. Bernor, R. L., Andrews, P. J., Solounias, N., Van Couvering, J. A. H. 1979. The evolution of "Pontian" mammal faunas: some zoogeographic, paleoecologic and chronostratigraphic consideration. *Ann. Geol. Pays Héll.*, Tome hors série 1:81–89
14. Bishop, N. W., Hill, A., Pickford, M. 1978. Chesowanja: a revised geological interpretation. See Ref. 11, pp. 307–27
15. Boaz, N. T. 1977. Paleoecology of early hominids in Africa. *Kroeber Anthro. Soc. Pap.* No. 50: 37–62. Berkeley: Univ. Calif.
16. Boaz, N. T. 1980. A hominoid clavicle from the Mio-Pliocene of Sahabi, Libya. *Am. J. Phys. Anthro.* 53:49–54
17. Boaz, N. T., Gaziry, A. W., El-Arnauti, A. 1979. New fossil finds from the Libyan upper Neogene site of Sahabi. *Nature* 280:137–40
18. DeBonis, L., Melentis, J. 1977. Les primates hominoides du Vallésian de Macédoine (Grece). *Geobios* 10:849–85
19. Bonnefille, R. 1979. Méthode palynologique et reconstitutions paléoclimatiques au Cenozoique dans le Rift East Africain. *Bull. Soc. Géol. France* 21:331–42
20. Brain, C. K. 1958. *The Transvaal Ape-Man-Bearing Cave Deposits. Mem. No. 11*, Pretoria: Transvaal Mus. 125 pp.
21. Brain, C. K. 1976. A re-interpretation of the Swartkrans site and its remains. *S. Afr. J. Sci.* 72:141–46
22. Bunn, H., Harris, J. W. K., Isaac, G., Kaufulu, Z., Kroll, E., Schick, K., Toth, N., Behrensmeyer, A. K. 1980. FxJ;50: an early Pleistocene site in northern Kenya. *World Archeol.* 12:109–36
23. Campbell, B. G., Amini, M. H., Bernor, R. L., Dickinson, W., Drake, R., Morris, R., Van Couvering, J. A., Van Couvering, J. A. H. 1980. Maragheh: a classical late Miocene vertebrate locality in northwestern Iran. *Nature* 287:838–41
24. Campbell, B. G., Bernor, R. L. 1976. The origin of the Hominidae: Africa or Asia? *J. Hum. Evol.* 5:441–54
25. Cerling, T. E., Hay, R. L., O'Neil, J. R. 1977. Isotopic evidence for dramatic climatic changes in East Africa during the Pleistocene. *Nature* 267:137–38
26. Chou, C. S., Li, C. K., Chou, C. T. 1979. The Chinese Neogene—a preliminary review of the mammalian localities and faunas. *Ann. Geol. Pays Héll.* 1:263–72, Intern. Congr. Mediterranean Neogene, 7th, Athens, 1979
27. Chavaillon, J., Coppens, Y. 1975. Découverte d'Hominidé dans un site Acheuléen de Melka Kunture (Ethiopie) *Bull. Mém. Soc. Anthropol. Paris* 2:125–28
28. Chow, M. 1958. Mammalian faunas and correlation of Tertiary and early Pleistocene of South China. *Pal. Soc. India* Memorial Number, Lucknow, 3: 125–27
29. Clark, J. D., Kurashina, H. 1979. Hominid occupation of the East-Central Highlands of Ethiopia in the Plio-Pleistocene. *Nature* 282:33–39
30. Crusafont-Pairó, M., Golpe-Posse, J. M. 1973. New pongids from the Miocene of Vallès Penedes Basin (Catalonia, Spain). *J. Hum. Evol.* 2:17–23
31. Curtis, G. H., Hay, R. L. 1972. Further geological studies and potassium-argon dating at Olduvai Gorge and Ngorongoro Crater. In *Calibration of Hominoid Evolution*, ed., W. W. Bishop, J. A. Miller, pp. 289–301. Edinburgh: Scottish Acad. 487 pp.
32. Dewey, J. F., Pitman, W. C., Ryan, W. B., Bonnin, J. 1973. Plate Tectonics and the evolution of the Alpine system. *Geol. Soc. Am. Bull.* 84:3137–80
33. Dorofeyev, P. I. 1966. Flora of *Hipparion* epoch. *Int. Geol. Rev.* 8:1109–16
34. Fergusen, D. K. 1972. The Miocene flora of Kreuzau, Western Germany. *Verhand. Afdeling Natuukunde* 60:1–29
35. Harris, J. W. K., Isaac, G. 1976. The Karari Industry: early Pleistocene archeological evidence from the terrain east of Lake Turkana, Kenya. *Nature* 262:1O2–7
36. Howell, F. C. 1972. Pliocene/Pleistocene Hominidae in Eastern Africa: absolute and relative ages. See Ref. 31, pp. 289–301
37. Howell, F. C. 1978. Chapter 10: Hominidae. In *Evolution of African Mammals*, ed. V. J. Maglio, H. B. S. Cooke, pp. 154–249. Cambridge: Harvard Univ. Press. 641 pp.
38. Howell, F. C. 1980. Zonation of late Miocene and early Pliocene circum-Mediterranean faunas. *Geobios* 13:653–57
39. Howell, F. C., Coppens, Y. 1976. An overview of Hominidae from the Omo succession, Ethiopia. See Ref. 10, pp. 522–32
40. Hu, C. C. 1973. Ape-man teeth from Yuanmou, Yunnan. *Acta Geol. Sin.* 1:65–71
41. Isaac, G. L. 1967. The stratigraphy of the Peninj Group - early middle Pleistocene formations west of Lake Natron, Tanzania. In *Background to Evolution in Africa*, ed. W. W. Bishop, J. D. Clark, pp. 229–57. Chicago: Univ. Chicago Press. 935 pp.

42. Isaac, G. L., Curtis, G. H. 1974. Age of early Acheulian industries from the Peninj Group, Tanzania. *Nature* 249:624–26
43. Jacob, T. 1973. Palaeoanthropological discoveries in Indonesia with special reference to the finds of the last two decades. *J. Hum. Evol.* 2:473–85
44. Johanson, D. C., Taieb, M., Gray, B. T., Coppens, Y. 1978. Geological framework of the Pliocene Hadar Formation (Afar, Ethiopia) with notes on paleontology including hominids. See Ref. 11, pp. 549–64
45. Kennett, J.P. 1977. Cenozoic evolution of Antarctic glaciation, the circum-Antarctic Ocean, and their impact on global paleooceanography. *J. Geophys. Res.* 82:3843–60
46. Kretzoi, M. 1975. New ramapithecines and *Pliopithecus* from the Lower Pliocene of Rudabanya in north-eastern Hungary. *Nature* 257:578–81
47. Leakey, M. D. 1971. *Olduvai Gorge, Excavations in Beds I and II*. Cambridge: Univ. Press 299 pp.
48. Leakey, M. D. 1978. Olduvai fossil hominids: their stratigraphic positions and associations. See Ref. 12, pp. 3–16
49. Leakey, M. D., Hay, R. L. 1979. Pliocene footprints in the Laetoli Beds at Laetoli, northern Tanzania. *Nature* 278:317–23
50. Leakey, M. D., Hay, R. L., Curtis, G. H., Drake, R. E., Jackes, M. K. 1976. Fossil hominids from the Laetolil Beds. *Nature* 262:460–66
51. Leakey, M. G., Leakey, R. E., eds. 1978. *Koobi Fora Research Project*, Vol. 1. Oxford: Clarendon. 191 pp.
52. Manabe, S., Hahn, D. G. 1977. Simulation of the tropical climate of an ice age. *J. Geophys. Res.* 82:3889–911
53. Martyn, J., Tobias, P. V. 1967. Pleistocene deposits and new fossil localities in Kenya. *Nature* 215:476–80
54. McFadden, P. L., Brock, A., Partridge, T. C. 1979. Paleomagnetism and the age of the Makapansgat hominid site. *Earth Planet. Sci. Lett.* 44:373–82
55. Nesbit Evans, E. M., Van Couvering, J. A. H., Andrews, P. 1981. Paleoecology of Miocene sites in western Kenya. *J. Hum. Evol.* 10:99–116
56. Ninkovich, D., Burkle, L. H. 1978. Absolute age of the base of the hominid-bearing beds of eastern Java. *Nature* 275:306–8
57. Ozansoy, F. 1970. *Ankarapithecus meteai*, pongidé fosille aux traits humains du Pliocène de Turquie. *Belleten Tûrk Tarih Kurumu* 34:1–15
58. Partridge, T. C. 1978. Re-appraisal of lithostratigraphy of Sterkfontein hominid site. *Nature* 275:282–87
59. Partridge, T. C. 1979. Re-appraisal of lithostratigraphy of Makapansgat Limeworks hominid site. *Nature* 279:484–88
60. Patterson, B., Behrensmeyer, A. K., Sill, W. D. 1970. Geology and fauna of a new Pliocene fauna in northwestern Kenya. *Nature* 226:918–21
61. Patterson, B., Howells, W. W. 1967. Hominid humeral fragment from the early Pleistocene of northwestern Kenya. *Azania* 2:1–15
62. Pei, W. C. 1962. Quaternary mammals from the Liucheng *Gigantopithecus* cave and other caves of Kwangsi. *Vert. Palasiat.* 6:211–18
63. Pickford, M. H. L. 1978a. Stratigraphy and mammalian paleontology of the late Miocene Lukeino Formation, Kenya. See Ref. 11, pp. 263–78
64. Pickford, M. H. L. 1978b. Geology, palaeoenvironments and vertebrate faunas of the mid-Miocene Ngorora Formation, Kenya. See Ref. 11, pp. 237–62
65. Pilbeam, D. 1979. Recent finds and interpretations of Miocene hominoids. *Ann. Rev. Anthropol.* 8:333–52
66. Pilbeam, D. 1980. Major trends in human evolution. In *Current Argument on Early Man*, ed. L. K. Konigsson, pp. 261–85. New York: Pergamon
67. Pilbeam, D. R., Simons, E. 1971. Humerus of *Dryopithecus* from Saint Gaudens, France. *Nature* 229:408–9
68. Pope, G. G. 1977. Hominids from the lower Pleistocene of South China. *Kroeber Anthr. Soc. Pap.* No. 50:63–73
69. Prakash, U. 1973. Palaeoenvironmental analysis of Indian Tertiary floras. *Geophytology* 2:178–205
70. Prasad, K. N. 1971. Ecology of the fossil Hominoidea from the Siwaliks of India. *Nature* 232:413–14
71. Qi, G. 1979. Pliocene mammalian fauna of Lufeng, Yunnan. *Vert. Palasiat.* 17:14–22
72. Xu, Q. H., Lu, Q. W. 1979. The mandibles of *Ramapithecus* and *Sivapithecus* from Lufeng, Yunnan. *Vert. Palasiat.* 17:12–13
73. Shackleton, R. M. 1978. Structural development of the East African Rift System. See Ref. 11, pp. 19–28
74. Shipman, P., Walker, A., Van Couvering, J. A., Hooker, P. J., Miller, J. A. 1981. The Fort Ternan hominoid site: Geology, age, taphonomy, and paleoecology. *J. Hum. Evol.* 10:49–72
75. Sickenberg, O. 1975. Die Gliederung des höheren Jungtertiärs und Altquartärs in der Türkei nach Vertebraten und ihre Bedeutung für die internationale Neogen-Stratigraphie. *Geol. Jahrbuch* B 5:3–167

76. Simons, E. L., Chopra, S. R. K. 1969. *Gigantopithecus* (Pongidae, Hominoidea) a new species from north India. *Postilla* 138:1–18
77. Simons, E. L., Pilbeam, D. R. 1965. Preliminary revision of the Dryopithecinae (Pondidae, Anthropoidea). *Folia Primatol*. 3:81–152
78. Solounias, N. 1979. The Turolian fauna from the island of Samos, Greece. In *Contributions to Vertebrate Evolution*, Vol. 6, ed. M. K. Hecht, F. S. Szalay. Basel: Karger. 232 pp.
79. Steininger, F. F., Papp. A. 1979. Current biostratigraphic and radiometric correlations of Late Miocene Central Paratethys stages and the Messinian Event in the Parathethys. *Newsl. Stratigr.* 8:100–10
80. Szalay, F. S., Delson, E. 1979. *Evolutionary History of the Primates*. New York: Academic. 580 pp.
81. Tekkaya, I. 1974. A new species of Tortonian anthropoid (Primates, Mammalia) from Anatolia. *Bull. Min. Res. Explor. Inst. Turkey* 83:148–65
82. Tobias, P. V. 1978. The South African Australopithecines in time and hominid phylogeny, with special reference to the dating and affinities of the Taung skull. See Ref. 12, pp. 45–84
83. Van Couvering, J. A., Berggren, W. A. 1977. Biostratigraphical basis of the Neogene time scale. In *Concepts and Methods in Biostratigraphy*, ed. E. G. Kauffman, J. E. Hazel, pp. 283–306. Stroudsburg: Dowden, Hutchinson, Ross
84. Van Couvering, J. A., Berggren, W. A., Drake, R. E., Aguirre, E., Curtis, G. H. 1976. The terminal Miocene event. *Mar. Micropaleontol.* 1:263–86
85. Van Couvering, J. A. H. 1980. Community evolution in East Africa during the late Cenozoic. In *Fossils in the Making*, ed. A. K. Behrensmeyer, A. P. Hill, pp. 272–98. Chicago: Univ. Chicago Press. 338pp.
86. Van Couvering, J. A. H., Van Couvering, J. A. 1976. Early Miocene mammal fossils from East Africa: aspects of geology, faunistics and paleoecology. In *Human Origins*, ed. G. Isaac, E. McCown, pp. 155–208. Menlo Park, Calif: Benjamin. 591 pp.
87. Vincens, A. 1979. Analyse palynologique du site archéologique FxJ:50. Formation de Koobi Fora, Est Turkana, (Kenya). *Bull. Soc. Géol. France* 21:343–47
88. Von Koenigswald, G. H. R. 1972. Ein unterkiefer eines fossilen Hominoiden aus dem unterploizän Griechenlands. *K. Ned. Akad. Wet. Proc.* 75:385–94
89. Vrba, E. S. 1975. Some evidence of chronology and paleoecology of Sterkfontein, Swartkrans and Kromdrai from the fossil Bovidae. *Nature* 254:301–4
90. Woo, J. 1958. New materials of *Dryopithecus* from Keiyuan, Yunnan. *Vert. Palasiat*. 2:38–42
91. Woodruff, F., Savin, S. M., Douglas, R. G. 1981. Miocene stable isotope record: a detailed deep Pacific Ocean study and its paleoclimatic implications. *Nature* 212:665–68
92. Zapfe, H. 1961. Ergebnisse einer Untersuchung der Austriacopithecus-Reste aus dem Mittelmiozän von Klein-Hadersdorf. *Stiz.-Ber. Akad. Wiss., Math.-Naturw., Wien* 170:139–48

Ann. Rev. Earth Planet. Sci. 1982. 10:61-108

DYNAMICAL CONSTRAINTS ON THE FORMATION AND EVOLUTION OF PLANETARY BODIES

Alan W. Harris and William R. Ward

Jet Propulsion Laboratory, California Institute of Technology, Pasadena, California

1. INTRODUCTION

In this paper we review a number of inferences as to the origin of planetary bodies based on the present dynamical state of the solar system, and point out some of the limitations that apply to these conclusions. Such inferences are generally based on the present orbits (spacing, eccentricity, and inclination), the rotational characteristics (period of rotation and tilt of the spin axis), internal heat (heat flow and evidence of past heat, such as crustal thickness and volcanism), and bulk composition. We discuss here only dynamical processes, specifically those processes that may have influenced the orbital or rotational properties of the planets and satellites.

The organization of the paper is as follows. In Section 2 we review the collisional processes often presumed to have produced the present dynamical state of the solar system: the size and spacing of the individual planets and their rotational motions. We note in Section 2.4 that some inferences from these calculations do not entirely agree with the present system. In Section 3 we discuss processes by which the original rotational motion of the planets, spin rate, and obliquity (tilt of the rotational axis to the orbit plane) may have been altered. The most important effects are tidal friction and resonances, sometimes acting in combination. In Section 4 we describe processes by which the orbital characteristics—spacing, eccentricity, and relative inclinations of the orbits—may have been altered. Again tidal and resonance interactions are most important. We note in Sections 3 and 4 that some resonance effects may

0084-6597/82/0515-0061$02.00

have been induced by the "solar nebula" disk from which the planets presumably formed. We conclude that a proper accounting for these effects may result in a scenario of planet formation considerably different from present ones, and one presumably free of most of the problems outlined in Section 2.4.

It is beyond the scope of this paper to thoroughly review such a broad range of topics. For subjects that have been reviewed previously (e.g. tidal evolution of the lunar orbit), we discuss only recent results and refer the reader to the earlier reviews for background information. For newer topics (e.g. disk dynamics) we provide a heuristic development of the subject to allow the reader to understand the results qualitatively. It is not our aim to provide a working mechanical formalism for any problem; we concentrate, instead, on providing a general overview of the many processes involved.

2. COLLISIONAL PROCESSES

The general features of terrestrial planet growth by collisional accumulation of planetesimals are reviewed by Wetherill (1980), so we mention only those aspects bearing directly on the final dynamic state of the planetary system at the conclusion of accumulation. The questions of timescale of planetary growth, mass distribution of growing protoplanetary bodies, and velocity dispersion during growth are all well summarized by Wetherill (1980). It suffices for our purpose to simply note that there is disagreement as to whether planetary accretion proceeded in such a way that most of the mass was always concentrated in the largest bodies (e.g. Safronov 1969), or whether a few planet embryos emerged and then quickly swept up the much smaller particles before they had a chance to grow significantly larger than their initial sizes (e.g. Greenberg et al 1978). In the former case, the "second largest bodies" are perhaps $\sim 10^{-3}$ (or larger) of the mass of the planet embryo and keep pace with it as it grows. The dispersion velocity is controlled by the planet embryo and is of the order of the surface escape velocity of that body. In the latter situation, the bulk of the mass remains in the small end of the mass distribution, and the dispersion velocity is controlled by those small bodies at a value near their surface escape velocity. Such low encounter velocities do not allow sufficient radial excursions for the present planets to clear the space between them; thus in the absence of intervening processes, accumulation stagnates with a large number of mini-planets rather than the actual four terrestrial planets. In the following three subsections, we examine the observational evidence that has been offered in support of the above possibilities.

2.1 Orbital Spacing

As the planetesimal swarm accumulates by mutual collisions into fewer bodies of larger size, there eventually comes a time when there are so few bodies separated by such large distances that collisions no longer occur. If this point is reached before the swarm is reduced to a few bodies of planetary size, then one must assume that some other process of radial transport of particles was also operative.

One approach to this question is to ask what relative velocity of a small planetesimal is required to assure that no matter what its orbital semimajor axis, it will cross the orbit of the nearest planet embryo somewhere in its own orbit. For the earth zone, a free orbital eccentricity of $\gtrsim 0.15$ will assure that a particle in such an orbit will intersect the orbit of Venus, Earth, or Mars no matter where between these planets the semimajor axis lies. This eccentricity corresponds to a velocity relative to the Earth at encounter of ~4 km/sec, which is very close to the value estimated by Safronov (1969) as the terminal random velocity generated by gravitational encounters between planetesimals and growing planet embryos. It was noted by Safronov, however, that in an isolated system containing only one massive planetary body, a gravitational encounter with a second ("massless") body will occur at the same orbital radius as the previous encounter; thus successive encounters will not "pump-up" eccentricity but only alter the orbit in random steps with no trend toward increasing eccentricity. Under these circumstances, the relative velocity may be controlled not by the planet embryo, but by bodies of the "second largest" size, presumed to be very numerous but much smaller. If this is the case, as has been argued by Levin (1978), then the random velocities of planetesimals never become large enough to allow sweep-up of all the matter from between the planets, and we must seek other mechanisms to transport matter into the narrow accretion zones of the planet embryos.

Safronov (1969) argues that stagnation will not occur, because velocities will remain high enough that a significant fraction of the planetesimals will cross not one but two embryo orbits, thus assuring that the pumping-up action continues. Wetherill (1977) showed by numerical calculation that such a two-planet pumping mechanism can yield relative velocities of ~7–10 km/sec in the earth zone.

The conclusion to be drawn from the above is that if relative velocities were ever as large as ~4 km/sec in the earth zone, then accumulation into as few as 4 planets seems assured. Unfortunately, the question of random velocity is unsettled because of uncertainty in the mass distribution of particles during planet growth.

One can approach the question from the opposite extreme: suppose a "massless" planetesimal were initially in a circular orbit near that of a planet embryo of mass m, also in circular orbit. What is the maximum orbit spacing, d, that would assure that the perturbed orbit would cross the planet's orbit after a single encounter? This distance is the minimum spacing between planets that could occur as an end point of accumulation. We neglect for the moment the curvature of the orbit motion. The test particle, initially moving tangentially to m with an impact parameter d, acquires a radial velocity impulse

$$\Delta v_{\perp} \approx \int_{-\infty}^{\infty} Gmd(v^2t^2 + d^2)^{-3/2}\, dt = 2Gm/vd, \tag{2.1}$$

where the approximation is valid for $\Delta v_{\perp} << v$. The radial excursion experienced by the particle in its new elliptic orbit is $\Delta v_{\perp}/\Omega$, where Ω is the orbit frequency about the sun. By equating this radial excursion with d we find the spacing at which the initially circular orbits just become crossing after one synodic pass. The relative velocity for Keplerian motion is $v = (3/2)\,\Omega\, d$, and the orbit frequency about the sun at orbit radius a is $\Omega^2 = GM_{\odot}/a^3$. The minimum separation is thus

$$d \approx \left(\frac{4}{3}\frac{m}{M_{\odot}}\right)^{1/3} a \approx 1.6 r_{\mathrm{L}_1}, \tag{2.2}$$

where r_{L_1} is the distance to the Lagrange point L_1 about m, which defines the "sphere of influence" of m. Numerical integrations of three-body motion (see Section 4.3, Figure 8) verify the dimensionality of (2.2), but with a lead coefficient of ~3.0. Nacozy (1976) reached a similar result in numerical integrations of the Sun/Jupiter/Saturn system with increased masses of Jupiter and Saturn. He further showed that the condition for long-term stability vs immediate instability is very sharp. Thus, while a system with two orbits separated by 3.0 r_{L_1} becomes unstable (orbits crossing) very quickly, a spacing of only 4.0 r_{L_1} remains stable for thousands of orbits—as long as one can integrate meaningfully on the computer. Lecar & Franklin (1973) considered the stability of hypothetical asteroid orbits between Mars and Jupiter and between Jupiter and Saturn. They found by numerical integration that asteroids closer to Jupiter than the 2:1 interior resonance ($a > 3.3$ AU) tended to be unstable. This corresponds to a distance of $\sim 5 r_{\mathrm{L}_1}$ from Jupiter's orbit. Similarly, they found that very few asteroid orbits between Jupiter and Saturn appear to be stable, even though an orbit at ~7.2 AU is ~5.4 r_{L_1} from either planet. This decreased stability is probably due to the inclusion of eccentricity in the orbits and the effect of resonances with the very massive planets.

From the above results, the present solar system appears somewhat overstable to the degree that if there were, say, three planets comprising the same mass as Jupiter and Saturn and occupying the same region between Mars and Uranus, they and their neighbors could remain stable. A similar configuration could probably be tolerated replacing Earth and Venus by three planets. One might wonder therefore why the mass of the solar nebula did not aggregate into a larger number of planets more closely spaced. The failure to do so suggests that there may have been other mechanisms contributing to radial transport of the matter that was accumulated into the planets (see Section 4).

2.2 *Planetary Rotation: Ordered Component*

It has long been suggested that the preferential prograde rotation of planets is somehow a result of the accumulation process. Safronov (1969) reviews earlier analytical attempts to solve the problem and concludes that they are all unsatisfactory. The first satisfactory approach was that of Giuli (1968), who showed by numerical integration that prograde rotation with a period of 10–20 hours resulted if Earth accumulated from planetesimals in earth-crossing orbits of low eccentricity ($e \sim 0.03$). Harris (1977) produced an analytical theory based on Giuli's model that allowed a wider range of conditions to be examined. The physical explanation for the prograde rotation can be seen in Figure 1. Consider the range of possible impact trajectories on a planet in circular orbit from a particle in a nearly tangent (interior or exterior) coplanar orbit. If one imagined a stream of particles rather than a single particle, the impacting stream would sweep inward across the planet until the planet passed the perihelion (aphelion) of the stream orbit, then the stream would reverse and reemerge on the same limb as it entered. Since particles in exterior orbits overtake the planet, while interior particles are overtaken by the planet, both streams contribute, on the average, a prograde angular momentum. A stream of particles sweeping completely across the planet (i.e. a fully crossing rather than tangential orbit) produces no significant angular momentum, prograde or retrograde. The increment of angular momentum, $\mathrm{d}h$, acquired as a planet accumulates an increment $\mathrm{d}m$ of mass can be written

$$\mathrm{d}h = \int_0^\infty n(v)f(v)\bar{\ell}v \,\mathrm{d}m\,\mathrm{d}v, \tag{2.3}$$

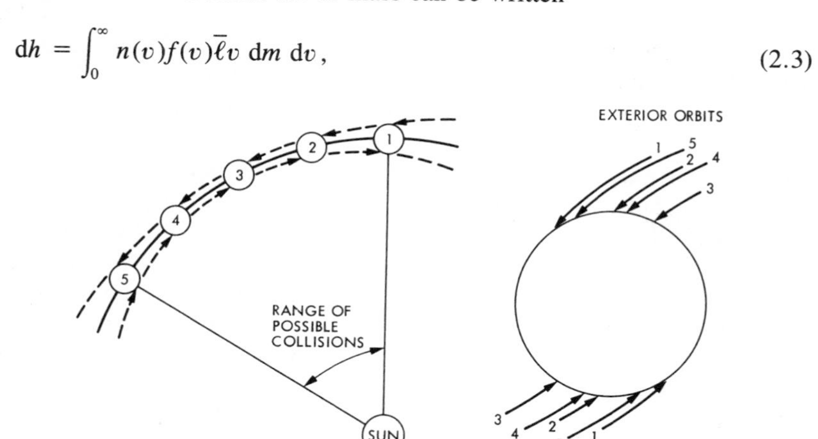

Figure 1 Collision geometry of streams of particles in exterior and interior grazing orbits in Sun- and planet-centered coordinates. Note that both streams result in net prograde rotation. (From Harris 1977; reproduced by permission of Academic Press.)

where $n(v)$ is the number density of planetesimals falling on the planet as a function of encounter velocity v (measured "at infinity," before acceleration by the planet's gravity). $n(v)$ is assumed to be Maxwellian, with v_o the mean squared value of v. $f(v)$ is the fraction of all possible orbits of encounter velocity v that are "near tangent" as opposed to "fully crossing." $\bar{\ell}$ is the mean impact parameter for all impacts from "near tangent" orbits. This turns out to be $\sim 1/7$ of the collision radius of the planet, independent of the collision velocity (Harris 1977). The limits of integration are zero to infinity. The practical limits are (1) velocities so low that the radial excursion of a planetesimal in its orbit about the sun is less than the width of the planet's sphere of influence throughout a full revolution, or (2) velocities exceeding the escape velocity from the solar system. In interpreting results one must be careful that these limits are not violated. Each of the above factors can be evaluated approximately and the integral of equation (2.3) can be analytically solved. By then integrating over the growth of the planet, an expression for the expected rotation period of the finished planet can be obtained (Harris 1977):

$$P \simeq 3 \frac{v_o}{v_e} (TT_o)^{1/2}, \tag{2.4}$$

where v_e is the surface escape velocity from the planet, T is the planet's orbit period about the sun, and T_o is the orbit period of a satellite at the surface of the planet. The result that higher impact velocities produce slower rotation is expected from the form of (2.3), since $f(v)$ decreases with increasing velocity and the product ℓv is constant for $v << v_e$. For the Earth and Mars, $(TT_o)^{1/2} \simeq 6$ days, which requires $v_o/v_e \sim 1/20$ in order to yield the correct value of P. Such a low value of v_o only barely satisfies the above stated condition for the lower limit on v. Giuli (1968) obtains numerical results for the earth in good agreement with (2.4), even for values of v near the lower limit of validity of the analytical theory. He furthermore finds that for even lower values of v (where the analytic theory is invalid) the angular momentum acquired decreases again, and in fact becomes slightly retrograde as $v \rightarrow 0$ (circular encounter orbits). This result can be qualitatively understood by noting that when the radial excursion becomes less than the sphere of influence, the particle streams (Figure 1) reverse direction, i.e. exterior particles at perihelion no longer *overtake* the planet, but are themselves *overtaken*, as in the case of circular particle streams. Hence, the net rotational impulse becomes less and in fact reverses for sufficiently low encounter velocity.

This implies that if the present rotation rates of the planets have been correctly interpreted, then the terrestrial planets accumulated from planetesimals in nearly circular orbits ($v_o/v_e \sim 1/20$ implies a mean eccentricity of the heliocentric planetesimal orbits of only ~ 0.02). This is about an order of magnitude below that inferred from the Safronov theory, and likewise an order of magnitude below the eccentricity necessary to provide crossing orbits from all orbital distances in the terrestrial zone.

2.3 *Stochastic Effects: Rotational Obliquities, Orbital Eccentricities and Inclinations*

If the planets accumulated from very small particles, one would expect them to acquire rotational motion, according to the last section, with their axes perpendicular to the orbital plane, and all of the planets would form in circular orbits in a common plane. The deviation from this pattern is commonly taken as a measure of the stochastic nature of accumulation from finite-sized bodies. Indeed, if the present rotational obliquities and orbital eccentricities and inclinations are regarded as primordial, one can estimate the sizes of the largest bodies that formed the planets (Safronov 1966, 1969, Safronov & Zvjagina 1969, Ziglina & Safronov 1976, Ziglina 1976, Pechernikova & Vityazev 1980). The first three of these references consider obliquity, the latter three orbital e and i. Harris (1979) applied a similar analysis to asteroid rotations, where the stochastic component of rotation is assumed to be completely dominant over the ordered component, i.e. the rotation axes are randomly directed (Harris & Burns 1979). We follow the development for planetary obliquities (cf Safronov 1969) as an example of the method, and then discuss the application to the other problems.

Assume that the particles colliding with the planet obey a power law number distribution with exponent q:

$$n(m')\,\mathrm{d}m' = m'^{-q}\,\mathrm{d}m'/m_1^{1-q}. \tag{2.5}$$

For $q < 2$, most of the mass is in the largest bodies, hence one must define an upper limit, m_1, to the distribution. The usual assumption, which is non-physical to some degree, is that the functional form of (2.5) is valid up to mass m_1, which represents the largest size of bodies present at any given time, and that there are no bodies larger. Equation (2.5) has been normalized for the case of just one end member of the distribution, of mass m_1. The total mass present in this distribution of particles is

$$\Delta m = \int_o^{m_1} m'n\,(m')\,\mathrm{d}m' = m_1/(2 - q).$$

It is further assumed that the total ensemble of particles that will form the planet is at the given time a multiple of (2.5); that is, there may be many particles of mass m_1, but none larger. The mass Δm is taken as the basic increment of growth, with the nature of the distribution not changing during the time Δm is accumulated. The first step of the calculation is to integrate the effect of the collisions of the particles comprising Δm. The second step, to integrate over the growth of the planet, must take into account the change in the planetesimal population that results from collisions between members of the population. In the present formalism, this is accomplished by allowing m_1, and perhaps also q, to change over the course of planet growth.

Proceeding now with the first step, the angular momentum impulses from the individual particles colliding with the planet embryo accumulate quadratically as in a random walk, assuming they are randomly directed:

$$\Delta(h^2) = \int_0^{m_1} m'^2 v^2 \ell^2 n(m')\mathrm{d}m', \tag{2.6}$$
$$= m_1^2 \ell^2 v^2/(3 - q),$$

where v^2 is the mean squared encounter velocity "at infinity" and ℓ^2 is the mean-squared impact parameter. Allowing for gravitational focusing of slow particles, we have $\ell^2 v^2 = (v^2 + v_e^2)r^2/2$, where r is the radius of the impacted body (Safronov 1966). By substituting the above relation into (2.6) and $(2 - q)\ \Delta m$ for one factor of m_1, a finite difference equation for h^2 is obtained:

$$\frac{\Delta(h^2)}{\Delta m} = \frac{2 - q}{2(3 - q)} \frac{m_1}{m} mr^2(v^2 + v_e^2). \tag{2.7}$$

If the mass law (2.5) were assumed valid all the way up to planet size (e.g. Safronov 1969), the rotation period would be ~ 2 hours. This appears to be an unsatisfactory result, since the Earth and Mars rotate considerably slower, and the mass distribution requires a largest body mass m_1 only a few times smaller than the finished planet. The result may have relevance for the smaller bodies involved in the accumulation process, however. Harris (1979) notes that if v is only modestly greater than v_e, particles are overspun by collisions (rotation velocity exceeds surface orbital velocity) and hence, they cannot grow by gravitational aggregation. This leads to an inconsistency in the Safronov accumulation scenario: If the random velocity is controlled by the largest bodies, then those only a few times smaller cannot grow, and therefore they fail to follow along with the growth of the planet embryo, as claimed by Safronov (1969).

Clearly in the case of a planet embryo, the mass law must break down at some point. Following Safronov (1966), we assume that m_1 represents a cutoff in the validity of (2.5) and that many bodies of mass $\sim m_1$ exist. The value of m_1 is constant over the first integration (2.6), but may vary as the planet grows (2.7), hence the two-step integration procedure. The simplest assumption is that the ratio m_1/m is constant whence by direct integration of (2.7) we have

$$h^2 = \frac{3(2 - q)}{20(3 - q)} \frac{m_1}{m} m^2 r^2 (v^2 + v_e^2). \tag{2.8}$$

In case of planetary rotations, the obliquity of the planetary spins is taken to be a measure of the out-of-plane component of h^2:

$$C^2\omega^2 \sin^2\epsilon = \frac{2}{3} h^2, \tag{2.9}$$

Table 1 Calculations of values of mass of largest projectile to mass of planet

Planet	Primordial rotation period	ϵ	m_1/m (ϵ)	$\overline{e^2}$	$\overline{i^2}$	m_1/m (e, i)
Mercury	?	—	—	.0324	.0168	17
Venus	?	—	—	.0012	.0010	.07
Earth	$\sim 10^h$	$\sim 12°$	.003	.0010	.0008	.04
Mars	$24^h\!.6$	$25°\!.2$	.004	.0067	.0039	.7
Jupiter	$9^h\!.9$	$3°\!.1$	.0006	.0022	.0000	.0004
Saturn	$10^h\!.5$	$26°\!.7$	.09	.0035	.0003	.0008
Uranus	$15^h\!.5$	$97°\!.9$	.1	.0020	.0003	.0007
Neptune	$18^h\!.5$?	$31°$	.01	.0001	.0001	.00003
Pluto	$\sim 8^h$?	$\sim 118°\!.5$	1	.0586	.0760	13

where C is the polar moment of inertia of the planet, ω the spin rate, and ϵ the obliquity. This can be substituted into (2.8) and rearranged to solve for m_1/m:

$$\frac{m_1}{m} = 10\,\frac{3-q}{2-q}\,K^2\,\frac{r^2\omega^2\sin^2\epsilon}{v^2+v_e^2}, \tag{2.10}$$

where the moment of inertia factor, $K = C/mr^2$, is 2/5 for a uniform sphere. Values of K for the planets are listed in Table 3.

Values of m_1/m are given in Table 1 for each planet for which primordial values of ω and ϵ are known. Primordial values of ω and ϵ for the Earth were estimated from Goldreich (1966). A mean value of $25°\!.2$ is used for the martian obliquity, although it should be noted that this quantity is highly variable on a short time scale (Ward 1974, 1979), introducing an order of magnitude uncertainty in m_1/m.

It has been assumed that $v_e >> v$ for all cases in evaluating (2.10). This assumption may be invalid for Mars and Pluto, since the random motions of planetesimals near those planets were probably influenced by their more massive neighbors.

One can make alternative assumptions regarding m_1 and q, such as m_1 = constant, $q = -\infty$ (all particles equal size), or that only one mass m_1 is responsible for a planet's obliquity, and all others are negligibly small. Safronov (1966, 1969) examined these and found modest variations in m_1/m for the different cases.

Ziglina & Safronov (1976) carried out a calculation similar to the above to evaluate the effect of large discrete collisions on the eccentricity and inclinations of the planetary orbits. Following the above calculation, the linear impulse received by the planet is computed as in (2.6), but with the factor ℓ^2 (which converts from linear to angular momentum) omitted:

$$\Delta(p^2) = m_1^2\,v^2/(3-q). \tag{2.11}$$

Proceeding as before and relating the accumulated random impulses to eccentricity and inclination by $p^2 = (\frac{5}{8} e^2 + \frac{1}{2} i^2) m^2 v_0^2$ (Safronov 1969), where v_0 is the planet's orbital velocity about the sun we obtain

$$\frac{m_1}{m} = \frac{1}{3} \frac{3 - q}{2 - q} (5e^2 + 4i^2) \left(\frac{v_0}{v} \right)^2 . \tag{2.12}$$

Ziglina (1976) corrected the above result by also including the effect of particles that do not physically collide with the planet, but are deflected by a large angle, thus transferring impulses just as if they had physically collided. Equation (2.12) can be corrected for this effect by replacing v^2 in the denominator by $v^2 + v_e^2$, thus allowing for the larger number of particles involved. Even more distant encounters contribute, although the deflections are small (see Safronov 1969), resulting in an additional factor in the denominator of order ln $(1 + D/d)$, where $d \approx rv_e/v$ is the range of strong deflection and D is the maximum range of any action. Chandrasekhar (1942) and Safronov (1969) argue that D can be taken to be the mean spacing of particles, but in any event cannot exceed the smallest dimension of the system, in this case the thickness of the protoplanetary disk. In the most extreme case ($v \sim 3$ km/sec), the log term is numerically ~ 6 in the earth zone. We take a more modest value of 4 and obtain

$$\frac{m_1}{m} \approx \frac{1}{12} \frac{3 - q}{2 - q} (5e^2 + 4i^2) \frac{v_0^2}{v^2 + v_e^2} . \tag{2.13}$$

Values of m_1/m from (2.13) are listed in the last column of Table 1. The tabulated values of e^2 and i^2 used to compute m_1/m are the mean-squared values of e and i for each planet, allowing for their secular variations (Brouwer & van Woerkom 1950; values for Pluto from Williams & Benson 1971). It is thus implicitly assumed that the planets "started out" at random phases in their secular variations. This need not have been the case. For example, the orbit of Mars can at times be quite circular. Hence, it is possible that very little of Mars' orbital eccentricity and inclination is primordial; the rest is due to secular perturbations. As with the obliquity problem, we have assumed $v_e >> v$, which may be invalid for Mars and Pluto.

2.4 Discussion

In Section 2.2, we argued that the present spin rates of the planets require a lower dispersion velocity than would allow particles at all orbital radii to reach the sites of terrestrial planet formation. If this is true, then some other process(es) must be present to move the planetesimals (or planets) radially so that accumulation can proceed. In particular, such radial motion must be more rapid than the accumulation timescale ($\sim 10^7$ years for the earth zone, assuming a dispersion velocity that yields "correct" planetary rotation rates), or the accumulation process will stagnate with too many mini-planets in the terrestrial zone. Even if a multitude of mini-planets succeed in colliding and coagulating into a few large planets following such a period of stagnation, the resulting orbits, at least the Earth's and Venus', would be much less regular than we observe today. In Section 4 we consider processes that may have caused radial drifts of planetesimals or planet embryos, thus avoiding this problem.

One must be mindful of the fact that the rotations of the planets may not have originated in the manner described in Section 2.2. Since most of the mass of the giant planets is gaseous, it is not clear that accumulation proceeded in the purely gravitational manner described, and even if so, the physical significance of v_0 is unclear also. It is certainly not the molecular thermal velocity, since the mean free path is short. It might be interpreted as a turbulence velocity, but a hydrodynamic calculation would be necessary to verify this. In the case of terrestrial planets, it is possible that there is no appreciable ordered component of spin at all, and that the rates are simply determined by the stochastic component of angular momentum, in which case values of m_1/m of $\sim 10^{-1}$ and 10^{-2}, respectively, would be inferred for the Earth and Mars. Since the initial spins of Mercury, Venus, and Pluto are unknown, we can deduce nothing from their origins. Another possibility, which has received only scant attention (Ruskol 1972, Harris 1977, 1978), is that some angular momentum may have been transferred to the planets from infall of part of a protosatellite disk.

The results summarized in Table 1 are discordant. The large values of m_1/m for the solid planets inferred from eccentricities and inclinations are improbable, if not impossible. We conclude from this that at least some of the present eccentricities and inclinations of these planets are the result of secular perturbations, perhaps enhanced by resonance passages during planetary formation and nebula removal (Section 4). These effects may have influenced the outer planet orbits as well. The values of m_1/m from the obliquities of Saturn, Uranus, and Neptune are difficult to reconcile, since such large values would lead to larger orbital values for e and i than have been observed. We discuss briefly the possibility of alteration of obliquity through resonance in Section 3; however, the obliquities of the outer planets must be regarded as an unsolved problem.

Pechernikova & Vityazev (1980) have introduced *ad hoc* (but plausible) models of variable m_1/m as a function of m in order to obtain acceptable agreement between obliquities and orbital e' s and i's of the terrestrial planets. However, the same models applied to the outer planets worsen the situation there.

The stochastic effects of gas accretion are probably nil; thus the values of

m_1/m for the giant planets are probably underestimated by a factor of the order of the gas/solids ratio. This increases the values based on obliquities to even less plausible levels. The existence of a gaseous disk during the formation of the planets may have damped the eccentricities of the growing planets (Goldreich & Tremaine 1981, Section 4.3), thus improving the agreement between estimates of m_1/m based on eccentricity vs obliquity for the giant planets.

We conclude this section on a dismal note, observing that in spite of the extensive literature on the subject, the present obliquities and orbital characteristics of the planets may tell us very little about the sizes and velocities of the bodies that accumulated to form the planets.

3. EVOLUTION OF ROTATIONAL MOTION

In the preceding section we reviewed the collision processes that presumably gave rise to the initial rotational motion of the planets. In this section we consider the subsequent evolution of planetary spins. Since ancient times it has been known that the Earth's spin axis changes direction in a regular fashion, i.e. the precession of the equinoxes, and it has also been known for a century that the rate of rotation of the Earth is slowly decreasing due to tidal friction. Only in the last few years have we come to realize that these same processes, coupled with orbital resonances, may have dramatically altered the spin states of some of the other planets and our own moon.

3.1 Spin State Evolution

The principal agent responsible for evolution in the spin rates of planets and satellites is tidal friction. Consider the case of the Earth-Moon system. The tide raised by the Moon on the Earth is carried out of alignment with the direction of the Moon by the Earth's rotation, resulting in a torque couple that tries to pull the bulge back into alignment. This transfers angular momentum from the Earth's rotation into the lunar orbit, lengthening of the day, and increasing the orbit radius (and orbit period) of the Moon. It can be shown that while angular momentum is conserved, energy is lost and appears as heat in the interior of the Earth. The torque (rate of transfer of angular momentum) between the Earth and Moon is given by (e.g. Goldreich & Soter 1966)

$$\dot{h} = \frac{3k_{2p}}{Q_p} \frac{Gm_s^2 r_p^5}{a^6}, \tag{3.1}$$

where m and r are mass and radius of a planet or satellite, a is orbit radius, and subscripts p and s refer to planet and satellite, respectively. Q is the specific energy dissipation function, the total tidal energy stored in the bulge divided by the energy lost per radian of the flexing cycle. By analogy with seismic Q, the tidal Q of a dry solid body is expected to be $\gtrsim 100$. Q might be greatly reduced by the existence of oceans, hydrated minerals, or a fluid core. The Love number k_2 is a measure of the elastic response of the planet to the tidal potential. For a homogeneous body of rigidity μ, k_2 is given by

$$k_2 = \frac{3/2}{1 + \dfrac{57}{8\pi}\dfrac{\mu}{G\rho^2 r^2}}, \tag{3.2}$$

where ρ and r are the density and radius of the body in question. For uncompressed but well-consolidated rock (e.g. granite), $\mu \approx 3 \times 10^{11}$ dynes/cm^2. For compressed rock in the interior of a planet or satellite, μ may be a few times greater. For μ in this range, the second term in the denominator of (3.2) dominates for all rocky bodies in the solar system (i.e. elasticity limits the tidal response to a small fraction of the zero-strength response), and k_2 is approximately proportional to r^2. k_2 for the Earth and Moon are 0.30 and 0.020, respectively (Ferrari et al 1980), in good agreement with the above generalization.

The effect of the torque couple (3.1) on the evolution of orbits is discussed in Section 4.1. We wish to consider here the effect on the planet's rotation. By dividing (3.1) by the planet's moment of inertia, C_p, we obtain the rate of change of rotation rate (e.g. Peale 1977):

$$\dot{\omega}_p = -\frac{3}{K_p}\frac{k_{2p}}{Q_p}\left(\frac{m_s}{m_p}\right)^2\left(\frac{r_p}{a}\right)^6 \rho_p \Omega_o^2, \tag{3.3}$$

where $\Omega_o = (\frac{4}{3}\pi G)^{1/2}$ is the orbit frequency at the surface of a sphere of unit density and is equal to 5.29×10^{-4} CGS units. K_p is the gyration constant, $C_p/m_p r_p^2$, and is equal to 2/5 for a homogeneous sphere. In the case of the Earth-Moon system, two complications exist: (1) there is an additional contribution to $\dot{\omega}_p$ from the tide raised by the Sun on the Earth, and (2) the orbit of the Moon is evolving rapidly, so that one must simultaneously follow the evolution of the lunar orbit in order to determine the evolution of the Earth's spin. This problem has been worked many times with various refinements (e.g. Darwin 1880, MacDonald 1964, Goldreich 1966). We do not discuss this problem further, except to note that the recent claim by Kahn & Pompea (1978), based on fossil-nautiloid growth patterns, that the Moon was much closer to the Earth 420 m.y. ago is not valid because they failed to correctly account for the dependence of $\dot{\omega}_p$ on lunar distance, a/r_p. Nevertheless, it is generally agreed that the Moon was probably once much closer to the Earth than at present, leading to an initial rotation period of the Earth of $\sim$ 6–8 hours (Goldreich 1966).

Equation (3.3) can be modified for the effect of solar tide on a planet or the planet tide on a nonsynchronous satellite as follows:

$$\dot{\omega}_s = -\frac{3}{K_s}\frac{k_{2s}}{Q_s}\left(\frac{r_p}{a}\right)^6 \frac{\rho_p^2}{\rho_s}\,\Omega_o^2, \tag{3.4}$$

where the subscripts p and s refer to "primary" and "secondary", i.e. to sun and planet, or to planet and satellite. If $m_s << m_p$ so that r_p/a remains nearly constant as the secondary despins, the time it takes to despin from an initial rate (presumed $\sim \Omega_o$) to the present rate can be found by direct integration of (3.4). For Mercury and all of the regular satellites of the solar system, this time is much shorter than the age of the solar system for any reasonable values of Q and k_2 (Peale 1977). The only marginal case is Venus, which requires $Q_p \lesssim 17$ (Goldreich & Soter 1966) in order to despin to its present rate. Such a low value is somewhat unexpected for a dry solid planet; however it appears that even the Moon may have a value of Q of this order (Ferrari et al 1980), presumably due to its fluid core, so this low value cannot be discounted. The atmospheric tide (Section 3.3), tends to spin-up the planet, so it cannot be responsible for the apparent low Q value from the above argument.

The recent discovery of a satellite of Pluto (Christy & Harrington 1978, Harrington & Christy 1980) added that planet to the list of tidally evolved bodies. We discuss this system in greater detail in Section 4. The present orbital configuration, $P = 6.3867$ days with the planet's rotation rate locked to the same value, and a mass ratio $m_s/m_p \approx 0.1$ (based on the brightness difference of the two bodies, Thomsen & Ables 1978), suggests that the initial spin period of Pluto could have been as short as 3–4 hours. The present slow spin of Pluto is thus no longer grounds for speculation that Pluto is an escaped satellite of Neptune that was tidally despun by its association with that planet (Goldreich & Peale 1968, Harrington & van Flandern 1979, Farinella et al 1980). In fact the contrary is true, since the Pluto/Charon system would have been tidally unstable as a binary satellite of Neptune (e.g. Burns 1973, Ward & Reid 1973). The primordial spin rate of Pluto, like those of Mercury and Venus, must be regarded as totally obscured by subsequent tidal evolution. Only Mars and the giant planets are likely to be spinning at near their primordial rates.

Resonant rotation Perhaps because the synchronous rotation of the Moon is so familiar, the possibility of a nonsynchronous tidal end-state of rotation escaped theoretical attention until 1965 when it was discovered that Mercury is spinning at a nonsynchronous rate (Pettengill & Dyce 1965). Peale & Gold (1965) noted that if Mercury were rotating at a rate only slightly faster than the synchronous rate, then the instantaneous rate of orbital motion would exceed the rotation rate over some fraction of the orbit near perihelion, resulting in a reversal of the tidal torque during that interval. Since the tidal torque is strongest at perihelion, for some tide models the time-averaged torque on a planet in an eccentric orbit will equal zero at a rotation rate greater than the synchronous value, hence a faster-than-synchronous tidal end-state. Colombo (1965) suggested that a permanent deformation of the planet could trap the spin in a higher-than-synchronous resonance if the time-averaged torque on the permanent bulge (characterized by the difference in equatorial moment of inertia, $B - A$), at some libration angle was large enough to counteract the time-averaged torque due to the tidal bulge. Since the former is proportional to $B - A$, while the latter is proportional to Q^{-1}, the existence of a stable spin-orbit resonance implies a limit on the product $Q(B - A)/C$ (e.g. Goldreich & Peale 1966, 1967, 1968). For example, the apparent resonance between the spin of Venus and the synodic orbit period between the Earth and Venus implies $(B - A)/C \gtrsim 1.6 \times 10^{-2}/Q$. Ananda et al (1980) find from Pioneer Venus orbiter tracking data that $(B - A)/C \lesssim 10^{-5}$, implying an implausibly large value of Q to stabilize the resonance. If Venus had such a high Q, solar tides would hardly have altered Venus' spin rate at all in 4.5×10^9 years. Recent radar data (Shapiro et al 1979) seem to confirm that Venus is in fact not in resonance with the Earth, in spite of the near coincidence of the observed rate to the resonant value.

One can constrain values of Q and $(B - A)/C$ for Mercury by the fact that it apparently passed through higher spin resonances from a rapid initial rotation rate before arriving at its present state. Goldreich & Peale (1966, 1967, 1968) found capture likely only for the 3/2 resonance for plausible values of $(B - A)/C$ and Q. Peale & Boss (1977a, b) reconsidered this problem in light of the probability that Mercury has a liquid core, and find that in order to avoid capture into the 2:1 resonance the liquid core must have a low viscosity (comparable to water), $(B - A)/C$ must be $\lesssim 10^{-5}$, and Q must be $\lesssim 100$ if the core/mantle boundary layer is laminar or $\lesssim 40$ if it is turbulent. The requirement on the core viscosity arises because viscous coupling increases the librational damping as the spin passes the resonant value, thus increasing the probability of capture into resonance. A low viscosity reduces this effect and enhances the chance of resonance passage.

The librations of Phobos If a satellite is locked into synchronous resonance but is in an eccentric orbit, the permanent bulge, which tries to remain aligned with the planet-satellite line, oscillates about that line due to the variation in orbital motion about the planet. This effect is called optical libration and is the primary reason that we see different parts of the Moon's surface at different times. On the other hand, a displacement of the tidal bulge from the planet-satellite line gives rise to a restoring torque that would cause the satellite to freely oscillate with a frequency $\omega_o = \Omega[3(B - A)/C]^{1/2}$, even if the orbit were circular. If a satellite were very irregular, in particular if $(B - A)/C \approx 1/3$, then the free libration frequency would be very near the orbit frequency, resulting in a large amplitude forced libration, a factor of $(\Omega^2 - \omega_o^2)^{-1}$ larger than the optical libration amplitude (Burns 1972). $(B - A)/C$ for Phobos is estimated to be ~ 0.228, leading to a three-fold increase in libration amplitude to $\sim 5°$, which was confirmed by Mariner 9 and Viking orbiter pictures of Phobos. Since $(B - A)/C$ for Deimos is comparable to that of Phobos but is less well determined, an even larger libration enhancement could exist and might be the answer to puzzling apparent differences in the internal structures of Phobos and Deimos (Yoder 1981, see Section 4.1).

3.2 *Spin Axis Precession and Resonance Variation*

The precession of the rotation axis of a planet in orbit about the Sun is rather analogous to the precession of a spinning top. The Sun exerts a torque on the equatorial bulge of the planet that tries to right the axis of the planet perpendicular to the direction to the Sun. Like any well-behaved top, this torque is translated into a motion of the spin axis perpendicular to the direction of the Sun, thus resulting in a precessional motion while preserving a constant tilt angle. The rate of motion of the spin axis unit vector is given by

$$\frac{d\hat{\mathbf{s}}}{dt} = -\alpha \sin 2\phi \frac{\hat{\mathbf{r}} \times \hat{\mathbf{s}}}{|\hat{\mathbf{r}} \times \hat{\mathbf{s}}|}, \qquad (3.5)$$

where ϕ is the angle between the spin axis unit vector $\hat{\mathbf{s}}$ and the Sun direction unit vector $\hat{\mathbf{r}}$. The constant α involves the gravitational harmonic J_2, the moment of inertia factor K defined earlier, the mean orbital motion Ω, and the spin rate ω:

$$\alpha = \frac{J_2}{K} \frac{\Omega^2}{\omega}. \qquad (3.6)$$

Since the angle ϕ varies from zero at times of equinox passage to a maximum value equal to the obliquity ϵ at solstice passage, the rate of motion of $\hat{\mathbf{s}}$ varies accordingly with a semiannual frequency. By averaging (3.5) over an orbit (assume for the moment a circular orbit that is not itself precessing), the *precessional* motion is obtained:

$$\frac{d\hat{\mathbf{s}}}{dt} = -\alpha(\hat{\mathbf{n}} \cdot \hat{\mathbf{s}})(\hat{\mathbf{n}} \times \hat{\mathbf{s}}), \qquad (3.7)$$

where $\hat{\mathbf{n}}$ is the orbit normal. The twice-annual cycle superimposed on this average motion is called *nutation*. The precession period T is obtained by dividing the length of the precession circle on the unit sphere, $2\pi \sin \epsilon$, by the rate $|d\hat{\mathbf{s}}/dt|$:

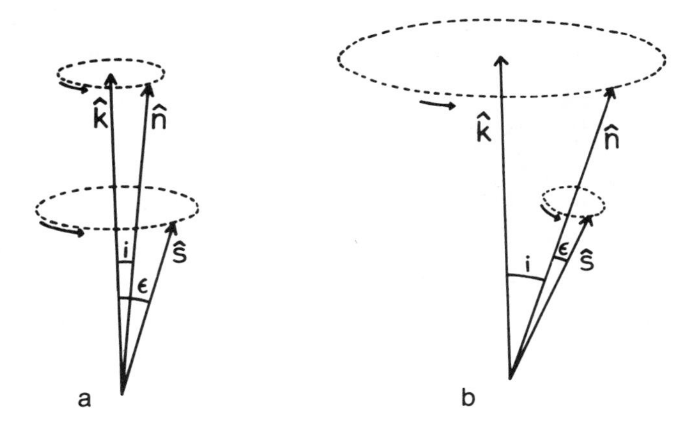

Figure 2 Spin axis precession when the orbit plane also precesses. (*a*) If the motion of the orbit normal, $\hat{\mathbf{n}}$, is much faster than the motion of the spin axis, then the spin axis, $\hat{\mathbf{s}}$, precesses at nearly constant obliquity ϵ about the *mean* direction of the orbit normal, i.e. the normal to the invariable plane, $\hat{\mathbf{k}}$. In the case of the lunar contribution to the Earth's precession, the lunar orbit precesses rapidly (~ 18 years) about the Earth's orbit normal. Hence, the average effect of the Moon is to cause precession of the Earth's spin axis about the Earth's orbit normal. Since this motion is in the same direction as the solar contribution, the two are simply additive. (*b*) If the motion of the rotation axis is much faster than the motion of the orbit normal, then the rotation axis precesses about the orbit normal at constant obliquity ϵ with respect to the orbit normal. This is the case for the solar contribution to the Earth's precession. (However, in the Earth's case, $\epsilon >> i$.)

$$T = \frac{2\pi}{\alpha \cos \epsilon}, \tag{3.8}$$

where the obliquity ϵ is the angle between $\hat{\mathbf{n}}$ and $\hat{\mathbf{s}}$. For small obliquity the precession frequency is equal to α. For the Earth, Equation (3.8) yields a precession period of ~ 83,000 years. However, in the case of the Earth an additional torque is introduced by the Moon. Since the lunar orbit plane precesses about the ecliptic plane on a time short compared to the rate of precession, the average effect is to produce an increase in the rate of precession of the Earth's axis about the normal to the ecliptic plane, while conserving the tilt of the axis, on average (Figure 2*a*). The short-term variations from the average rate (with periods of 1/2 month and the 18 year period of the precession of the lunar orbit about the ecliptic) constitute additional nutation terms of the axis motion. When the effect of the Moon is included, the precession period is ~ 26,000 years. Finally, the Earth's orbit is precessing about the invariable plane of the solar system. This precession is a composite of several frequencies and amplitudes (see Table 2), but the most important one has a period of ~ 69,000 years. Since this period is longer than

Table 2 Eigenperiods of secular perturbations in the solar system (from Brouwer & van Woerkom 1950)

Inclination terms	Period (yrs)	Planets principally affected
1	249,000	1, 2, 3
2	197,000	1, 2, 3
3	69,000	2, 3, 4
4	73,500	4
5	∞	—
6	50,400	4, 5, 6
7	446,500	7
8	1,913,000	8
Eccentricity terms		
1	237,000	1
2	176,500	1, 2, 3
3	74,800	2, 3, 4
4	72,000	2, 3, 4
5	301,700	1, 2, 3, 4, 5, 6, 7
6	46,700	4, 5, 6
7	477,000	7, 8
8	2,046,000	8
9	67,600	—
10	25,300	—

the mean precession period of the Earth's axis, the Earth tends to maintain a nearly constant obliquity to the ecliptic, with the axis tending to follow along with the orbit normal as it moves in space (Figure 2*b*). The behavior of the spin axis is like the response of a forced oscillator. If the driving frequency is much faster than the natural response frequency, the oscillator moves at near its natural frequency about the mean position of the driver, with a low amplitude wiggle at the driving frequency superimposed. This motion is analogous to the precession due to the Sun and Moon, with the nutation caused by the high frequency variations of the forcing function. If the oscillator is driven at a frequency much below the natural response frequency, then the oscillator moves at near its natural frequency and with constant amplitude about the instantaneous location of the driver. That is, it tracks the driving motion while at the same time oscillating just as it would in the absence of the driving motion. This is analogous to the precessional motion that follows the orbit normal as the latter moves slowly in space.

The mutual perturbations between the planets result in long-term "secular" perturbations in the eccentricity and inclination of the planetary orbits. The periods of the largest amplitude terms (from Brouwer & van Woerkom 1950) are listed in Table 2. Each orbit is perturbed by some amount at each frequency, but different terms dominate for different planets. The fifth inclination term is just the inclination of the coordinate system chosen (ecliptic 1950.0) to the invariable plane of the solar system. We are interested in the inclination terms, since these variations constitute forcing functions to the planetary spin axes.

As long as the various frequencies of orbit precession remain well below that of spin axis precession, the obliquity can be regarded as an *adiabatic invariant* and will show essentially no secular change. However, if the axis precession frequency is nearly matched by one of these frequencies of orbital precession, the axis motion may be amplified by the orbital precession, much as the response of a forced oscillator if driven at near its natural frequency. However, since the spin precession rate depends on obliquity, the analogy to a linear-forced oscillator breaks down near resonance. In the case of the Earth, the current period of precession of the spin axis is $\sim$ 26,000 years. In the past, the period was even shorter. (A shorter day produces a slower precession, but this is more than offset by the increased equatorial bulge resulting from faster rotation, which increases the torque coupling. In addition, the Moon was closer in the past, also resulting in increased precessional torque.) Since the shortest eigenperiod associated with the orientation of the Earth's orbit is $\sim$ 50,000 years, and the dominant period is even longer, 69,000 years (Table 2), the Earth's obliquity presently varies by only $\sim 2°$ (e.g. Ward 1974, Berger 1976). In the past it varied even less since the driving and response frequencies were even more widely separated then. Even so, it has been suggested that these small variations may have triggered the Earth's ice ages (e.g. Hays et al 1976). It is interesting to note however, that the Earth's precession frequency will pass through resonance with the above eigenperiods in the future, as the lunar orbit evolves through distances of $\sim$ 66.5 and $\sim$ 68.0 Earth radii. Ward (1981d) has estimated that this will occur in $\sim$ 2 by, if tidal evolution continues at its present rate, and will result in obliquity variations up to as much as $\sim 60°$ on a timescale of $\sim 10^5$ years.

Variation of the martian obliquity It is largely because of the Moon that the Earth's pole precession frequency is so rapid, thus avoiding the natural frequencies of orbit variation. The situation is quite different for Mars, where the pole precession period is $\sim$ 175,000 years, considerably longer than the largest amplitude terms of the orbit plane motion and very close to the period of one of the smaller amplitude terms (197,000 years). Ward (1973, 1974, 1979) showed that because of these interactions, the motion of the martian spin axis is quite complex, and indeed the obliquity of Mars can vary by as much as $\pm 13.6°$ from a mean value of $\sim 24.4°$. The oscillations are controlled by two basic periodicities: a $\sim 1.2 \times 10^5$-year cycle, which is modulated with a longer period of $\sim 1.2 \times 10^6$ years (Figure 3). By coincidence, Mars is

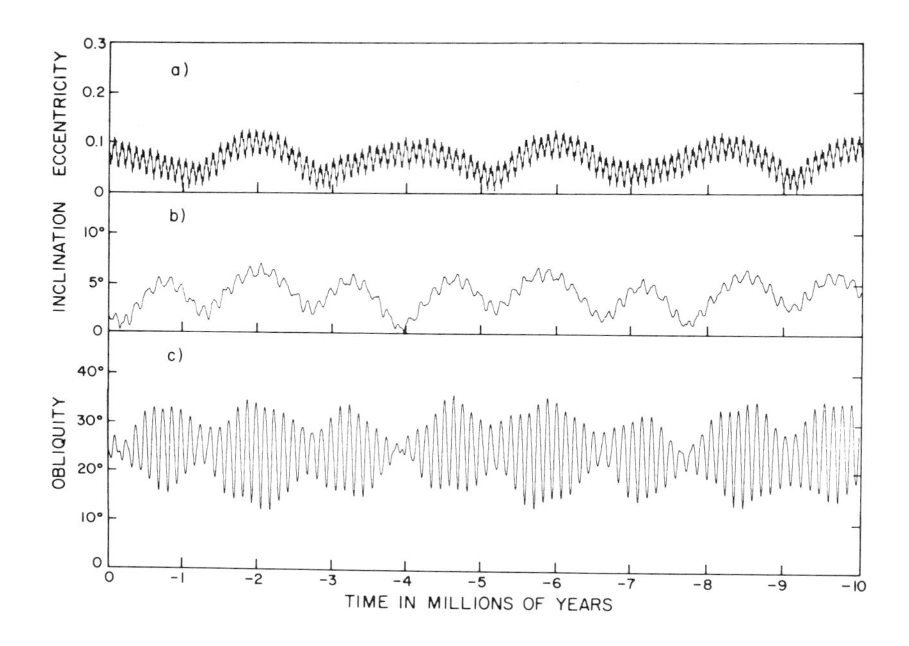

Figure 3 (*a*) Eccentricity and (*b*) inclination of the orbit of Mars for the past 10^7 years. (*c*) Variation in the obliquity of Mars taking into account the precession of the spin axis. (From Ward 1979; reproduced by permission of Am. Geophys. Union.)

presently near the mean value of the short period oscillation and also near a node in the longer period modulation. Thus, it has been $\sim 5 \times 10^5$ years since Mars executed large-scale excursions of its obliquity. Ward et al (1974, 1979) and Toon et al (1980) speculate that the large variation in polar insolation during these cycles may be responsible for the climatic variations suggested by the polar-cap layering seen on the martian surface. They also note (Ward et al 1979) that the partially uncompensated Tharsis uplift results in a value of J_2 of Mars that is $\sim 6\frac{1}{2}\%$ larger than the hydrostatic value. If at some time in the past the martian gravity figure were hydrostatic (pre-Tharsis), then the pole-precession period would be indistinguishably different from the 197,200-year period of one of the orbit precession terms. They show that if this were the case, then Mars could have been driven to even more extreme obliquities, as low as 9° and as high as 46° or more.

The importance of this work to our discussion is that if Mars' obliquity has varied over such extremes in the past, then the *initial* obliquity from which subsequent evolution occurred could have been any value within that range.

Table 3 Rotational properties of the planets

Planet	Rotation period	Obliquity	$K = (C/mr^2)$	J_2	Satellite	m_s/m_p	Axial precession period (yr)
Mercury	$58^d.6$	0°	[a]	[a]	—	—	2,000[a]
Venus	$243^d.0$	178°	0.34	6×10^{-6} [b]	—	—	21,500
Earth	$23^h.9$	23°.45	0.335	0.001083	Moon	0.0123	26,000
Mars	$24^h.6$	25°.2	0.3654	0.001955[c]	—	—	173,000
Jupiter	$9^h.9$	3°.1	0.26[d]	0.01473[e]	Io	4.705×10^{-5} [f]	4.5×10^5
					Europa	2.522×10^{-5} [f]	
					Ganymede	7.806×10^{-5} [f]	
					Callisto	5.665×10^{-5} [f]	
Saturn	$10^h.5$ [g]	26°.7	0.22[d]	0.01646[h]	Titan	2.37×10^{-4} [h]	1.8×10^6
Uranus	$15^h.5$* [i]	97°.9	0.20[i]	0.003354[i]	Ariel	8×10^{-6}* [k]	5.7×10^8*
					Umbriel	2×10^{-6}* [k]	
					Titania	1×10^{-5}* [k]	
					Oberon	1×10^{-5}* [k]	
Neptune	$18^h.5$* [l]	31°* [m]	0.19[j]	0.0036* [m]	Triton	0.00134* [n]	1.4×10^7*
Pluto	$6^d.39$ [o]	118°.5[p]	0.4	—	Charon	0.1* [q]	7.3×10^6

*Uncertain values in need of confirmation or improvement.

[a]The axial precession rate of Mercury is locked to the orbital precession, since it is in a Cassini state (see Section 3.5). The obliquity is near 0°, the exact value depending on K and J_2. The latter is unknown but presumed small ($\lesssim 10^{-4}$).

[b]Ananda et al (1980).

[c]Reasenberg (1977).

[d]K for Jupiter and Saturn computed from interior models of Slattery (1977).

[e]Null (1976).

[f]Masses of the Galilean satellites from Voyager flyby data (Synnott, private communication 1980). Values are essentially the same as given by Null (1976).

[g]Kaiser & Desch (1980).

[h]Anderson et al (1980).

[i]The value of J_2 for Uranus is inferred from the observed apsidal precession rate of the ϵ ring (Nicholson et al 1978, Elliot et al 1981). With this value of J_2 and the optical flattening observed by stellar occultations (f=0.033, Elliot et al 1981) the rotation rate can be computed uniquely, subject only to the assumption of hydrostatic equilibrium. The computed value of $15^h.5$ for the rotation period (Elliot et al 1981) is probably more reliable than those values reported from direct observation, which range from ~ 10 to ~ 24 hours. The value of K is also uniquely determined from these values of J_2 and f, and is in reasonable agreement with those obtained from theoretical interior models (Hubbard & MacFarlane 1980).

[j]Thevalueof K for Neptune is estimated from theoretical interior models (e.g. Hubbard & MacFarlane).

[k]Masses of the uranian satellites are inferred from photometric data (Cruikshank 1980) and are consistent with products of masses determined by Greenberg (1976) from satellite dynamics.

[l]Slavsky &Smith (1978), based on photometric variation. This value is not to be taken as firm, since the same technique applied to Uranus yields an improbable result (24 hr).

[m]Preliminary values based on a reanalysis of the precession of the orbit plane of Triton. The interior models of Hubbard & MacFarlane (1980) favor a value of $J_2 \lesssim 0.003$, or a shorter rotation period than the $18^h.5$ value we have adopted.

[n]The mass of Triton was determined by measuring the wobble of Neptune's position due to its motion about the Neptune/Triton barycenter (Alden 1943). The quoted mass corresponds to a barycentric offset of Neptune of only ~ 0.02 arcsec. We consider this offset only marginally detectable at best, and hence doubt the correctness of the value of m_s/m_p. From the photometric brightness of Triton and an assumed density of 1–3 gm/cm^3, the mass ratio probably lies in the range 0.00025–0.0015 (Cruikshank et al 1979).

[o]The rotation period of Pluto has been inferred from light variations (Harris 1961). The discovery of a satellite tidally locked to the planet at the same orbit period confirms the earlier value (Christy & Harrington 1978, Harrington & Christy 1980).

[p]Harrington (private communication 1980).

[q]Based on assumed equal density and albedo of planet and satellite and a brightness difference of 1.7 magnitudes (Thomsen & Ables 1978). While this value of m_s/m_p is uncertain, the precession rate of the Pluto/Charon system turns out to be nearly independent of the mass ratio.

Outer planet obliquities It is clear from Table 1 that the obliquities of the giant planets (with the possible exception of Jupiter) cannot be "primordial" in the sense discussed in Section 3.2. Aside from the values of m_1/m required to produce the present obliquities being implausibly large for planets that are mostly gaseous, the collisions of such large bodies would have induced much larger eccentricities and inclinations of the orbits of the giant planets. We therefore seek a different explanation for the obliquities of these planets.

The rates of precession of the spin axes of the outer planets are dominated by their respective satellite systems. The orbits of these satellites are effectively coupled to the planet's oblateness, thus the torque exerted on the satellites by the Sun is added to that received by the planet. The axial precession rates of the planets are listed in Table 3, based on current estimates of satellite masses and oblatenesses according to equations given by Ward (1975a). The periods for Jupiter and Saturn are remarkably close to two of the eigenperiods of orbital inclination, 4.5×10^5 years and 1.9×10^6 years. (The apparent exact match for Jupiter is not significant, mainly because of uncertainty in the moment of inertia of the planet.) If a slow change in either the axial or the orbital precession frequencies occurred since the formation of the planets, then the resulting resonances might have substantially altered the directions of the spin axes of these planets (Ward, in preparation). One can only speculate as to what may have caused variations in the frequencies. A more massive "proto-satellite disk" during planetary formation might have produced shorter axial precession periods. This might have been important for Uranus and Neptune, where the present precession periods are much too long to be in resonance with any of the inclination periods. The presence of the "solar nebula" (the excess H, He, and other volatiles not accumulated into the planetary system) would have substantially reduced the periods of orbital precession from the present values. If this material was dissipated slowly, the precession rates of some of the planets might have been in resonance with one or more of the orbital precession frequencies long enough to alter the obliquity considerably. A slow decrease in the solar mass, resulting in outward spiraling of the planet orbits, could have had a similar effect since the orbital eigenfrequencies and the spin precession rates scale differently with semimajor axis. Finally, slow contractions of the giant planets as they cool with attendant change in J_2, and/or the slow tidal evolution of a satellite system, might cause the precession period of the planet to pass through resonance. Since most of these processes are understood qualitatively at best, it is hard to say with certainty which, if any, were important, but with such a range of possibilities one must be cautious in assuming that any of the present obliquities is primordial.

The orbit normal of Pluto precesses about the invariable plane of the solar system at a nearly constant rate corresponding to a period of 3.7×10^6 years (Williams & Benson 1971). This is reasonably close to the estimated precession period, computed by holding all angles constant at present values. We expect that the obliquity history of Pluto is quite complex owing to this near commensurability plus the large angles of inclination and obliquity involved. For our present purpose it suffices to note that Pluto's spin axis is probably highly altered from its initial value.

3.3 Tidally Evolved Rotation—Cassini States

In 1693, Cassini recognized three laws that described the rotational motion of the moon:

1. The rotation period is equal to the orbit period.
2. The rotation equator is inclined by a constant angle of $\sim 1°.5$ to the ecliptic.
3. The ascending node of the lunar orbit on the ecliptic coincides with the descending node of the lunar equator. Hence the spin axis and orbit normal precess at the same rate about the ecliptic normal.

It has long been recognized that these laws describe a dynamically stable configuration (e.g. Danby 1962), presumably an end-state of tidal evolution. The first step toward generalization of these laws was prompted by the discovery that Mercury's rate of rotation is faster than synchronous (Pettengill & Dyce 1965). Simultaneously, theorists noted that tidal friction may produce a rotational end-state faster than the synchronous value (Peale & Gold 1965); in particular it might become trapped in a 3/2 resonance (Colombo 1965) or other faster-than-synchronous resonances (see Goldreich & Peale 1968 for a review). Colombo (1966) and Peale (1969) generalized the second and third Cassini laws by showing that the spin axis of a planet is in equilibrium if it occupies any one of the four "Cassini states" (Figure 4). If the spin axis is not in a Cassini state, it will precess about one of the states 1, 2, or 3, but will diverge away from state 4 to circulate about one of the other states. Peale (1974) and Ward (1975a) investigated these spin states in more detail and showed that states 1 and 2 can be end-points of tidal evolution.

Consider the idealized case of a satellite or planet in an orbit that maintains a constant inclination, i, to an inertial plane and precesses about that plane at a uniform rate. The rate of motion of the spin axis, $d\hat{\mathbf{s}}/dt$, is given by (3.7). If the motion of the spin axis is rapid compared to that of the orbit normal, $\hat{\mathbf{n}}$, then the spin axis will precess about the orbit normal while maintaining a constant angle to that vector. If the spin axis motion is slower than the orbit precession motion, then the precession occurs about the average direction of the orbit normal, i.e. the normal to the inertial plane ($\hat{\mathbf{k}}$). The Cassini states defined by Colombo (1966) are those values of ϵ for which the resulting motion of the spin axis exactly follows the rate of precession of the orbit normal, keeping the three vectors $\hat{\mathbf{s}}$, $\hat{\mathbf{k}}$, and $\hat{\mathbf{n}}$ in the same plane:

$$\frac{2\pi|\hat{\mathbf{s}} \times \hat{\mathbf{k}}|}{|d\hat{\mathbf{s}}/dt|} = \frac{2\pi}{\dot{\Omega}} \tag{3.9}$$

which can be written

$$\alpha \sin \epsilon \cos \epsilon + \dot{\Omega} \sin (\epsilon - i) = 0, \tag{3.10}$$

where $\dot{\Omega}$ is the precession frequency of the orbit node (or orbit normal). [Note that $\dot{\Omega}$ used here is not the derivative of the orbit frequency (mean motion), which is denoted by Ω elsewhere in the text.] It is clear from the form of (3.10) that four solutions for ϵ exist if $\alpha >> \dot{\Omega}$, and two solutions exist if $\dot{\Omega} >> \alpha$. These correspond to the present situations for Mercury and the Moon, respectively, and are illustrated in Figures 4*a* and 4*b*. The unit sphere is viewed from a near polar aspect. The normal to the invariable plane is $\hat{\mathbf{k}}$, and remains fixed. The normal to the orbit plane is $\hat{\mathbf{n}}$, which precesses about $\hat{\mathbf{k}}$. The plane containing both vectors at some initial time is represented by the solid great circle, and the same plane at a time Δt later by the dashed circle. If the spin axis $\hat{\mathbf{s}}$ were initially in the common plane with $\hat{\mathbf{k}}$ and $\hat{\mathbf{n}}$, it would precess freely in a direction perpendicular to $\hat{\mathbf{n}}$, arriving at a point on the dotted curve after the time Δt. If the spin axis is located at one of the obliquities where the dotted curve and the dashed circle intersect, then the axis precession exactly keeps step with the motion of the orbit normal so that the three vectors $\hat{\mathbf{k}}$, $\hat{\mathbf{n}}$, and $\hat{\mathbf{s}}$ remain in a common plane, thus satisfying the generalization of the third of Cassini's laws. In the case of Mercury, the orbit precession rate is very slow, hence for the axis rate to be equally slow, values of ϵ must be near 0°, 180°,

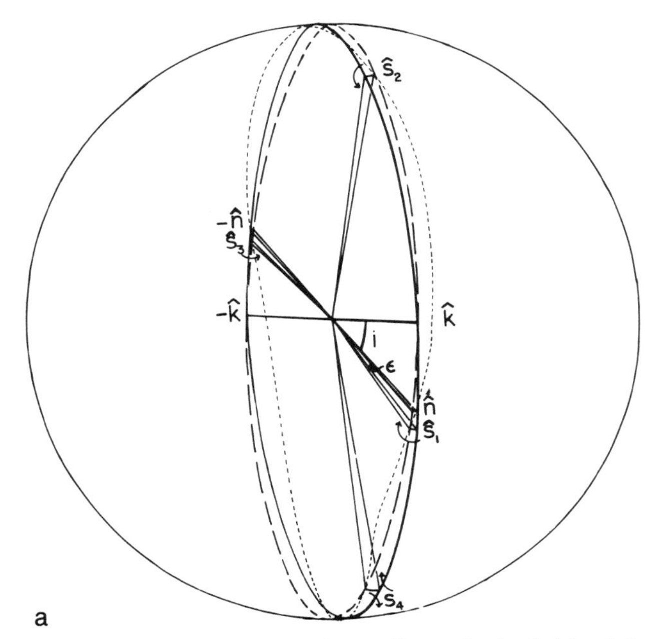

Figure 4a Graphical representation of Cassini states. See text for detailed description. If the spin axis motion can exceed the motion of the orbit normal, four Cassini states exist, denoted $\hat{\mathbf{s}}_1$ through $\hat{\mathbf{s}}_4$ (Mercury case).

and ±90°, where the quantity sin 2ϵ is very small. These positions are indicated by $\hat{\mathbf{s}}_1$ through $\hat{\mathbf{s}}_4$ in Figure 4*a*. In the case of the Moon, the orbit precession motion is very rapid; thus the spin axis can keep up only if it lies very close to the normal to the invariable plane so that the small precession angle about $\hat{\mathbf{n}}$ constitutes a large angle about the much closer axis $\hat{\mathbf{k}}$. Only two Cassini states exist, labeled $\hat{\mathbf{s}}_2$ and $\hat{\mathbf{s}}_3$ in Figure 4*b*. By imagining a slight displacement from $\hat{\mathbf{s}}$ from a Cassini state, one can see that the resulting motion of the spin axis is to trace closed trajectories about states 1, 2, and 3, but divergent trajectories from state 4 (small arrows in Figures 4*a* and 4*b*). Peale (1974) and Ward (1975a) found that solid body tidal friction causes the spin axis to spiral *out* from state 3, but *in* toward states 1 or 2. Thus Cassini States 1 and 2 are indeed end-states of tidal evolution.

Spin state of Mercury The J_2 of a planet is generally assumed to consist of a hydrostatic component, proportional to ω^2, and a nonhydrostatic component due to random variations of the figure and density of the planet. The latter component is limited by the strength of the body, which leads to a depen-

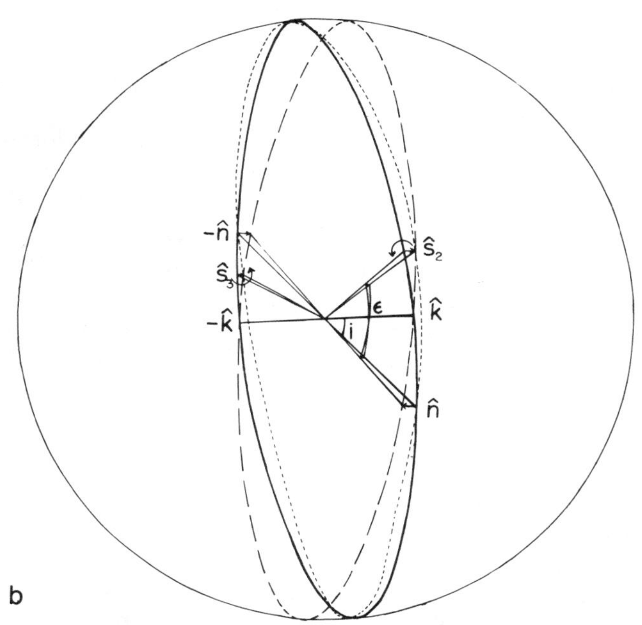

Figure 4b If the spin axis motion is slow compared to the motion of the orbit normal, only two Cassini states are possible, denoted $\hat{\mathbf{s}}_2$ and $\hat{\mathbf{s}}_3$ (Lunar case). If the system depicted in (*a*) were evolving such that the rate of spin axis precession decreased with time (amplitude of dotted line decreasing), it is clear that states 1 and 4 would merge and then cease to exist, leaving only the two states as depicted in (*b*).

dence of r^{-2} when scaled from one planet or satellite to another. Hence, if a planet despins,

$$J_2 \sim J_{20} + J' \omega^2, \tag{3.11}$$

where $J' \approx 2 \times 10^5$ sec^2 for a homogeneous planet of rock-like density. From the nonhydrostatic gravity moments of the Earth and the Moon, we can infer $J_{20} \sim 10^{-6} (r_\oplus/r)^2$. With this functional form of J_2 in (3.6), it is clear that if Mercury was despun from an initially rapid rate, α at first decreased while J_2 was primarily hydrostatic, and then increased again as J_2 became constant at the nonhydrostatic value. If at any point α was small enough that only two Cassini states existed, then Mercury would have tidally evolved toward state 2. As α then increased again, it would probably continue to damp into Cassini state 2 rather than 1. In order for this to happen, Peale (1974) finds that J_{20} must be $\lesssim 10^{-6}$, rather than the value of $\sim 10^{-5}$ expected from scaling arguments. If the present J_2 (essentially J_{20}) were as small as $\sim 10^{-6}$, Cassini state 2 would lie several degrees from the orbit normal, whereas the pole is observed to lie within 1° of the orbit normal, thus requiring Mercury to be in state 1. Peale (1974) therefore concludes that Mercury's J_{20} must be $\gtrsim 10^{-6}$ so that transition to state 2 never occurred.

History of the lunar spin axis Ward (1975b) applied a similar analysis to the evolution of the lunar spin axis. He found that when the Moon was close to the Earth, only Cassini state 1 was at low obliquity and was therefore the likely spin state of the Moon. As it evolved outward under the effect of tidal friction, the pole precession rate decreased as the Earth's torque on the lunar figure decreased with increasing distance, and the orbit precession rate increased as the solar perturbations became stronger relative to the Earth's gravity. Thus, states 1 and 2 merged when the orbit radius reached 34.2 Earth radii. The spin axis then underwent obliquity variations (up to 77°) as the pole position began precessing about state 2 with a large amplitude, finally settling down to the direction of Cassini state 2 under the action of tidal friction.

The spin state of Venus An essentially correct dynamical explanation for Mercury's spin was discovered so quickly that it was published simultaneously with the radar observation of the correct spin rate (Pettengill & Dyce 1965, Peale & Gold 1965). The dynamical explanation of Venus' spin state is still uncertain fifteen years after the radar measurement of the correct period. We have already noted that the despinning of Venus from a rapid initial rotation rate requires an unexpectedly low tidal Q, and that in spite of a remarkable near coincidence of the rotation rate (to 0.1%!) with a resonance with the Earth-Venus synodic orbit period, the planet is measurably not in resonance. The same radar measurements indicate a pole position somewhat different from Cassini state 3 (Ward & DeCampli 1979). Yoder & Ward (1979) suggest

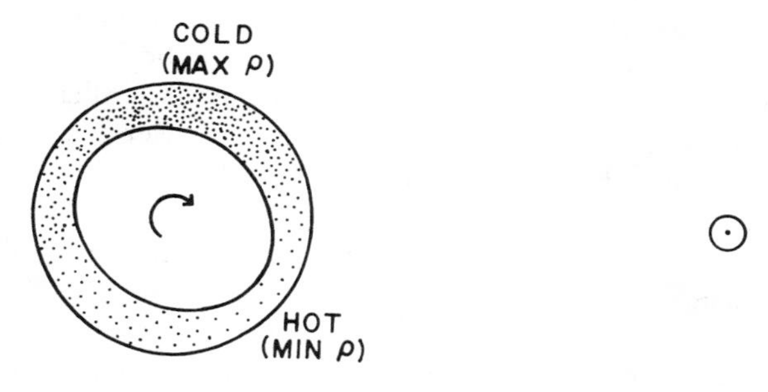

Figure 5 Atmospheric and solid-body tides on Venus. Rotation is clockwise (*arrow*). The solid-body tidal bulge is carried past the subsolar point, thus resulting in a counterclockwise (retarding) torque. An equipotential (constant pressure) surface in the atmosphere is negligibly distorted from spherical. However, since the morning temperature is lower than the afternoon temperature, a greater mass of gas is contained below a given equipotential surface on the morning side than the afternoon side. This results in a quadrupole moment to the figure, the same as the tidal bulge, but this time leading the Sun position, producing a clockwise, or accelerating, torque.

that the deviation may be due to a large-amplitude polar wobble analogous to the Chandler wobble of the Earth. They point out that the timescale of wobble damping is long ($\sim 10^9$ years), while the timescale of generation of the wobble may be more rapid (as it is for the Earth), thus leading to a "random walk" growth of wobble amplitude. Such a motion could lead to a time-averaged effective J_2 for Venus that would be much smaller than the real roughness of the second-order gravity field. However, gravity solutions to data from the Pioneer Venus orbiter (Ananda et al 1980) do not show the requisite large C_{21} and S_{21} components that would be diagnostic of a large-amplitude wobble, and the position of the spin axis remains a puzzle.

As we already noted, solid-body tidal friction will tend to drive Venus' spin axis away from Cassini state 3, hence toward prograde rotation. Goldreich & Peale (1970) note that core-mantle friction would tend to damp the precessional motion about a Cassini state, thus evolving the spin axis onto the Cassini state. This could stabilize the rotation in Cassini state 3 for plausible values of core viscosity and spin rate, but does require an initially retrograde spin.

The possible role of the atmospheric tide in stabilizing Venus in or near Cassini state 3 was first suggested by MacDonald (1964), and elaborated on by Gold & Soter (1969). They pointed out in qualitative terms that, while solid-body tides lag the tide-raising body (in this case the Sun), the atmospheric tide, because of solar heating of the atmosphere, *leads* the position of the Sun (Figure 5). Thus while the solid-body tide will cause the spin to evolve toward the prograde synchronous value, atmospheric tides alone would evolve the spin away from that value in either direction. A planet initially spinning retrograde with respect to the Sun (such that the Sun rises in the west and sets in the east) would thus be driven by the atmospheric tide in the direction of increasing retrograde motion, while a planet rotating faster than synchronous would be driven to ever-increasing prograde spin. Hence a spin reversal appears nearly impossible, and one must conclude that the initial spin of Venus was retrograde.

Since the present spin rate is apparently not resonance controlled, it can represent a stable end-state only if the solid and/or atmospheric tides are frequency dependent, so that the sum of the tidal torques cancel at the present spin rate, but drive it toward that value from either direction. Dobrovolskis & Ingersoll (1980) and Dobrovolskis (1980) developed the atmosphere tide model quantitatively in an attempt to evaluate the plausibility of an atmospherically-driven spin state of Venus. The tidal torque on the atmosphere creates a rapid retrograde circulation, which transfers torque to the planet through wind-shear stress at the surface. Dobrovolskis & Ingersoll (1980) find that the surface wind speeds of $\sim$ 1–10 m/sec are required to produce the required torque on the solid planet.

The principal factor driving the wind circulation is the delay in heating the surface—that is, how far past noon is the hottest time of the day? They find a range of plausible atmosphere and surface models that could produce the requisite conditions. The surface wind speeds measured by Veneras 8, 9, and 10 appear to be a factor of several too slow, but Dobrovolskis & Ingersoll (1980) note that the Venera anemometers may have been too close to the ground, within the frictional boundary layer. The wind speeds near, but not on, the surface measured by the Pioneer Venus entry probes also seem to be too low, $\sim$ 1 m/sec (Counselman et al 1979).

4. EVOLUTION OF PLANETARY ORBITS

There are a number of mechanisms (i.e. Poynting–Robertson, Yarkovsky effect, gas drag, etc.) that can move small objects in the solar system. A recent review of radiation processes (Burns et al 1979) is available, while gas drag on solid particles in the early solar system is discussed by Weidenschilling (1977). We restrict our attention here to mechanisms capable of altering the orbits of satellite and/or planet-sized objects. Such mechanisms include tides, density waves, mean-motion resonances, and secular resonances. Of these, we have chosen to omit a discussion of mean-motion resonance, since a number of reviews on this subject have been conducted of late. In particular, we call the reader's attention to the *Annual Review* article by Peale (1976). Our discussion of tides is limited to recent results, since good background reviews already exist (e.g. Burns 1977).

4.1 Tides

The evolution of the lunar orbit is the classic example of tidal friction (e.g. Darwin 1880, MacDonald 1964, Goldreich 1966). Since tides have not significantly altered the orbit of any planet, we consider only planet/satellite tides. The equations that we use are taken (with some rearrangement) from Goldreich & Soter (1966). The tidal torque between the planet's spin and the satellite's orbit (Equation 3.1) causes the orbital semimajor axis a to evolve as follows:

$$\frac{\dot{a}}{a} = 3\,\frac{k_{2p}}{Q_p}\frac{m_s}{m_p}\left(\frac{r_p}{a}\right)^{13/2}\rho_p^{1/2}\,\Omega_o \sin\left(\omega_p - \Omega\right), \tag{4.1}$$

where the notation is the same as in Section 3.1. The eccentricity of the satellite's orbit is increased by the tide raised on the planet, but damped by dissipation of tidal energy in the satellite:

$$\frac{a}{e}\frac{de}{da} = \frac{19}{8}\,\mathrm{sign}\,(2\omega_p - 3\Omega) - \frac{7}{2}\left(\frac{\rho_p}{\rho_s}\right)^2 \frac{r_p}{r_s}\frac{Q_p}{Q_s}\frac{k_{2s}}{k_{2p}}. \tag{4.2}$$

The above equations are first order in e with coefficients appropriate for a "Darwin" tide with constant lag angle for all components (Goldreich 1963). The sign of (4.1) is positive for prograde satellites outside of synchronous orbit. For a satellite inside of synchronous (e.g. Phobos) or in retrograde orbit (e.g. Triton), the sign is negative and evolution is inward. The sign of the first term of (4.2) is negative for a satellite with an orbit period less than 3/2 of the planet's rotation period, or in retrograde orbit. The sign of the second term is always negative.

Damping of satellite eccentricities Goldreich (1963) and Goldreich & Soter (1966) pointed out that while the Q of the giant planets must be large in order to accommodate the limited outward drift of their inner satellites, the Q's of the satellites are probably much lower. Hence, the second term of (4.2) is dominant by a large factor and probably effective in a timespan short compared to the age of the solar system. Hence the near circularity of the orbits of many of the natural satellites may not reflect their primordial values.

Satellite loss The direction of tidal evolution depends on the sign of $(\omega - \Omega)$. If the planet spins more slowly than, or in the opposite direction from, the satellite's mean motion, the tidal bulge lags behind the position of the satellite and the angular momentum is transferred from orbit to spin with a resulting orbital decay. Such is the case for the present orbits of Phobos and Triton. Three body tidal systems are unstable in that if two of the three objects achieve synchroneity, the third can continue to draw angular momentum from them (Burns 1973, Ward & Reid 1973). Application to Mercury and Venus reveals that a large range of hypothetical satellites of either of these planets would first tidally evolve outward until reaching synchronization with the planet's spin, and then evolve back inward as the Sun continued to despin the planet, eventually spiraling all the way into the planet.

Satellites of Mars The synchronous point ($\omega_p = \Omega$) about Mars is at ~ 6.03 r_p. Hence, Phobos at 2.76 r_p is undergoing orbital decay while Deimos at 6.92 r_p is undergoing orbital expansion. Tracing their orbit backward reveals their semimajor axes were closer in the past. Singer (1968, 1971) traced the evolution of both semimajor axis and eccentricity for frequency-dependent tides and concluded that a large primordial eccentricity for Phobos could have been decayed. This led to the suggestion that either or both objects could have been captured. Lambeck (1979) included the effects of significant radial tides in the satellites—a possibility if their rigidity is less than that of Mars. He predicts an even more rapid decay of orbital eccentricity. On the other hand, a large eccentricity for Phobos results in a crossing orbit with Deimos and the collisional time scale is only of order $\sim 10^5$ days, i.e. much shorter than the relevant tidal time scales (e.g. Yoder 1981). In addition, the inclinations of both satellites are very small, and yet tides could not have decayed the large inclinations expected for captured objects. Cazenave et al (1980a, b) pointed out that to produce a close orbit nearly in the equatorial plane of Mars from an initially elliptical one with a large semimajor axis, capture must occur in the Mars orbit plane. This is because the decaying orbit tracks the local Laplacian plane, which varies from lying near the orbit plane when far out to near the equatorial plane when close to the planet. However, this plane seems no more likely to be selected by capture than does any other special plane.

Yoder (1981) offered a way out of this dilemma, but in doing so introduced another problem. He showed that passage of Phobos through various resonances, most notably the 2:1 resonance with Mars' longitudinal-gravity variation due to the Tharsis bulge (when $a = 3.8r_p$) could have generated increments to the free eccentricity, so that its current value need not be a tidally decayed remnant of its initial value (see Figure 6). Indeed, Phobos' eccentricity could have been small throughout its history. Unfortunately, one resonance encountered is the 2:1 resonance with Deimos when $a = 4.3r_p$, which pumps the eccentricity of the orbit of Deimos up to ~ 0.002, i.e. four times its current value. (Because of the greater mass of Phobos, the resonance has a negligible effect on the eccentricity of its orbit.) It thus appears that dissipation in Deimos has been unusually effective in circularizing its orbit, implying $\mu Q \approx 10^{10}$ dynes/cm^2, compared with $\mu Q \gtrsim 10^{12}$ dynes/cm^2 for Phobos. Yoder (1981) notes, however, that if $(B - A)/C$ of Deimos is extremely close to $1/3$, then the libration amplitude of Deimos may be enhanced as discussed in Section 3.1, thus allowing the requisite dissipation to result from a higher value of μQ, perhaps comparable to that of Phobos. Otherwise one must conclude that the internal structure of Deimos is somehow different from Phobos to account for the higher rate of dissipation.

Galilean satellites The damping of orbital eccentricities by dissipation in the satellites contributes along with other sources (i.e. radionuclides) to heating their interiors. This is usually self-limiting, since a more vigorous dissipation (i.e. smaller Q_s) simply decays the eccentricity faster, the total amount of energy deposited being the same. However, if there exists an additional agency to pump-up the eccentricity, the energy deposition can continue unabated. For Io, such an agency exists in the form of gravitational perturbations from the next further satellite, Europa. These two satellites occupy a 2:1 orbit-orbit resonance, in which each conjunction occurs near Io's perijove. As a consequence, there is an eccentricity forced into Io's orbit of $e \sim 0.004$. Radial tides in Io attempt to damp this eccentricity, but are unable to since it is continually replenished by Europa's perturbations. As a result, it is believed that Io may currently be the most intensely heated terrestrial-type body in the solar system (Peale et al 1979), and that the spectacular volcanism revealed by

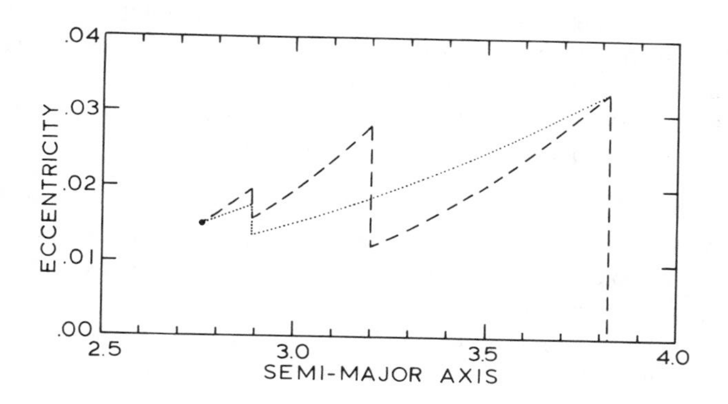

Figure 6 The evolution of eccentricity of the orbit of Phobos. The eccentricity is increased to 0.032 from any lower value by passage through the 2:1 resonance with the planet's rotation at $a = 3.8\ r_p$. At $3.2\ r_p$, the eccentricity may be increased by resonance between the apse precession rate and Mars' orbit motion around the Sun. The magnitude of this effect can vary from zero (*dotted line*) to as much as ˜ 0.016 (*dashed line*), depending on the particulars of Mars' orbit at the time of resonance passage. The third excitation of 0.004 at $2.9\ r_p$ is due to the 3:1 resonance with the planet's spin. The two curves, both terminating at the present values of a and e of Phobos, thus bracket possible histories of the evolution of eccentricity, assuming $e < .032$ when the first resonance was encountered. The dashed curve corresponds to greater tidal dissipation in Phobos and is used to place a lower limit of $\mu Q \gtrsim 10^{12}$ dynes/cm^2 for Phobos (Yoder 1981).

Voyager cameras, as well as the long-observed sodium and sulfur halos, are probably a direct consequence of its dynamic environment.

In addition to the Io/Europa commensurability, Europa and the next satellite Ganymede also occupy a 2:1 resonance. The forced eccentricity for Europa is $e \sim .011$, but the greater distance from Jupiter results in a less severe tidal dissipation rate and gentler internal heating. Even so, effects on Europa's internal structure may not be negligible (Cassen at al 1979). Yoder & Peale (1981) presented a detailed exposition of how the present resonance state was established via jovian tides with the tidal expansion of Io's orbit being the driver. The Io/Europa and Europa/Ganymede resonances are established sequentially. In particular, both 2:1 resonances now act in concert to produce the well-known Laplace relationship

$$\Omega_{\mathrm{Io}} - 3\Omega_{\mathrm{Europa}} + 2\Omega_{\mathrm{Ganymede}} \leqslant 10^{-8},$$

where Ω_i are the satellite mean motions. The associated resonance variable is

$$\lambda_{\mathrm{Io}} - 3\lambda_{\mathrm{Europa}} + 2\lambda_{\mathrm{Ganymede}} = \phi,$$

where λ_i are mean longitudes, and ϕ librates about 180° with an amplitude $\sim 0.066° \pm 0.013°$ and a period of 2074 days (Lieske 1980). This means that whenever Europa and Ganymede are in conjunction, Io is in opposition to them. Yoder & Peale (1981) show that if the libration amplitude is assumed to have been tidally damped (via dissipation in Io) from a starting value of 180° at resonance formation, the three-body lock may have formed some ~ 1600 Q_{J} yrs ago, where Q_{J} is Jupiter's dissipation factor. For a "plausible" $Q_{\mathrm{J}} \sim 4 \times 10^5$, the time is of order $\sim 6 \times 10^8$ yrs.

Pluto-Charon The recently discovered satellite of Pluto (Christy & Harrington 1978, Harrington & Christy 1980) is the only known example of a tidal end-state, i.e. both planet and satellite spins are synchronous with the satellite's mean motion. The satellite is large enough ($m_s/m_p \approx 0.1$) to have easily achieved synchronization in less time than the age of solar system, if we assume any reasonable value of Q. Counselman (1973) showed that for a given planet/satellite system of specified angular momentum, two synchronous states exist (for the primordial Earth/Moon, but neglecting solar tides, these were at orbit radii of ~ 2.3 and ~ 90 Earth radii). Evolution is always away from the inner synchronous point, and toward the outer one. This is because at the inner synchronous point a conservative exchange of rotational for orbital angular momentum changes the orbital more than the rotational frequency. Hence, a satellite slightly outside (inside) the synchronous point finds its orbit period lengthening (shortening) more rapidly than the planet's rotation period, and the difference between the two periods diverges. At the outer synchronous point the situation is reversed. A satellite slightly outside (inside) the synchronous point finds its orbit period lengthening (shortening) more slowly than the planet's rotation period and the two rates converge. The condition for whether a given synchronous state is an inner one or an outer one can be expressed as

$$3\,(C_p + C_s) < \frac{mM}{M + m}\,a^2, \tag{4.3}$$

where C_p and C_s are the polar moments of inertia of the planet and satellite, of masses M and m, respectively. The radius of a synchronous point is given by a. If the above condition is satisfied, then the synchronous point is an outer one, and evolution is toward that state; hence, it is a stable end-state of evolution. For Pluto/Charon, $a \approx 17$ planet radii, and the above criterion implies $m_s/m_p \gtrsim 0.004$. This is a lower limit to the plausible mass ratio of the satellite, given that it is found in the above tidal end-state. The estimated mass ratio given previously exceeds this limit comfortably.

4.2 Secular Resonances

Secular resonances involve 1:1 commensurabilities between various aspidal or nodal line precession rates. Since these rates are determined by the quadrupole (and higher) moments of the gravitational potential, the locations of such resonances are sensitive to the distribution of mass within the central body, as well as to the distribution of mass in orbit around the central body (e.g. other planets, a protoplanetary or protosatellite disk, etc). In the case of an evolving system, such as during the clearing of the solar nebula or the contraction phase of the sun or a planet, the locations of these resonances may "scan" through the orbital phase space occupied by planets or satellites. Such resonances can affect angular momentum exchange, thereby altering orbital eccentricities and inclinations. They have been invoked to explain certain observed characteristics of the solar system, as well as to constrain scenarios of planet/satellite formation by the requirement that their disruptive influence be avoided.

Figure 7 shows a typical secular resonance situation: a smaller object, m, perturbed by a larger one, m', lying in an eccentric orbit at a further distance from the primary ($a' > a$). If we time-average the perturbations from m', or equivalently, consider its mass to be spread out over its orbit, the radial and tangential components of force experienced by m are, to order $e'(a/a')^2$,

$$F_r = \Omega'^2 a' \left\{ \frac{1}{2}\left(\frac{r}{a'}\right) + \frac{9}{8}\left(\frac{r}{a'}\right)^2 e' \cos(\theta - \tilde{\omega}') \right\},$$

$$F_\theta = -\frac{3}{8}\,\Omega'^2 a' \left(\frac{r}{a'}\right)^2 e' \sin(\theta - \tilde{\omega}'), \tag{4.4}$$

where r and θ are the polar coordinates of the position of m, and $\tilde{\omega}'$ is the

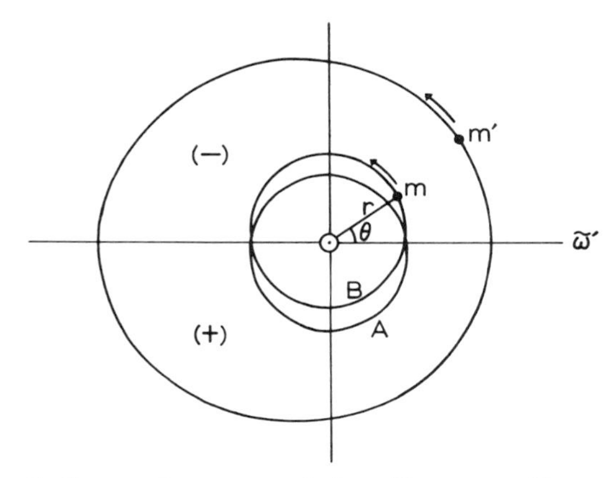

Figure 7 Schematic diagram of secular perturbations. The average effect of m' (perihelion in the direction $\tilde{\omega}'$) on m is to decrease the eccentricity when the orbit is oriented as in A, or increase it when the orbit is oriented as in B. If the orbit of m precesses relative to that of m', a small-amplitude periodic perturbation results. If the precession rates are equal, the eccentricity may grow to a large value (secular resonance).

longitude of periapse of m'. If $\mathrm{d}E/\mathrm{d}t = \boldsymbol{v} \cdot \boldsymbol{F} = \dot{r}\mathrm{F}_r + r\dot{\theta}F_\theta$ is integrated over an orbital cycle of m, $\oint (\mathrm{d}E/\mathrm{d}t)\,\mathrm{d}t = 0$. Since the orbital energy remains constant, secular perturbations do not cause variations in the semimajor axes. However, changes in the angular momentum do occur and are given by $\mathrm{d}H/\mathrm{d}t = rF_\theta$. Hence, during the half-orbit as m moves from the pericenter of m' ($\theta = \tilde{\omega}'$) to its apocenter ($\theta = \tilde{\omega}' + \pi$), the angular momentum decreases, with the "off-center" ring of material trying to retard the orbital motion. During the subsequent half-cycle back to $\tilde{\omega}'$, H increases. If the orbit of m is circular, these effects are largely compensatory (although not quite, since an eccentricity *is* forced in the orbit of m, which folds back into the perturbation equations and can result in a growing e). However, if the orbit of m is eccentric, the torque is larger at its apocenter and the orbital velocity is slower, so that m spends more time there. Hence, there is a net increase in angular momentum for orbit A in Figure 7, and a net decrease for orbit B. Since the semimajor axis is unchanged, $e\Delta e \approx -\Delta H/H$ (e.g. Burns 1977), and e decreases and increases for orbits A and B, respectively. If the apsidal lines of m and m' precess at different rates, $(\tilde{\omega} - \tilde{\omega}')$ will in general rotate through 2π and the eccentricity will undergo a periodic variation. If m and m' were isolated, their mutual perturbations would also determine $\dot{\tilde{\omega}}$ and $\dot{\tilde{\omega}}'$ so that the system's motion would not evolve. However, if there are other sources of a quadrupole field, such as an oblate primary or gas disk that can change with time, the relative apsidal line motion can be driven through a 1:1 comensurability, during which the oscillations may become severe. Such a passage is termed a secular resonance and can have the net effect of generating a large contribution to the eccentricity. A similar argument applies to orbital inclinations and precessions of the nodes.

The orbit of Mercury The orbit of Mercury is anomalously irregular, with a mean eccentricity (0.175) and inclination (7°.2) nearly twice as large as any other major planet, excepting Pluto. Ward et al (1976) suggested secular resonances with Venus as the cause of this orbital irregularity. The secular variations of the planetary system exhibit discrete characteristic frequencies (i.e. eigenfrequencies) in their oscillations (Table 2). In this scheme, Mercury is driven through resonance by a slowly decaying quadrupole moment of the Sun's gravity field during solar spin down. This can cause Mercury's dominant apsidal and nodal frequencies ($j = 1$) to drift through one or more of the other eigenfrequencies. A minimum solar $J_2 = 1.6 \times 10^{-3}$ is necessary for the $j = 1$ frequencies to begin above the frequencies of the nearest eigenvector, $j = 2$, associated with Venus. This corresponds to a solar rotation period of 5–6 hours, which is reasonably consistent with rotation rates for young solar-mass stars as estimated by extrapolation of observational data (Kraft 1967, 1972). The resulting eccentricity perturbation is proportional to $(\Delta\dot{S})^{-1/2}$, where $\Delta\dot{S} = \dot{S}_1 - \dot{S}_2$ is the rate at which the differential precession frequency drifts through zero (Ward et al 1976). Resonances can account for the present eccentricity and inclination if $\Delta\dot{S} \sim (10^{-26}\,\mathrm{sec}^{-2})$. If this is, in turn, related to the loss of the solar quadrupole field during spin-down, the required characteristic spin-down time is $\omega_\odot^{-1}\,d\omega/dt \sim 10^{-6}\,\mathrm{yr}^{-1}$. The Sun is generally believed to have lost its primordial angular momentum through the magnetic braking action of the solar wind (e.g. Spiegel 1970, Fricke & Kappenhahn 1972, Gilman 1974). Scaling the magnetic field as $\omega_\odot$ (e.g. Durney 1972) the implied solar-mass loss rate becomes $M_\odot^{-1}\,dM_\odot/dt \sim 10^{-8}\,\mathrm{yr}^{-1}$, which is the same order of magnitude as estimated loss rates from T-Tauri stars (e.g. Ezer & Cameron 1971, Kuhi 1964, 1966).

Solar nebula removal An indirect application of secular resonances can be made to the question of planetary stability during solar nebula dispersal (Ward 1980, 1981c). If the planetary system were initially embedded in a $10^{-2}\,M_\odot$ nebula of surface density $\sigma \propto a^{-k}$, where a is heliocentric distance and k is an exponent presumed to lie in the range $1 \lesssim k \lesssim 2$ (cf Weidenschilling 1977), the initial eigenfrequencies of the system's secular variations would be dominated by the nebula and correspond to individual planetary precession rates that would vary monotonically with distance. The current planetary precession rates (which actually involve a superposition of all eigenfrequencies to some degree) would then constitute a partial inversion of such an original ordering (see Table 2). As gas left the system and the "background" potential of the nebula weakened, the system then could have passed through a number of secular resonances. In fact, it seems unlikely that a sweep of powerful resonances through the inner solar system could have been avoided. The reason for this is straightforward; the most important resonances involve either Jupiter or Saturn. The principal eccentricity eigenfrequencies associated with these planets (i.e. S_5, S_6) now bound the present terrestrial planet eigenfrequencies (S_1, S_2, S_3, S_4) from both above and below. However, for a nebula density monotonically varying with distance as postulated above, the inner planet frequencies were not so bound initially. Hence, at least one major resonance must be passed to arrive at present conditions. For inclinations, $S_5' = 0$, so the present terrestrial frequencies are only bound from above (shorter period). However, since the nebula augments nodal regression, the terrestrial frequencies were initially faster than at present. For the nebula density postulated, with $k > 1/2$, the initial frequencies would have been faster than S_6', while at present they are slower than S_6', again implying resonance passage.

The consequences of resonance passage are similar to the Mercury orbit problem except that, instead of a single planet's orbit being perturbed, it is the eigenvector amplitudes that are pumped-up. A single eigenvector may involve significant e's or i's for more than one planet. (Again, the strength of the effect varies inversely with the square root of the relative deceleration, $|\dot{S}_j - \dot{S}_n|^{1/2}$.)

The current eigenvector amplitudes can thus be used to determine a critical deceleration rate $|\dot{S}_j - \dot{S}_n|_{crit}$ that would be capable of exciting the entire terrestrial amplitude with this (j, n) resonance; slower decelerations would produce larger amplitudes. The strength of the resonance also depends in part on the eigenvector configuration at the moment of resonance passage. This must be determined by tracking their behavior in the particular dispersal model employed. The critical deceleration must then be related to a time scale of nebula dispersal, τ. Again this is somewhat model dependent. Several idealized dispersal routines have been considered by Ward (1981c); values for τ for the most powerful resonances were typically of order (few) $\times$ 10^5 yrs. This is short compared to the typical accretion timescales of order 10^7–10^8 years for the terrestrial planets (Wetherill 1980) and may place strong constraints on models of solar system formation. In particular, the possibility that the terrestrial planets postdate both giant planet formation and nebula dispersal must be considered (Ward 1980).

Asteroid belt Although the best known features of the asteroid belt's morphology, the Kirkwood gaps, are associated with mean motion commensurabilities, secular resonance may also have played an important role in the belt's evolution. The three resonance frequencies that are most important for the asteroid belt are a nodal precession rate of $-25''.7$ yr^{-1}, and apsidal precession rates of $27''.8$ yr^{-1} and $4''.3$ yr^{-1}. The first of these is associated primarily with a co-precession of Jupiter and Saturn nodal lines, the last two with the apsidal precessions of Saturn and Jupiter, respectively. Main belt (non–Mars-crossing) asteroids with $a < 2.6$ au are severely depleted at these resonances (Williams 1971).

Secular resonances have been suggested as a mechanism for material transport from the asteroid belt, furnishing a source for meteorites. Collisional debris from asteroids adjacent to resonance zones are ejected into the zone where their eccentricities are pumped-up until they are Mars-crossing. Subsequent close encounters with Mars random-walk the orbits until Earth-crossing orbits are achieved (Wetherill 1977, Wetherill & Williams 1979, Wetherill 1979).

For small free eccentricity and inclination, the nodal resonance is located at ~ 1.9 au near the inner edge of the belt, the fast apsidal resonance lies at ~ 2.0 au, and the slow apsidal resonance does not lie in the belt at all. However, the positions of the resonances change for large e and i, so that their complete description involves mapping their surfaces in (a, e, i) phase space. Recently, Williams & Faulkner (1981) mapped these principal resonances for semimajor axes between 1.25 and 3.5 au. The slow apsidal resonance penetrates the region for high inclination ($\gtrsim 23°$).

The locations of these resonances would vary with any change of characteristics of the planetary system. One possibility is, again, removal of the solar nebula. However, since for most of the belt the nodal and apsidal precessions are faster than the highest frequency resonance, a model that reverses this situation (i.e. that increases the planetary eigenfrequencies associated with Jupiter and Saturn more than the asteroidal precession frequencies) must have a surface density that drops off more slowly than $r^{-1/2}$ or even increases with r throughout the region. Heppenheimer (1980) partially circumvented this restriction by pointing out that objects immersed in a gas nebula tend to reverse the direction of their apsidal line rotation. This arises from the strong local torque exerted by that portion of the nebula alternately inside and outside of the eccentric orbit. As a result, the asteroid orbits may have initially regressed, but then reversed direction as the nebula was removed. Their $\dot{\tilde{\omega}}$ thus runs through the apsidal resonance frequencies from below even for a nebula with density profile $\sigma \propto r^{-3/2}$. With a characteristic nebula dispersal time of $\tau = \sigma/\dot{\sigma} \sim (10^{4-5}$ yrs), large eccentricities can be generated in the belt as the resonance(s) scan(s) through. However, there is no corresponding inclination resonance in the scheme because a reversal of the nodes' precession would require evacuation of the nebula's mid-plane, in violation of vertical hydrostatic equilibrium.

A similar scenario, but one involving mean motion resonances between asteroids and Jupiter, is proposed by Torbett & Smoluchowski (1980). A large nebula density is required to produce significant drift in this type of resonance.

Iapetus A related problem involves the unusual orbit of Iapetus, which is inclined by $\sim 8°$ to the local Laplacian plane, although its eccentricity is small ($e = 0.0283$). Ward (1981b) considered the effect of a circumplanetary disk, such as the one that may have been the progenitor of the satellite system. This disk and the satellites would be in the Laplacian plane, which would be warped from its present value by the mass of the disk. If the disk mass were dispersed more rapidly than the nodal precession rate of Iapetus, then that satellite would fail to track the changing Laplacian plane and would be left in an inclined orbit. Although results are somewhat model dependent, a disk dispersal rate of about half the mass of Titan per 100 years seems to be required. Such a rapid dispersal suggests turbulence as the dissipation mechanism.

4.3 Disk Dynamics and Disk-Satellite Interactions

Disk-satellite torque Another mechanism for moving matter about in the solar nebula involves a tide-like interaction between a discrete massive planet (or satellite) and a neighboring "fluid" disk of small particles, i.e. a protoplanetary swarm of a planetary ring. The most proper way to consider this effect is in the framework of density wave mechanics analogous to that applied to galactic structure (see Goldreich & Tremaine 1978b, 1979b, 1980, 1981). The most important result for our purposes, the tide-like torque on a ring by a nearby satellite, can be derived approximately by a simple impulse approximation (Lin & Papaloizou 1979a, b). Consider the gravitational interaction between two masses $m_r << m_s$ passing one another at velocity v and impact parameter d. Following the encounter, m_r has received an impulse perpendicular to the initial velocity as given by (2.1) Since the total relative velocity must remain unchanged, the parallel component of velocity must be decreased by

$$\Delta v_{\parallel} \approx \frac{1}{2}\, v \left(\frac{\Delta v_{\perp}}{v}\right)^2 = \frac{2G^2 m_s^2}{d^2 v^3}\,. \tag{4.5}$$

If m_r and m_s are two satellites initially in circular, coplanar orbits of radii a and $a + d$ about a planet of mass m_p, the relative velocity is $v = (3/2)\Omega d$, where $\Omega = (Gm_p/a^3)^{1/2}$ is the orbit frequency. Following the encounter, the impulse causes a radial velocity $\Delta v_{\perp}$, which results in an eccentric orbit for m_r, and a tangential impulse, which tends to reduce the relative velocity between m_r and m_s. Note that if m_r is exterior to m_s, it is *overtaken* by m_s during the encounter, so $\Delta v_{\parallel}$ is added to the actual orbit motion thus moving the new orbit farther out. If m_r is interior, it *overtakes* m_s, so $\Delta v_{\parallel}$ opposes the actual orbit motion, moving the new orbit inward. Thus, in either case the impulse results in the two satellite orbits moving away from one another. Figure 8 illustrates this effect with a numerical integration. The exchange in angular momentum is

$$h = am_r\Delta v_\parallel \approx \frac{2G^2m_s^2m_ra}{d^2v^3}. \tag{4.6}$$

The time between encounters is $\Delta t = 2\pi/\Delta\Omega \approx 4\pi a/3\Omega d$. Hence that rate of exchange of angular momentum (torque) between m_r and m_s is

$$\dot{h} = \frac{\Delta h}{\Delta t} = \frac{2}{3\pi}\frac{m_s^2m_r}{m_p^2}\frac{\Omega^2a^6}{d^4}, \tag{4.7}$$

where we have substituted expressions for v and Ω appropriate to Keplerian motion (m_r, $m_s << m_p$) in order to remove v and G from the expression. Goldreich & Tremaine (1980) derived an expression dimensionally identical to the above, but with a lead coefficient of 0.399 rather than $(2/3)\pi(\approx 0.21)$.

There is an important limitation to this effect: once the particles begin moving in eccentric orbits, subsequent impulses will tend to become random in direction as they occur at random phases in the eccentric motion. Thus, the momentum exchange becomes a random walk, with no net tendency of the orbit spacing to increase or decrease. In order to continue the effect beyond the first encounter, the induced eccentricity must be damped. It is for this reason that the interaction is important only between a satellite and a "fluid" disk. In such a disk, two mechanisms exist whereby the eccentric motion may be damped. The more obvious is simple collisional damping. As the particles

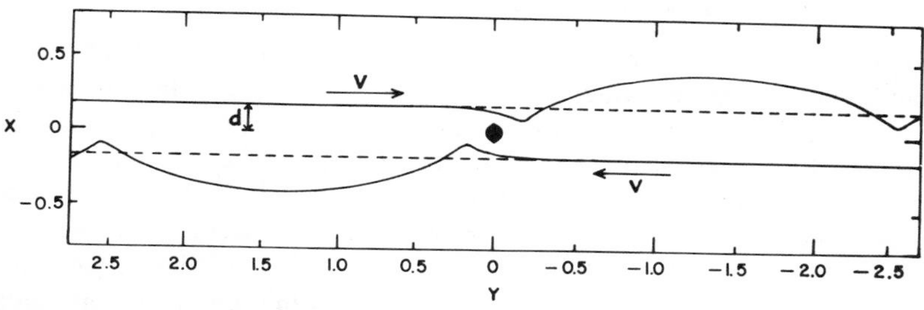

Figure 8 The motion of "massless" particles initially in circular orbits interior and exterior to a secondary body of mass $\mu = 10^{-12}$ that of the primary, which is also in circular orbit. The motion was computed numerically in rotating coordinates centered on the secondary with $+X$ radially outward and $+Y$ in the direction of motion of the secondary. The dimensions are in units of 10^{-3} of the primary-secondary orbit radius. The secondary is represented by a spot which fills its Roche lobe—that is, the inner and outer tips of the spot are the L_1 and L_2 Lagrange points of the secondary. The magnitude of the perturbations scale as $\mu^{1/3}$. Hence, if $\mu = 10^{-15}$, the axis units become 10^{-4} radii and the figure remains valid as drawn. The unperturbed motion of each particle is shown by the dashed lines. Note that following encounter, the mean radial (X) coordinates of the particles are farther away from the secondary orbit than before encounter. Hence, the particles have been repelled. If the cyclic motion (eccentricity) of the particles ceases prior to the next encounter, then the process will be repeated, leading to a clearing out of the zone near the secondary.

bump into one another, they suffer collisions, inelastic to some degree, which eventually reestablish the circular orbital motion. One problem with this is that the perturbations induced in neighboring particles are nearly equal, so the resulting epicyclic motion is nearly coherent. That is, the relative motion between neighboring particles is only a small fraction of the total velocity relative to the circular orbit reference point, thus damping is very slow. A second problem is that the collisional interactions can be thought of as a viscosity in the "fluid" ring, which is experiencing shear stress due to the differential Keplerian velocity. It can be shown that in many cases, the transfer of angular momentum from viscous shear exceeds the disk-satellite torque. A more subtle effect is operative, which assures the success of the disk-satellite torque: The perturbations in the particle motions create density variations (waves) in the ring, which through their own self-gravity propagate across the ring. Much in the same way that water waves propagate away and leave the site of the original disturbance calm, density waves remove the disturbance from the ring edge near the satellite where the interaction is strongest, and leave the site ready for the next impulse. The resulting particle distribution consists of a spiral wave pattern, and the attraction of the perturber for this distribution results in a torque. The waves must be damped eventually but, as in the analogy of the water waves, this may take much longer than the time between impulses. The important point is that the rate of wave propagation is of the order of the orbit frequency, whereas the rate of impulses is much slower for a ring perturbed by a nearby satellite.

Cassini division One application of density wave theory indicating that disturbances in Saturn's rings are dissipated in this way is the problem of Cassini's division. It has long been known that Cassini's division lies very near the 2:1 resonance with the satellite Mimas and is probably associated with that resonance. However, the range over which perturbations by Mimas would be expected to clear particles from the ring is much narrower than the observed width of the gap (e.g. Franklin & Colombo 1970). Goldreich & Tremaine (1978b) proposed a density wave explanation for this problem. The initial disturbance, generated in a very narrow zone near the resonance point, propagates outward as a long trailing spiral density wave. No long waves are propagated inward. The wave carries a "negative" angular momentum in the sense that the particles through which the wave passes lose angular momentum in the process of damping the wave, and thus spiral inward. This creates a zone that is cleared outward from the resonance point to a distance at least as far as the scale over which damping occurs, rather than the width over which the disturbance is generated. Goldreich & Tremaine (1978b) estimate that the width of Cassini's division is in plausible agreement with the range over which dissipation occurs. The zone may be further widened by particle diffusion, which we discuss next.

Viscous diffusion Returning now to the matter of the torque exerted on a ring by a nearby satellite, we must consider the opposing torque, mentioned briefly above, that is the viscous shear stress existing within the ring due to the random ("thermal") motions of particles coupled with the shear velocity gradient due to the differential orbital velocity (Lynden-Bell & Pringle 1974, Brahic 1977, Goldreich & Tremaine 1978a). The shear stress on a differentially rotating fluid is (e.g. Safronov 1969, p. 70)

$$S \equiv \rho \nu a \frac{\mathrm{d}\Omega}{\mathrm{d}a}. \tag{4.8}$$

The above expression defines the kinematic viscosity ν. The density of the "fluid" is ρ, and the velocity gradient is $a\,\mathrm{d}\Omega/\mathrm{d}a$, which for Keplerian motion is equal to $-3/2\,\Omega$. In order to find the torque couple acting on the ring, the above stress is multiplied by a to convert from force to torque, integrating around the ring (multiplied by $2\pi a$), and integrated vertically through the ring (replace the density ρ by the surface density $\sigma = \int \rho\,\mathrm{d}z$). The resulting expression for torque, or time rate of change of angular momentum, is

$$\dot{h} = 2\pi a^3\,\sigma\nu \frac{\mathrm{d}\Omega}{\mathrm{d}a} = -3\pi a^2\,\sigma\nu\Omega. \tag{4.9}$$

From the form of 4.8, it is clear that the kinematic viscosity must be of the following functional form:

$$\text{stress (force/area)} = \begin{pmatrix}\text{mass/area/time moved}\\ \text{across velocity gradient}\end{pmatrix}\begin{pmatrix}\text{distance}\\ \text{moved}\end{pmatrix}\begin{pmatrix}\text{velocity}\\ \text{gradient}\end{pmatrix}$$

$$\sim (\rho\Delta a\omega_c)\,(\Delta a)\left(a\frac{\mathrm{d}\Omega}{\mathrm{d}a}\right). \tag{4.10}$$

Comparing (4.10) with (4.8), we see that $\nu = \Delta a^2\omega_c = (1/3)\,\lambda^2\omega_c$, where ω_c is the collision frequency and λ is the mean free path. The factor $1/3$ arises since only one of the three components of the random velocity is radial (see Safronov 1969 and Goldreich & Tremaine 1978a).

The collision frequency is approximately $\omega_c \sim \Omega\tau$, where τ is the normal optical depth of the ring. For an optically thick ring, the mean free path is simply $\lambda \sim v/\omega_c = v/\Omega\tau$, where v is the random velocity between particles. If the collision frequency is much less than the orbit frequency ($\tau << 1$), the mean free path in the radial direction is limited by the maximum radial excursion of the particle over the entire orbit, and $\lambda \sim v/\Omega$. Goldreich & Tremaine (1978a) show that to a good approximation the mean free path for arbitrary τ can be taken as

$$\lambda^2 \approx \frac{v^2}{\Omega^2(1+\tau^2)}. \tag{4.11}$$

The kinematic viscosity is thus

$$\nu \approx \frac{1}{3} \frac{v^2 \tau}{\Omega(1 + \tau^2)}. \tag{4.12}$$

This is the same as Goldreich & Tremaine's (1978a) equation (2) except that we used the total mean-squared dispersion velocity v^2, whereas they used only the radial component of v^2, which is $(1/3)v^2$ if v is isotropic. The torque on the ring thus becomes

$$\dot{h} \approx -\pi a^2 \sigma v^2 \frac{\tau}{(1 + \tau^2)}. \tag{4.13}$$

The viscous spreading of a ring has been discussed in terms of a random walk (Brahic 1977, Goldreich & Tremaine 1978b, 1979a). A particle moving in random steps of length λ and collision frequency ω_c will move a distance $n^{1/2}\lambda = (\omega_c t)^{1/2}\lambda$ after time t. Allowing for the fact that the radial direction is only one of three directions of motion, the mean-squared radial excursion is $w^2 = \omega_c t\, \lambda^2/3$. We substitute expressions for ω_c and λ to obtain $w^2 = (v^2 t\tau/3\Omega)(1 + \tau^2)$. By differentiating this expression with respect to time and identifying the spreading rate, $\dot{w}$, with the rate of change in orbit radius (half of the mass is moving outward at $\sim \dot{w}/2$, while the other half is moving inward), one can recover (4.13) as the torque required to produce this rate of spreading. As must be expected of dimensional arguments, the constant coefficients are not exactly the same.

Brahic (1977) noted that for Saturn's rings the random velocity v must be less than ~ 0.1 cm/sec in order that the diffusion spreading in 4.5×10^9 years does not exceed the present width of the rings. Goldreich & Tremaine (1978b) place a more stringent requirement on v by noting that diffusion must be limited to a distance of the order of the width of the Enke Division ($\sim 10^3$ km), since their density wave theory predicts clearing of gaps to a width of either the damping range of the density waves or the diffusion range of particles into the resonance zone (whichever is larger). This limit on v is $\sim 10^{-2}$ cm/sec, corresponding to a ring thickness ($z_0 \sim v/\Omega$) of only ~ 1 meter. We note however that this is a pre-Voyager conclusion and does not take into account the "record-groove" structure, which we discuss below. Goldreich & Tremaine (1979a) note that for uranian rings, $w \lesssim 10$ km in some cases; the rings, if unconfined, would have to be thinner than $z_0 \sim 1/3$ cm. A ring this thin, even if totally solid, would decay by Poynting-Robertson drag in less than 4.5×10^9 years. They conclude that the uranian rings must be confined by some restoring torque and propose pairs of "guardian" satellites, which would exert opposing torques according to (4.7).

Guardian satellites In the most simplified case of two satellites, each of mass m_s, with orbits an equal distance d inside and outside of a ring of width

$w << d << a$, the net torque (torque from outer satellite minus torque from inner satellite) at the edge of the ring can be equated with the diffusion torque (Goldreich & Tremaine 1979a):

$$\frac{8}{3\pi}\frac{m_s^2 m_r}{m_p^2}\frac{\Omega^2 a^6 w}{d^5} \approx \pi a^2 \sigma v^2 \frac{\tau}{(1+\tau^2)}. \tag{4.14}$$

The above expression can be simplified considerably by substituting $m_r \approx 2\pi r w \sigma$ and $v \sim \Omega z_o$:

$$\frac{z_o}{w} \sim 2\left(\frac{m_s}{m_p}\right)\left(\frac{a}{d}\right)^{2.5}\left(\frac{1+\tau^2}{\tau}\right)^{1/2} \tag{4.15}$$

A second condition that may be imposed on the ring/satellite system is that the "guardians" not be receding from the ring rapidly compared to the age of the solar system. The rate of recession, obtained by equating the torque (4.7) with the change in satellite angular momentum, is

$$\dot{h} = \frac{1}{2} m_s \Omega a \dot{a} = \frac{2}{3\pi}\frac{m_s^2 m_r}{m_p^2}\frac{\Omega^2 a^6}{d^4}. \tag{4.16}$$

The characteristic time of recession is thus

$$T \sim \frac{d}{\dot{a}} = \frac{3\pi}{4}\frac{m_p^2}{m_s m_r}\left(\frac{d}{a}\right)^5 \Omega^{-1} \gtrsim 4.5 \times 10^9 \text{ yrs}. \tag{4.17}$$

Numerically, this reduces to

$$\frac{m_s m_r}{m_p^2} \lesssim 10^{-13}\left(\frac{d}{a}\right)^5. \tag{4.18}$$

Goldreich & Tremaine (1979a) present graphical solutions to the constraints (4.15) and (4.18). There are two apparent applications to their work: the uranian rings and Saturn's F ring with its attendant "guardians." In general, (4.15) predicts reasonable ring thicknesses (~ 10 m) for expected or known values of m_s, d/a, and τ. However, (4.17) predicts that the rate of recoil of the satellites for reasonably massive systems ($m_s/m_p \sim m_r/m_p \sim 10^{-10}$) should be rapid compared to the age of the solar system, hence (4.18) is probably violated by both Saturn's F ring and the uranian rings. Goldreich & Tremaine (1979a) suggest that resonances with larger outer satellites may preserve the system. If the "guardian" satellites are trapped in resonance with larger satellites, the rate of recession is reduced approximately by the mass ratio of the resonant pair, which is plausibly $\sim 10^{-3}$–10^{-4}. This improves condition (4.18) to an almost acceptable level, although the inferred masses are still very low. A remaining difficulty is that satellites evolving away from one another cannot, in general, be trapped into resonance (Greenberg 1973,

Yoder 1973). Hence, the inner guardian satellite would not be trapped as it moved inward past resonances with exterior satellites.

The situation may be improved because the viscous torque could be considerably less due to the breakup of the ring into alternating high and low density zones, as suggested by Lin & Bodenheimer (1981) and Ward (1981a). They point out that a ring will not remain uniform if the viscous stress can be reduced by breaking up into alternating high and low density ringlets. The shear stress must be conserved across the boundary, which requires that the stress be lower at values of τ both above and below the value of τ for a uniform ring. This breakup into a lower stress state was proposed by the above authors as an explanation of the "record-groove" structure of Saturn's rings revealed by Voyager I. This lower-stress state will slow the viscous spreading rate of a ring, thus allowing higher random motions of particles in some parts of the ring than inferred by Brahic (1977) and Goldreich & Tremaine (1978a, b). The restoring torque required to confine a narrow ring might also be reduced, alleviating the situation of the rapid recoil of the "guardian" satellites.

Planetary and satellite formation Several authors have applied the above results to the problem of planetary formation and evolution. The piling up of ring matter just interior to the 2:1 resonance as in Saturn's rings suggests a mechanism for triggering formation of a planet or satellite near the 2:1 resonance with an earlier formed planet or satellite embryo in the proto-planetary or satellite "nebula." This might account for some of the commensurabilities in the satellite systems of Jupiter and Saturn (Goldreich & Tremaine 1978b). The torque that exists between a disk and a massive body orbiting near or within it can cause densifications at the boundaries as it pushes the ring edges away from its orbit. This in turn might trigger formation of additional planet embryos near the sites of growing planets. Perhaps more importantly, if there is a radial gradient to the density of the solar nebula, the torque from one side on a planet embryo will be different from that on the other, and the embryo will be propelled inward or outward by the torque imbalance. Goldreich & Tremaine (1980) note that Jupiter would migrate by a substantial amount ($\Delta a/a \sim 1$) on a time scale of $\sim 10^4$ years, suggesting that outer planet formation and dispersal of the residual solar nebula must have occurred very rapidly. This mechanism might have resulted in large-scale migrations of planet embryos in the solar nebula, thus allowing them to overtake and sweep-up neighboring smaller embryos and avoid the stagnation problem discussed in Section 1.2. Similar migrations may have played a role in determining the size and spacing of satellites about the outer planets.

We have not mentioned the evolution of eccentricity as a result of disk-satellite interaction, because it is difficult to treat by our simple impulse model. Goldreich & Tremaine (1980, 1981) considered eccentricity evolution in the context of density wave theory. They show that torques from Lindblad resonances tend to increase the eccentricity of both the satellite and the ring, while those from co-rotation resonances tend to damp it. For a uniform density disk the latter effect dominates and the orbits are circularized. However, if the co-rotation resonances are strong enough to clear zones in the disk, the effectiveness of these resonances is reduced and the eccentricity is increased. Goldreich & Tremaine (1980, 1981) apply these results to the eccentricity of the ϵ ring of Uranus and to the orbit of Jupiter in the solar nebula. The latter result is more relevant to the present discussion, because it is yet another way in which orbital eccentricity may have been altered since (or during) planet formation. They note that for a uniform solar nebula, Jupiter's orbit eccentricity should be damped on a time scale $\sim$ 100 yrs, or 20 times shorter than the rate of radial drift. Hence, the eccentricities of the outer planet orbits may have been substantially damped by this mechanism, even if the orbit spacings were not substantially affected.

Literature Cited

Alden, H. L. 1943. Observations of the satellite of Neptune. *Astron. J.* 50:110–11

Anada, M. P., Sjogren, W. L., Philips, R. J., Wimberly, R. N., Bills, B. G. 1980. A low order global gravity field of Venus and dynamical implications. *J. Geophys. Res.* 85:8303–18

Anderson, J. D., Null, G. W., Biller, E. D., Wong, S. K., Hubbard, W. B., MacFarlane, J. J. 1980. Pioneer Saturn Celestial Mechanics Experiment. *Science* 207: 449–453

Berger, A. L. 1976. Obliquity and precession for the last 5,000,000 years. *Astron. Astrophys.* 51:127–35

Brahic, A. 1977. Systems of Colliding bodies in a gravitational field. I. Numerical simulation of the standard model. *Astron. Astrophys.* 54:895–907

Brouwer, D., van Woerkom, A. J. 1950. The secular variations of the orbital elements of the principal planets. *Astron. Pap. Amer. Ephemeris & Naut. Alm.* 13, Pt.2

Burns, J. A. 1972. Dynamical characteristics of Phobos and Deimos. *Rev. Geophys. Space Phys.* 10:463–83

Burna, J. A. 1973. Where are the satellites of the inner planets? *Nature* 242:23–25

Burns, J. A. 1977. Orbital evolution. In *Planetary Satellites*, ed. J. A. Burns, pp. 113–56. Tucson: Univ. Ariz. Press. 598 pp.

Burns, J. A., Lamy, P. L., Soter, S. 1979. Radiation forces on small particles in the solar system. *Icarus* 40:1–48

Cassen, P., Reynolds, R. T., Peale, S. J. 1979. Is there liquid water on Europa? *Geophys. Res. Lett.* 6:731–34

Cazenave, A., Dobrovolskis, A., Lago, B. 1980a. Evolution of the inclination of Phobos. *Nature* 284:430–31

Cazenave, A., Dobrovolskis, A., Lago, B. 1980b. Orbital history of the Martian satellites with inferences on their origin. *Icarus* 44:552–607

Chandrasekhar, S. 1942. *Principles of Stellar Dynamics*. Chicago: Chicago Univ. Press. Reprinted 1960, New York: Dover. 313 pp.

Christy, J. W., Harrington, R. S. 1978. The satellite of Pluto. *Astron. J.* 83:1005–8

Colombo, G. 1965. Rotation period of the planet Mercury. *Nature* 208:575

Colombo, G. 1966. Cassini's second and third laws. *Astron. J.* 71:891–96

Counselman, C. C. III. 1973. Outcomes of tidal evolution. *Astrophys. J.* 180:307–14

Counselman, C. C., III, Gourevitch, S. A., King, R. W., Loriot, G. B., Prinn, R. G. 1979. Venus winds are zonal and retrograde below the clouds. *Science* 205:85–87

Cruikshank, D. P. 1980. Near-Infrared studies of the satellites of Saturn and Uranus. *Icarus* 41:246–58

Cruikshank, D. P., Stockton, A., Dyck, H. M., Becklin, E. E., Macy, W. 1979. The diameter and reflectance of Triton. *Icarus* 40:104–14

Danby, J. M. A. 1962. *Fundamentals of Celestial Mechanics*. New York: Macmillan. 348 pp.

Darwin, G. H. 1880. On the secular change in the elements of the orbit of a satellite revolving about a tidally distorted planet. *Philos. Trans. R. Soc. London* 171:713–891

Dobrovolskis, A. R. 1980. Atmospheric tides

and the rotation of Venus. II. Spin evolution. *Icarus* 40:18–35
Dobrovolskis, A. R., Ingersoll, A. P. 1980. Atmospheric tides and the rotation of Venus. I. Tidal theory and balance of torques. *Icarus* 40:1–17
Durney, B. 1972. Comments on solar rotation. In *Solar Wind*, ed. C. P. Sonett, P. J. Coleman, J. M. Wilcox, pp. 282–86. Washington DC: NASA.
Elliot, J. L., French, R. G., Frogel, J. A., Elias, J. H., Mink, D., Liller, W. 1981. Orbits of nine Uranian Rings. *Astron. J.* 86:444–55
Ezer, D., Cameron, A. G. W. 1971. Pre-main sequence stellar evolution with mass loss. *Astrophys. Space Sci.* 10:52–70
Farinella, P., Milani, A., Nobili, A. M., Valsecchi, G. B. 1980. Some remarks on the capture of Triton and the origin of Pluto. *Icarus* 44:810–12
Ferrari, A. J., Sinclair, W. S., Sjogren, W. L., Williams, J. G., Yoder, C. F. 1980. Geophysical parameters of the earth-moon system. *J. Geophys. Res.* 85:3939–51
Franklin, F. A., Colombo, G. 1970. A dynamical model for the radial structure of Saturn's Rings. *Icarus* 12:338–47
Fricke, K. J., Kippenhahn, R. 1972. Evolution of rotating stars. *Ann. Rev. Astron. Astrophys.* 10:45–72
Gilman, P. A. 1974. Solar rotation. *Ann. Rev. Astron. Astrophys.* 12:47–70
Giuli, R. T. 1968. On the rotation of the earth produced by gravitational accretion of particles. *Icarus* 8:301–23
Gold, T., Soter, S. 1969. Atmospheric tides and the resonant rotation of Venus. *Icarus* 11:356–66
Goldreich, P. 1963. On the eccentricity of satellite orbits in the solar system. *Mon. Not. R. Astron. Soc.* 126:257–68
Goldreich, P. 1966. History of the lunar orbit. *Rev. Geophys* 4:411–39
Goldreich, P., Peale, S. 1966. Spin-orbit coupling in the solar system. *Astron. J.* 71: 425–38
Goldreich, P., Peale, S. 1967. Spin-orbit coupling in the solar system. II. The resonant rotation of Venus. *Astron. J.* 72:662–68
Goldreich, P., Peale, S. J. 1968. The dynamics of planetary rotations. *Ann. Rev. Astron. Astrophys.* 6:287–320
Goldreich, P., Peale, S. J. 1970. The obliquity of Venus. *Astron. J.* 75:273–84
Goldreich, P., Soter, S. 1966. Q in the solar system. *Icarus* 5:375–89
Goldreich, P., Tremaine, S. 1978a. The velocity dispersion in Saturn's rings. *Icarus* 34: 227–39
Goldreich, P., Tremaine, S. 1978b. The formation of the Cassini Division in Saturn's rings. *Icarus* 34:240–53
Goldreich, P., Tremaine, S. 1979a. Towards a theory for the Uranian rings. *Nature* 277:97–99
Goldreich, P., Tremaine, S. 1979b. Precession of the ϵ ring of Uranus. *Astron. J.* 84:1638–41
Goldreich, P., Tremaine, S. 1980. Disk-satellite interactions. *Astrophys. J.* 241: 425–41
Goldreich, P., Tremaine, S. 1981. The origin of the eccentricities of the rings of Uranus. *Astrophys. J.* 243:1062–75
Greenberg, R. 1973. Evolution of satellite resonances by tidal dissipation. *Astron. J.* 78:338–46
Greenberg, R. 1976. The Laplace relation and the masses of Uranus' satellites. *Icarus* 29:427–33
Greenberg, R., Wacker, J. F., Hartmann, W. K., Chapman, C. R. 1978. Planetesimals to planets: Numerical simulation of collisional evolution. *Icarus* 35:1–26
Harrington, R. S., Christy, J. W. 1980. The satellite of Pluto II. *Astron. J.* 85:168–70
Harrington, R. S., Christy, J. W. 1980. The satellite of Pluto II. *Astron. J.* 85:168–70
Harrington, R. S., van Flandern, T. C. 1979. The satellites of Neptune and the origin of Pluto. *Icarus* 39:131–36
Harris, A. W. 1977. An analytical theory of planetary rotation rates. *Icarus* 31:168–74
Harris, A. W. 1978. Satellite formation, II. *Icarus* 34:128–45
Harris, A. W. 1979. Asteroid rotation rates II. A theory for the collisional evolution of rotation rates. *Icarus* 40:145–53
Harris, A. W., Burns, J. A. 1979. Asteroid rotation I. Tabulation and analysis of rates, pole positions, and shapes. *Icarus* 40: 115–44
Harris, D. L. 1961. Photometry and colorimetry of planets and satellites. In *Planets and Satellites*, ed. G. P. Kuiper, B. M. Middlehurst, pp. 272–342. Chicago: Chicago Univ. Press. 601 pp.
Hays, J. D., Imbrie, J., Shackleton, N. J. 1976. Variations in the earth's orbit: Pacemaker of the ice ages. *Science* 194:1121–32
Heppenheimer, T. A. 1980. Secular resonances and the origin of eccentricities of Mars and the asteroids. *Icarus* 41:76–88
Hubbard, W. B., MacFarlane, J. J. 1980. Structure and evolution of Uranus and Neptune. *J. Geophys. Res.* 85:225–34
Kahn, P. G. K., Pompea, S. M. 1978. Nautiloid growth rhythms and dynamical evolution of the earth-moon system. *Nature* 275:606–11
Kaiser, M. L., Desch, M. D. 1980. Voyager detection of non-thermal radio emission from Saturn. *Bull. Amer. Astron. Soc.* 12:510

Kraft, R. P. 1967. Studies of Stellar rotation V. *Astrophys. J.* 150:551–70
Kraft, R. P. 1972. Evidence for changes in the angular velocity of the surface regions of the sun and stars. In *Solar Wind,* ed. C. P. Sonett, P. J. Coleman, J. M. Wilcox, pp. 276–81
Kuhi, L. V. 1964. Mass loss from T Tauri stars. *Astrophys. J.* 140:1409–1533
Kuhi, l.V. 1966. Mass loss from T Tauri stars II. *Astrophys. J.* 143:991–93
Lambeck, K. 1979. On the orbital evolution of the Martian Satellites. *J. Geophys. Res.* 84:5651–58
Lecar, M., Franklin, F. A. 1973. On the original distribution of the asteroids. I. *Icarus* 20:422–36
Levin, B. J. 1978. Relative velocities of planetesimals and the early accumulation of planets. *The Moon and the Planets* 19: 289–96
Lieske, J. H. 1980. Improved ephemerides of the Galilean satellites. *Astron. Astrophys.* 82:340–48
Lin, D. N. C., Bodenheimer, P. 1981. On the stability of Saturn's rings. *Astrophys. J. Lett.* In press
Lin, D. N. C., Papaloizou, J. 1979a. Tidal torques on accretion discs in binary systems with extreme mass ratios. *Mon. Not. R. Astron. Soc.* 186:799–812
Lin, D. N. C., Papaloizou, J. 1979b. On the structure of circumbinary accretion discs and the tidal evolution of commensurable satellites. *Mon. Not. R. Astron. Soc.* 188: 191–201
Lynden-Bell, D., Pringle, J. E. 1974. The evolution of viscous discs and the origin of the nebular variables. *Mon. Not. R. Astron. Soc.* 168:603–37
MacDonald, G. J. F. 1964. Tidal Friction. *Rev. Geophys* 2:467–541
Nacozy, P. E. 1976. On the stability of the solar system. *Astron. J.* 81:787–91
Nicholson, P. D., Persson, S. E., Matthews, K., Goldreich, P., Neugebauer, G. 1978. The rings of Uranus: Results of the April 10, 1978, occultation. *Astron. J.* 83:1240–48
Null, G. W. 1976. Gravity field of Jupiter and its satellites from Pioneer 10 and Pioneer 11 tracking data. *Astron. J.* 81:1153–61
Peale, S. J. 1969. Generalized Cassini's laws. *Astron. J.* 74:483–89
Peale, S. J. 1974. Possible histories of the obliquity of Mercury. *Astron. J.* 79:722–44
Peale, S. J. 1976. Orbital resonances in the solar system. *Ann. Rev. Astron. Astrophys.* 14:215–46
Peale, S. J. 1977. Rotation histories of the natural satellites. In *Planetary Satellites*, ed. J. Burns, pp. 87–112. Arizona: Univ. Ariz. Press. 598 pp.
Peale, S. J., Boss, A. P. 1977a. A spin-orbit constraint on the viscosity of a Mercurian liquid core. *J. Geophys. Res.* 82:743–49
Peale, S. J., Boss, A. P. 1977b. Mercury's core: The effect of obliquity on the spin-orbit constraints. *J. Geophys. Res.* 82:3423–29
Peale, S. J., Gold, T. 1965. Rotation of the planet Mercury. *Nature* 206:1240–41
Peale, S. J., Cassen, P., Reynolds, R. T. 1979. Melting of Io by tidal dissipation. *Science* 203:892–94
Pechernikova, G. V., Vityazev, A. V. 1980. Evolution of orbital eccentricities of the planets in the process of their formation. *Sov. Astron. J. A.* 24:460–467
Pettengill, G. H., Dyce, R. B. 1965. A radar determination of the rotation of the planet Mercury. *Nature* 206:1240
Reasenberg, R. D., 1977. The moment of inertia and isostasy of Mars. *J. Geophys. Res.* 82: 369–75
Ruskol, E. L. 1972. The role of the satellite swarm in the origin of the earth's rotation. *Astron. Vestn.* 6:91–95. English trans. in *Sol. Syst. Res.* 6:80–83
Safronov, V. S. 1966. Sizes of the largest bodies falling onto the planets during their formation. *Soviet Astron. - A. J.* 9:987–91
Safronov, V. S. 1969. *Evolution of the Protoplanetary Cloud and Formation of the Earth and Planets.* Moscow: Nanka. Transl. Israel Program for Scientific Translations, 1972. NASA TTF-677.
Safronov, V. S., Zvjagina, E. V. 1969. Relative sizes of the largest bodies during the accumulation of the planets. *Icarus* 10:109–15
Shapiro, I. I., Campbell, D., DeCampli, W. 1979. Nonresonance rotation of Venus? *Astronpys. J. Lett.* 230:L123–26
Singer, S. F. 1968. The origin of the moon and geophysical consequences. *Geophys. J. R. Astron. Soc.* 15:205–26
Singer, S. F. 1971. The Martian Satellites. In *Physical Studies of the Minor Planets*, ed. T. Gehrels, pp. 399–402. Washington: NASA SP-267.
Slattery, W. L. 1977. The structure of the planets Jupiter and Saturn. *Icarus* 32:58–72
Slavsky, D. B., Smith, H. J. 1978. The rotation period of Neptune. *Astrophys. J. Lett.* 226:L49–52
Spiegel, E. A. 1970. A history of solar rotation. In *Physics of the Solar System*, pp. 63–91. Greenbelt, Md: Goddard Inst. Space Studies, 4th Summer Inst.
Thomsen, B., Ables, H. D. 1978. Measurement of the angular separation and magnitude difference for the Pluto/Charon system. *Bull. Am. Astron. Soc.* 10:586
Toon, O. B., Pollack, J. B., Ward, W. R., Burns, J. A., Bilski, K. 1980. The astronomical theory of climatic change on Mars. *Icarus* 44:552–607

Torbett, M. Smoluchowski, R. 1980. Sweeping of the Jovian resonances and the evolution of the asteroids. *Icarus* 44:722–29
Ward, W. R. 1973. Large-scale variations in the obliquity of Mars. *Science* 181:260–62
Ward, W. R. 1974. Climatic variations on Mars 1. Astronomical theory of insolation. *J. Geophys. Res.* 79:3375–86
Ward, W. R. 1975a. Tidal friction and generalized Cassini's laws in the solar system. *Astron. J.* 80:64–70
Ward, W. R. 1975b. Past orientation of the lunar spin axis. *Science* 189:377–79
Ward, W. R. 1979. Present obliquity oscillations of Mars: Fourth order accuracy in orbital e and i. *J. Geophys. Res.* 84:237–41
Ward, W. R. 1980. Scanning secular resonances: A cosmogonical broom? *Lunar Planet. Sci. XI*, pp. 1199–1201
Ward, W. R. 1981a. On the radial structure of Saturn's Rings. *Geophys. Res. Lett.* 8: 641–43
Ward, W. R. 1981b. Orbital inclination of Iapetus and the rotation of the Laplacian Plane. *Icarus* 46:97–107
Ward, W. R. 1981c. Solar nebula dispersal and the stability of the planetary system. I. Scanning secular resonance theory. *Icarus* 47:234–64
Ward, W. R. 1981d. Comments on the long-term stability of the Earth's obliquity. *Icarus*. In press
Ward, W. R., DeCampli, W. 1979. Comments on the Venus rotation pole. *Astrophys. J. Lett.* 230:L117–21
Ward, W. R., Reid, M. J. 1973. Solar tidal friction and satellite loss. *Mon. Not. R. Astron. Soc.* 164:21–32
Ward, W. R., Burns, J. A., Toon, O. B. 1979. Past obliquity oscillations of Mars: The role of the Tharsis Uplift. *J. Geophys. Res.* 84:243–59
Ward, W. R., Colombo, G., Franklin, F. A. 1976. Secular resonance, solar spindown, and the orbit of Mercury. *Icarus* 28:441–52
Ward, W. R., Murray, B. C., Malin, M. C. 1974. Climatic variations on Mars 2. Evolution of carbon dioxide atmosphere and polar caps. *J. Geophys. Res.* 79:3387–95
Weidenschilling, S. J. 1977. Aerodynamics of solid bodies in the solar nebula. *Mon. Not. R. Astron. Soc.* 180:57–70
Wetherill, G. W. 1977. Evolution of the earth's planetesimal swarm subsequent to the formation of the earth and moon. *Proc. Lunar Sci. Conf. 7th*, pp. 1–16
Wetherill, G. W. 1979. Steady state populations of Apollo-Amor objects. *Icarus* 37:96–112
Wetherill, G. W. 1980. Formation of the terrestrial planets. *Ann. Rev. Astron. Astrophys.* 18:77–113
Wetherill, G. W., Williams, J. G. 1979. Origin of differentiated meteorites. In *Origin and Distribution of the Elements, Second Symposium*, ed. L. H. Ahrens, pp. 19–31. Oxford: Pergamon.
Williams, J. G. 1971. Proper elements, families, and belt boundaries. In *Physical Studies of Minor Planets*, ed T. Gehrels, pp. 177–81
Williams, J. G., Benson, G. S. 1971. Resonances in the Neptune-Pluto system. *Astron. J.* 76:167–77
Williams, J. G., Faulkner, J. 1981. The positions of the secular resonance surfaces. *Icarus* 46:390–99
Yoder, C. F. 1973. On the establishment and evolution of orbit-orbit resonances. PhD thesis. Univ. Calif., Santa Barbara. 303 pp.
Yoder, C. F. 1982. Tidal rigidity of Phobos. Submitted to *Icarus*
Yoder, C. F., Peale, S. J. 1981. Tides on Io. *Icarus* 47:1–35
Yoder, C. F., Ward, W. R. 1979. Does Venus wobble? *Astrophys. J. Lett.* 233:L33–37
Ziglina, I. N. 1976. Effect on eccentricity of a planet's orbit of its encounters with bodies of the swarm. *Sov. Astron. - A. J.* 203: 730–33
Ziglina, I. N., Safronov, V. S. 1976. Averaging of the orbital eccentricities of bodies which are accumulating into a planet. *Sov. Astron. - A. J.* 20:244–48

Ann. Rev. Earth Planet. Sci. 1982. 10:109-28

THIRTEEN YEARS OF DEEP-SEA DRILLING

Kenneth J. Hsü

Geological Institute, ETH, Zurich, Switzerland

INTRODUCTION

On June 24, 1966, Scripps Institution of Oceanography of the University of California at San Diego received a contract from the US National Science Foundation to fund a Deep-Sea Drilling Project (DSDP). The scientific guidance of the project has been given by the Joint Oceanographic Institutions Deep Earth Sampling (JOIDES) and drilling has been done by the *Glomar Challenger* of Global Marine Inc. On August 11, 1968, scientific drilling (Leg 1) officially started in Mexico. The original 18-month Phase I of DSDP was followed by Phases II and III, totalling five and one half years. In November 1975, Germany, France, Great Britain, Japan, and the Soviet Union joined JOIDES, and DSDP went into the International Phase of Ocean Drilling (IPOD). We are now in the second phase of IPOD, which will end in 1983. Although plans for additional ocean drilling are being made, this review serves both as an information circular and as an index to help those not familiar with the project to search out the relevant cruise reports for further reference.

ORIGIN OF OCEAN BASINS AND MOVEMENT OF CONTINENTS

The theory that present ocean basins are young geological features is embodied in the idea of seafloor spreading, advanced by Hess (1962) and Dietz (1961). That idea became a theory when Vine &Matthews (1963) postulated the spreading apart of ocean crust as an explanation for the linear magnetic anomalies under the seafloor. Vine & Wilson (1965) developed the theory

0084–6597/82/0515–0109$02.00

further when they found a direct correlation between the width of magnetic anomaly belts on the seafloor and the duration of the last few epochs of polarity reversals; the correlation indicated a linear rate of seafloor spreading. Extrapolating back 100 million years, Heirtzler et al (1968) were able to predict the age of the seafloor under the world's oceans on the basis of magnetic data.

A corollary of seafloor-spreading theory is that the continents have shifted their relative positions on the earth's surface, an idea advocated by Alfred Wegener in the early decades of this century. Synthesizing the old with the new, Morgan (1968) and McKenzie & Parker (1967) simultaneously and independently developed the theory of plate tectonics. Using data from magnetic surveys of the seafloor, Le Pichon (1968) reconstructed relative motions between the various continents during the last hundred million years. The time was ripe for a revolution in the earth sciences when DSDP got underway in 1968. Geologists working on land then, including myself, were not ready to accept the new ideas, which were formulated mainly on the basis of oceanographic data, until new theoretical predictions could be confirmed by a well-established geologic method. The best way to achieve such a confirmation would be to date ocean crust by drilling into the ocean floor. The adventures of *Glomar Challenger* began as a geological experiment to provide this critical test of a revolutionary new theory.

The objective of Legs 2 and 3 of DSDP was to determine the ages of the ocean crust on both flanks of the mid-Atlantic Ridge. Unfortunately Leg 2 across the Central Atlantic had to be shortened for logistical reasons (Peterson et al 1970); the decisive test of the seafloor-spreading theory was thus postponed until the South Atlantic drilling during Leg 3. A transect of seven holes was drilled along the 30°S parallel on both sides of the mid-Atlantic Ridge. The age of the ocean crust had been predicted to increase linearly with distance from the ridge axis. The age of the oldest sediments overlying basement confirmed predictions. The plot of basement age against distance from the ridge axis gives a straight line (Figure 1), verifying the assumptions of a linear rate of seafloor spreading over the last 70 million years (Maxwell et al 1970).

After the spectacular results of Leg 3, the theory of seafloor spreading received wide acceptance. The remaining cruises of the Phase I drilling (Legs 5–9) determined the ages of seafloor anomalies in the Pacific Ocean. Young ocean crust was encountered near the center of seafloor spreading on the East Pacific Rise. The crust is progressively older toward the west. Cretaceous and Jurassic seafloors were found next to the ocean trenches fringing the island arcs of the Western Pacific (McManus et al 1970, Fischer et al 1971, Winterer et al 1971, Tracey et al 1971, Hays et al 1972). Later, the M-series of magnetic anomalies were dated during Leg 32 to Provide a key to the detailed history of Mesozoic seafloor spreading (Larson et al 1975).

A drilling program involving six cruises (Legs 22–27) in 1971–1972 in-

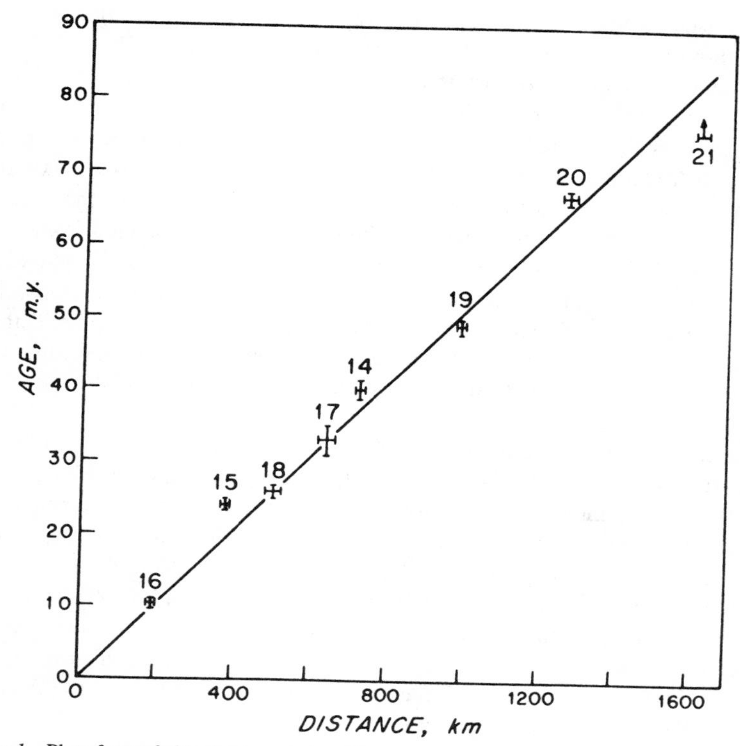

Figure 1 Plot of age of oldest sediment above basement as a function of distance to mid-Atlantic Ridge axis. (Maxwell et al 1970).

vestigated the Indian Ocean (von der Borch et al 1974, Whitmarsh et al 1974, Fisher et al 1974, Simpson et al 1974, Davies et al 1974, Veevers et al 1974). Four subsequent legs (28, 29, 35, 36) drilled the Southern Ocean during the austral summers of 1972–1974 (Hayes et al 1975, Kennett et al 1975, Hollister et al 1976, Barker et al 1976). The history of seafloor spreading that led to the fragmentation and dispersal of the Gondwanaland was clarified by using drilling results to interpret magnetic-survey data. The motion of the plates not only created the Indian and Southern Oceans, it also led to the collision of India with Eurasia, which gave rise to the Himalaya Mountains.

The acceptance of the seafloor-spreading theory also opened up the possibility of determining the relative movements between Europe and Africa through an analysis of the history of the Atlantic. The cruises to the Atlantic during the first year of the Phase II drilling (Legs 11–14) provided critical information on the ages of magnetic anomalies (Hollister et al 1972, Laughton et al 1972, Ryan et al 1972, Hayes et al 1972), which Pitman & Talwani

(1972) used to work out the seafloor-spreading history of the Atlantic. Fragmentation of the supercontinent Pangea began in the Triassic. By early Jurassic, Pangea was split into northern and southern continents, and the Central Atlantic was born where Africa was torn apart from North America and Europe. After Africa had moved 2000 km sinistrally with respect to Europe, the North Atlantic spreading began at 81 m.y. BP, as Europe broke away from North Africa. The rate of eastward march of Europe was faster than that of Africa, so that the movement between the two continents changed from sinistral to dextral. Smith (1971), Hsü (1971a), and Dewey et al (1973) applied the kinematic analyses of the Atlantic spreading to the geology of the Alps. The sinistral movement of Africa away from Europe created the Alpine Tethys. The dextral movement brought Africa and Europe together, resulting in a continental collision, which caused the demise of the Tethys and the rise of the Alps.

The seafloor-spreading theory postulates formation of new ocean crust at a submarine elevation of 2500–2700 m depth where the heatflow is high and the density of the mantle is abnormally light. The outer flanks of the ridges are regions of normal heatflow where the mantle density is greater, in response to the cooling of the lithospheric plates as they move away from the ridge axes. Where the crust is older than 50 million years, the seafloor has often subsided to a depth of more than 5000 m. Sclater et al (1971) formulated a theoretical model to predict the ocean-crust depth and the subsidence history of the seafloor. Prior to the end of the Phase II drilling, the results from the Atlantic and the Pacific confirmed the validity of the subsidence curve (Sclater & Detrick 1973, see also Figure 2). Since then it has become a routine practice to deduce the depth of ancient seafloor on the basis of such a "Sclater Curve."

GENERATION OF OCEAN CRUST AND MID-PLATE VOLCANISM

Studies of the ocean crust during the second half of the Deep-Sea Drilling Project were less concerned with the age than with the nature of the crust. Two deep holes were drilled almost 600 m into the Atlantic basement, but no deep crustal penetrations of the East Pacific Rise were possible because of mechanical difficulties.

The volcanic rocks constituting the second layer of ocean crust are mainly tholeiitic basalts, forming either pillow lavas or breccias; a minor amount of intrusive rocks such as gabbros and serpentinites have been encountered at a few sites. The chemistry of the basalts is remarkably similar everywhere; almost all samples analyzed fall within the defined limits of mid-ocean ridge basalts (MORB), characterized by a depletion of large-ion lithophiles (LIL).

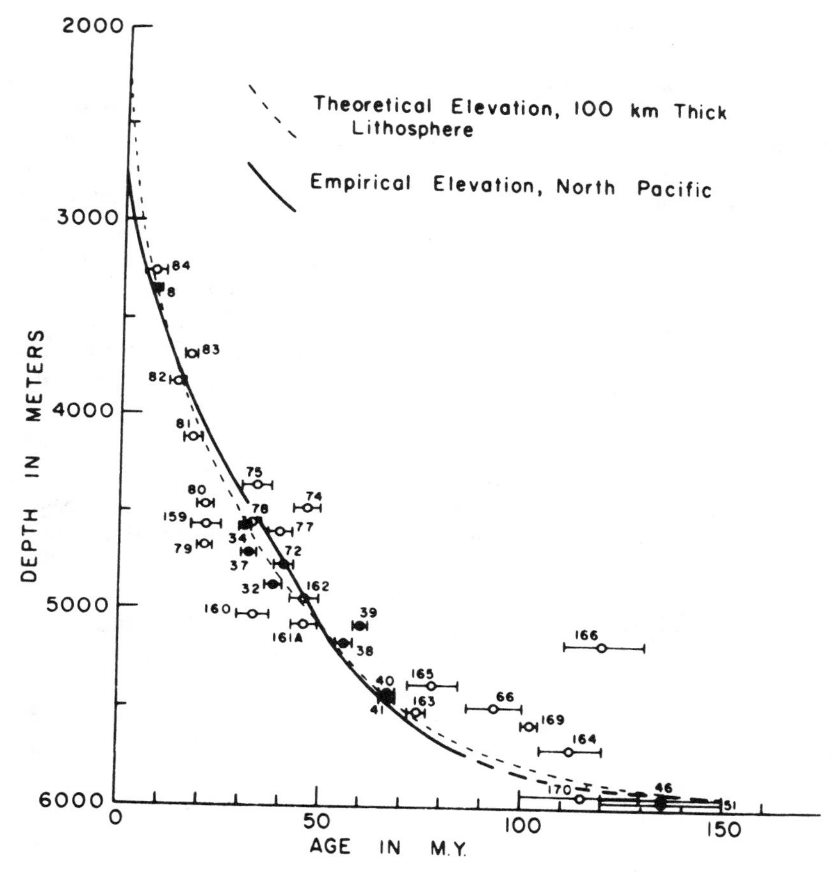

Figure 2 Subsidence of aging crust (Sclater & Detrick 1973).

The concentration of the various rare earth elements are also what one expects from MORB: the heavy rare earth elements (HREE) show very little fractionation, whereas the light (LREE) have been comparatively depleted. The chemistry of the basalts suggests derivation of the magmas from a homogeneous mantle source. Regional and secular variations have been observed, but they do not show systematic trends and are apparently a manifestation of the great complexity of the igneous processes of partial melting, magmatic differentiation, and magma mixing. These conclusions have been drawn largely on the basis of Atlantic drilling, during Legs 36, 45, 46, and 51–53 (Aumento et al 1977, Melson et al 1978, Dimitriev, et al 1978, Donnelly et al 1979), and have been confirmed by the results of the Pacific drilling during Legs 34 and

54 (Yeats et al 1976, Rosendahl et al 1980). Only the basalt samples from the North Atlantic obtained during Leg 49 showed sufficient chemical difference from MORB to suggest mantle heterogeneity (Luyendyk et al 1978).

The Pacific floor is dotted with innumerable active and extinct submarine volcanoes, or seamounts, which tend to be arranged linearly to form seamount chains. Wilson (1963) noted that the seamounts farthest away from the active volcanoes of Hawaii are the oldest and have sunk deepest below sea level. He proposed the hypothesis of mantle "hot spots" to account for the origin of the Hawaiian seamount chain. Later, Christofferson (1968) suggested that the Emperor Seamounts constitute the northern continuation of the chain. The two, one trending northwest and the other north, might be joined together with a kink, or bend. This was considered as evidence that the Pacific Plate made a half turn to the right during its forward march. Morgan (1972) extended the Wilsonian postulate to interpret other seamount chains of the Pacific.

Drilling during Legs 17, 33, and 61 contradicted the predictions by Morgan. The Line-Tuomoto and the Marshal-Austral seamount chains were created by regionally synchronous mid-plate volcanism during the Cretaceous, which produced a thick pile of lava flows covering millions of square kilometers of ocean floor (Winterer et al 1973, Schlanger et al 1976, Larson et al 1981). The "hot spot" hypothesis was given a last chance during Leg 55, and was proven correct when the Emperor Seamount Chain was drilled (Jackson et al 1980). Paleonotological dating on board ship and radiometrical dating on land gave ages that confirmed the predicted northward movements of the Pacific Plate. The latitudinal shifts are also shown by the magnetic inclination of the basalt flows, and by the presence of coral reefs as the oldest sediments on seamounts. The basalts are tholeiitic, belonging to the oceanic-island type. They are also similiar in chemistry to the Hawaiian basalts, and thus indicative of a common origin of the two. A remarkably linear relation between the ages of the seamounts and the distances from Hawaii exists, which projects the speed of movement of the Pacific Plate at about 8 cm/yr (Figure 3). The change in direction of the movement that bent the chain took place 43 million years ago, almost exactly the date Morgan had predicted.

The ocean basalts encountered by drills in the South Pacific and on the seamounts are products of mid-plate volcanism. Drilling in the Indian Ocean and in the South Atlantic revealed submarine volcanism on aseismic ridges along or near transform-fault margins. The Ninety-east Ridge is a good example. This remarkably straight aseismic ridge runs along the Ninety-east longitude from 15°N to 31°S, a distance of almost 6000km. For most of its length, the ridge stands some 1500 to 2000 m above the adjacent seafloor. The basalts on the Ninety-east Ridge also belong to the oceanic-island type; they are enriched in LIL and LREE elements, which are depleted in normal MORB. Computer modeling indicates that the Ninety-east Ridge was probably created by the northward movement of the Indian Plate over two fixed hot spots that now lie under the Amsterdam–St. Paul and Kerguelen Islands (Luyendyk 1977).

TECTONIC EVOLUTION OF PASSIVE OCEAN MARGINS

Geologists studying sedimentary deposits in coastal mountains have long noted a common paleogeographical pattern, which suggests that the detritus making up those sediments came from sources that now lie under the oceans. For many years the burning question was, why did such ancient landmasses beyond the present continental margins disappear? Elevation with respect to sea level is not the only distinction between continents and oceans. A more fundamental difference is the thickness of the earth's crust: the continents have a thick crust, 30–50 km, whereas the ocean crust is only 5–10 km thick. To convert a continent into an ocean requires not only subsidence, but also a change in crustal thickness. Speculations on this subject have been numerous. Gilluly (1955), assuming the removal of continental crust where convection currents descend, suggested subcrustal erosion. Beloussov (1962) postulated oceanization of continental crust through subcrustal chemical processes. These speculations have not been adequately supported and do not seem to be viable working hypotheses. Hsü (1965) suggested that the continental margins may have been uplifted and eroded at a time when the density of the underlying mantle was reduced by a steepening of the geothermal gradient. The continental crust was thinned and the subsidence of passive continental margins could thus be related to subsequent cooling of the mantle. This idea was developed into a quantitative model by Sleep (1971). More recently McKenzie (1978) suggested crustal thinning by stretching, or "necking," and he also related subsidence to mantle density changes.

The current model on the tectonic evolution of passive margins depicts several stages of development. First a continent is stressed under extension. The continental crust is pulled apart, forming rift valleys. The geothermal gradient in the mantle is steep, causing a partial melting of the mantle at depth and subaerial volcanisms at the surface. This initial-rifting stage of the Atlantic has been recorded by the New Red Sandstones on both sides of the ocean. Some regions, such as the Rhein Graben and the East African Rift Zone, remained in this stage of arrested development. Where extension has gone further, the continental crust has pulled apart completely. Lavas coming up from the mantle form new seafloor in the crack. The Red Sea and the Gulf of California have progressed this far, whereas the Atlantic went past this stage during the Jurassic. After the formation of the new seafloor, the geothermal gradient should still be high in the mantle. Accumulations of basalt flows or sills eventually build up an ocean crust of normal thickness. With the con-

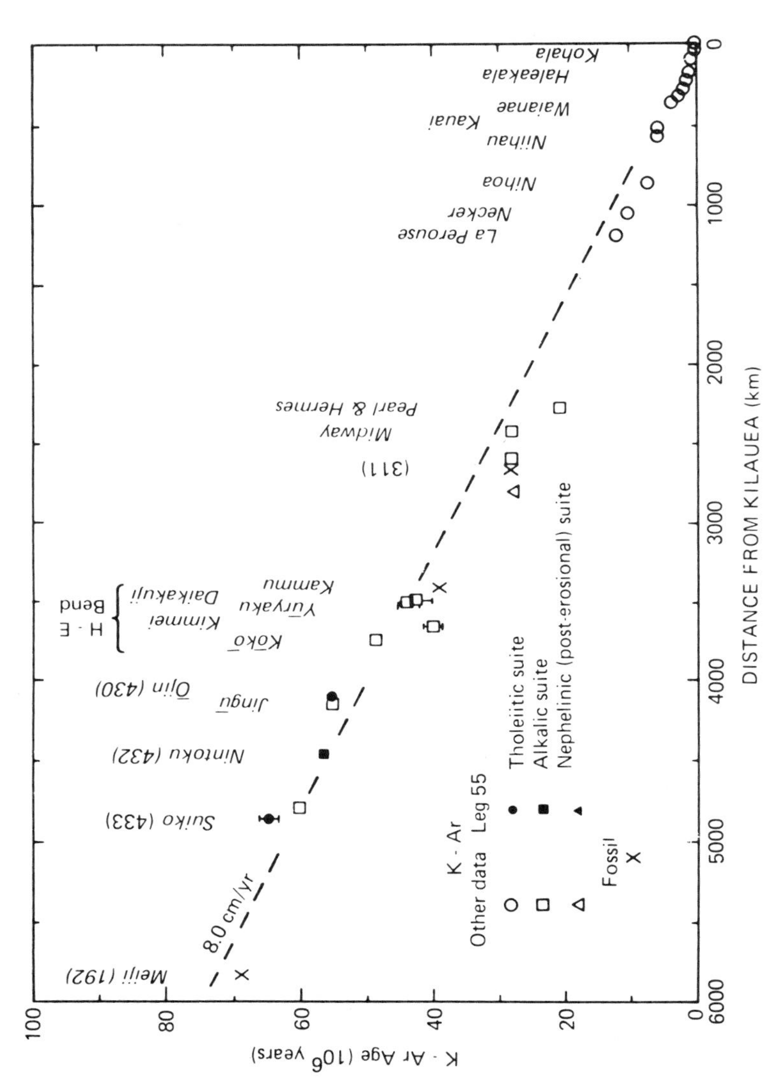

Figure 3 Ages of volcanoes in the Hawaiian-Emperor chain as a function of distance from Kilauea Volcano (Jackson et al 1980).

tinued spreading of the seafloor, the continental margins move away from the regions of high heatflow. The geological history is then one of sedimentation and subsidence, characterized by initial transgression followed by the largely regressive build-up of the margins.

The development of this tectonic model depends greatly upon geological investigations on land and geophysical investigations of the ocean margins. The model predicts geologic structures, which can best be studied by seismic methods. The purpose of deep-sea drilling is to furnish the fourth dimension (time), so as to convert a geometric into a kinematic analysis. Many deep-sea drilling cruises have been scheduled to investigate the Atlantic ocean margins, particularly during JOIDES Phase III and IPOD, including Legs 36 (Barker et al 1976), 38 (Talwani et al 1976), 39 (Supko et al 1977), 40 (Bolli et al 1978), 41 (Lancelot et al 1977), 43 (Tucholke et al 1979), 44 (Benson et al 1978), 47A (von Rad et al 1979), 47B (Sibuet et al 1979), 48 (Montadert et al 1979), and 50 (Lancelot et al 1980). Seven more legs (76–82) are being, or will be, drilled into the Atlantic margins. The tremendous investment of time and effort has produced a wealth of data on regional marine geology.

Two of the most interesting "passive-margin" cruises have been sent to the Indian and the Pacific Oceans to investigate the initial stages of seafloor spreading. Leg 23B drilling of the Red Sea Basin confirmed that the most recent seafloor spreading there has been going on at a 0.9 cm/yr rate during the last 2.4 million years (Whitmarsh et al 1974). The Gulf of California, drilled during Leg 64 also has axial basins formed by seafloor spreading during the past four million years. One bore hole penetrated the granite basement of a thinned continental crust, at a marginal site only 10 km away from a site that penetrated ocean basalt to define the sharp continent-ocean transition (Curray et al 1979).

SUBDUCTION AT OCEAN TRENCHES

The creation of new seafloor requires the elimination or "consumption" of the old. Evidence that ocean crust has been crumpled, fragmented, and consumed has been found in the ophiolitic mélanges of the Circum-Pacific mountains and in the suture zones of continental collision (Hsü 1971b). The on-going subductions of oceanic lithospheric plates register as earthquakes along the Circum-Pacific Benioff Zones (Isaacs et al 1968). The geology of mélanges and geophysical studies of ocean trenches indicate the accretion of a mixture of broken slabs of oceanic crust and pelagic sediments onto the edge of active continental margins, forming an "accretional wedge" of deformed sediments. Drilling of the Astoria Fan and Alaskan Trench during Leg 18 encountered deformed sediments, which apparently belong to an accretional wedge (Kulm et al 1973). Subsequently, *Glomar Challenger* drilled the Tonga Trench during Leg 21 (Burns et al 1973), the Timor Trench during Leg 27 (Veevers et al 1974), the New Hebrides Trench during Leg 30 (Andrews et al 1975), and the Nankai Trough during Leg 31 (Karig et al 1975), and the drill results have been commonly interpreted on the basis of the "accretional wedge" model. An exception to the rule was discovered during the 1970 drilling of the Hellenic Trench south of the Island Arc of Crete, where the rocks under the inner trench wall are mainly Cretaceous carbonate-platform deposits (Ryan et al 1972).

Several cruises were sent to the Pacific during IPOD to investigate the active margins fringed by ocean trenches. Drilling of the Middle American Trench during Leg 66 seems to have fulfilled the prediction of underthrust, with the oldest (Miocene) sediments encountered high upon the trench wall and the youngest (Pleistocene) near the foot (Moore et al 1979). However, other IPOD cruises failed to find large accretional wedges. The current views on the tectonic processes at active ocean margins distinguish a "tectonic erosion" or "drag-down" model from the "accretional wedge" or "jack-up" model (Scholl et al 1980). The drillings of Japan Trench during Legs 56 and 57 (Scientific Party, 1980), of Mariana Trench during Leg 60 (Hussong et al 1978), and another part of Middle American Trench during Leg 67 (von Huene et al 1980) all indicate that the subduction of the ocean crust in those areas has dragged down the continental margin to form the inner trench wall. The subsidence of the margin was accompanied by a thinning of continental crust through subcrustal erosion (Figure 4).

MARGINAL SEAS

The origin of the basins beneath marginal seas has been a favorite theme of speculation. Beloussov (1962) postulated oceanization of continental crust to explain the origin of marginal seas. The modern concept has been proposed by Karig (1970) on the basis of geophysical investigations of the Tonga Basin. He postulates that the back-arc basins have been produced by the rise of mantle-convection currents behind island arcs. The tensional stress produced by the lateral movement of the currents broke strips of lithosphere away from the margins of continents to form island arcs, and thereby created deep-sea basins in the cracks behind the arcs.

Karig's theory predicts the presence of ocean crust, not continental crust, under marginal seas. Leg 30 sampled the basalt crust of the Coral Sea Basin (Andrews et al 1975). Subsequent drilling of the Philippine Sea behind the Mariana Arc (Legs 31, 58, and 59) confirmed back-arc seafloor spreading (Karig et al 1975, de Vries Klein et al 1980, Kroenke et al 1981). One hole penetrated more than 600 m into the ocean crust of the Philippine Sea and found that the chemistry of basalts from this basinal site is indistinguishable from that of normal MORB.

The Mediterranean marginal seas may also owe their origin to seafloor spreading. Drilling during Leg 42A penetrated 200 m of ocean crust in the Tyrrhenian Sea; the basalts there are oceanic tholeiites, characterized by a depletion of LIL elements, but they show affinity to oceanic-island type basalts, because the LREE elements are less than normally depleted. The geology of the Mediterranean back-arc basins indicates that their genesis was during the Cenozoic. The Aegean Basin is still largely underlain by continental crust, and the dredging of the Tyrrhenian Abyssal Plain has sampled granite basement locally. These young basins are undergoing initial stages of development; only the Balearic Basin has proceeded so far as to become an inactive back-arc basin underlain by a typical ocean crust (Hsü et al 1978).

Karig's theory of back-arc basin genesis related back-arc spreading to the subduction of oceanic lithosphere under the trench in front of the arc. The age of the youngest ocean floor behind the arc is, as a rule, younger than that being subducted. One exception is the Caribbean Basin; the Cretaceous basalts underlying that basin are older than the Eocene basement encountered east of Barbados Ridge (Bader et al 1970). Furthermore, these basalts are about the same age in three widely separated holes drilled during Leg 15 (Edgar et al

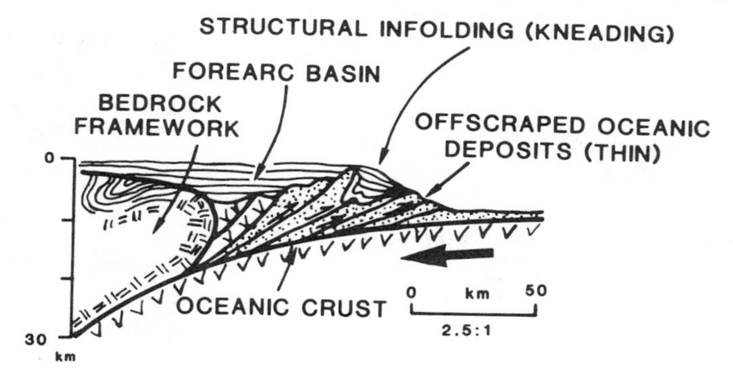

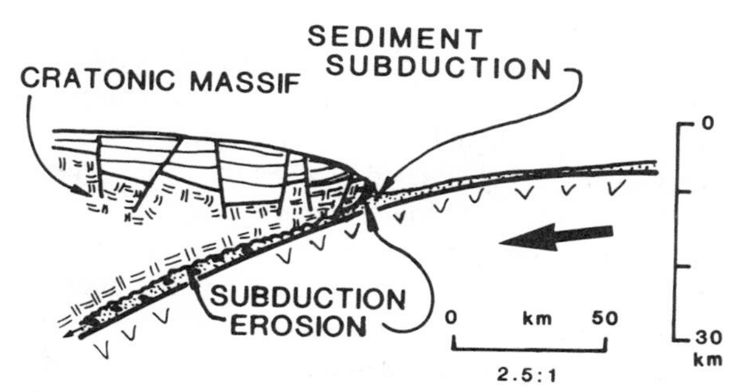

Figure 4 Development of active margins. (*above*) Accretional-wedge ("jack-up") model. (*below*) Subduction-erosion ("drag-down") model (Scholl et al 1980).

1973); they are more likely the product of regional mid-plate volcanism than that of back-arc spreading. Recent drilling in the Pacific has uncovered evidence suggesting that the Caribbean crust was originally formed in the South Pacific and may have belonged to the same volcanic province as the mid-plate basalts of the Nauro Basin (Larson et al 1981). This fragment of the Pacific crust was separated from the great ocean after the orogenic uplift of the Panama Isthmus.

PALEOCEANOGRAPHY AND PALEOCLIMATOLOGY

Precise dating is a prerequisite for deciphering the chronology of events and appreciating the rates of processes. The study of well-preserved micro- and nannofossils in ocean sediments has led to increasingly refined biostratigraphy. A superposition of foraminiferal and nannofossil zonations permits an accuracy of relative Cenozoic ages down to a fraction of a million years. These zones are locally correlated with radiolarian and/or diatom zones.

The absolute ages of paleontological zones have been calibrated by magnetostratigraphy and by radiometric chronology. Core disturbance and incomplete recovery hampered the use of magnetostratigraphic methods to date deep-sea drilling cores until a major technical breakthrough was achieved with the development of hydraulic piston-coring (HPC) (Prell & Gardner 1980). With the use of HPC, the precision biostratigraphy and magnetostratigraphy of sedimentary sequences have permitted seafloor dating back to the time of Anomaly 32 (late Cretaceous) and an exact correlation of the polarity-reversal record recovered in sediments with the record registered in seafloor basalts during spreading (Hsü et al, in preparation).

Analysis of the microfaunas or the nannofloras from deep-sea cores has permitted solutions to paleoceanographical problems. Mapping the distribution of biogenic sediments has delineated the past positions of the high-productivity equatorial zone (van Andel et al 1973, Heezen et al 1973). The northward shift of the fossil equatorial belts gave a measure of the rate of Pacific Plate motion commensurable to that deduced by studying seamount chains. Mapping diatom occurrences in high latitude ocean sediments portrayed the changing position of the polar fronts (Creager et al 1973, Kennett et al 1975, Ludwig et al 1980) and comparison of planktonic faunas from the two sides of the Panama Isthmus dated precisely the time when the isthmus was formed (Prell & Gardner 1980).

Calcareous nannoplankton and foraminifera constitute the main source of ocean sediments. The ocean waters at depth are undersaturated with calcite, but calcitic sediments are deposited where the rate of supply exceeds the rate of dissolution. Calcite-compensation depth (CCD) is the ocean depth at which the dissolution of calcitic fossils is exactly compensated by the supply. Below

CCD only red clays could be deposited. Red clays are now most common in the North Pacific in the gyre regions of the middle latitudes where the planktonic production is low and where the bottom water is relatively rich in CO_2 and, therefore, most corrosive. In the Atlantic, Holocene sediments accumulating on the seafloor at less than 5000 m depth are often calcitic.

At the end of the Cretaceous the CCD rose a few thousand meters, but the common presence of Miocene red clays in the Atlantic indicates significant variations in the CCD level there. A current notion relates the rise of CCD to the generation of Antarctic Bottom Waters (AABW); it was thought that these waters, rich in dissolved CO_2, should cause extensive dissolution of calcitic sediments along their flow path. Drilling during Leg 73 indicated, however, a lower CCD on the west side of the mid-Atlantic Ridge where the AABW have been more active. There is also a correlation of the lowering of CCD with the rapid climatic coolings at the beginning of Oligocene and during late Miocene (Hsü et al, in preparation). Thus it seems that the initiation of AABW may have flushed out preexisting CO_2-rich waters, and thereby caused a drop, not a rise, of the CCD level.

Deep-sea drilling has repeatedly encountered sediments rich in organic carbon. The Neogene sediments of the Mediterranean include numerous sapropel layers. The bottom stagnation was related to the presence of a low-density surface layer resulting from mixture with the inflow from brackish Black Sea waters (Ryan et al 1972, Hsü et al 1978). More remarkable was the evidence of widespread occurrences of Cretaceous black shales, found mainly in Atlantic drilling during Legs 1, 11, 14, 15, 36, 39, 40, 41, 43, 44, 47, 50, and 75. Cretaceous black shales have also been found on Hess Rise in the North Pacific (Larson et al 1975, Thiede et al 1981) and in the Indian Ocean west of Australia (Davies et al 1974, Veevers et al 1974). The rich organic matter in the sediments could be related to the high production rate in nutrient-rich waters and/or enhanced preservation in oxygen-minimum zones of the oceans, although some of the Atlantic occurrences seem to indicate basin wide stagnation (Tucholke et al 1979, Arthur & Natland 1979).

Determinations of paleotemperatures are made by measuring the ratio of oxygen isotopes: $^{18}0$ to $^{16}0$. On land, the oxygen isotope ratios may be modified by postdepositional changes, so that the measured values cannot give information on the temperatures of ancient oceans. However, the deep-sea sediments are commonly not altered diagenetically if the burial depth is not more than a few hundred meters, and the isotope method has produced reliable results. Both the surface and the bottom temperatures at various sites have been determined by analyzing planktonic foraminifera and benthic foraminifera separately (Shackleton & Kennett 1975, Boersma & Shackleton 1977, Vergnaud-Grazzini 1979). The trend, as shown by Figure 5, shows a fluctuating, but unmistakable, increase of $\delta^{18}0$ values in younger ocean sediments. The two most noteworthy rapid changes took place during the end of Eocene and during late Neogene. The oxygen isotope shifts during the last few million years have been related to changes in the ice volume of polar ice caps, but the Cenozoic trend indicates decreasing temperatures (Shackleton & Kennett 1975). Savin et al (1975) found that data from the widely separate sites of the Atlantic and Pacific could be fitted into one general pattern. A closer look indicated, however, some variations in the timing and magnitude of the climatic cooling. Parallel to the oxygen isotope shifts are variations in carbon isotope values, indicating accompanying changes in ocean chemistry.

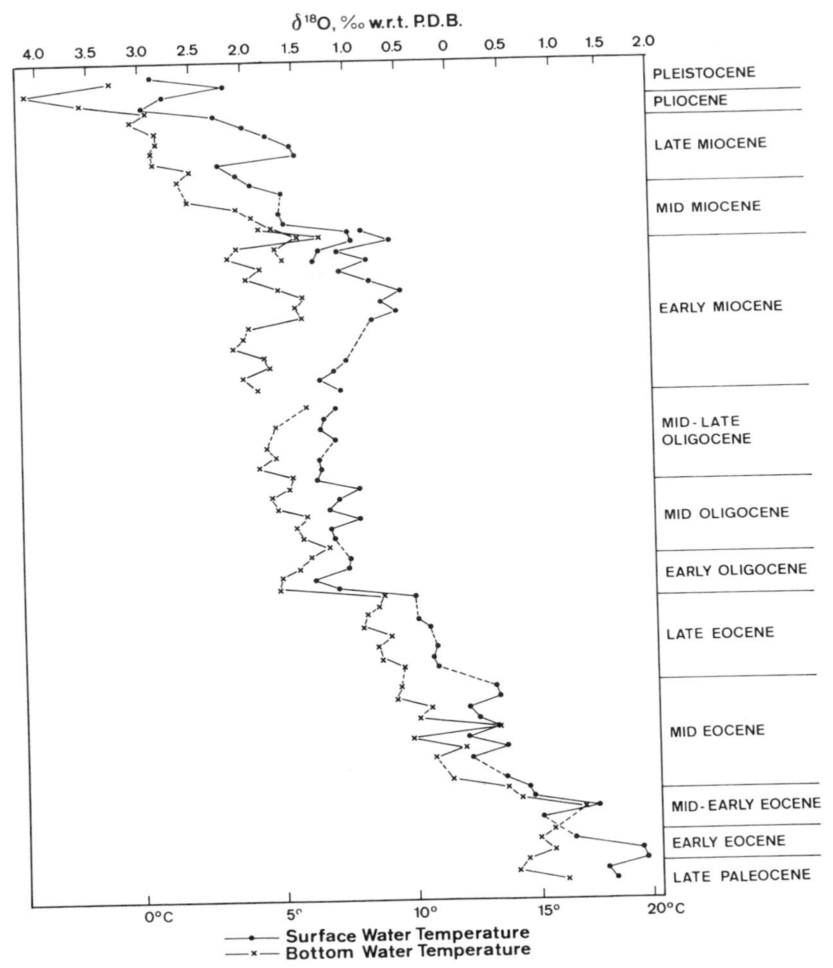

Figure 5 Decline of ocean temperatures during the Cenozoic, exemplified by the isotope data from a South Pacific site (Shackleton & Kennett 1975).

The terminal Eocene decrease of ocean temperature is registered everywhere and is a very important event in the Cenozoic history. The ocean temperatures in high southern latitudes during early Oligocene were apparently not much different from those of today. The near-freezing surface temperature there suggests that the Antarctic glaciers must have descended down to (or nearly to) sea level, and that sea ice may have been forming in the Southern Ocean. The North Atlantic data also emphasize the important and sudden cooling at about 38 m.y. BP, when cold-bottom environment was established to enable the evolution of psychospheric (cold-water) ocean faunas.

Information on the start of glaciation in polar regions is provided by the glacial marine sediments in high-latitude bore holes. Recovery of "dropstones" from the North Atlantic drilling gave a late Pliocene (3 m.y. BP) date for the beginning of glaciation in the Northern Hemisphere (Laughton et al 1972). Drilling in the Ross Sea shelf area indicated the initiation of ice rafting there in early Oligocene and a major expansion of the Ross Ice Shelf during late Miocene (Hayes et al 1975). These sedimentological conclusions are in agreement with the record of Cenozoic temperature changes given by oxygen isotope data.

RARE EVENTS AND NEO-CATASTROPHISM

The uniformitarianism of Lyell is founded on two premises: physical laws are immutable, and the rates of physical processes have been "uniform" since the beginning of geologic time. While the first premise remains the foundation of science, the second has never been more than an unproven assumption accepted all too readily by geologists during the last century. Deep-sea drilling has made two discoveries of unusual events of catastrophic proportions, which negate the second premise of Lyellian uniformitarianism. In fact, new data on extinction rates are also causing a reexamination of some aspects of the Darwinian theory of evolution.

One of the discoveries made during Leg 13 was that the Mediterranean Sea was desiccated during the late Miocene, a little over 5 million years ago. Salt-dome-like structures under the deep waters of the Gulf of Mexico, the Mediterranean, and the South Atlantic have been revealed by geophysical investigations. The presence of large salt deposits under the ocean floor has been accepted, since the inaugural cruise of *Glomar Challenger* drilled into the caprock of a salt dome (Ewing et al 1969), but the prevailing opinion was to assume that a foundering of continental crust accounted for the origin of the salts. The 1970 drilling of the Mediterranean penetrated a thick evaporite formation beneath the deep sea. The real surprise was provided by the wealth of geological and geophysical data indicative of salt precipitation in desiccated deep basins formed by seafloor spreading long before the beginning of the salinity crisis (Ryan et al 1972). Although the evidence was convincing, at least to most of us, a second drilling cruise was sent to the Mediterranean, staffed primarily by scientists who had kept an open mind. After the completion of the Leg 42A cruise report, authored by more than a hundred investigators (Hsü et al 1978), no one (except a few diehards) continued to question the theory of desiccated deep basins. Drilling in the Red Sea and Black Sea yielded evidence to suggest that these inland waters were also desiccated during the late Miocene (Whitmarsh et al 1974, Ross et al 1978). The interdisciplinary implications of the Mediterranean are manifold; the deep erosion of continental margins while the Mediterranean was desiccated provides explanations for the origin of many of the peculiar land forms in the Circum-Mediterranean countries and under the Mediterranean Sea. These features include the deeply cut valleys on land, the Southern Alpine lakes, the Mediterranean submarine canyons, and the "cobblestone topography" (or "sink holes") on Mediterranean ridge. Desiccation, followed by the formation of large euryhaline lakes in desiccated basins, also provides the key to many of the mysteries of biogeography. However, the greatest contribution to geology made by the discovery was to shake the faith in substantive uniformitarianism. The immutability of physical laws only demands that evaporites are formed in an enclosed water-body where evaporative losses have exceeded influx. The laws do not specify the size of the body. We no longer need to assume that all salt pans have been as small as those on coastal salinas today. The evaporating pan could be a dried-up deep-sea basin! With the breakthrough in the Mediterranean, there are no more a priori reasons to counter suppositions that the Jurassic salts of the Central Atlantic and Gulf of Mexico and the Cretaceous salts of the South Atlantic were also residues from seawaters deposited in desiccated ocean basins.

Another major discovery by the deep-sea drilling was the catastrophic rate of the terminal Cretaceous extinction. The Darwinian theory postulates evolutionary extinction as a consequence of the struggle for existence, with survivors being the fittest. Darwin himself was troubled by the abrupt extinction of ammonites at the end of Cretaceous. The paleontological records since that time have reinforced the impression of a terminal Cretaceous catastrophe. The two groups most affected were the marine plankton (ammonites, planktonic foraminifera, and nannoplankton) and the large terrestrial vertebrates (dinosaurs). For more than a decade, the deep-sea drill cores provided materials to decipher the environmental changes that may have caused, or accompanied, the terminal Cretaceous extinction. Studies of the Cretaceous-Tertiary (C/T) boundary indicated that the CCD rose sharply at the end of the Cretaceous, causing the deposition of red clay everywhere (Worsley 1974).

This evidence of a terminal Cretaceous catastrophe was later confirmed by analyses of oxygen and carbon isotopes in fossil skeletons across the C/T boundary in deep-sea drill cores: large oxygen and carbon isotopic shifts indicate drastic changes in ocean temperature and chemistry (Boersma et al 1979, Thierstein & Berger 1978). Impressed by the suddenness of the temperature increase, I postulated cometary impact as the cause of terminal Cretaceous extinction (Hsü 1980). A similar idea of asteroid impact was put forward by Alvarez et al (1980) on the basis of their discovery of unusual concentrations of iridium in the red clay just above the C/T contact at Gubbio, Italy. This iridium anomaly has since been found in deep-sea drill cores also (Kyte et al 1980, Hsü et al, in preparation).

During Leg 73 drilling, a sequence of rapidly deposited late Cretaceous and early Tertiary sections was penetrated, and the sediments have been dated by precision stratigraphy (Hsü et al, in preparation). Detailed analyses show a steady decrease of $\delta^{13}C$ values, with a maximum decrease of about 3‰ in 40,000 years after a terminal Cretaceous event. We interpret the isotopic shift as evidence of large-scale destruction of ocean life by an extraterrestrial event. A less systematic shift in oxygen isotopes also took place during the first 40,000 years after the catastrophe, suggesting a temperature increase of a few degrees. The thermal stress of this climatic warming may have accelerated the extinction of dinosaurs. It is premature to claim that we have found the answer to the "great-dying" at the end of Cretaceous. However, the analyses of deep-sea drilling cores will yield data to test the various theories now being formulated to explain this most puzzling evolutionary problem. If a theory invoking an extraterrestrial cause is accepted, we might begin to wonder if chance has played an important role in determining the direction of biologic evolution. The terminal Cretaceous event produced environmental changes, which selectively destroyed the marine planktons and the dinosaurs. Other catastrophic events may have taken place at the end of the Paleozoic, the Triassic, and/or the Eocene with different evolutionary consequences.

SUMMARY

Thirteen years of deep-sea drilling have enabled the successful completion of the revolution in earth sciences inspired by the seafloor-spreading and plate-tectonic theories. The geological data from the oceans brought a basic change in our understanding of the origin of mountains and ocean basins, and enabled us to interpret past environmental and biological changes. The discoveries of rare catastrophic events are causing us to modify some of the fundamental premises in geology and paleontology.

Literature Cited

Note: *Initial Reports of the Deep Sea Drilling Project,* Washington (U.S. Government Printing Office) has been cited repeatedly and will be abbreviated as ICR DSDP.

Alvarez, W., Alvarez, L., Asaro, F., Michel, H. V. 1980. Extraterrestrial cause for the Cretaceous-Tertiary Extinction. *Science* 208:1095–1108

Andrews, J. E., Packham, G. et al. 1975. *ICR DSDP* 30. 753 pp.

Arthur, A., Natland, J. H. 1979. Carbonaceous sediments in the North and South Atlantic. In *Deep Sea Drilling Results in the Atlantic Ocean,* ed. M. Talwani et al, pp. 375–401. Washington D.C: Am. Geophys. Union

Aumento, F., Melson, W. G. et al. 1977. *ICR DSDP* 37. 1008 pp.

Bader, R. G. et al. 1970. *ICR DSDP* 4. 753 pp.

Barker, P. F., Dalziel, I. W. D. et al. 1976. *ICR DSDP* 36. 1080 pp.

Beloussov, V. V. 1962. *Basic Problems in Geotectonics*. New York: McGraw Hill

Benson, W. E., Sheridan, R. E. et al. 1978. *ICR DSDP* 44. 1005 pp.

Boersma, A., Shackleton, N. 1977. Tertiary oxygen and carbon isotope stratigraphy, Site 357 (middle latitude South Atlantic). *ICR DSDP* 39:911–24

Boersma, A., Shackleton, N., Hall, H., Given, Q. 1979. Carbon and oxygen isotope records at DSDP Site 384 (North Atlantic) and some Paleocene paleotemperatures and carbon isotope variations in the South Atlantic. *ICR DSDP* 43:695–717

Bolli, H. M., Ryan, W. B. F. et al. 1978. *ICR DSDP* 40. 1079 pp.

Burns, R. E., Andrews, J. E. et al. 1973. *ICR DSDP* 21. 931 pp.

Christofferson, E. 1968. *Am. Geophys. Union Trans.* 49, 214 (Abstr.)

Creager, J. S., Scholl, D. W. et al. 1973. *ICR DSDP* 19. 913 pp.

Curray, J. R., Moore, D. G. et al. 1979. Leg 64 seeks evidence on development of basins. *Geotimes* 24(7):18–20.

Davies, T. A., Luyendyk, B. P. et al. 1974. *ICR DSDP* 26. 1129 pp.

de Vries Klein, G., Kobayarshi, K. et al. 1980. *ICR DSDP* 58. 1022 pp.

Dewey, J. F., Pitman, W. C., Ryan, W. B. F., Bonnin, J. 1973. Plate tectonics and the evolution of the Alpine system. *Geol. Soc. Am. Bull.* 84:3137–50.

Dietz, R. S. 1961. Continent and ocean basin evolution by spreading of the seafloor. *Nature* 190:854–57Dimitriev, L., Heirtzler, J. et al. 1978. *ICR DSDP* 46. 436 pp.

Donnelly, T., Francheteau, J., Bryan, W., Robinson, P., Flower, M., Salisbury, M. et al. 1979. *ICR DSDP* 51–53. 1613 pp.

Edgar, T. N., Saunders, J. B. et al. 1973. *ICR DSDP* 15. 1137 pp.

Ewing, M. et al. 1969. *ICR DSDP* 1. 672 pp.

Fischer, A. G. et al. 1971. *ICR DSDP* 6. 1329 pp.

Fisher, R. L., Bunce, E. T. et al. 1974. *ICR DSDP* 24. 1183 pp.

Gilluly, J. 1955. Geologic contrast between continents and oceans. *Geol. Soc. Am. Spec. Pap. No. 62,* pp. 7–18

Hayes, D. E., Frakes, L. W. et al. 1975. *ICR DSDP* 28. 1017 pp.

Hayes, D. E., Pimm, A. C. et al. 1972. *ICR DSDP* 14. 975 pp.

Hays, J. D. et al. 1972. *ICR DSDP* 9. 1205 pp.

Heezen, B. C., MacGregor, I. D. et al. 1973. *ICR DSDP* 20. 858 pp.

Heirtzler, J. R., Dickson, G. O., Herron, E. M., Pitman, W. C., Le Pichon, X. 1968. Marine magnetic anomalies, geomagnetic field reversals, and motions of the ocean floor and continents. *J. Geophys. Res.* 73, 2119–36

Hess, H. H. 1962. History of ocean basins. In *Petrologic Studies,* ed. A. E. J. Engel et al, pp. 599–620. New York: Geol. Soc. Am.

Hollister, C. D., Craddock, C. et al. 1976. *ICR DSDP* 35, 929 pp.

Hollister, C. D., Ewing, J. I. et al. 1972. *ICR DSDP* 11. 1077 pp.

Hsü, K. J. 1965. Isostasy, crustal thinning, mantle changes, and the disappearance of ancient land masses. *Am. J. Sci.* 263:97–109

Hsü, K. J. 1971a. Origin of the Alps and western Mediterranean. *Nature* 233:44–8

Hsü, K. J. 1971b. Franciscan melanges as a model for eugeosynclinal sedimentation and underthrusting tectonics. *J. Geophys. Res.* 76:1162–70

Hsü, K. J. 1980. Terrestrial catastrophe caused by cometary impact at the end of Cretaceous. *Nature* 285:201–3

Hsü, K. J., Montadert, L. C. et al. 1978. *ICR DSDP* 42(A). 1249 pp.

Hussong, D., Uyeda, S. et al. 1978. Near the Philippines, Leg 60 ends in Guam. *Geotimes* 23(10):19–22

Isaaks, B., Oliver, J., Sykes, L. R. 1968. Seismology and new global tectonics. *J. Geophys. Res.* 73:5855–99

Jackson, E. D., Koisumi, I. et al. 1980. *ICR DSDP* 55. 868 pp.

Karig, D. E. 1970. Ridge and basins of the Tonga-Kermadec island-arc system. *J. Geophys. Res.* 75:239–54

Karig, D. E., Ingle, J. C. et al. 1975. *ICR DSDP* 31. 927 pp.

Kennett, J. P., Houtz, R. E. et al 1975. *ICR DSDP* 29. 1197 pp.

Kroenke, L., Scott, R. et al. 1981. *ICR DSDP* 59. 820 pp.

Kulm, L. D., von Huene, R. et al. 1973. *ICR DSDP* 18. 1077 pp.

Kyte, F. T., Zhou, Z., Wasson, J. T. 1980. Siderophile-enriched sediments from the Cretaceous-Tertiary boundary. *Nature* 288:651–56

Lancelot, Y., Seibold, E. et al. 1977. *ICR DSDP* 41. 1259 pp.

Lancelot, Y., Winterer, E. L. et al. 1980. *ICR DSDP* 50. 868 pp.

Larson, R. L., Moberly, R. et al. 1975. *ICR DSDP* 32. 980 pp.

Larson, R. L., Schlanger, S. O. et al. 1981. *ICR DSDP* 61. In press

Laughton, A. S., Berggren, W. A. et al. 1972. *ICR DSDP* 12. 1343 pp.

Le Pichon, X. 1968. Seafloor spreading and continental drift. *J. Geophys. Res.* 73:3661–97

Ludwig, W. L., Krashenninikov, V. et al. 1980. Tertiary and Cretaceous paleo-environments in the southwest Atlantic Ocean: Preliminary results of DSDP Leg 71. *Geol. Soc. Am. Bull.* 91:655–64

Luyendyk, B. P., Cann, J. R. et al. 1978. *ICR DSDP* 49. 1020 pp.

Luyendyk, B. P. 1977. Deep sea drilling on the Ninetyeast Ridge: synthesis and tectonic model. In *Indian Ocean Geology and Biostratigraphy,* ed J. R. Heirtzler et al, pp. 165–88. Washington, D.C.: Am. Geophys. Union.

Maxwell, A. E. et al. 1970. *ICR DSDP* 3. 806 pp.

McKenzie, D. P. 1978. Some remarks on the development of sedimentary basins. *Earth Planet. Sci. Lett.* 40:25–32

McKenzie, D. P., Parker, R. L. 1967. The North Pacific: An example of tectonics on a sphere. *Nature* 216:1276–80

McManus, D. A. et al. 1970. *ICR DSDP* 5. 827 pp.

Melson, W. G., Rabinowitz, P. D. et al. 1978. *ICR DSDP* 45. 717 pp.

Montadert, L. C., Roberts, D. G. et al. 1979. *ICR DSDP* 48. 1183 pp.

Moore, J. C., Watkins, J. R. S. et al. 1979. Off Mexico, Middle American Trench. *Geotimes* 24(9):20–22

Morgan, W. J. 1968. Rises, trenches, great faults, and crustal blocks. *J. Geophys. Res.* 73:1959–82

Morgan, W. J. 1972. Deep mantle convection plumes and plate motions. *Am. Assoc. Petrol. Geol. Bull.* 56:203–13

Peterson, M. N. A. et al. 1970. *ICR DSDP* 2. 491 pp.

Pitman, W. C., Talwani, M. 1972. Seafloor spreading in the North Atlantic. *Geol. Soc. Am. Bull.* 83:619–46

Prell, W. L., Gardner, J. V. 1980. Hydraulic piston coring of late Neogene and Quaternary sections in the Carribean and equatorial Pacific: Preliminary results of DSDP Leg 68. *Geol. Soc. Am. Bull.* 91:433–44

Rosendahl, B. R., Hekinian, R. et al. 1980. *ICR DSDP* 54. 957 pp.

Ross, D. A., Neprochnov, Y. P. et al. 1978. *ICR DSDP* 42(B). 1244 pp.

Ryan, W. B. F., Hsü, K. J. et al. 1972. *ICR DSDP* 13. 1447 pp.

Savin, S. M., Douglas, R. G., Stehli, F. G. 1975. Tertiary marine temperatures. *Geol. Soc. Am. Bull.* 86:1499–510

Schlanger, S. O., Jackson, E. D. et al. 1976. *ICR DSDP* 33. 973 pp.

Scholl, D. W., von Huene, R., Vallier, T. L., Howell, D. G. 1980. Sedimentary masses and concepts about tectonic processes at underthrust ocean margins. *Geology* 8:564–68

Scientific Party. 1980. *ICR DSDP* 56–57. 1417 pp.

Sclater, J. G., Detrick, R. 1973. Elevation of mid-ocean ridges and the basement ages of JOIDES drilling sites. *Geol. Soc. Am. Bull.* 84:1547–54

Sclater, J. G., Anderson, R. N., Bell, M. L. 1971. Elevation of ridges and evolution of the central eastern Pacific. *J. Geophys. Res.* 76:7888–915

Shackleton, N. J., Kennett, J. P. 1975. Late Cenozoic Oxygen and Carbon isotopic changes at DSDP Site 284. *ICR DSDP* 29:801–8

Sibuet, J. C., Ryan, W. B. F. et al. 1979. *ICR DSDP* 47(B). 787 pp.

Simpson, E. S. W., Schlich, R. et al. 1974. *ICR DSDP* 25. 883 pp.

Sleep, N. H. 1971. Thermal effects of the formation of Atlantic continental margin by continental breakup. *Geophys. J. R. Astron. Soc.* 24:325–50

Smith, A. G. 1971. Alpine deformation and the oceanic areas of the Tethys. *Mediterr. Atl. Geol. Soc. Am. Bull.* 82:2039–70

Supko, P. R., Perch-Nielsen, K. et al. 1977. *ICR DSDP* 39. 1139 pp.

Talwani, M., Udintsev, G. et al. 1976. *ICR DSDP* 38. 1255 pp.

Thiede, J., Vallier, T. et al. 1981. *ICR DSDP* 62. In press

Thierstein, H. R., Berger, W. H. 1978. Injection events in ocean history. *Nature* 276:461–66

Tracey, J. I. et al. 1971. *ICR DSDP* 8. 1037 pp.

Tucholke, B. E., Vogt, P. R. et al. 1979. *ICR DSDP* 43. 1115 pp.

van Andel, T. H., Ross, G. R. et al. 1973. *ICR DSDP* 16. 949 pp.

Veevers, J. J., Heirtzler, J. R. et al. 1974. *ICR DSDP* 27. 1060 pp.

Vergnaud-Grazzini, C. 1979. Cenozoic paleotemperatures at Site 398, eastern North Atlantic. *ICR DSDP* 47(B):507–12

Vine, F. J., Matthews, D. H. 1963. Magnetic

anomalies over ocean ridges. *Nature* 199:947–49
Vine, F. J., Wilson, J. T. 1965. Magnetic anomalies over a young oceanic ridge off Vancouver Island. *Science* 150:485–89
von der Borch, C. C., Sclater, J. G. et al. 1974. *ICR DSDP* 22. 890 pp.
von Huene, R., Aubouine, J. et al. 1980. DSDP Middle America Trench transect off Guatemala. *Geol. Soc. Am. Bull.* 91:421–32
von Rad, U., Ryan, W. B. F. et al. 1979. *ICR DSDP* 47(A). 835 pp.
Whitmarsh, R. B., Weser, O. E., Ross, D. A. et al. 1974. *ICR DSDP* 23. 1179 pp.
Wilson, J. T. 1963. A possible origin of the Hawaiian Islands. *Can. J. Phys.* 41:863–70
Winterer, E. L. et al. 1971. *ICR DSDP* 7. 1757 pp.
Winterer, E. L., Ewing, J. I. et al. 1973. *ICR DSDP* 17. 930 pp.
Worsley, T., 1974. The Cretaceous-Tertiary boundary event in the ocean. *Soc. Econ. Paleontol. Mineral. Spec. Publ. No. 20*, pp. 94–125
Yeats, R. S., Hart, S. R. et al. 1976. *ICR DSDP* 34. 813 pp.

Ann. Rev. Earth Planet. Sci. 1982. 10:129-54

CORDILLERAN METAMORPHIC CORE COMPLEXES —From Arizona to Southern Canada

Richard Lee Armstrong

Department of Geological Sciences, University of British Columbia, Vancouver, British Columbia, Canada, V6T 2B4

INTRODUCTION

Cordilleran metamorphic core complexes occur in a sinuous belt that lies west of the Cordilleran fold and thrust belt from Canada to California. It then continues southeastward through the Basin and Range country of Arizona, where it lies athwart the northeast edge of the fold and thrust belt across Arizona, before continuing south into Mexico (Figure 1). This curious geographic distribution, in addition to the relatively recent recognition of the young age of metamorphic fabrics in many areas, has attracted attention to these complexes and led to a variety of hypotheses for their origin.

The Shuswap complex in Canada is the largest and longest recognized metamorphic core complex and is considered the type example (Coney 1980). Only during the past two decades has an awareness of the complexes in the US blossomed. This awareness reached its fullest expression in the recent Geological Society of America memoir devoted to discussion of these metamorphic complexes (Crittenden et al 1980). Because of the richness of that source, this review focuses on ideas and interpretations rather than descriptive details, but some examples must be given to demonstrate both variability and common features.

The investigation of each complex has tended to follow a similar historical pattern. Prior to 1960 most were regarded as exposures of pre-Phanerozoic crystalline basement or granitic intrusive bodies, and thus not structurally active parts of the Mesozoic orogen. In the 1960s, field work and reconnaissance K-Ar geochronometry drew attention to the complexes as sites of Mesozoic and Cenozoic deformation and metamorphism affecting Phanerozoic supracrustal rocks. During the last two decades numerous detailed

0084-6597/82/0515-0129$02.00

studies of these complexes have revealed a polyepisodic history, with metamorphic protolith ages ranging from early Precambrian to Cenozoic and deformation histories of varying complexity and length.

Coney (1980) reviewed much of the history of discovery and study of these complexes. In Canada the work of Wheeler (1963, 1965, 1966) and Reesor

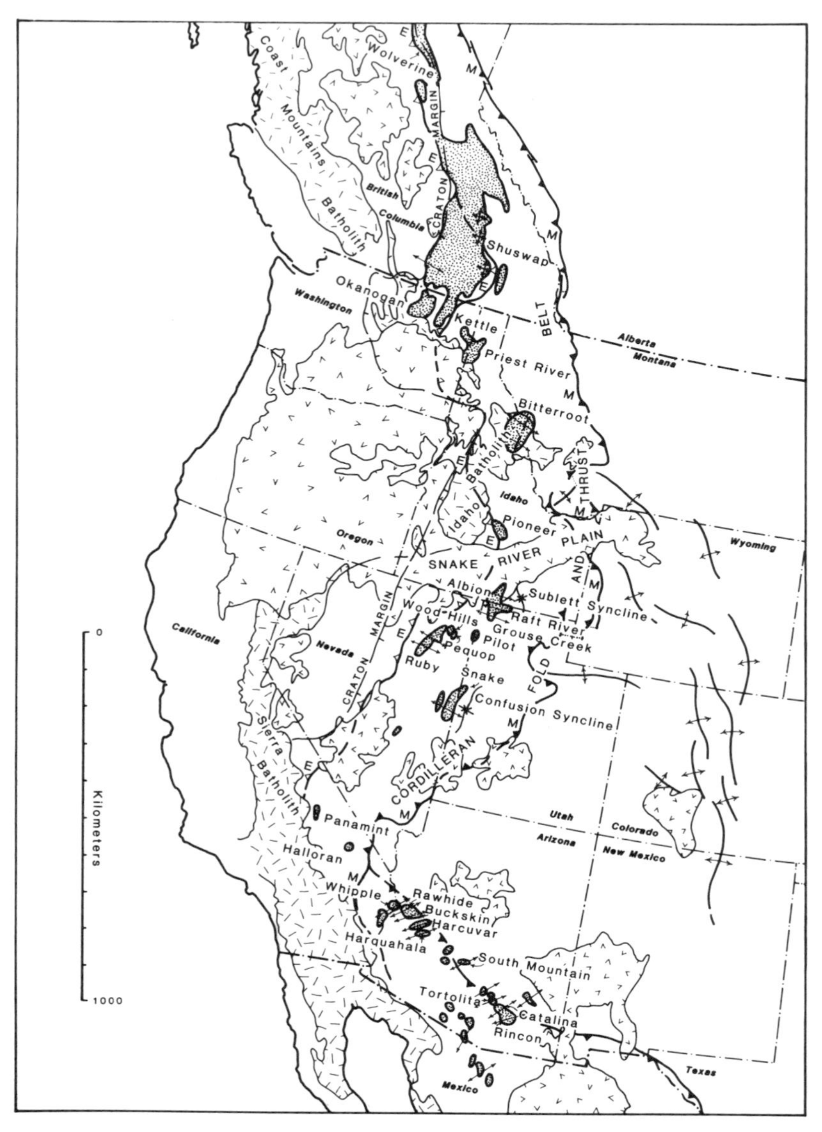

(1965, 1970, Reesor & Moore 1971) brought out the importance of domal structures along the eastern margin of the Shuswap complex. They reviewed evidence for Mesozoic metamorphism and its temporal overlap with emplacement of granitic rocks. Wheeler (1966) used the term Shuswap "metamorphic complex" and in later papers often referred to the area as a "metamorphic core zone." These terms were blended by Coney to "metamorphic core complex"; at the same time there was a shift in emphasis to the complexes further south, especially to those in Nevada and Arizona.

In the US the work of Peter Misch and his students and co-workers (Misch 1960, Misch & Hazzard 1962, Nelson 1969, Dover 1969, Thorman 1970) showed that Mesozoic metamorphism has affected rocks of the Cordilleran miogeosyncline in Nevada, Utah, and Idaho. These papers put emphasis on the low-angle "decollement" faulting of younger-on-older style, which is regionally associated with the metamorphic exposures.

Early hints at the importance of Cenozoic denudation (Jones 1963) and metamorphism (Mauger et al 1968) in Arizona, and the description by Davis (1975) of gravity gliding in the Rincon Mountains, led to the development of an influential "megaboudin" model for the Arizona core complexes (Davis & Coney 1979).

In a series of papers attempting to relate geochronometry and geologic information for the eastern Great Basin, I introduced the concept of a mobile Mesozoic "infrastructure" in the hinterland of the Sevier Orogenic Belt; pointed out that uplift and cooling of the metamorphic complexes was a Cenozoic phenomena; and suggested that many of the low-angle younger-on-older faults were probably Cenozoic extension and gravity slide structures (Armstrong 1964, Armstrong & Hansen 1966, Armstrong 1972). Controversy arose as various workers attempted to integrate the metamorphic areas into models for Cordilleran structural evolution—with varying degrees of success and agreement (Armstrong 1968b, Price & Mountjoy 1970, Mudge 1970, Campbell 1973, Price 1973, Hose & Daneś 1973, Roberts & Crittenden 1973,

Figure 1 Distribution and tectonic setting of Cordilleran metamorphic core complexes (similar to figures published by Coney 1979, 1980). The complexes are heavily stippled, the trends of regionally consistent late lineations are shown by double headed arrows. Three boundaries of the craton edge are shown. From east to west these are (*a*) the east edge of the miogeosyncline, marked with M, usually a major thrust of the Cordilleran fold and thrust belt; (*b*) the eastern limit of eugeosynclinal rocks, marked with E, usually the limit of material thrust eastward over the western part of the continental margin sediment wedge (this tectonic contact is shown with open thrust symbols); and (*c*) the west limit of older Precambrian basement, labeled "CRATON MARGIN", as indicated by strontium isotope ratios in granitic rocks. The Cordilleran fold and thrust belt, with filled in thrust symbols, diverges from the miogeosyncline (M) in southern California and Arizona. The major Mesozoic batholiths are shown with a scrambled dash pattern and large patches of Cenozoic volcanic rocks with a scattered V pattern. Major basement uplifts of Laramide age are shown by anticline symbols and dejected belts in the hinterland of the fold and thrust belt by syncline symbols.

Scholten 1973, Fox et al 1977, Brown 1978, Allmendinger & Jordan 1981). Recent reviews of Cordilleran core complexes emphasize Cenozoic deformation and its consequences, as exemplified by the core complexes in Arizona (Davis & Coney 1979, Coney 1979). This emphasis aroused protest from DeWitt (1980), who cited the evidence for Mesozoic development of the core complexes from California to Canada.

Core complexes are controversial because the evidence for timing of deformation is contradictory. In numerous cases structural elements thought to belong to one deformation episode have been shown to be of different age in nearby areas, and, thus, attempts at simple interpretations have failed. In reality most complexes are multiepisodic, with the effects of each deformation episode heterogeneously distributed rather than coincident. An episode of ductile to brittle Cenozoic deformation is common to all core complexes, but its significance declines northward. Geologists working north of 50° latitude in Canada assign it a very minor role.

The orientations of stress axes have locally remained similar in successive episodes because of a constant disposition of zones of weak and rigid lithosphere—large-scale movements are easiest either toward or away from the unremobilized cratonic lithosphere. Major longitudinal strike-slip motion is not important in core complex geology until northern British Columbia and the Yukon are reached. Those areas are not included in this review.

Structural behavior of the rocks in core complexes varies from ductile to brittle as these thermal and strain-rate controlled structural regimes move through the rocks. Price (1972) emphasized the inherent diachronism in the superposition of structures of different style in an evolving orogenic belt. The general sequence is an evolution from soft sediment structures through ductile structures of succeeding higher metamorphic grades; and then into brittle structures as the rocks undergo accumulation, tectonic burial and magma injection, and unroofing. Regional correlation of locally observed strain episodes is fraught with uncertainty.

I have visited many of the 25 complexes listed by Coney (1980); done geochronometry in the Mojave Desert, Great Basin, Idaho-Washington, and Canadian complexes; and spent seven field seasons mapping part of one complex, the Albion Mountains and Middle Mountain in southern Idaho, that shares features with all of them. No doubt these experiences affected my thinking and are evident in the examples cited and concepts developed herein.

UNIFYING FEATURES

All the metamorphic core complexes of the Cordillera display an association of lithologic, structural, and chronometric features: gently dipping foliation, in many places a distinctly cataclastic foliation; well-developed lineation, ductile and/or cataclastic, that is regionally consistent in orientation, and nearly parallel with minor fold axes; intrusive igneous rocks ranging from

Mesozoic to Cenozoic in age that show a variable structural overprint; Cenozoic K-Ar and FT dates for metasedimentary rocks, even when far from intrusive igneous bodies; and evidence of tectonic denudation along low-angle faults formed in a brittle structural regime that has been clearly superimposed on rocks previously deformed in a ductile fashion. Younger-on-older, nonmetamorphic-on-metamorphic, low-angle tectonic contacts are typical. Brecciation is common, and in its extreme development, sheets of breccia, which are most likely the result of gravity slides, are present.

Metamorphic Fabrics

The gently dipping foliation has been a matter of controversy since the disagreement between Daly (1912) and Gilluly (1934) on its origin in the Shuswap complex. Detailed descriptions of rock fabrics now abound and there is general agreement as to the strain involved: flattening perpendicular to foliation and stretching in the direction of the lineation.

Metamorphic fabrics in the core complexes affected by Mesozoic metamorphism and deformation are too varied to receive detailed discussion in this review. The generalizations about gently dipping, commonly cataclastic foliations apply fairly rigorously to Cenozoic structures. Gently dipping foliations are only part of the Mesozoic structural pattern, which also includes upright foliations, spectacular foliation fans, and varied examples of superimposition of structures. The development of flat foliations in an environment of regional compression and nappe movement is not unreasonable. It could be the result of progressive simple shear where large horizontal transport has occurred; or flattening above upwelling material in gneiss domes; or the axial plane foliation of isoclinal recumbent folds.

Notable detailed studies of metamorphic fabrics are those of Jones (1959), Reesor (1965), Hyndman (1968), Ross (1968), Campbell (1970), Fyles (1970), Fyson (1970), Preto (1970), McMillan (1973), Ross & Christie (1979), and Simony et al (1980) in Canada; Compton et al (1977), Compton (1980), Todd (1980), and Miller (1980, 1982) in the Albion-Raft River-Grouse Creek area of Utah and Idaho; Howard (1968, 1980) and Snoke (1980) in the Ruby Mountains of Nevada; Davis et al (1980) in the Whipple Mountains of California; and Banks (1980), G. A. Davis (1980), and Reynolds & Rehrig (1980) in Arizona. The orientation of the prominent Mesozoic and/or Cenozoic late stretching lineation in core complexes is shown diagramatically in Figure 1.

Igneous Rocks

The intrusive igneous rocks associated with core complexes are moderately variable in composition, mostly from biotite-hornblende granodiorite to biotite-muscovite granite, calcalkaline to mildly alkaline, and met- to peraluminous. They range in size from sills and dikes to batholiths. Their initial strontium isotope ratios are relatively radiogenic (Kistler & Peterman 1978, Armstrong et al 1977, Chase et al 1978, Armstrong 1979) and they are typically aluminous in character (Mursky 1972, Swanberg & Blackwell 1973, Best et al 1974, Keith et al 1980, Miller & Bradfish 1980, Anderson & Rowley 1981); these features distinguish these rocks from the granitic rocks typical of Circumpacific batholiths and provide evidence of an origin involving melting or assimilation of crustal rock, rather than direct magma derivation from a subduction zone. At present levels of exposure the abundance of granitic rock in most core complexes is much less than in the coastal batholith belts, and is not greatly different from that in the intermontane zone separating the metamorphic core zone and batholith belt. The major exceptions to this are in the Okanogan (Fox et al 1976, 1977); Kettle (Cheney 1980), and Valhalla (Reesor 1965) domes where large tongues or sheets of Mesozoic (?) granitic gneiss are incorporated into domed metamorphic rock sequences; the Bitterroot lobe of the Idaho batholith (Hyndman 1980), in which the chemical and structural characteristics of the core complexes are superimposed onto the batholith belt in the one zone where it swings far inland from its usual coastal position; and the South Mountain (Reynolds & Rehrig 1980) and Catalina-Rincon-Tortolita (Banks 1980, Keith et al 1980) complexes of Arizona, which include relatively large amounts of Cenozoic granitic rocks.

As a general rule the peraluminous granitic rocks, often with muscovite and garnet as accessories, are younger than the metaluminous hornblende-bearing granitic rocks located nearby. They also do not fit as neatly into the cycles of waxing and waning Cordilleran igneous activity (Armstrong & Suppe 1973, Armstrong et al 1977, Gabrielse & Reesor 1974) as do the metaluminous granitic rocks whose ages define those cycles. Typical examples are the White Creek (Wanless et al 1968, Mursky 1972) and Galena Bay (Read & Wheeler 1976) plutons in Canada, the Bitterroot (Swanberg & Blackwell 1973, Chase et al 1978) and Almo (Armstrong & Hills 1967) plutons in Idaho, the Kern (Best et al 1974) and Ruby Mountains (Kistler & Willden 1969) plutons in Nevada, the Whipple (Anderson & Rowley 1981) and Coyote Mountains (Wright & Haxel 1980) plutons in California, and the Wilderness (Keith et al 1980) pluton in Arizona. Many of the earliest granitic rocks in the regions containing core complexes are distinctly alkaline (Read 1973, Gabrielse & Reesor 1974, Fox et al 1977, Miller 1978).

The ages of granitic complexes in and near the core complexes vary widely as do their structural settings. In general the time span of ductile deformation overlaps the times of pluton emplacement, and the pre-, syn-, and post-kinematic relationships have been uniquely important in establishing the ages of structures.

Cenozoic Isotopic Dates

The Cenozoic K-Ar and FT dates that characterize core complexes came as a glaring contradiction to the scattered evidence for Mesozoic deformation and the once firmly established view that in the Cordillera the Cenozoic was a time of brittle crustal extension rather than regional metamorphism. The early papers by Armstrong & Hansen (1966), Mauger et al (1968), and Gabrielse & Reesor (1964) drew attention to these young dates, and numerous subsequent studies have closely examined and reconfirmed these observations (Ross 1974, Medford 1975, Archibald et al 1977, Mathews 1981, Armstrong 1974, Miller & Engels 1975, Fox et al 1976, Kistler & O'Niel 1975, Martin et al 1980, Dokka & Lingrey 1979, Banks 1980, Reynolds & Rehrig 1980, Keith et al 1980).

Denudation Faults

Arguments for Cenozoic denudation in the eastern Great Basin were marshalled in a paper by Armstrong (1972). This paper reviewed previous observations of denudation structures on a variety of scales and styles, and pointed out that this aspect of the regional synthesis had not received sufficient emphasis. Since then, studies of denudation have flourished. Coney (1974) reexamined the Snake Range "decollement" and Snoke (1980) the Secret Pass area of the Ruby Mountains and both agreed that Cenozoic denudation was the culminating process in the development of these core complexes. Cheney (1980) and Rhodes & Cheney (1981) described faults bounding the Kettle Dome in northern Washington as denudation faults similar to those observed in the southwestern US. The Newport Fault (Miller 1971), which lies on the Priest River complex, is now viewed by many geologists as an early Cenozoic denudation structure (Cheney 1980, Ewing 1981, Reynolds et al 1981, Price et al 1981a, b).

Spectacular examples of Cenozoic denudation in the Mojave-Sonoran desert region of California-Arizona have been described by Shackelford (1980) and Davis et al (1980), and a recent US Geological Survey conference (Howard et al 1981) gave much attention to these and related structures. The core complex memoir gives detailed descriptions of the denudation complexes in Arizona (Rehrig & Reynolds 1980, Reynolds & Rehrig 1980, Banks 1980, G. H. Davis 1980, Keith et al 1980).

In two areas brittle denudation faults show a special relationship to reset K-Ar dates. In the Snake Range (Lee et al 1970, 1980) and in the Whipple Mountains (Martin et al 1980), the dates decrease upward in lower-plate rocks, reaching minimum values of 17.0 and 15.3 Ma, respectively, for samples close to the master detachment-denudation fault.

SIGNIFICANT CONTRASTS

Most confusion concerning core complexes arises because of differences in age of structures and multiplicity of deformation events. These differences are of two major types:

(*a*) From Canada to California the complexes are polygenetic—all contain evidence of Mesozoic metamorphism and deformation—which is related to Cordilleran orogenic development in a setting of plate convergence. All the complexes have also been overprinted by an episode of crustal extension during the Cenozoic. In Arizona most complexes are monogenetic—exclusively the result of Cenozoic extension.

(*b*) The Cenozoic creation or modification of core complexes in an extensional tectonic setting is the consequence of different episodes of crustal extension on the two sides of the Snake River Plain. North of the plain, the extension is an Eocene event. To the south it is Miocene. Episodes of regional extension during the Mesozoic have not been clearly resolved, and potentially are further complexities of the polygenetic core complexes.

The Shuswap, Albion–Raft River–Grouse Creek, and Whipple-Rawhide-Buckskin areas can be used as examples of polygenetic complexes in order to illustrate the timing and nature of Mesozoic core complexes of the Sevier-Laramide hinterland. The Catalina-Rincon-Tortolita complex exemplifies the monogenetic core complexes of Arizona.

Shuswap Complex

Understanding of this large and only partly well-exposed region has come about gradually as detailed mapping and fossil and isotope geochronology have proceeded. Major issues remain in flux but a general outline (Brown et al 1981, Price et al 1981b) is possible. The premetamorphic protoliths that compose the complex include early Precambrian crystalline basement (Chamberlain et al 1979, Brown 1980); a middle Proterozoic rift basin filled with clastic strata (Gabrielse 1972); late Proterozoic through Paleozoic to Triassic sediments, mostly types deposited outboard of the carbonate bank (Read & Wheeler 1976); and allochthonous Paleozoic to Triassic oceanic rocks—including a Devonian volcanic arc assemblage with granitic batholiths (Okulitch 1979)—emplaced tectonically in late Triassic or early Jurassic time (Rees 1981, Parrish 1981). Tectonic imbrication and ductile deformation had affected parts of the protolith assemblage, but no detailed reconstruction of this structural stage is yet possible (Read & Wheeler 1976, Brown 1978).

Igneous activity began anew in late Triassic–early Jurassic time and by the end of the Jurassic, numerous large plutons were emplaced (Gabrielse & Reesor 1974, Pigage 1977). These postdate the main structural development of the complex—an aggregation of Alpine-style nappes with associated metamorphic fabrics (Morrison 1980, Read & Klepacki 1981). The metamorphic culmination in many areas was reached about 180 to 160 Ma ago, a conclusion well documented by batholith geochronometry circumscribing the complex.

Pluton emplacement and movement along major faults continued on into the Cretaceous as the nappe-batholith complex was gradually unroofed (Price et al 1981b, Archibald et al 1977, Brown 1978, Brown et al 1981). At the same time, the entire complex was translated more than 100 kilometers toward cratonic North America while the Rocky Mountain fold and thrust belt developed (Price & Mountjoy 1970). Evidence for Cretaceous ductile deformation is not yet well documented. Doming is a relatively late and modest modification of the nappes that is poorly dated (Read & Klepacki 1981). Some doming may be as old as Jurassic; the final stages were as recent as Eocene.

In the Eocene, after Rocky Mountain thrusting had ceased, an episode of crustal heating and extension further modified the metamorphic complex (Price 1979, Price et al 1981a, Ewing 1981). Igneous activity, extension and denudation structures, and dome accentuation occurred while the crystalline rocks were still at or being raised to, temperatures of 300° to 400°C. This dramatic episode terminated abruptly about 45 Ma ago. Over a large area near coincident with sillimanite-grade rocks, K-Ar and FT dates of minerals were set as isotherms moved rapidly down into the crust. Ductile to cataclastic foliation of Eocene age has been proven in a few Eocene igneous rocks (Ross 1974, Solberg 1976) and may be widespread in the reset K-Ar date terrane. Mylonitization associated with low-angle faults and low-angle faults that juxtapose rocks of contrasting metamorphic grade have been observed on both sides of the complex. However, these features are not as spectacularly developed as in complexes further south and their age is not firmly established (Ross 1973, Brown et al 1981, Murphy 1981, Lane 1981).

Albion–Raft River–Grouse Creek Complex

The chronology of metamorphism and deformation in this area has been resolved as the result of 15 years of study by myself (Armstrong 1968a, 1970, 1976, in preparation, Armstrong & Hills 1967), Compton & Todd (Compton 1980, Compton et al 1977, Compton & Todd 1979, Todd 1980), and Miller (1980, 1982).

The protolith assemblage was early Precambrian crystalline basement with a Precambrian (?) and Paleozoic to Triassic cover sequence that is related to the continental margin miogeosyncline, but thinner and more pelitic; and an allochthonous quartzite-dominated later Precambrian or Paleozoic sedimentary sequence, present only in northern parts of the complex. During the Paleozoic the autochthon may have been a slowly subsiding outer high (Schuepbach & Vail 1980) developed on a late Precambrian divergent continental margin—outboard of the shallow-water carbonate bank. Further offshore in a rise or slope environment lay the depositional environment of the quartzite assemblage.

Regional metamorphism reached a first amphibolite facies culmination in Jurassic time, more than 160 Ma ago. This was followed by a Cretaceous period of imbrication and ductile deformation under conditions of decreasing pressure and temperature. Cretaceous biotite-muscovite granites were emplaced in northwestern parts of the complex.

Profound further modification of the area took place in early to mid-Cenozoic time, accompanied by further emplacement of granitic rock. Near and in the granitic injection complex, temperatures rose to sillimanite grade, and rock strength was dramatically reduced while the area was subject to regional extension. The several basement-cored domes may have risen at this time, but this is not well dated and their growth may be largely Cretaecous. Both interference structure (Armstrong in preparation) and polydiapiric (Miller 1982) explanations for the domes have been advocated. As a result of high temperatures and extreme extension, the nappes were reactivated and thinned while in the Grouse Creek Mountains, near a Cenozoic pluton, the basement became locally remobilized and intruded its sedimentary cover. A strong mylonitic foliation and lineation, with lineation trend nearly parallel to Cretaceous fold axes and lineations, developed in areas deformed at this time. The effects of the Cenozoic episode dominate the structural story in Utah, but only affect the westernmost part of the Albion Mountains. As a result, the distinction of Mesozoic and Cenozoic structures is possible there. Relatively late features are the development of brittle denudation and detachment faults, breccia sheets, and far-traveled gravity slide masses. A remarkably similar overall structural chronology has been worked out in the Ruby Mountains-Wood Hills-Pequop Mountains area (Thorman 1970, Howard 1980, Snoke 1980) and probably also applies to the Snake Range (Misch & Hazzard 1962, Nelson 1969, Coney 1974).

Whipple-Rawhide-Buckskin Mountains

The spectacular denudation structure of the Whipple Mountains and the structural history of the rocks exposed by denudation have been the subject of recent intensive study (Davis et al 1980, Dickey et al 1980, Martin et al 1980, Anderson & Rowley 1981). There, a middle Precambrian basement and scattered remnants of its late Proterozoic and Paleozoic platformal cover have been subject to Jurassic metamorphism and Jurassic and Cretaceous intrusion of granitic rocks. During later Cretaceous time, structurally deeper rocks were intensely mylonitized—with the development of cataclastic foliation and lineation synchronous with the emplacement of granitic sheets parallel to foliation.

Distinctly later, in the Miocene, brittle detachment faulting removed much of a Cenozoic volcanic and sedimentary cover. Slickensides and structures in the disrupted cover indicate that the movement was approximately parallel to the Mesozoic lineation, tempting geologists to find a common genesis for both (Lucchitta et al 1981) in spite of the considerable difference in age.

Catalina-Rincon-Tortolita Complex

The geology of this long-studied area was recently synthesized by G. H. Davis (1980), Banks (1980), and Keith et al (1980). The core complex protolith was middle Precambrian crystalline basement with platform cover of late Precambrian to Mesozoic age. The peripheral effects of latest Cretaceous and early Cenozoic Laramide orogeny (Drewes 1978, Davis 1979) may have been present in the form of detached and deformed sedimentary cover and brittle-fault bounded basement-cored uplifts, but no regional metamorphism had affected the area before the Cenozoic.

Igneous activity started in Laramide time with the emplacement of 75 to 60 Ma old calc-alkaline granodiorite. This was followed by a large laccolithic body of peralkaline granite of Eocene (50 to 44 Ma) age and a final calc-alkaline intrusive of Miocene (29 to 25 Ma) age. Cataclastic flattening and stretching occurred after each of these three intrusive episodes but were largely confined to the time interval from late in the second to late in the third igneous episode. Uplift and rapid cooling, with setting of K-Ar and FT mineral dates, came between 30 and 20 Ma, outlasting the last igneous episode.

During the height of deformation the granites and enclosing country rock were partially converted to mylonitic augen gneiss, with gently dipping foliation and regionally consistent lineation. Stretching also produced ductile normal faults, and flattening created a variety of recumbent folds. High-temperature extension was superseded by brittle denudation, with unmetamorphosed cover moving radially off rising domes along low-angle faults (Davis 1975). The metamorphic cores now stand fringed with chaotic, broken, and folded bits of unmetamorphosed cover that lie in brittle-fault contact with deformed basement, its pre-Cenozoic sediment cover, and intrusive granitic rocks. Davis & Coney (1979) describe the overall structural pattern as one of "megaboundins," with deformation localized at low levels in the Phanerozoic sediment cover where granite spreading was concentrated. This same zone was one of steep metamorphic gradients during early to mid-Cenozoic time.

GEOPHYSICAL EXPRESSION

Metamorphic core complexes do not stand out on geophysical maps of the Cordillera. Seismicity and heat flow reflect late Cenozoic tectonic activity and thus show absolutely no association with metamorphic exposures (Eaton 1980). There is no expression of individual complexes or domes on magnetic anomaly maps, but the complexes all occur in a broad belt of low magnetic relief that is caused by thick sedimentary cover and high crustal temperatures (Berry et al 1971, Mabey et al 1978). The gravity field in areas of the complexes is intermediate (Bouguer anomaly -90 to -160 milligals). Crustal thickness ranges from 20 to 45 km. It is typically about 25 km under Mojave and Arizona complexes; 30 km under Nevada, Utah, and Idaho complexes; and 40 km under complexes in southern Canada (Eaton et al 1978, Smith 1978, Forsyth et al 1974, Berry & Mair 1977, Cumming et al 1979). Late Cenozoic crustal extension can explain the steady southward decrease in crustal thickness. Cady (1980) observed that local gravity highs (10 to 20 milligals) correlated with individual gneiss domes in southern Canada and northern Washington, where Cenozoic modifications of the gravity field are minimal. In the metamorphic core zones of southern Canada and northern Washington, crustal seismic velocities and densities are generally higher than in surrounding areas (Cady 1980, Cumming et al 1979) and no crustal roots are present. The thickening of "lower crustal" rocks in the core zones is consistent with the idea of compressive crustal thickening during Mesozoic orogeny followed by deep erosion and isostatic recovery (Cady 1980).

CRUSTAL EXTENSION

Regional extension is a widely accepted explanation for much of the character of core complexes, particularly for those features acquired during Cenozoic time (Coney 1979, 1980, G. A. Davis 1980). The timing of extension seems to be directly related to concurrent igneous activity: Eocene in Canada and the northwestern US (Lipman et al 1972, Armstrong 1974, Ewing 1981), and Oligocene-Miocene south of the Snake River Plain (Christiansen & Lipman 1972, Snyder et al 1976). Most authors view the extension process as one where shallow rocks undergo brittle fracture and block rotation due to movement along listric normal faults, while ductile necking of warm lower crust occurs simultaneously (Hamilton & Myers 1966, Stewart 1978, Coney 1979, Eaton 1980, G. A. Davis 1980). A counter-proposal (Wernicke 1981a, b) is that low-angle normal faults continue through the crust to root in the mantle. This solves the problem of finding a stretched terrane synchronous in movement and complementary to each low-angle denudation structure, a difficulty that forced some authors to attempt a surficial, gravity-glide explanation for large-scale detachment (Davis et al 1980). A complete description of crustal extension probably incorporates both propositions. The depth to the brittle-ductile transition is clearly variable and under some circumstances may even lie below the crust, but in others it has been within supracrustal strata, as for example in the Catalina-Rincon-Tortolita complex. Gravity gliding cannot be denied for situations where detached rocks have moved across Cenozoic deposits in basins, as in the Rawhide-Buckskin area (Davis et al 1980) or Grouse Creek Mountains (Todd 1980).

The logical structural succession for rocks that have moved from a metamorphic environment to surface conditions is the order observed in core complexes. Ductile recrystallization-flow structures are succeeded by cataclastic flow, then brittle cataclasis, and finally overprinted by local gravity-glide structures, including the development of breccia sheets. This sequence could develop in one protracted extension episode as an overlapping continuum, while rocks from a depth of several kilometers are tectonically denuded and brought to the surface (as in the Catalina-Rincon-Tortolita complex); or it could develop in distinct stages—Mesozoic ductile or cataclastic fabrics overprinted by Cenozoic ductile and brittle faulting (as in the Shuswap, Albion–Raft River–Grouse Creek, and Whipple complexes). Some low-angle detachment surfaces show large-scale corrugations that parallel the extension direction inferred from other structural data (Rehring & Reynolds 1980, Cameron et al 1981).

The most popular plate tectonic explanations for the two Cenozoic episodes of crustal extension are oblique rifting due to a diffuse transform interaction of North America and offshore lithosphere plates (Atwater 1970, Ewing 1981, Price 1979, Price et al 1981a); and back-arc spreading or spreading over a hole in the descending slab due to upwelling asthenosphere (Scholz et al 1971, Dickinson & Snyder 1979, G. A. Davis 1980). These proposals are not mutually exclusive. They are different views of the same process, and they involve an interplay of globally created stress fields, mantle flow patterns, magma generation, and consequent failure of plates as they are weakened by heating.

LOCALIZATION OF THE MESOZOIC METAMORPHIC CORE ZONE

Crustal extension does not explain the restricted geographic location of the metamorphic core complexes. Something more is required, and in the case of the polygenetic complexes of the Sevier-Laramide hinterland, it is almost certainly the presence of the thickened and metamorphosed sialic crust that was generated during Mesozoic orogeny. Superimposition of nonuniform crustal heating and stretching on irregularly thickened and heterogeneous crust could explain the irregular distribution of US core complexes. The alignment of Cenozoic core complexes across Arizona may represent the coincidence of magmatism and heating of sialic crust with regional extension—as in the "megaboudin" model of Davis & Coney (1979).

Dual Thermal Culmination

The formation of Mesozoic metamorphic infrastructural zones in a belt that lies inland from contemporaneous coastal batholith belts requires explanation.

The usual "Cordilleran" or "Andean" model has only one broad magmatic arc—thermal culmination (Burchfiel & Davis 1975, Dickinson 1976). The locus of Mesozoic infrastructural zones is clearly a thermal culmination that is spatially separate from the culmination associated with the batholith belts; the Idaho batholith is the only significant exception. The dual thermal culmination has always been evident in Canada (Monger & Hutchison 1971), and the distribution of the polygenetic core complexes in the US indicates that it is present there as well.

Study of active subduction zones may provide an explanation for dual thermal culminations and thereby explain the Mesozoic thermal pattern of the Cordillera. In an active island arc like Japan (Sugimura & Uyeda 1973) volcanic activity is sharply focused in a narrow belt with a well-defined cutoff toward the trench. This sharp boundary is called the *volcanic front*. In the opposite direction there is an exponential decline over a distance of several hundred kilometers in the production rate of volcanic rocks. This is analogous to the distribution of granitic rocks of any given age in Cordilleran batholith belts. Heat carried into the crust by magma is an explanation for one thermal culmination.

For hundreds of kilometers behind the zone of maximum magma production, a broad zone of high heat flow is present (Sugimura & Uyeda 1973). It is largely coincident with scattered volcanic activity, but the observed heat flux is not correlated with volcanic production rates. A widely accepted explanation for this zone of high heat flow follows from the original suggestions of McKenzie (1969) and Griggs (1972) that the descending slab induces flow of mantle material in the triangular prism of the asthenosphere bounded by floating and sinking lithosphere slabs (Andrews & Sleep 1974, Anderson et al 1976, Toksöz & Bird 1977a, b, Uyeda 1977). Numerical models of Andrews & Sleep (1974) illustrate the consequences of this type of process (Figure 2). As subduction continues from an initial condition of horizontal isotherms, a broad band of the floating lithosphere undergoes heating from below. In the model illustrated, the thermal culmination, which is purely a consequence of flow in the mantle and stretching of the overlying lithosphere, is localized about 300 km from the earth surface point of contact of the plates. This is well behind the expected locus of the magmatic culmination, which would be about 150 km from the same point of contact. Thus there is a possible explanation for two thermal maxima inland from an active subduction zone—one due to magmatic heat transfer and the other due to induced mantle flow. The second culmination could be augmented by magmatic heat transfer, as rising mantle and heated crust undergo partial melting, and by heat generation in sialic basement of the continental margin.

Crustal Shortening

Where the lithosphere plate floating above an active subduction zone is subjected to heating, it will weaken, and may fail, by shortening or elongation. Asthenosphere flow merely provides favorable conditions for lithosphere failure behind a magmatic arc. Integrated global stress patterns dictate whether the failure in a given area will be shortening or elongation. Geologic evidence indicates consistent trench-craton convergence during Mesozoic time along the Pacific Margin of North America (Hamilton 1978); this convergence is accepted here as an observation without explanation.

The detailed structural style of crustal shortening can be exceedingly varied. The heterogeneity of the crust and variable position of the brittle-ductile transition within the crust will both be critical factors in control of structural style, and these will change as deformation proceeds. Figure 3 illustrates three of the many possible patterns that can occur where crystalline basement underlies a stratified cover. If the basement is fairly rigid, large thrust structures may form. A shallow-basement example of this is the Wind River thrust in Wyoming (Smithson et al 1978). Deeply buried examples of large thrust

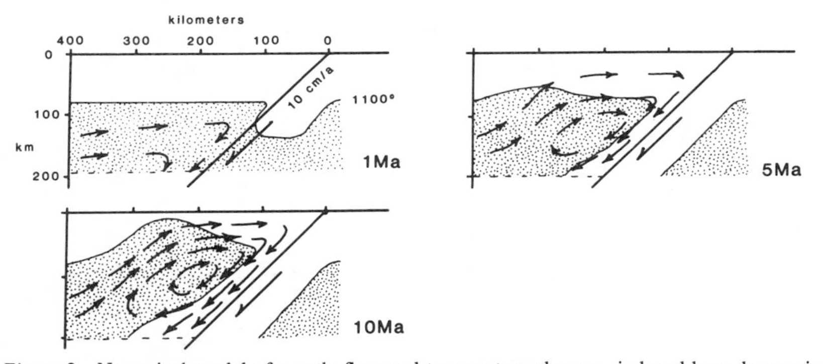

Figure 2 Numerical model of mantle flow and temperature changes induced by a downgoing slab (Andrews & Sleep 1974). The 1100°C isotherm that is shown is approximately the lithosphere-asthenosphere boundary. The scaling is only approximate and will vary as subduction rate, subduction angle, and physical properties of the mantle and lithosphere are changed. Nevertheless, the deduction, based on reasonable choices of physical properties, is that induced flow will occur, and this will change the thermal structure of a broad region above the subducting plate. An exact correspondence with Cordilleran tectonics during the Mesozoic is not expected because the calculation was intended to simulate the formation of marginal basins. The models of Toksoz & Bird (1977a, 1977b) for continental plateaus are similar and equally applicable to the discussion. Numerical models designed to simulate induced flow and thermal evolution of the Cordillera are needed. In these models the radiogenic heat production of the crystalline basement may need to be taken into account to produce the metamorphic core complex thermal culmination.

steps may include the Snake Range and Albion–Raft River–Grouse Creek core complexes. A slightly more ductile basement may fail in thin slices or wedges. This style is observed in the massifs of the Alps (Labhart 1966, 1968, Steck 1968) and is described in the Shuswap complex (Morrison 1980) and Wasatch Mountains of northern Utah (Bruhn & Beck 1981). Basement-cored fold nappes are formed where basement becomes very ductile, and where there is negligible ductility contrast between basement and cover. This is seen in the Pennine zone of the Alps (Milnes 1974) and in the Shuswap complex (Brown et al 1981, Read & Klepacki 1981). In both areas are examples where early basement wedges were overprinted by more ductile structures as metamorphic grade increased (Milnes 1974, Ross 1968, Morrison 1980, 1981).

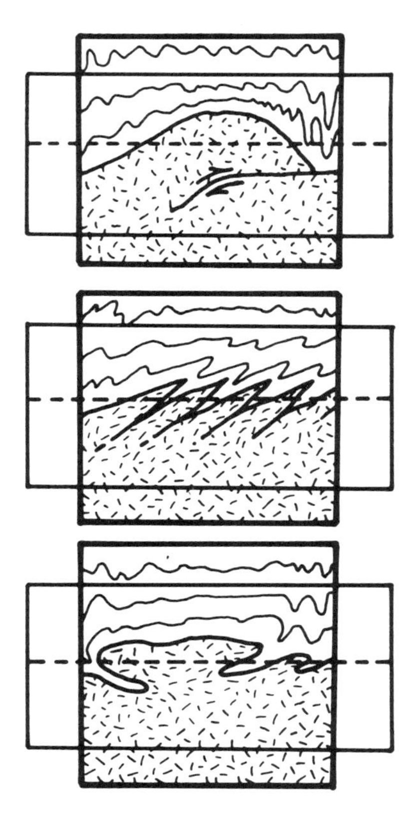

Figure 3 Three styles of crustal shortening, shown very diagramatically. A large thrust involving basement results in considerable structural relief on the basement-cover contact. Imbrication of thin basement wedges and slices or ductile folding together of basement and cover can accomplish similar amounts of shortening but produce less structural relief.

The different structural styles all accomplish crustal shortening, even; though their surface expression may vary dramatically, all presumably played a role during Mesozoic crustal shortening in the Cordillera.

Where thick geosynclinal sediments are involved, the surface expression of crustal shortening need not directly overlie the location of basement shortening. Cordilleran thin-skinned fold and thrust belts are a surficial expression of crustal shortening in basement farther west, including the rocks within or beneath metamorphic core complexes (Royse et al 1975, Price et al 1981b). The area of shortened and thickened crust provides the slope and push to drive supracrustal rocks toward fold and thrust belts (Kehle 1970, Price 1973, Elliott 1976, Chapple 1978).

In the Albion Mountains, telescoping of stratigraphic units appears to have gone on during fold and thrust belt deformation, whereas in the Shuswap complex much of the visible structure predates deformation along the eastern edge of the deformed belt (Brown 1978, Brown et al 1981, Price et al 1981b). Both situations are possible. As the core zone is thrust eastward, climbs thrust ramps, and is exposed by erosion from above, the brittle-ductile transition will move downward, and the zone where deep accommodation of surface shortening occurs will sink deeper into the crust and shift eastward. Earlier episodes of deformation will be frozen into the rocks that are now exposed at the surface, while shortening is still in progress at depth. During later stages of orogenesis the active thrusts will have shifted deeper and eastward, so that the upper levels of the metamorphic core will be passively transported cratonward. This view of upwelling and structural diachronism explains the seeming contradiction that metamorphic core ductile structures predate the later stages of marginal fold and thrust belt deformation.

The 100 to 200 km of crustal shortening observed in supracrustal rocks is compatible with the amount of sialic basement aggregated in Cordilleran metamorphic core zones—if two factors are taken into account (Brown 1978, Price et al 1981b). The first is that at the end of geosyncline subsidence, the sialic basement in polygenetic core complex areas was probably thin, attenuated by faulting and ductile stretching, and partially replaced by sima, as is now the situation along divergent margins. The second factor is Cenozoic extension, which may have removed any thickened crustal roots that were present at the end of the Mesozoic. The present exposed area of polygenetic core complex rocks in any regional cross section is reasonably well correlated with geologic estimates for the amount of shortening in the corresponding part of the fold and thrust belt.

Uplifted and Dejected Belts

Where a thick suprastructure is still present in the hinterland of the Cordilleran fold and thrust belt, there may be ductile folding or multiple thin-slice basement wedging at depth, with little surface expression. In contrast, large thrust steps are expressed in a particular pattern that is observed in the Snake Range and Albion–Raft River–Grouse Creek areas. This pattern has been called an uplifted infrastructure-dejected belt couple (Armstrong 1978). A geometric clue to a large thrust step is provided by the large local structural relief. In both cases the arched ranges, exposing metamorphic infrastructure, are paired with exceptionally deep structural depressions, the dejected belts, that lie immediately to the east. In the case of the Snake Range the depression is the Confusion Range synclinorium (Hose 1977); in that of the Albion–Raft River–Grouse Creek area, it is the Sublett synclinorium (Armstrong et al 1978). Both depressions contain rocks as young as Triassic and are the only places where rocks that young are preserved between the metamorphic core and the fold and thrust belt. The inferred deep structure from the Snake Range to the fold and thrust belt is shown in Figure 4. A similar geometric logic has been used in interpreting deep structure in the metamorphic core of the Canadian Rocky Mountains (Simony et al 1981, Price & Fermor 1981, Price et al 1981b), following the rules for balanced sections discussed by Dahlstrom (1970).

CONCLUSION

There are a variety of processes and events responsible for Cordilleran metamorphic core complexes. The polygenetic complexes originated as metamorphic infrastructure in the hinterland of the Cordilleran fold and thrust belt as a result of lithosphere heating above a long-lived subduction zone. Their origin was also partly a consequence of mid-Mesozoic imbrication of oceanic terranes and the craton margin. Crustal shortening and thickening in the metamorphic core zone produced a large volume of deformed rock and were responsible for bringing rocks from depths of 10 to 20 km to surface exposure. Isostatic response to crustal thickening and ramping up large thrust steps were parts of the uplift process. The irregular exposure of US core complexes is explained by the variable structural style of crustal shortening and different depths of erosion through the suprastructure. At the end of the Mesozoic the metamorphic core rocks that we now see at the surface were within a few kilometers of the surface and were probably still warmer, more buoyant, and more ductile than surrounding rocks, which had not undergone such dramatic excursions into ductile structural regimes.

Cenozoic volcanism and upwelling of hot asthenosphere again led to increased lithosphere temperatures and structural failure, this time extensional. The Mesozoic infrastructure was remobilized, and accidents of block faulting and tectonic denudation, following irregularly distributed deep-seated crustal stretching, led to exposure of the polygenetic core complexes as we see them

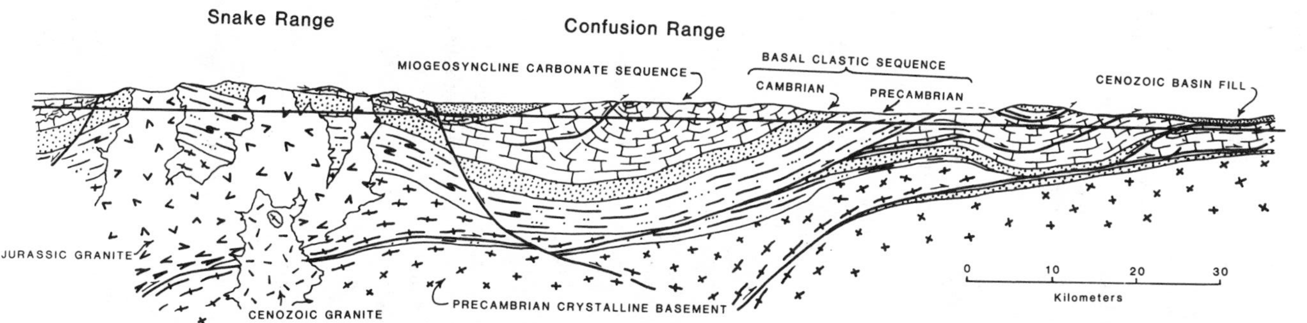

Figure 4 Schematic cross section from metamorphic core complex to fold and thrust belt. The Snake Range–Confusion Range uplifted infrastructure–dejected belt couple are shown as an example of structural relief produced by a thrust step involving crystalline basement. This section is similar to one drawn by Coney (1979, 1980), based on an earlier shallow section published by Armstrong (1972).

today. Gravitational glide structures were formed as a consequence of topographic relief on uplifted blocks. The same back-arc weakening of lithosphere above a descending plate that operated during Mesozoic time may have had a role in localizing the Cenozoic core complexes.

In Arizona during mid-Cenozoic time, magmatism and lithosphere failure encroached cratonward, even beyond the Mesozoic orogenic front—something that did not occur farther north in the Cordillera. As a consequence of this stepping forward of back-arc thermal effects, a special type of core complex—the monogenetic "megaboudin"—was created. The continuous zone of Cenozoic lithosphere failure, with its varied geological consequences, links the two core complex types.

A core complex can be described in a few words: it is an exposure of rocks that were once ductile lower crust, on which shallow brittle extensional features have been superimposed. In these special areas we have an opportunity to view the myriad effects and complexities of lithosphere failure. No simple single prescription of events and processes can explain all the complexes. Each has its own unique protolith and deformation history and provides a new geological puzzle.

There are lessons to be learned in the study of Cordilleran core complexes that are applicable to the study of metamorphic core zones in other Pacific-type orogenic belts. In addition, our understanding of the process of crustal extension, such as has occurred whenever divergent continental margins have been formed on the site of waning orogenic belts, is enriched.

ACKNOWLEDGMENTS

My reserach on core complexes has been funded by the US National Science Foundation and the Canadian Natural Sciences and Engineering Research Council. The list of people who have shared core complex experience with me would be as long as the list of authors cited in this paper, and would be much the same. My thanks go to all of them and to R. R. Parrish and W. H. Mathews for reviews of this manuscript.

Literature Cited

Allmendinger, R. W., Jordan, T. E. 1981. Mesozoic evolution, hinterland of the Sevier Orogenic Belt. *Geology*. 9:308–13

Anderson, J. L., Rowley, M. C. 1981. Synkinematic intrusion of two-mica and associated metaluminous granitoids, Whipple Mountains, California. *Can. Mineral.* 19:83–101

Anderson, R. N., Uyeda, S., Miyashiro, A. 1976. Geophysical and geochemical constraints at converging plate boundaries–Part I: Dehydration in the downgoing slab. *Geophys. J. R. Astron. Soc.* 44:333–57

Andrews, D. J., Sleep, N. H. 1974. Numerical modelling of tectonic flow behind island arcs. *Geophys. J. R. Astron. Soc.* 38: 237–51

Archibald, D. A., Glover, J. K., Farrar, E. 1977. K-Ar ages from the Bayonne batholith and some nearby plutons, S. E. British Columbia, and their geological implications. *Geol. Assoc. Can. Abstr.* 2:5

Armstrong, R. L. 1964. *Geochronology and geology of the eastern Great Basin in Nevada and Utah*. PhD thesis. Yale Univ. 202 pp.
Armstrong, R. L. 1968a. Mantled gneiss domes in the Albion Range, southern Idaho. *Geol. Soc. Am. Bull.* 79:1295–1314
Armstrong, R. L. 1968b. The Sevier orogenic belt in Nevada and Utah. *Geol. Soc. Am. Bull.* 79:429–58
Armstrong, R. L. 1970. Mantled gneiss domes in the Albion Range, southern Idaho: a revision. *Geol. Soc. Am. Bull.* 81:909–10
Armstrong, R. L. 1972. Low-Angle (denudation) faults, hinterland of the Sevier orogenic belt, eastern Nevada and western Utah. *Geol. Soc. Am. Bull.* 83:1729–54
Armstrong, R. L. 1974. Geochronometry of the Eocene volcanic-plutonic episode in Idaho. *Northwest Geol.* 3:1–15
Armstrong, R. L. 1976. The geochronometry of Idaho. *Isochron/West.* 15:1–33
Armstrong, R. L. 1978. Core complexes, dejected zones, and an orogenic model for the eastern Cordillera. *Geol. Soc. Am. Abst. with Programs* 10:360–61
Armstrong, R. L. 1979. Sr isotopes in igneous rocks of the Canadian Cordillera and the extent of Precambrian rocks. *Cordilleran Sect. Geol. Assoc. Can., Programme and Abstracts, 1979 Meet., Vancouver, B. C.* p. 7
Armstrong, R. L., Hansen, E. C. 1966. Cordilleran infrastructure in the eastern Great Basin. *Am. J. Sci.* 264:112–27
Armstrong, R. L., Hills, F. A. 1967. Rubidium-strontium and potassium-argon geochronologic studies of mantled gneiss domes, Albion Range, southern Idaho, U.S. *Earth Planet. Sci. Lett.* 3:114–24
Armstrong, R. L., Smith, J. F. Jr., Covington, H. R., Williams, P. L. 1978. Preliminary geologic map of the west half of the Pocatello 1° by 2° quadrangle, Idaho. *US Geol. Surv. Open File Rep. 78–833*
Armstrong, R. L., Suppe, J. 1973. Potassium-argon geochronometry of Mesozoic igneous rocks in Nevada, Utah, and southern California. *Geol. Soc. Am. Bull.* 84:1375–92
Armstrong, R. L., Taubeneck, W. H., Hales, P. O. 1977. Rb-Sr and K-Ar geochronometry of Mesozoic granitic rocks and their Sr isotopic composition,, Oregon, Washington and Idaho. *Geol. Soc. Am. Bull.* 88:397–411
Atwater, T. 1970. Implications of plate tectonics for the Cenozoic tectonic evolution of Western North America. *Geol. Soc. Am. Bull.* 81:3513–36
Banks, N. G. 1980. Geology of a zone of metamorphic core complexes in southeastern Arizona. *Geol. Soc. Am. Mem.* 153:177–215
Berry, M. J., Jacoby, W. R., Niblett, E. R., Stacey, R. A. 1971. A review of geophysical studies in the Canadian Cordillera. *Can. J. Earth Sci.* 8:788–801
Berry, M. J., Mair, J. A. 1977. The nature of the earth's crust in Canada. *Am. Geophys. Union Geophys. Monograph* 20:319–48
Best, M. G., Armstrong, R. L., Graustein, W. C., Embree, G. F., Ahlborn, R. C. 1974. Mica granites of the Kern Mountains pluton, eastern White Pine Country, Nevada: remobilized basement of the Cordilleran miogeosyncline. *Geol. Soc. Am. Bull.* 85:1277–86
Brown, R. L. 1978. Structural evolution of the southeast Canadian Cordillera: A new hypothesis: *Tectonophysics* 48:133–51
Brown, R. L. 1980. Frenchman Cap Dome, Shuswap Complex, British Columbia: A progress report. *Geol. Surv. Can. Pap.* 80–1A, pp. 47–51
Brown, R. L., Fyles, J. T., Glover, J. K., Höy, T., Okulitch, A. V., Preto, V. A., Read, P. B. 1981. Southern Cordillera cross-section-Cranbrook to Kamloops. *Field guides to geology and mineral deposits, Calgary, 1981. Geol. Assoc. Can. Meet.*, pp. 335–72
Bruhn, R. L., Beck, S. L. 1981. Mechanics of thrust faulting in crystalline basement, Sevier orogenic belt, Utah. *Geology* 9:200–4
Burchfiel, B. C., Davis, G. A. 1975. Nature and controls of Cordilleran orogenesis, western United States; extensions of an earlier synthesis. *Am. J. Sci.* 275–A:363–96
Cady, J. W. 1980. Gravity highs and crustal structure, Omineca crystalline belt, northeastern Washington and southeastern British Columbia. *Geology* 8:328–32
Cameron, T. E., Frost, E. G., John, B. 1981. Development of regional arches and basins and their relationship to mid-Tertiary detachment faulting in the Chemehuevi Mountains, San Bernardino County, California, and Mojave County, Arizona. *Geol. Soc. Am. Abstr. with Programs* 13:48
Campbell, R. B. 1970. Structural and metamorphic transitions from infrastructure to suprastructure, Cariboo Mountains, British Columbia. *Geol. Assoc. Can. Spec. Pap.* 6:67–72
Campbell, R. B. 1973. Structural cross-section and tectonic model of the southeastern Canadian Cordillera *Can. J. Earth Sci.* 10:1607–20
Chamberlain, V. E., Lambert, R. St. J., Baadsgaard, H., Gale, N. H. 1979. Geochronology of the Malton Gneiss Complex of British Columbia. *Geol. Surv. Can. Pap. 79–1B*, pp. 45–50
Chapple, W. M. 1978. Mechanics of thin-skinned fold-and-thrust belts. *Geol. Soc. Am. Bull.* 89:1189–98
Chase, R. B., Bickford, M. E., Tripp, S. E.

1978. Rb-Sr and U-Pb isotopic studies of the northeastern Idaho batholith and border zone. *Geol. Soc. Am. Bull.* 89:1325–34
Cheney, E. S. 1980. Kettle dome and related structures of northeastern Washington. *Geol. Soc. Am. Mem.* 153:463–83
Christiansen, R. L., Lipman, P. W. 1972. Cenozoic volcanism and plate tectonic evolution of the Western United States II: Late Cenozoic. *Philos. Trans. R. Soc. London, Ser. A* 271:249–84
Compton, R. R. 1980. Fabrics and strains in quartzites of a metamorphic core complex, Raft River Mountains, Utah. *Geol. Soc. Am. Mem.* 153:385–98
Compton, R. R., Todd, V. R. 1979. Oligocene and Miocene metamorphism, folding, and low-angle faulting in northwestern Utah: Reply to discussion by M. D. Crittenden, Jr. *Geol. Soc. Am. Bull.* 90:307–9
Compton, R. R., Todd, V. R., Zartman, R. E., Naeser, C. W. 1977. Oligocene and Miocene metamorphism, folding, and low-angle faulting in northwestern Utah. *Geol. Soc. Am. Bull.* 88:1237–50
Coney, P. J. 1974. Structural analysis of the Snake Range 'decollement', east-central Nevada. *Geol. Soc. Am. Bull.* 85:973–78
Coney, P. J. 1979. Tertiary evolution of Cordilleran metamorphic core complexes. In *Cenozoic Paleogeography of the Western United States,* pp. 15-28. Los Angeles, Calif: Pac. Sect. Soc. Econ. Paleon. and Mineral.
Coney, P. J. 1980. Cordilleran metamorphic core complexes: An overview. *Geol. Soc. Am. Mem.* 153:7–31
Crittenden, M. D. Jr., Coney, P. J., Davis, G. H., eds. 1980. *Cordilleran metamorphic core complexes*. Geol. Soc. Am. Mem. 153. 490 pp.
Cumming, W. B., Clowes, R. M., Ellis, R. M. 1979. Crustal structure from a seismic refraction profile across southern British Columbia. *Can. J. Earth Sci.* 16:1024–40
Dahlstrom, C. D. A. 1970. Structural geology in the eastern margin of the Canadian Rocky Mountains. *Bull. Can. Petrol. Geol.* 18:322–406
Daly, R. A. 1912. Reconnaissance of the Shuswap Lakes and vicinity: south-central British Columbia. *Geol. Sur. Can. Ann. Rep. 1911*. 12 pp.
Davis, G. A. 1980. Problems of intraplate extensional tectonics, western United States. In *Continental Tectonics,* pp. 84-95. Washington D. C.: US Natl. Acad. Sci., Studies in Geophysics
Davis, G. A., Anderson, J. L., Frost, E. G., Shackelford, T. J. 1980. Mylonitization and detachment faulting in the Whipple-Buckskin-Rawhide Mountains terrane, southeastern California and western Arizona. *Geol. Soc. Am. Mem.* 153:79–129
Davis, G. H. 1975. Gravity-induced folding off a gneiss dome complex, Rincon Mountains Arizona. *Geol. Soc. Am. Bull.* 86:979–90
Davis, G. H. 1979. Laramide folding and faulting in southeastern Arizona. *Am. J. Sci.* 279:543–69
Davis, G. H. 1980. Structural characteristics of metamorphic core complexes, southern Arizona. *Geol. Soc. Am. Mem.* 153:35–77
Davis, G. H., Coney, P. J. 1979. Geologic development of the Cordilleran metamorphic core complexes. *Geology* 7:120–24
DeWitt, E. 1980. Comment on 'Geologic development of the Cordilleran metamorphic core complexes,' *Geology* 8:6–9
Dickey, D. D., Carr, W. J., Bull, W. B. 1980. Geologic map of Parker NW, Parker, and parts of the Whipple Mountains SW and Whipple Wash. quadrangles California and Arizona. *US Geol. Surv. Misc. Inv. Ser. I-1124*
Dickinson, W. R. 1976. Sedimentary basins developed during evolution of Mesozoic-Cenozoic arc-trench system in western North America. *Can. J. Earth Sci.* 13:1268–87
Dickinson, W. R., Snyder, W. S. 1979. Geometry of subducted slabs related to San Andreas transform. *J. Geol.* 87:609–27
Dokka, R. K., Lingrey, S. H. 1979. Fission track evidence for a Miocene cooling event, Whipple Mountains, southeastern California. See Coney 1979, pp. 141–45
Dover, J. H. 1969. Bedrock geology of the Pioneer Mountains, Blaine and Custer Counties, central Idaho. *Idaho Bur. Mines Geol. Pam. 142*. 61 pp.
Drewes, H. 1978. The Cordilleran orogenic belt between Nevada and Chihuahua. *Geol. Soc. Am. Bull.* 89:641–57
Eaton, G. P. 1980. Geophysical and geological characteristics of the crust of the Basin and Range province. See Davis, G. A. 1980, pp. 96-113
Eaton, G. P., Wahl, R. R., Prostka, H. J., Mabey, D. R., Kleinkopf, M. D. 1978. Regional gravity and tectonic patterns: Their relation to late Cenozoic epeirogeny and lateral spreading in the western Cordillera. *Geol. Soc. Am. Mem.* 152:51–91
Elliott, D. 1976. The motion of thrust sheets. *J. Geophys. Res.* 81:949–63
Ewing, T. E. 1981. Paleogene tectonic evolution of the Pacific Northwest. *J. Geol.* 88:619–38
Forsyth, D. A., Berry, M. J., Ellis, R. M. 1974. A refraction survey across the Canadian Cordillera at 54°N. *Can. J. Earth Sci.* 11:533–48
Fox, K. F. Jr., Rinehart, C. D., Engels, J. C. 1977. Plutonism and orogeny in north-

central Washington. *US Geol. Surv. Prof. Pap. 989*. 27 pp.

Fox, K. F. Jr., Rinehart, C. D., Engels, J. C., Stern, T. W. 1976. Age of emplacement of the Okanagan gneiss dome, north-central Washington. *Geol. Soc. Am. Bull.* 87:1217–24

Fyles, J. T. 1970. Structure of the Shuswap metamorphic complex in the Jordan River area, northwest of Revelstoke, British Columbia. *Geol. Assoc. Can. Spec. Pap.* 6:87–98

Fyson, W. K. 1970. Structural relations in metamorphic rocks, Shuswap Lake area, British Columbia. *Geol. Assoc. Can. Spec. Pap* 6:107–122

Gabrielse, H. 1972. Younger Precambrian of the Canadian Cordillera. *Am. J. Sci.* 272:521–36

Gabrielse, H., Reesor, J. E. 1964. Geochronology of plutonic rocks in two areas of the Canadian Cordillera. *R. Soc. Can. Spec. Publ.* 8:96–138

Gabrielse, H., Reesor, J. E. 1974. The nature and setting of granitic plutons in the central and eastern parts of the Canadian Cordillera. *Pac. Geol.* 8:109–38

Gilluly, J. 1934. Mineral orientation in some rocks of the Shuswap terrane as a clue to their metamorphism. *Am. J. Sci.* 28: 182–201

Griggs, D. T. 1972. The sinking lithosphere and the focal mechanism of deep earthquakes, In *The Nature of the Solid Earth,* ed. E. C. Robertson, pp. 361-84. New York: McGraw-Hill.

Hamilton, W. 1978. Mesozoic tectonics of the western United States. In *Mesozoic Paleogeography of the Western United States*. pp. 33-70. Los Angeles, Calif: Pac. Sect. Soc. Econ. Paleontol. Mineral.

Hamilton, W., Myers, W. B. 1966. Cenozoic tectonics of the western United States. *Rev. Geophys.* 4:509–49

Hose, R. K. 1977. Structural geology of the Confusion Range, west-central Utah. *US Geol. Surv. Prof. Pap. 971*. 9 pp.

Hose, R. K., Daneś, Z. F. 1973. Development of the late Mesozoic to early Cenozoic structures of the eastern Great Basin. In *Gravity and Tectonics,* ed. K. A. DeJong, R. Scholten, pp. 429-41. New York: Wiley.

Howard, K. A. 1968. Flow direction in triclinic folded rocks. *Am. J. Sci.* 266:758–65

Howard, K. A. 1980. Metamorphic infrastructure in the northern Ruby Mountains, Nevada. *Geol. Soc. Am. Mem.* 153:335–47

Howard, K. A., Carr, M. D., Miller, D. M., eds. 1981. Tectonic framework of the Mojave and Sonoran Deserts, California and Nevada. *US Geol. Surv. Open File Rep. 81-503*. 125 pp.

Hyndman, D. W. 1968. Mid Mesozoic multiphase folding along the border of the Shuswap metamorphic complex. *Geol. Soc. Am. Bull.* 79:575–88

Hyndman, D. W. 1980. Bitterroot dome-Sapphire tectonic block, an example of a plutonic-core gneiss-dome complex with its detached suprastructure. *Geol. Soc. Am. Mem.* 153:427–43

Jones, A. G. 1959. Vernon map-area British Columbia. *Geol. Surv. Can. Mem. 296*. 186 pp.

Jones, R. W. 1963. Structural evolution of part of southeast Arizona. *Am. Assoc. Petroleum Geol. Mem.* 2:140–51

Kehle, R. O. 1970. Analysis of gravity sliding and orogenic translation. *Geol. Soc. Am. Bull.* 81:1641–64

Keith, S. B., Reynolds, S. J., Damon, P. E., Shafiqullah, M., Livingston, D. E., Pushkar, P. D. 1980. Evidence for multiple intrusion and deformation within the Santa Catalina-Rincon-Tortolita crystalline complex, southeastern Arizona. *Geol. Soc. Am. Mem.* 153:217–67

Kistler, R. W., O'Neil, J. R. 1975. Fossil thermal gradients in crystalline rocks of the Ruby Mountains, Nevada as indicated by radiogenic and stable isotopes. *Geol. Soc. Am. Abst. with Programs* 7:334–35

Kistler, R. W., Peterman, Z. E. 1978. Reconstruction of crustal blocks of California on the basis of initial strontium isotopic compositions of Mesozoic granitic rocks. *US Geol. Surv. Prof. Pap. 1071*. 17 pp.

Kistler, R. W., Willden, R. 1969. Age of thrusting in the Ruby Mountains, Nevada. *Geol. Soc. Am. Abstr. with Programs* 1(5):40–41

Labhart, T. P. 1966. Mehrphasige alpine Tektonik am Nordrand des Aarmassivs. *Eclogae Geol. Helv.* 59:803–30

Labhart, T. P. 1968. Der Bau des nordichen Aarmassivs und seine Bedeutung fur die alpine Formungsgeschichte des Massivraumes. *Schweiz. Min. Pet. Mitt.* 48: 525–37

Lane, L. S. 1981. Brittle fractures of the Columbia River Fault in a damsite excavation near Revelstoke, British Columbia. *Geol. Assoc. Can. Abstr.* 6:A–33

Lee, D. E., Marvin, R. F., Stern, T. W., Peterman, Z. E. 1970. Modification of potassium-argon ages by Tertiary thrusting in the Snake Range, White Pine County, Nevada. *US Geol. Surv. Prof. Pap. 700D*, pp. 92–102

Lee, D. E., Marvin, R. F., Mehnhert, H. H. 1980. A radiometric age study of Mesozoic-Cenozoic metamorphism in eastern White Pine County, Nevada, and nearby Utah. *US Geol. Surv. Prof. Pap. 1158-C,* pp. 17–28

Lipman, P. W., Prostka, H. J., Christiansen, R. L. 1972. Cenozoic volcanism and plate tectonic evolution of the Western United States. I: Early and Middle Cenozoic. *Phil. Trans. R. Soc. London Ser. A.* 271:217–48

Lucchitta, I., Suneson, N., Shackelford, T. J. 1981. Comment and reply on Tertiary tectonic denudation of a Mesozoic-early Tertiary(?) gneiss complex, Rawhide Mountains, western Arizona. *Geology* 9:50–52

Mabey, D. R., Zietz, I., Eaton, G. P., Kleinkopf, M. D. 1978. Regional magnetic patterns in part of the Cordillera in the western United States. *Geol. Soc. Am. Mem.* 152:93–106

Martin, D. L., Barry, W. L., Krummenacher, D. 1980. K-Ar dating of mylonitization and detachment faulting in the Whipple Mountains, San Bernardino County, California and the Buckskin Mountains, Yuma County, Arizona. *Geol. Soc. Am. Abstr. with Programs* 12:118

Mathews, W. H. 1981. Early Cenozoic resetting of potassium-argon dates and geothermal history of North Okanagan area, British Columbia. *Can. J. Earth Sci.* 18:1310–19

Mauger, R. L., Damon, P. E., Livingston, D. E. 1968. Cenozoic argon ages on metamorphic rocks from the Basin and Range Province. *Am. J. Sci.* 266:579–89

McKenzie, D. P. 1969. Speculations on the consequences and causes of plate motions. *R. Astron. Soc. Geophys. J.* 18:1–32

McMillan, W. J. 1973. Petrology and structure of the west flank, Frenchman's Cap Dome, near Revelstoke, British Columbia, *Geol. Surv. Can. Pap. 71-29.* 88 pp.

Medford, G. A. 1975. K-Ar and fission track geochronometry of an Eocene thermal event in the Kettle River (west half) map area, southern British Columbia. *Can. J. Earth Sci.* 12:836–43

Miller, C. F. 1978. An early Mesozoic alkalic magmatic belt in western North America. See Hamilton 1978, pp. 163-73

Miller, C. F., Bradfish, L. J. 1980. An inner Cordilleran belt of muscovite-bearing plutons. *Geology* 8:412–16

Miller, D. M. 1980. Structural geology of the northern Albion Mountains, south-central Idaho. *Geol. Soc. Am. Mem.* 153:399–423

Miller, D. M., 1982. Interpretation of a strain field measured on a gneiss dome, Albion Mountains, Idaho, *Am. J. Sci.* In press

Miller, F. K. 1971. The Newport fault and associated mylonites, northeastern Washington. *US Geol. Surv. Prof. Pap. 750 D,* pp. 77–79

Miller, F. K., Engels, J. C. 1975. Distribution and trends of discordant ages of the plutonic rocks of northeastern Washington and northern Idaho, *Geol. Soc. Am. Bull.* 86:517–28

Misch, P. 1960. Regional structural reconnaissance in central-northeast Nevada and some adjacent areas: observations and interpretations. *Intermountain Assoc. Pet. Geol. 11th Ann. Field Conf., Guidebook* pp. 17–42

Misch, P., Hazzard, J. C. 1962. Stratigraphy and metamorphism of late Precambrian rocks in central northeastern Nevada and adjacent Utah. *Am. Assoc. Pet. Geol. Bull.* 46:289–343

Milnes, A. G. 1974. Post-nappe folding in the western Lepontine Alps. *Eclogae Geol. Helv.* 67:333–48

Monger, J. W. H., Hutchison, W. W. 1971. Metamorphic map of the Canadian Cordillera. *Geol. Surv. Can. Pap 70-33.* 61 pp., Suppl. 19 pp.

Morrison, M. L. 1980. Basement involvement on the southwest flank of the southern Canadian Rockies. *26th Congr. Geol. Int., Paris, 1980, Résumés* 1:366

Morrison, M. L. 1981. Basement involvement as thrust and fold nappes in the Columbian Orogen, the Malton Gneiss, southeast British Columbia. *Geol. Assoc. Can. Abstr.* 6:A–41

Mudge, M. R. 1970. Origin of the disturbed belt in northwestern Montana. *Geol. Soc. Am. Bull.* 81:377–92

Murphy, D. C. 1981. Structural analysis of mylonitic rocks, Columbia River Fault Zones, British Columbia. *Geol. Asso. Can. Abstr.* 6:A–42

Mursky, G. 1972. Origin and significance of zonation in a granitic intrusion. *24th Int. Geol. Congr., Montreal, 1972, Sect. 2,* pp. 181–90

Nelson, R. B. 1969. Relation and history of structures in a sedimentary succession with deeper metamorphic structures, eastern Great Basin. *Am. Assoc. Pet. Geol. Bull.* 53:307–39

Okulitch, A. V. 1979. Thompson-Shuswap-Okanagan. *Geol. Surv. Can. Open File 637*

Parrish, R. 1981. Geology and regional tectonics of the Nemo Lakes Belt, northern Valhalla Range, British Columbia. *Can. J. Earth Sci.* 18:944–58

Pigage, L. C. 1977. Rb-Sr dates for granodiorite intrusions on the northeast margin of the Shuswap Metamorphic Complex, Cariboo Mountains, British Columbia. *Can. J. Earth Sci.* 14:1690–95

Preto, V. A. 1970. Structure and petrology of the Grand Forks Group, British Columbia. *Geol. Surv. Can. Pap. 69-22.* 80 pp.

Price, R. A. 1972. The distinction between displacement and distortion in flow, and the origin of diachronism in tectonic overprinting in orogenic belts. See Mursky. 1972, Sect. 3, pp. 545–51

Price, R. A. 1973. Large-scale gravitational

flow of supracrustal rocks, southern Canadian Rockies. See Hose & Daneš 1973, pp. 491–502

Price, R. A. 1979. Intracontinental ductile crustal spreading linking the Fraser River and northern Rocky Mountain Trench transform fault zones, south-central British Columbia and northeast Washington. *Geol. Soc. Am. Abstr. with Programs* 11:499

Price, R. A., Fermor, P. R. 1981. Three sections through the southern part of the Rocky Mountain Thrust and Fold Belt in southern Canada. *Geol. Assoc. Can. Abstr.* 6:A–47

Price, R. A., Mountjoy, E. W. 1970. Geologic structure of the Canadian Rocky Mountains between Bow and Athabasca rivers—a progress report. *Geol. Assoc. Can. Spec. Pap.* 6:7–25

Price, R. A., Archibald, D., Farrar, E. 1981a. Eocene stretching and necking of the crust and tectonic unroofing of the Cordilleran metamorphic infrastructure, southeastern British Columbia and adjacent Washington and Idaho. *Geol. Assoc. Can. Abstr.* 6:A–47

Price, R. A., Monger, J. W. H., Muller, J. E. 1981b. Cordilleran cross-section—Calgary to Victoria. See Brown et al 1981, pp. 261–334

Read, P. B. 1973. Petrology and structure of Poplar Creek map-area, British Columbia. *Geol. Surv. Can. Bull. 193*. 144 pp.

Read, P. B., Wheeler, J. O. 1976. Lardeau W$\frac{1}{2}$ Map and marginal notes. *Geol. Surv. Can. Open File 432*

Read, P. B., Klepacki, D. W. 1981. Stratigraphy and structure: northern half of Thor-Odin nappe, Vernon east-half map area, southern British Columbia. *Geol. Surv. Can. Pap. 81–1A,* pp. 169–73

Rees, C. J. 1981. Western margin of the Omineca Belt at Quesnel Lake, British Columbia. *Geol. Surv. Can. Pap. 81-1A,* pp. 223–26

Reesor, J. E. 1965. Structural evolution and plutonism in Valhalla gneiss complex, British Columbia. *Geol. Surv. Can. Bull 29*. 128 pp.

Reesor, J. E. 1970. Some aspects of structural evolution and regional setting in part of the Shuswap metamorphic complex. *Geol. Assoc. Can. Spec. Pap.* 6:73–86

Reesor, J. E., Moore, J. M. Jr. 1971. Petrology and structure of Thor-Odin gneiss dome, Shuswap metamorphic complex. *Geol. Surv. Can. Bull. 195*. 147 pp.

Rehrig, W. A., Reynolds, S. J. 1980. Geologic and geochronologic reconnaissance of a northwest-trending zone of metamorphic core complexes in southern and western Arizona. *Geol. Soc. Am. Mem.* 153:131–57

Reynolds, S. J., Rehrig, W. A. 1980. Mid-Tertiary plutonism and mylonitization, South Mountains, central Arizona. *Geol. Soc. Am. Mem.* 153:159–75

Reynolds, S. J., Rehrig, W. A., Armstrong, R. L. 1981. Reconnaissance Rb-Sr geochronology and tectonic evolution of the Priest River crystalline complex of northern Idaho and northeastern Washington. *Geol. Soc. Am. Abstr. with Programs* 13:103

Rhodes, B. P., Cheney, E. S. 1981. The low-angle Kettle River fault: The eastern contact of Kettle Dome, northeast Washington. *Geology* 9:366–69

Roberts, R. J., Crittenden, M. D. Jr. 1973. Orogenic mechanisms, Sevier orogenic belt, Nevada and Utah. See Hose & Daneš 1973, pp. 409–28

Ross, J. V. 1968. Structural relations at the eastern margin of the Shuswap Complex, near Revelstoke, southeastern British Columbia. *Can. J. Earth Sci.* 5:831–49

Ross, J. V. 1973. Mylonitic rocks and flattened garnets in the southern Okanagan of British Columbia. *Can. J. Earth Sci.* 10:1–17

Ross, J. V. 1974. A Tertiary thermal event in south-central British Columbia. *Can. J. Earth Sci.* 11:1116–22

Ross, J. V., Christie, J. S. 1979. Early recumbent folding in some westernmost exposures of the Shuswap Complex, southern Okanagan, British Columbia. *Can. J. Earth Sci.* 16:877–94

Royse, F. Jr., Warner, M. A., Reese, D. L. 1975. Thrust belt structural geometry and related stratigraphic problems. In *Deep Drilling Frontiers of the Central Rocky Mountains,* pp. 41–54. Denver, Colo: Rocky Mountains Assoc. Geol.

Scholten, R. 1973. Gravitational mechanisms in the northern Rocky Mountains of the United States. See Hose & Daneš 1973, pp. 473–84

Scholz, C. H., Barazangi, M., Sbar, M. L. 1971. Late Cenozoic evolution of the Great Basin, western United States, as an ensialic interarc basin. *Geol. Soc. Am. Bull* 82:2979–90

Schuepbach, M. A., Vail, P. R. 1980. Evolution of outer highs on divergent continental margins. See Davis, G. A. 1980, pp. 50–61

Shackelford, T. J. 1980. Tertiary tectonic denudation of a Mesozoic-early Tertiary(?) gneiss complex, Rawhide Mountains, western Arizona. *Geology* 8:190–94

Simony, P. S., Ghent, E. D., Craw, D., Mitchell, W., Robbins, D. B. 1980. Structural and metamorphic evolution of northeast flank of Shuswap complex, southern Canoe River area, British Columbia. *Geol. Soc. Am. Mem.* 153:445–61

Simony, P. S., Oke, C., Morrison, M. L. 1981. Cover-basement relationships on the west flank of the southern Canadian Rocky Mountains. *Geol. Assoc. Can. Abstr.* 6:A–52

Smith, R. B. 1978. Seismicity, crustal structure, and intraplate tectonics of the interior of the western Cordillera. *Geol. Soc. Am. Mem.* 152:111–44

Smithson, S. B., Brewer, J., Kaufman, S., Oliver, J., Hurich, C. 1978. Nature of the Wind River thrust, Wyoming, from COCORP deep-reflection data and from gravity data. *Geology* 6:648–52

Snoke, A. W. 1980. Transition from infrastructure to suprastructure in the northern Ruby Mountains, Nevada. *Geol. Soc. Am. Mem.* 153:287–333

Snyder, W. S., Dickinson, W. R., Silberman, M. L. 1976. Tectonic implications of space-time patterns of Cenozoic magmatism in the western United States. *Earth Planet. Sci. Lett.* 32:91–106

Solberg, P. H. 1976. *Structural relations between the Shuswap and "Cache Creek" complexes near Kalamalka Lake, southern British Columbia*. MSc thesis. Univ. B.C. 90 pp.

Steck, A. 1968. Die alpidischen Strukturen in den Zentralen Aarengraniten des westlichen Aarmassivs. *Eclogae geol. Helv.* 61:19–48

Stewart, J. H. 1978. Basin-range structure in western North America: A review. *Geol. Soc. Am. Mem.* 152:1–31

Sugimura, A., Uyeda, S. 1973. *Island arcs: Japan and its environs*. Amsterdam: Elsevier. 247 pp.

Swanberg, C. A., Blackwell, D. D. 1973. Areal distribution and geophysical significance of heat generation in the Idaho Batholith and adjacent intrusions in eastern Oregon and western Montana. *Geol. Soc. Am. Bull.* 84:1261–82

Thorman, C. H. 1970. Metamorphosed and nonmetamorphosed Paleozoic rocks in the Wood Hills and Pequop Mountains, northeast Nevada. *Geol. Soc. Am. Bull.* 81:2417–48

Todd, V. R. 1980. Structure and petrology of a Tertiary gneiss complex in northwestern Utah. *Geol. Soc. Am. Mem.* 153:349–83

Toksöz, M. N., Bird, P. 1977a. Formation and evolution of marginal basins and continental plateaus. *Am. Geophys. Union, Maurice Ewing Ser.* 1:379–93

Toksöz, M. N., Bird, P. 1977b. Modelling of temperatures in continental convergence zones. *Tectonophysics* 41:181–93

Uyeda, S. 1977. Some basic problems in the trench-arc-back arc system. *Am. Geophys. Union, Maurice Ewing Ser.* 1:1–14

Wanless, R. K., Loveridge, W. D., Mursky, G. 1968. A geochronological study of the White Creek batholith, southeastern British Columbia. *Can. J. Earth Sci.* 5:375–86

Wernicke, B. 1981a. Geometric similarity between thin-skin compression and extension. *EOS* 62:398–99

Wernicke, B. 1981b. Low-angle normal faults in the Basin and Range Province: Nappe tectonics in an extending orogen. *Nature* 291:645–48

Wheeler, J. O. 1963. Rogers Pass map-area, British Columbia and Alberta. *Geol. Surv. Can. Pap. 62-32.* 32 pp.

Wheeler, J. O. 1965. Big Bend map-area, British Columbia. *Geol. Surv. Can. Pap. 64-32.* 37 pp.

Wheeler, J. O. 1966. Eastern tectonic belts of Western Cordillera in British Columbia. *Can. Inst. Min. Metall. Spec. Vol.* 8:27–45

Wright, J. E., Haxel, G. 1980. Uranium-lead isotopic systematics of zircons from a garnet- and white-mica-bearing granite, Coyote Mountains, southern Arizona. *Geol. Soc. Am. Abstr. with Programs* 12:160

Ann. Rev. Earth Planet. Sci. 1982. 10:155-90

MID-OCEAN RIDGES: Fine Scale Tectonic, Volcanic and Hydrothermal Processes Within the Plate Boundary Zone

Ken C. Macdonald

Department of Geological Sciences and Marine Science Institute, University of California, Santa Barbara, California 93106

INTRODUCTION

A first order model of spreading centers as idealized linear boundaries of crustal and lithospheric generation provides only a gross understanding of global scale plate kinematics. As we attempt to understand the complexity of crustal and lithospheric structure of two thirds of the earth's surface, it is becoming increasingly necessary to study the tectonic, volcanic, and hydrothermal processes within the spreading center plate boundary zone. All oceanic crust bears the imprint of these processes. This review focuses on a few selected topics concernining the fine scale tectonics and geophysics of the active axial zone of mid-ocean ridges with reference to associated volcanic and hydrothermal processes. It draws heavily on recent studies that use deeply towed instrument packages, multi-beam bathymetric mapping, ocean bottom instruments, and ALVIN (e.g. the Famous, AMAR, RISE, and Galapagos expeditions).

We begin with a review of the large-scale structure of spreading centers. We then take a close look at the axial neovolcanic zone and progress away from the axis through the active tectonic zones. Next we consider the characteristics of the axial magma chamber and associated hydrothermal actvity, as well as the generation of magnetic anomaly "stripes" and their implications for crustal generation. One of our findings is that the initial two-dimensional model of volcanic and tectonic zones must be expanded upon to allow for variations

0084-6597/82/0515-0155$02.00

along strike and for episodicity. While this is primarily a review paper, in the process of synthesis I hazard a number of suggestions and speculations, some of which are new, and most of which require further work for verification or disposal.

STRUCTURE AND TECTONICS OF THE AXIAL ZONE

Spreading rates, which vary from 1–18 cm/yr, seem to control the gross morphology of spreading centers (Figure 1; Menard 1967). At slow total opening rates of 1–5 cm/yr, a 1.5–3.0 km deep rift valley marks the axis. Rough and faulted topography created in the rift valley is largely preserved in the older ocean basin. The Mid-Atlantic Ridge (MAR) is a classic example (Figure 2; Van Andel & Bowin 1968, Loncarevic et al 1966).

At intermediate rates of 5–9 cm/yr, the rift valley is only 50–200 m deep. This shallow rift is superposed on a broad axial high, and the flanking topography is relatively smooth. The East Pacific Rise (EPR) at 21°N (RISE study area) and the Galapagos spreading center are examples (Larson 1971, Klitgord & Mudie 1974). At fast spreading rates (greater than 9 cm/yr) there is no rift valley, but a triangular-shaped axial high is observed (e.g. EPR south of 15°N, Rea 1978). The topography is relatively smooth with a fine scale horst and graben structure. A category of "ultra-fast" spreading centers has been pro-

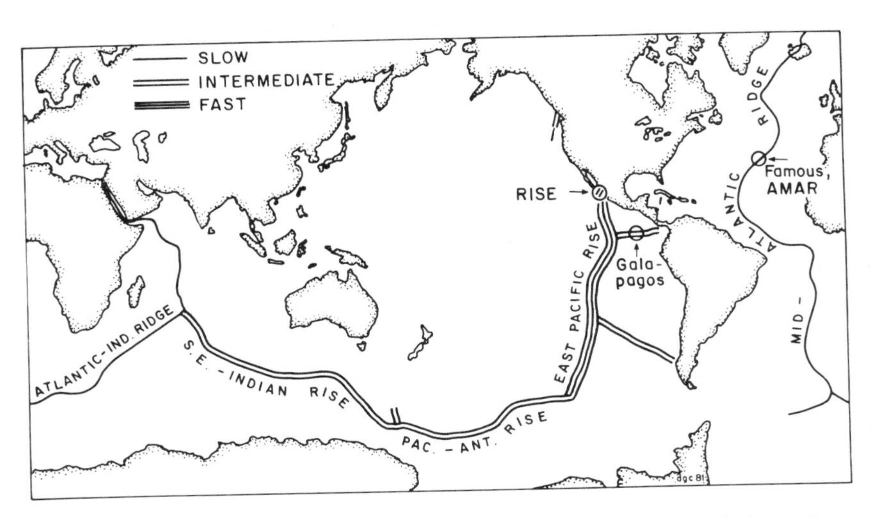

Figure 1 Major seafloor spreading centers shown schematically; transform faults, back-arc spreading centers, and subduction zones omitted. Slow spreading rates, 1.0–5.0 cm/yr; intermediate rates, 5.0–9.0 cm/yr; fast rates, 9.0–18.0 cm/yr. Mid-ocean ridge diving-expeditions indicated.

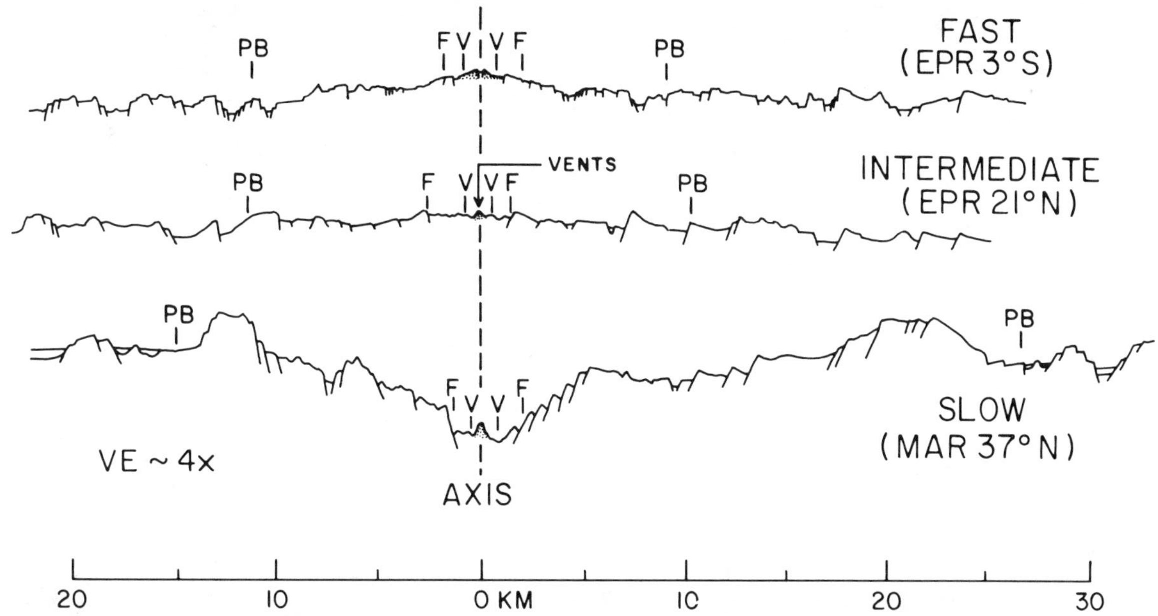

Figure 2 High resolution deep-tow profiles of mid-ocean ridges at fast, intermediate, and slow rates. Neovolcanic zone bracketed by Vs, zone of fissuring by Fs, plate boundary zone (width of active faulting) by PBs. The neovolcanic zone is generally very narrow (~1 km). Active faulting occurs up to 10–30 km off axis. Data from Lonsdale (1977), Normark (1976), Shih (1980), Macdonald et al (1975), and Macdonald & Luyendyk (1977).

posed (Lonsdale 1977) but is omitted here as there is insufficient evidence for any significant morphologic or structural distinction between the fast and "ultra-fast" ridges.

Several hypotheses have been proposed to explain why a deep rift valley occurs at slow spreading rates but not at fast rates (an exception being the hot spot–dominated Reykjanes Ridge). One is the "hydraulic head loss" model proposed by Sleep (1969) with subsequent elaborations (Lachenbruch 1973, 1976, Sleep & Rosendahl 1979). Along the sides of an idealized conduit tapping deep magma sources, viscous forces are sufficient to cause a significant loss of hydraulic head, resulting in a topographic depression over the spreading center. To conserve energy, this head loss is regained by uplift of the rift valley walls relative to the valley floor. The head loss is directly proportional to the upwelling velocity and inversely proportional to the cube of the conduit width. A deep rift valley is present at slow spreading rates because material upwells through a narrow conduit formed by cool, old lithosphere. At faster spreading rates there is much less head loss because a wider conduit overwhelms the dependence on flow rate. The rift valley is replaced by flat topography or a crestal peak, which may be caused by the presence of a low density crustal magma chamber. Thus the cross section of fast spreading ridges closely approaches that expected from buoyancy in a relaxed state, while slow spreading ridges exhibit significant dynamic effects.

A relatively new hypothesis invokes "steady-state necking" of the lithosphere as the cause of the median valley (Tapponnier & Francheteau 1978). In this model, the rift valley is caused by necking or thinning in a ductile layer beneath the rift valley. The analogy is that of a beam plastically necking out under tensional stress. The layer does not actually break like a necking beam, because new material is added constantly from below (maintaining steady state), while the entire region is continually uplifted by buoyancy forces. At slow spreading rates, the strength of the crust in the axial zone is presumed great enough for necking to be significant, creating a rift valley. At faster rates, the young crust is too hot and weak at shallow levels for this process to be significant. Other models explain rift valleys and central peaks as caused by imbalances in the supply of new material versus crustal acceleration within the axial zone (Deffeyes 1970, Anderson & Noltimier 1973, Reid & Jackson 1981, Nelson 1981). These models are not mutually exclusive and some combination of them may apply.

Beyond these first order differences, high resolution instruments reveal that fine scale crustal structure and tectonics evolve in a pattern that is largely independent of spreading rate. This is surprising considering the magnitude of the first-order differences discussed above. On this scale, spreading rate seems to influence primarily the continuity in time and in space of volcanic, magmatic, and tectonic processes, and the amplitude of faulting, but the fundamental processes and structural evolution change little.

The axis of spreading is characterized by a narrow zone of recent volcanism, which is flanked by zones of crustal fissuring (Figure 2). Away from the axis, a zone of active normal faulting is characterized by significant vertical disruption of the crust (Needham & Francheteau 1974, Macdonald et al 1975, CYAMEX 1981). At some distance off-axis the crust becomes essentially stable and rigid, as assumed by plate tectonics. The zone in which 95% of crust created by volcanic and plutonic activity is of Holocene age is termed the "crustal accretion zone" (Luyendyk & Macdonald 1976), and the surface volcanic component of this zone is called here the "neovolcanic zone." The region in which active faulting and deformation occurs is the "plate boundary zone," and is subdivided into zones of fissuring and faulting. Let us consider each of these volcano-tectonic zones in greater deail.

The Neovolcanic Zone

The zone of recent and ongoing volcanism at the spreading center is usually remarkably narrow, on the order of 1–2 km wide (Figure 2). The narrowness of the central zone of volcanism has been verified by submersible observations in regions where total opening rates are 2–7 cm/yr (Ballard & van Andel 1977, Bryan & Moore 1977, Corliss et al 1979, Spiess et al 1980, CYAMEX 1981) and by deeply towed camera vehicles at rates up to 18 cm/yr (Lonsdale 1977, Ballard & Francheteau personal communication). The neovolcanic zone is characterized by fresh, glassy lava flows and an almost complete lack of sediment cover. Volcanic processes account for essentially all of the topography in this zone.

At slow spreading-rates the axial zone is marked by a highly discontinuous chain of central volcanoes (Figure 3; Needham & Francheteau 1974, Macdonald et al 1975). Central volcanoes are elongate parallel to the spreading axis and appear to be accumulations of fresh, sediment-free pillow basalts (Ballard & van Andel 1977, Luyendyk & Macdonald 1977). Mt Venus in the Famous area is a typical example with dimensions of 1 by 4 km and a height of 250 m (ARCYANA 1975). At intermediate spreading-rates, the volcanoes are more continuous along strike, except where interrupted by small (< 1 km) *en echelon* offsets. Sheet flow basalts, similar in morphology to pahoehoe, are more frequently observed (Ballard et al 1979, Normark 1976). The central volcanoes seem to reach a maximum height of only 50 m on axis (Klitgord & Mudie 1974, Crane 1979). At fast spreading rates the nature of the central volcano changes considerably. It resembles a very elongate Hawaiian-type shield volcano with gently sloping sides and a summit rift zone caused by keystone collapse (Lonsdale 1977). The central volcano is 1–2 km wide, as at slower spreading rates, but is remarkably continuous (up to 100 km along strike) and is interrupted only by transform faults (Searle et al 1981). Both pillow lavas and sheet flows are observed.

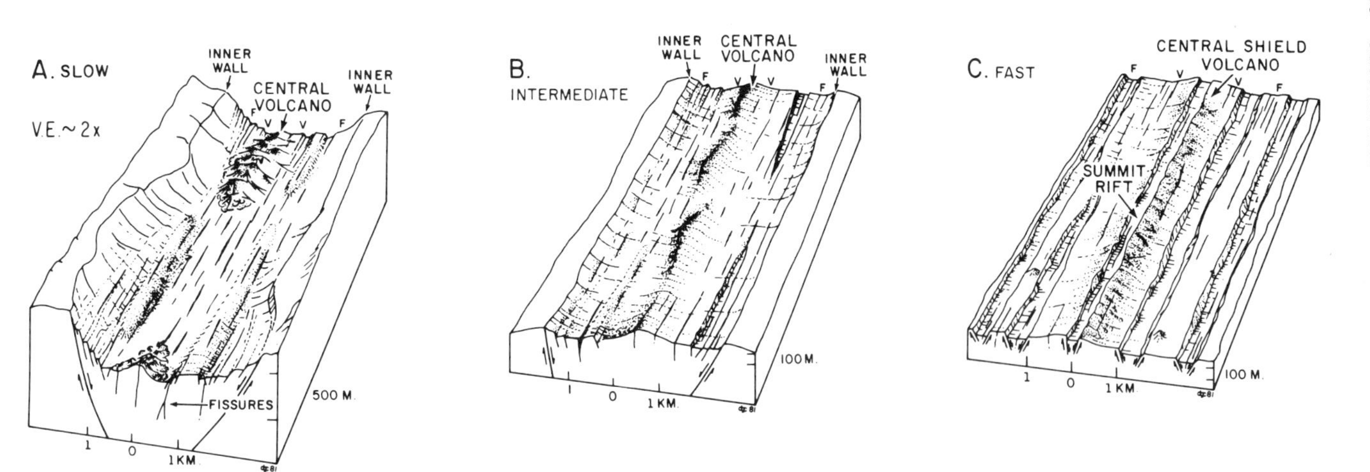

Figure 3 Schematic illustrations of the neovolcanic zone at different spreading rates. The central volcano is highly discontinuous at slow rates (*A*), moderately continuous with *en echelon* offsets at intermediate rates (*B*), and often almost perfectly continuous at fast rates (*C*). At fast rates the volcano resembles a Hawaiian shield volcano with a summit rift. At slow to intermediate rates it is a volcanic construction of pillow lavas. Fissuring of the crust appears to be greatest adjacent to the neovolcanic zone but may occur within it as well. Labels V and F as in Figure 2. (Sketch *A* modified after Moore et al 1974.)

PILLOWS VS. SHEET FLOWS: VOLCANIC CYCLES Careful analysis of the occurrence of sheet flows and pillow lavas provides important information about possible volcanic cycles along the spreading axis. It has been suggested that pillow lavas and sheet flows are the submarine equivalents of tube-fed and surface-fed pahoehoe, respectively (Ballard et al 1979). If so, then sheet flows erupt from a new volcanic vent at very high effusion rates during the initial stage of the volcanic cycle. As the volcanic edifice builds, the lava starts to flow through a volcanic catacomb of tunnels and tubes rather than erupting directly from fissures. Channeling of lava through the volcanic plumbing system and diminishing effusion rates produce pillow lavas rather than sheet flows (Figure 4). Pillow lavas and sheet flows should occur on ridge crests regardless of the spreading rate. However, at a slow spreading rate it is more likely that the late-stage pillow lavas will mask the sheet flows, while at fast spreading rates, there is a greater chance that sheet flows will remain exposed

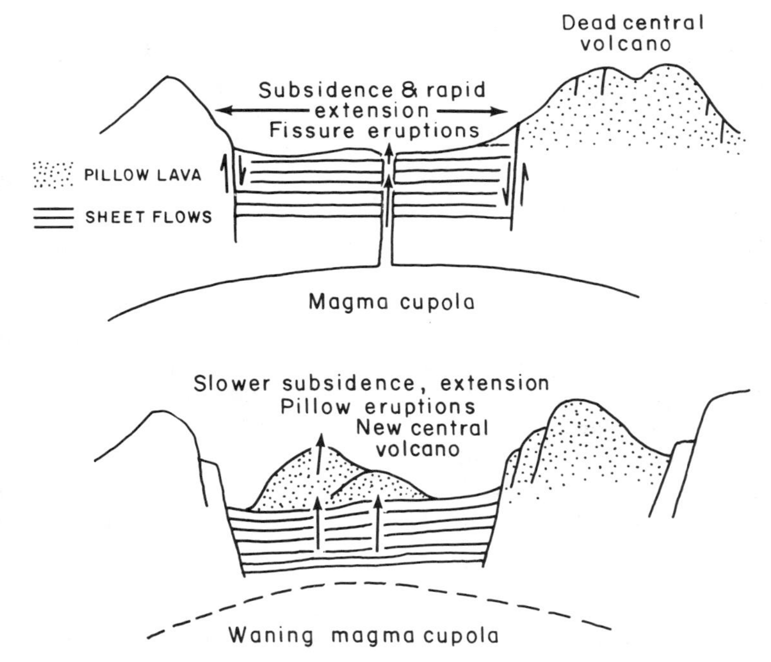

Figure 4 A hypothetical cross section of the neovolcanic zone based on the assumption that sheet flows erupt first during early stage fissure eruptions, followed by pillow lavas, which form steep volcanic constructions (modified from van Andel & Ballard 1979). Several eruptive cycles will create an approximately 1 km thick lava section that is a complex melange of pillow lavas and sheet flows (not shown). Here (*top*) the new eruptive phase is shown occurring in crust adjacent to the most recent central volcano. It is also possible for the new eruption to occur along the axis as the previous central volcano is split in two.

in many places. So far, field observations from ALVIN of pillow/sheet flow spatial relationships support this concept of volcanism (Atwater 1979, van Andel & Ballard 1979, Ballard et al 1981). It should be noted that field mapping in ophiolites indicates episodes of volcanism, but not necessarily the orderly sequence of sheet flows to pillow lavas summarized here (Hopson personal communication). A chaotic mix of sheet flows and pillow lavas is observed instead. Episodes of tectonism and hydrothermal activity may be linked to these volcanic episodes. This is discussed in later sections.

FREQUENCY OF VOLCANIC ERUPTIONS If volcanic cycles occur at spreading centers, what is their periodicity? Consider first the slowly spreading MAR. Since the approximate thickness of the volcanic section (1.0 km) and the dimensions and spacing of volcanoes are known, the spatial density of volcanoes in the crustal section can be estimated. When combined with the spreading rate, the frequency of major eruptive cycles can be estimated to be once every 5,000–10,000 years (Bryan & Moore 1977, Atwater 1979). This result is supported by deep-sea drilling results from the Atlantic (Hall 1976). In a similar exercise I arrive at an eruption frequency of once every 300–600 years for the intermediate spreading rate RISE area. For the fast spreading EPR, a slightly different analysis yields an eruption interval of approximately 50 years (Lonsdale 1977). While these calculations are all quite crude, it appears that the frequency of major volcanic eruptions increases as approximately the square of the spreading rate. We see later that fine scale studies of magnetic anomalies support this relationship.

Do axial eruptions occur rapidly with long periods of intervening quiescence, or is activity fairly continuous at a slow rate? Analogy with terrestrial eruptions suggests the former. Perhaps the best evidence is from Deep-Sea Drilling Project (DSDP) holes. For deep holes (> 500 m), thick crustal units occur in which magnetic, petrologic, and geochemical properties are nearly uniform and are significantly different from crustal sections above or below. In the presence of secular variation of the magnetic field, this suggests eruption episodes of short (1–100 yr) duration (Hall 1976) separated by long periods of quiescence.

STABILITY OF THE NEOVOLCANIC ZONE The neovolcanic zone is usually restricted to a zone only 1–2 km wide and appears to remain so for long periods. Submersible and photographic studies have delineated the narrowness of this zone in the Famous, AMAR, RISE and Galapagos study areas (Bryan & Moore 1977, Luyendyk & Macdonald 1977, Normark 1976, Spiess et al 1980, van Andel & Ballard 1979). Observations of fresh lavas and sparse sediment cover, however, give only an instantaneous view of the volcanic zone.

One way to observe the width and stability in time of the neovolcanic zone is through high resolution deep-tow studies of magnetic anomaly transitions.

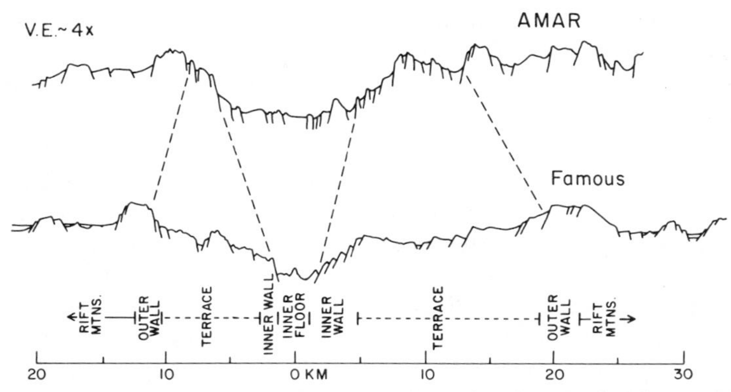

Figure 5 Deep-tow profiles of the Famous and AMAR rift valleys. Dashed lines connect the corresponding inner and outer walls (terminology at bottom after Macdonald et al 1975). These are typical end-members in the evolution of a rift valley which may have a narrow inner floor and wide terraces (Famous) or vice versa (AMAR). Magnetic anomalies may be clearly recorded when the inner floor is narrow, and "smeared out" with wide transitions when the inner floor is wide.

The magnetic anomaly polarity transition width is a measure of the total width of the crustal accretion zone, including the neovolcanic zone and magnetized plutonics (discussed in detail later) (Harrison 1968, Macdonald 1977). Transition widths at intermediate to fast spreading rates suggest that the crustal accretion zone has remained narrow (1–3 km) and localized for millions of years (Klitgord et al 1975, Macdonald et al 1980a). At slow spreading rates, the zone appears to vary between 1 and at least 8 km in width (Macdonald 1977). Thus for all spreading rates the crustal accretion zone is remarkably narrow compared to the lateral dimensions of the plates, but at slow spreading rates there may be a greater tendency for the crustal accretion zone to wander laterally, or to periodically widen to 5–10 km within the rift valley.[1]

The variation in transition width for slow spreading ridges, and thus the width of the zone of crustal accretion, may reflect a time-varying median valley structure (Macdonald 1977). The valley has either a wide inner floor and narrow terraces, in which case the neovolcanic zone is wide and magnetic anomalies are poorly recorded (wide transition zones), or it has a narrow inner floor and well-developed terraces (Figure 5). The neovolcanic zone is then narrow and anomalies are clearly recorded (narrow transition widths). The median valley of any slow spreading ridge may vary between these two extreme structures with time as well as along strike. On the MAR, the Famous (at 36°45′N) and AMAR (36°25′N) rifts are two end-member examples (Macdonald & Luyendyk 1977).

[1]There is some controversy here in that surface tow magnetic studies show a different variation in transition widths than the deep-tow results reviewed here (Blakely & Lynn 1977). The discrepancy may be due to resolution limits of surface tow magnetic studies (Miller 1977).

Another approach to the stability of the neovolcanic zone is to consider the mechanism by which volcanoes are transported out of the neovolcanic zone; do they move away as intact units or are they split along the axis? A model has been proposed for the Famous area in which volcanoes are transported out of the rift valley as whole units. The plate boundary shifts laterally up to 1 km, or 1 volcano width, and a new central volcano is born along the shifted axis (Ballard & van Andel 1977). However, at intermediate to fast spreading rates, there is growing evidence that central volcanoes may occasionally split along the axis. A portion of the volcano moves to each side and is rafted away on the diverging plates. In the RISE area approximately one seventh of the volcanoes appear to be split and in each case the rifted face is toward the spreading axis (Macdonald et al 1980a). A statistical model suggests that the zone of splitting must be less than 1.6 km wide on the average for this to occur (Macdonald 1982). This model agrees well with the narrowness and stability of the intrusion zone implied by the single-sided chilling of feeder dikes in ophiolites (Kidd 1977) and with the magnetic and observational data for the width of the neovolcanic zone.

Sparse observations suggest that the tendency for axial volcanoes to split is greater at intermediate to fast spreading rates than at slow. If so, this agrees well with the magnetic anomaly transition studies that suggest a wider or less stable neovolcanic zone at slow spreading rates. Consider the following model. At slow spreading centers, major volcanic eruptions occur only every 5,000–10,000 years. The crust cools during intervening quiescent periods, thickening and gaining brittle strength along the axial zone. This is enhanced by rapid deep cooling due to hydrothermal circulation. With the preexisting zone of weakness largely erased, the next episode of rifting and volcanism 10^4 years later may occur anywhere within the inner floor of the rift valley. (There may be a preference for rifting along the edge of the last volcano, where the crust may be thinnest.) Thermal models also suggest a thicker and stronger lid over the magma chamber at slow spreading rates (Sleep 1975). At fast spreading rates, the periods of quiescence between eruptions are shorter, only 50–600 years. Even in the presence of hydrothermal cooling, the system is likely to have a thermal memory locating the preexisting zone of weakness along the axial feeding system of the last volcano erupted (Macdonald 1982). As a result, the tendency for splitting of the central volcano will be greater and the neovolcanic zone will be narrower and more stable.

Needless to say, off-axis volcanism occurs, especially at slow spreading rates (Heirtzler & Ballard 1977, Luyendyk & Macdonald 1977). In the Famous area, deep-tow magnetic data indicate that up to 10% of the volcanism occurs outside the main neovolcanic zone in crust 0.5–2.0 m.y. old, i.e. 5–20 km off-axis (Macdonald 1977, Atwater 1979). At faster spreading rates sheet lavas may flow up to 4 km off-axis (Spiess et al 1980, Ballard et al 1979).

However, the volume of lava is usually small, and the basic model of a stable and centered neovolcanic zone seems to be valid.

Tectonic Zones

Intense crustal fissuring becomes apparent at the edges of the neovolcanic zone (Figures 2 and 3). Within 2–3 km of the axis some of these fissures develop significant vertical offset by normal faulting. In older crust, faulting diminishes significantly. We now discuss these three tectonic zones in some detail and consider the problems of steady-state maintenance of mid-ocean ridge structure.

ZONE OF CRUSTAL FISSURING Before the seafloor is ~100,000 years old, the crust becomes intensely fissured. At slow spreading rates, where the neovolcanic zone is discontinuous, fissures are also observed along the spreading axis. At intermediate to fast spreading rates, fissuring of the crust probably occurs along the axis but is obscured by continuous central volcanoes. At all spreading rates, the most intense observable fissuring occurs in bands 1–2 km wide flanking the central volcanoes. These fissures closely resemble the *gjar* in Iceland and are typically 1–3 m wide, extending 10 m to 2 km along strike (Luyendyk & Macdonald 1977, Ballard & van Andel 1977). Their azimuth closely parallels the strike of the ridge, which suggests that they are caused by tensional failure of the crust during spreading rather than cracking due to thermal contraction (Luyendyk & Macdonald 1977).

The tensional stresses producing this pervasive fissuring are caused by the horizontal acceleration of crust from zero at the idealized center of the neovolcanic zone to the full spreading rate at the edge of the plate boundary zone. With an overburden pressure of nearly 300 bars from the water layer, one might expect failure under shear rather than simple tension. However, the effective pressure is close to zero at the seabed because of high crustal permeability, and failure occurs under simple tension for several tens of meters into the young crust (Macdonald et al 1982a).

It is likely that these fissure fields provide access for cold seawater to penetrate the young, hot oceanic crust, creating the recharge system for hydrothermal convection (Lister 1972, Lowell 1975). The intensity of fissuring may control the vigor and exit temperature of hydrothermal convection. For example, the 350° hydrothermal vents ("black smokers") in the RISE area occur in a relatively unfissured portion of the spreading center (Macdonald et al 1980b, Ballard et al 1981). Areas that are intensely fissured are more efficiently cooled and have either ceased vigorous hydrothermal activity or have high temperature activity at depth with considerable subsurface mixing. Examples of the latter are the Famous and AMAR areas of the MAR (Fehn et al 1977), the TAG geothermal area (MAR 26°N, Scott et al 1974), the RISE area only a few km north of the black smokers (Crane & Normark 1977), and the Galapagos spreading center (Green et al 1981, Edmond et al 1979).

Crustal fissuring is the likely cause for the seismically defined "layer 2A" in the ocean basin. This layer is on the order of 500 m thick and has a bulk velocity of only 2.5–3.8 km/sec (e.g. Houtz & Ewing 1976), considerably lower than the velocities of 5.0–6.0 km/sec found in hand specimens. Cracking and other forms of porosity cause the very low velocities. Eventually the fissures fill with sediment and are sealed by low temperature diagenetic cementation. In addition, exiting of high temperature metalliferous solutions tends to fill cracks with hydrothermal minerals. As these processes continue, the seismic velocity of layer 2A will increase to that of layer 2 (approximately 5.5 km/sec) and the cracked layer will "disappear" as a seismically detectable entity (Christiansen & Salisbury 1975).

ACTIVE FAULT ZONE At a distance of 1–4 km from the spreading axis, some fissures develop large vertical offsets by normal faulting, with most of the faults dipping toward the spreading axis (Figures 2 and 3). At slow spreading centers, the individual faults have vertical throws of 200 m or greater. A series of these fault slivers creates scarps 600 m or greater in height (Macdonald & Luyendyk 1977), resulting in the ubiquitous deep rift valley characteristic of slow spreading ridges. The rift valley varies in depth from 1.2–3.0 km. Its shape may resemble a "U" with a single set of rift valley walls, or a nested "V" having an inner and outer set of walls with intervening horizontal areas, or "terraces" (Macdonald et al 1975) (Figure 5). These shapes represent end-members in the evolutionary stages of the rift valley in which the terraces are non-steady state. This variation in structure may control the width of the neovolcanic zone and the recording of magnetic anomalies as discussed earlier.

At intermediate spreading rates, the faults dipping toward the axis develop throws of only 50 m or less and the rift valley is shallower (Figures 2 and 3). The upfaulted relief is essentially cancelled by a gentle (~5°) back-tilting of the fault blocks (Klitgord & Mudie 1974).

At fast spreading rates, no rift valley is evident (Figure 2). Normal faulting creates axially dipping fault scarps with throws of 50 m or less. Here however, this relief may be cancelled by both back-tilting and outward-dipping normal faults (Lonsdale 1977). The result is an undulating horst and graben terrain of typical Pacific abyssal hills. An alternative hypothesis is that back-tilting of fault blocks is dominant at fast rates as well (Rea 1975). At present, the high resolution data base for fast spreading centers is too sparse to conclude which model is generally correct.

Linearity On the fast-spreading East Pacific Rise, the major fault scarps continue uninterrupted for tens of kilometers from transform fault to transform fault (Searle et al 1981). On the slow spreading ridges, the gross inner and outer walls continue from one transform fault to the next, but individual faults as large as 200 m in throw may disappear in only 1–2 km, or merge with other faults along strike (Macdonald et al 1975, Macdonald & Luyendyk 1977). The spreading rate dependence of faulting continuity is probably a result of two factors: tectonics at slower spreading rates may be more episodic, and greater crustal thicknesses may result in less uniform stress fields and resulting strain.

Fault dips and crustal tilt Many of the faults are nearly vertical at the top indicating failure under tension. Larger throw scarps have dips of approximately 50°–60°, indicating a transition to failure under shear at approximately 20–100 m depth in the crust (Macdonald & Luyendyk 1977). First motion solutions for earthquakes on spreading centers have tension axes perpendicular to the spreading axis, appropriate for normal faulting, and also yield dips of 50° to 60° (Sykes 1967).

Fault blocks on slow-spreading centers are typically tilted 5°–15° away from the spreading axis (Atwater & Mudie 1973, Macdonald & Luyendyk 1977). Observations from ALVIN indicate that some major blocks such as those bounding the outer walls of the rift valley may be back-tilted in excess of 30° (Macdonald & Atwater 1982). Shallow magnetic inclinations measured in DSDP holes have led Verosub & Moores (1981) to hypothesize tilts in excess of 60° by movement along listric normal faults whose dips shallow with depth. Tilts of 3°–5° and occasionally up to 10° appear to be typical of intermediate-to-fast-spreading crust (Klitgord & Mudie 1974). While the data set from faster spreading centers is too sparse for a reliable comparison, it appears that crust at slow-spreading centers suffers greater tectonic disruption through tilting than crust at faster spreading centers. Radical disruption of slow-spreading crust may be caused by creation of the 1.5–3.0 km deep rift valley and its subsequent transformation into the relatively horizontal, undulating rift mountains. A spreading rate dependence in tectonic tilt may be one of several reasons why magnetic anomalies are clearer in the Pacific than in the Atlantic (Macdonald et al 1982b).

Antithetic faults Small throw faults that dip away from the axis frequently occur at the base of large axially dipping faults, especially at slow spreading centers. These small antithetic faults create an apparent "reverse drag" on the parent fault. They are likely to be caused by a shallowing of fault dip with depth on the listric parent fault and a filling in of the resulting gap with antithetically down-dropped fault blocks (see Figure 8, Macdonald & Luyendyk 1977). These antithetic faults may play a major role in exposing deeper crustal units by repeated chopping and uplifting of the crust. This mechanism may be particularly important at spreading center/transform fault intersections where crust may be anomalously thin (Stroup & Fox 1981).

Horizontal extension The faults and fissures result in a significant horizontal extension of the crust. In the Famous area the extension is 11% to the west and 18% to the east, which is in the same sense as the spreading rate asymmetry of 0.7 cm/yr to the west and 1.3 cm/yr to the east (Macdonald & Luyendyk 1977). This suggests that asymmetric spreading is accomplished by asymmetric crustal extension as well as by asymmetric crustal accretion. Crustal extension also implies crustal thinning to a degree that could be a significant fraction of the thickness of the crust. Extension of the crust due to faulting is less at faster spreading rates and is on the order of 5% (Shih 1980).

Width of the active fault zone Unfortunately earthquake locations are neither numerous enough nor accurate enough to determine the width of the plate boundary zone. With precise bathymetric data it is possible to evaluate the cumulative fault displacement as a function of distance. Where the slope becomes constant, active faulting has presumably diminished. In such a way, Macdonald & Atwater (1978a) find that most of the active faults on the MAR occur within ±5 km of the rift axis and dip toward the axis. The faulting is characterized by significant microearthquake activity (Reid & Macdonald 1973, Spindel et al 1974). Faulting on planes dipping away from the axis and tilting of faulted blocks continues in crust up to ±30 km off-axis in the rift mountains (Figures 5 and 6). Using a similar analysis for intermediate to fast spreading centers, Shih (1980) finds that active faulting occurs within ±4 to ±10 km of the spreading axis, apparently narrower than for slowly spreading ridges. A fault zone width of ±10 km was verified during submersible investigations in the RISE area (CYAMEX 1981). Beyond the active fault zone, the oceanic lithosphere is relatively stable and rigid as assumed in plate tectonics. This marks the edge of the plate boundary zone and the beginning of the rigid plate, although mid-plate earthquakes attest to some continued activity in this stable region.

EVOLUTION OF THE RIFT VALLEY The ubiquity of a deeply rifted valley at slow spreading centers has lead to the hypothesis that the rift valley is a steady-state feature (Deffeyes 1970). If this is true, a problem arises in explaining the "disappearance" of the axially dipping regional slope of the rift valley as it is transformed into the horizontal, undulating relief of the rift mountains (Figure 5). One model is that the rift valley walls are tilted back to approximately horizontal in the rift mountains (Figure 6*A*). The rift valley/rift mountain transition may be accomplished by a modest rotation (5–9°) of the entire rift valley half-section as it passes into the rift mountains. A second model is that the rift valley relief is undone by "unfaulting" along the preexisting inward-facing faults (Figure 6*B*). Thus, as new normal faults are created near the center of the valley, the relict normal faults are collapsed by reverse faulting at the valley edges. A third hypothesis is that the rift valley staircase is

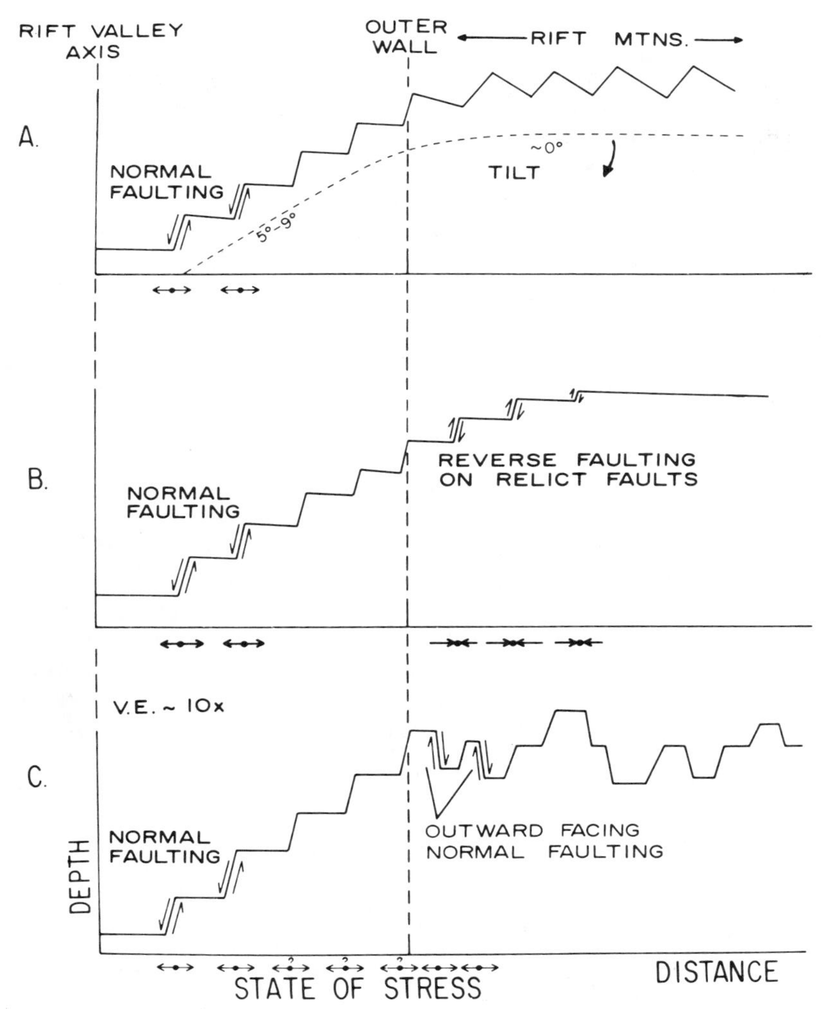

Figure 6 Three idealized models for transformation of the rift valley into the rift mountains (after Macdonald & Atwater 1978a). *A*. Regional tilting of the fossil rift valley walls in the rift mountains. *B* Reverse faulting at the outer walls and in the rift mountains. *C* Outward-facing normal faulting in the rift mountains just beyond the outer walls. Relative motion on presumed active faults shown by arrows. State of stress indicated; diverging arrows—tension, converging arrows—compression.

effectively overprinted by normal faults, which dip away from the valley axis (Figure 6*C*). These may be new fault planes or reactivated faults that previously had small offsets. While at first I favored the outward-faulting model, it now seems that all three processes must be acting in the rift mountains to maintain a steady-state rift valley (Macdonald & Atwater 1978a, b, Harrison

& Stieltjes 1977). The dominant mechanisms appear to be related to a significant tilting of fault blocks away from the rift axis by as much as 5°–50°. This tilting is often manifested by flexure and resulting failure of the crust by outward-dipping normal faulting, as well as by simple tilting (Macdonald & Atwater 1982). These processes occur as far as 30 km off-axis, which accounts for the greater width of the plate boundary zone on slow spreading ridges (~60 km) compared with fast spreading centers (~8–20 km). The relief that results from these processes is the ubiquitous abyssal hills of the Atlantic Ocean basin (Heezen et al 1959).

AXIAL MAGMA CHAMBER AND HYDROTHERMAL ACTIVITY

It has been proposed that crustal volcanic and plutonic rocks are formed by differentiation of mantle-derived parent magmas in a shallow crustal magma chamber, rather than by injection and eruption directly from the mantle (Figure 7, *top*). The magma chamber model has been strongly supported by analysis of ophiolites, petrologic studies (e.g. Cann 1974, Rhodes & Dungan 1979), thermal models (Sleep 1975), and seismic experiments (Orcutt et al 1975). Let us consider the geophysical evidence. The first strong seismic indication of a magma chamber came from ocean bottom seismometer refraction studies on the axis of the East Pacific Rise near 9°N. The primary evidence here is the presence of a substantial shadow zone beginning at ranges of 15 km,

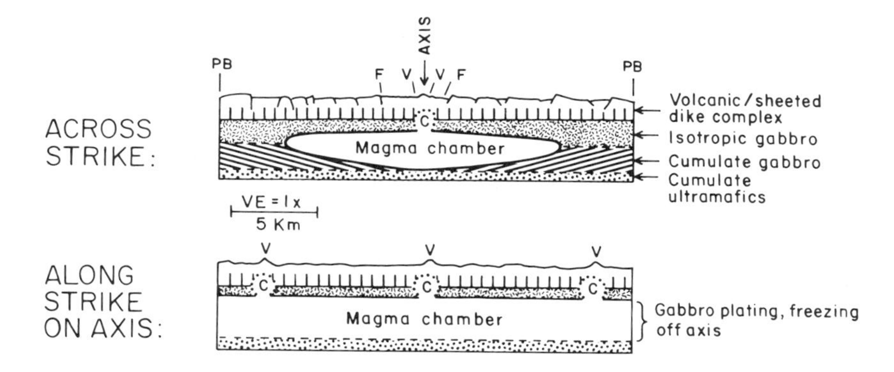

Figure 7 Hypothetical cross section of the axial magma chamber at an intermediate to fast spreading rate ridge. Topography from EPR 21°N (RISE), no vertical exaggeration. Labels F, V, PB as in Figure 2. Depth and width of chamber loosely constrained by seismic data (see text), precise shape unconstrained, C represents a possible non-steady-state magma cupola. Notice stratigraphic relation of crustal rock types to magma chamber and dependence of stratigraphy on chamber shape, width, and depth. (*Bottom*) Hypothetical section parallel to strike along the axis. Vs now correspond to active or very recent central volcanoes. Cupola spacing totally unconstrained. Along strike variation in magma chamber configuration would be difficult to detect.

in which wave amplitudes are significantly attenuated and travel times are delayed (Orcutt et al 1976, Rosendahl et al 1976). Such data require a low velocity zone, which is interpreted as a shallow magma chamber beneath the spreading axis. Subsequent refraction studies have indicated axial magma chambers beneath the EPR at 22°N (McClain & Lewis 1980), 21°N (Reid et al 1977), 12–13°N (ROSE in preparation), 10°S (Bibee et al 1981), and the GSC at 86°W (Bibee et al 1981). Additional evidence for a shallow magma chamber beneath the EPR has come from attenuation of shear waves from microearthquakes (Reid et al 1977) and from multichannel reflection work (Herron et al 1980).

Numerous seismic refraction studies over the slowly spreading MAR have not provided clear evidence for an axial magma chamber, with the continued exception of the Reykjanes Ridge (Keen & Tramontini 1970, Poehls 1974, Whitmarsh 1975, Fowler 1976). In addition, measurements of microearthquakes near the axis do not indicate attenuation of shear waves as would be expected if a magma chamber were present (Francis & Porter 1973, Reid & Macdonald 1973, Spindel et al 1974, Francis et al 1977). While it is not possible to rule out magma pockets less than a seismic wavelength in dimension (~1 km), magma chambers of the size proposed by Bryan & Moore (1977) and Hekinian et al (1976) conflict with the seismic evidence. Microearthquakes on the axis of the MAR at 45°N are up to 10 km deep (Lilwall et al 1977) and preclude a shallow steady-state magma chamber in this area.

Is the Magma Chamber Steady State?

We have seen that seismic evidence demonstrates the presence of a shallow axial magma chamber at the six carefully studied fast- and intermediate-rate spreading centers. Conclusive evidence for a magma chamber beneath the slow spreading MAR is still lacking, although closely spaced fracture zones and rough topography make seismic experiments difficult. Petrologically, the spectrum of basaltic glass compositions show different degrees of fractionation. This seems to require at least a temporary magma chamber at both fast and slow spreading rates (e.g. Juteau et al 1980, Spiess et al 1980, Bryan & Moore 1977). Furthermore, petrologic evidence suggests that the magma chambers fractionate as open systems with repeated replenishment and magma mixing, even at slow spreading rates. Thus, the seismic and petrologic data at slow spreading centers appears to be in conflict.

A reasonable hypothesis is that the magma chamber beneath intermediate to fast spreading centers is steady state while beneath slow spreading centers it is transitory. Two additional lines of reasoning support this hypothesis.

Thermal models suggest that a steady-state magma chamber cannot persist at opening rates less than 2.0 cm/yr (MAR rates), but should be present at intermediate and fast (EPR) rates (Sleep 1975). The case for occasional "freezing" of the magma chamber at slow spreading centers is particularly strong when the added cooling of hydrothermal circulation is considered. While apparently strong petrological arguments can be made for or against a steady-state chamber at slow spreading rates, the thermal arguments lead me to side with the "freezers." Nisbet & Fowler (1978) propose that if there is any magma chamber beneath the MAR, it is a narrow vertical slot. I suggest that the chamber may occasionally grow in size, but only as a non-steady-state feature during volcanic episodes. The cutoff spreading rate for a steady-state chamber is not well defined. It depends on the chamber shape, degree of partial melt, frequency of magma replenishment, and perhaps most importantly, on the depth and degree of hydrothermal circulation. There are likely to be cases in which a slow-spreading ridge segment may have a steady-state chamber either because hydrothermal penetration is lacking or unusual heat sources are present. In the latter case, Icelandic hot spot volcanism may support a steady-state magma chamber beneath the Reykjanes ridge as well as a non-rifted fast spreading center morphology (Sleep & Rosendahl 1979). Conversely, unusually extensive hydrothermal penetration may occasionally "freeze out" a normally steady-state magma chamber at intermediate rates, though probably not at fast rates.

The morphology of the neovolcanic zone outlined earlier supports this model (Figure 3). At fast spreading rates, the axial shield volcano is remarkably continuous, interrupted only by transform faults. Recent Gloria side-scan sonar data clearly shows 100 km segments of the axial shield volcano near EPR 3°S to be perfectly continuous complete with a narrow summit graben less than 500 m wide (R. Searle personal communication). It would be difficult to maintain such perfect two-dimensionality and uniform depth without a steady-state magma chamber and frequent eruptions. In contrast, slow spreading ridges have a highly discontinuous string of volcanoes of varying height and morphology in the neovolcanic zone. Only the gross tectonic structure of the rift valley shows transform-to-transform continuity. Here the magma chamber is likely to be transitory in time and discontinuous along strike. At intermediate rates, the chain of central volcanoes is frequently *en echelon*, but continuous enough to suggest an underlying continuity in the magma source. The case, however, is certainly not as strong as for fast spreading ridges.

It is possible that magma chambers at any spreading rate develop transitory peaks beneath the axis that periodically penetrate to the surface to feed lava flows (Figure 7). These "cupolas" to the magma chamber may only be feeder dikes, or may form significant shallow penetrations of the magma chamber into the dike complex (Macdonald & Luyendyk 1981, Sleep oral communication). On-bottom gravity measurements from ALVIN at EPR 21°N reveal a short-wavelength gravity minimum on the axis that is consistent with a shallow, narrow magma cupola at 1 km depth, approximately 1 km wide (Spiess et al 1980, Luyendyk in preparation). The narrowness of the neovolcanic zone has also been interpreted as suggesting a narrow, shallow magma reservoir only 1 km below the seafloor (Ballard et al 1981). Inspection of the dike-gabbro contact in ophiolites can apparently be used to either support (N. Sleep personal communication) or refute (C. Hopson personal communication) the possibility of non-steady-state cupolas. Further verification of shallow magma cupolas is difficult. If they are as small as the gravity data indicates, they are not resolvable from seismic refraction. In addition, it is likely that they are non-steady state, and disappear by magma drain-back and subsequent faulting. These cupolas may provide temporary zones of weakness at shallow levels, which spatially stabilize the zone of dike intrusion and the neovolcanic zone. Indeed, the single-sided chilling of dikes in ophiolites (Kidd 1977) and the occurrence of split volcanoes attest to this stability (Macdonald et al 1980a, Macdonald 1982).

Depth and Dimensions of the Magma Chamber

The width, shape,and depth of the axial magma chamber are critical parameters governing the petrology, structure, and stratigraphy of oceanic crust (Figure 7; Pallister & Hopson 1981). These parameters are also important boundary conditions for hydrothermal models. The total stratigraphic thickness of the volcanic section (sheet flows and pillow lavas) plus the sheeted dike complex is governed by the depth to the magma chamber. The extent of the plutonic gabbro section is determined by the thickness of the magma chamber. The uppermost zone of isotropic gabbro is thought to have crystallized downward from the chamber roof and is described as "plated gabbro" (Dewey & Kidd 1977). Magma chamber solidification apparently involves "plating" of gabbros down from the roof while gabbroic and ultramafic cumulates deposit progressively upward from the floor. The downward- and upward-solidifying parts of the chamber meet in a "sandwich zone." Here the fractionating magma reaches its most evolved composition, yielding quartz-bearing gabbros, diorites, and minor plagiogranite.

The shape of the magma chamber determines the relative thicknesses of the plated (isotropic) and cumulate gabbro sections, as well as the location of the highly fractionated sandwich zone (Figure 7, *top*). For example, a funnel-shaped chamber would yield a thick cumulate section, a thin plated gabbro section, and a highly fractionated zone at shallow levels at distances 5–15 km away from the spreading axis, depending on the size of the chamber. A bell-shaped model in which the chamber widens downward would yield a very different crustal stratigraphy (see Pallister & Hopson 1981, Figures 17 and 18). The width of the chamber will influence magma mixing, scale of crustal heterogeneity, off-axis volcanism, and overall structure and tectonics of the ridge axis. A qualified petrologist/geochemist could expound on many other implications; these are only meant to be examples.

Let us now consider the geophysical constraints from intermediate to fast spreading centers, taking depth to the top of the magma chamber first. Travel time inversion of first arrivals alone (such as τ-p inversion) provides bounds on velocity as a function of depth, but cannot confirm the presence of a low velocity zone (Kennett & Orcutt 1976). Synthetic seismograms, which model the travel time and amplitude behavior of the entire seismogram, can be used to resolve low velocity zones in a forward-modeling sense (Kennett 1976). Using these techniques Orcutt et al (1976) resolved the top of a magma chamber at only 2–3 km depth on the East Pacific Rise at 9°N. Very shallow depths of 2–3 km were found on the East Pacific Rise at 22°N and 21°N as well (Reid et al 1977, McClain & Lewis 1980). In addition a multichannel profile at 9°N revealed a reflector at 2 km depth tentatively identified as the top of the magma chamber (Herron et al 1980). However, an alternative interpretation of refraction experiments at the Galapagos spreading center and the East Pacific Rise at 10°S suggest a magma chamber at 6 km depth, which would place it beneath the moho (Bibee et al 1981). The difference in the models centers primarily on the interpretation of larger amplitude arrivals in the wave train between the 25 km to 40 km range. Both synthetic seismogram analyses are limited to a one-dimensional assumption for crustal structure, i.e. no lateral variations. One hopes that this is a plausible assumption for shooting parallel to the spreading axis, but it may not be. A very high density experiment with arrays and using three-dimensional ray tracing may be necessary to resolve this controversy. For example, it is possible (even likely at slow to intermediate spreading rates) that the magma chamber varies significantly in depth along strike (Figure 7, *bottom*). This cannot be resolved with existing data and certainly not with synthetic seismogram algorithms, which assume lateral homogeneity. Orcutt's interpretation of a shallow (2 km deep) crustal magma chamber is in far better agreement with ophiolite models and with thermal models, which predict a 1 km deep chamber at intermediate spreading rates (Sleep 1978). A steady state 6 km deep chamber is difficult to reconcile with ophiolite and thermal models.

The width (and, therefore, shape) of the magma chamber is also difficult to determine. Refraction across the East Pacific Rise at 22°N and along the rise at 9°N suggest a magma chamber no wider than 10 and 20 km, respectively (McClain & Lewis 1980, Rosendahl et al 1976). Attenuation of shear waves at 21°N also suggests a chamber less than 20 km wide (Reid et al 1977). Existing data therefore indicates a narrow axial magma chamber (<20 km), with a shallow roof (2–6 km) and with an unspecified shape. Clearly much remains to be learned about the stratigraphic location of the magma chamber within the oceanic crust and the resulting effects of petrology and structure (see Lewis 1978 for review).

Hydrothermal Activity in the Axial Zone

The large discrepancy between measured conductive heat flow and theoretical cooling-plate models suggests that at least 40% of the heat loss at mid-ocean ridges and 20% of the Earth's total heat loss is accomplished by hydrothermal circulation near spreading centers (Lister 1972, Williams & Von Herzen 1974, see Lister 1980 for review). This was first directly verified on the Galapagos spreading center (Weiss et al 1977). Hydrothermal fluids with temperatures of 20°C discharge from several sites along the Galapagos rift axis, creating a life-support system for an exotic benthic community (Corliss et al 1979). The vents were apparently associated with swarms (up to 80 per hour) of very shallow microearthquakes recorded in 1972 (Macdonald & Mudie 1974).

The discovery of the RISE hydrothermal field in 1979 allowed the first direct estimate to be made of axial hydrothermal heat flux (Macdonald et al 1980b). Here hydrothermal fluids flow from discrete chimneys in many cases, rather than diffusing around pillows. Waters blackened by sulfide precipitates jet out at rates of 1–5 m/sec at temperatures of up to 350°C. These are by far the hottest water temperatures and highest flow rates ever measured at a seafloor hydrothermal vent. These fluids are thought to be pristine and undiluted by subsurface mixing (Edmond 1980).

The entire RISE hydrothermal field is 6.2 km long with at least 12 separate vent clusters of chimneys and mineralized mounds. The field lies entirely within the neovolcanic zone in a band less than 500 m wide (Spiess et al 1980). The vents here are also characterized by shallow microearthquakes and possible harmonic tremors of the type associated with volcanic eruptions (Macdonald et al 1980c).

The resulting heat flux is approximately $(6 \pm 2) \times 10^7$ cal/sec for a single black smoker chimney. This is between three and six times the total theoretical heat flow along a 1 km segment out to a distance of 30 km on each side (crustal age 1 m.y.; see Figure 8). At least 12 major individual chimneys were found in a narrow linear zone less than 1 km long; obviously the total heat flux from the vents is overwhelming. The rate of heat loss is so great that it is highly unlikely that these vents are steady state. Macdonald et al (1980b) estimate that individual vents have a lifetime on the order of ten years. This is in keeping with the time estimated for the sulfide mound edifices to be built by precipitation (Haymon & Kastner 1981, Finkel et al 1980), and with the age distribution of clams near the vents (Killingley et al 1980, Turekian & Cochran 1981).

On the other hand, recent surveys in the Pacific indicate that high temperature vents are now commonly found on most intermediate to fast spreading centers (Spiess, et al 1980, Francheteau personal communication). This possibility raises serious questions regarding the size and longevity of the axial magma chamber once again. For example, given a simple cross-sectional model of a magma chamber beneath a single black smoker chimney, I calculate that in only 10^2–10^3 years the magma chamber will totally freeze. A shallow, 1 km diameter cupola would freeze in only 10^1–10^2 years.

It is unlikely that the spreading center hydrothermal system is either sufficiently two-dimensional or of sufficient duration to freeze the major chamber at intermediate to fast spreading rates. However, vigorous hydrothermal activity may periodically depress the depth of the chamber roof. If the chamber penetrates to shallow depths during eruptive cycles (e.g. creating a shallow magma cupola), then subsequent hydrothermal activity may act to drive the solidus back down. Magma withdrawal and subsequent faulting may also act to depress the solidus to the depth of the main chamber.

It is difficult to place bounds on the depth of hydrothermal circulation. Hydrothermal penetration should be slightly less deep than the depth of the magma chamber roof, where a chamber is present. In the RISE hydrothermal area shallow microearthquake focal depths (1–3 km) suggest that circulation on the axis is shallow (Macdonald et al 1980c). Off-axis, however, oxygen isotope studies in ophiolites suggest circulation to greater than 5 km depths, penetrating at least as deep as the moho locally (Gregory & Taylor 1981). Discrepancy between theoretical and measured conductive heat flow profiles suggests that hydrothermal activity may persist in crust up to 80 m.y. old

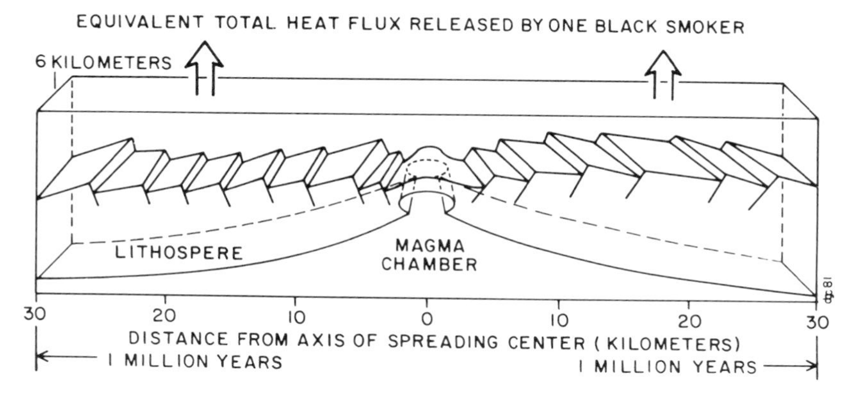

Figure 8 Heat flux from high-temperature axial hydrothermal vents make a significant contribution to the total heat budget of the Earth. The heat output of a single "black smoker" vent is equivalent to the total theoretical conductive heat flux for a spreading segment 6 km along axis out to 1 m.y. age to either side (±30 km at 6 cm/yr).

(Anderson et al 1977). However, high-temprature (~350°C) shallow-penetration (1–3 km) hydrothermal activity appears to be resticted to the neovolcanic zone and immediate surrounds.

CRUSTAL MAGNETIZATION AND IMPLICATIONS

The study of marine magnetic anomalies on mid-ocean ridges has gone beyond the calculation of spreading rates to the unraveling of oceanic crustal emplacement processes, fine scale spreading behavior, and formation of the magnetic source layer. Previously, I alluded to the use of magnetic studies in constraining the width and stability of the neovolcanic zone, estimating the frequency and duration of volcanic eruptions at various spreading rates, and detecting off-axis volcanism. Here I summarize a detailed study of a typical magnetic reversal boundary, in the RISE area, (Figure 9) and consider the implications for crustal structure and evolution.

In the first stage of the study, we conducted a dense, gridded deep-tow magnetic survey of the Brunhes/Matuyama reversal transition (Macdonald et al 1980a). The data were analyzed using a Fourier inversion method including the effects of topography (Parker & Huestis 1974). The method was used in three dimensions, thus avoiding the usual assumption that the magnetized sources and bathymetry are perfectly lineated. In fact, we found that the transition is extremely linear on all scales down to hundreds of meters, and very narrow, only 1000–1400 m wide (Figure 9*A*). Encouraged and slightly surprised by the results, since the anomalies here are poorer than average for the Pacific, we extended the resolution of our study. A three component magnetometer and vertical gradiometer were mounted on ALVIN so that the magnetic polarity of individual lava flows and faulted outcrops could be determined. This gave us a spatial resolution of 0.5–1.0 m versus 200–400 m for deep-tow data (due to filtering required by inversion) and 2–4 km for surface tow data.

The 280 polarity determinations made in situ with ALVIN yielded several surprises (Figure 9*B*). Even on long traverses across both sides of the boundary, nearly every magnetic target had the correct polarity, i.e. the same polarity as that of the regional magnetic stripe defined by the deep-towed magnetometer (Macdonald et al 1982b). This observation was not too surprising for the younger side of the boundary, because newer positive-polarity crust, with the same polarity as the earth's present magnetic field, would be expected to overlie older, negatively polarized crust. What was surprising was that there were no outlying regions of new crust on the older side of the boundary. The transition in the outcropping volcanic section was sharp and linear, delineated in some cases by an actual geologic contact of opposing flow fronts, and no wider than 150 m in other crossings.

We found that the magnetic-reversal boundary surveyed with the ALVIN is displaced about 500 meters further away from the spreading axis than the boundary position calculated for the three-dimensional inversion studies. The calculated boundary marks the average position of the magnetic reversal for the entire source layer. The fact that the boundary mapped on the sea floor surface is displaced 500 meters from the calculated average position indicates a spillover of basalt away from the volcanic vents over older, negatively polarized crust. By this measure, the total width of the neovolcanic zone circa 0.7 m.y. ago was approximately 1000 m. This is in excellent agreement with submersible observations in the present neovolcanic zone, which vary from 400 m to 1200 m in width (Spiess et al 1980, CYAMEX 1981). Now consider again the 1000–1400 m width found for the magnetic transition from deep-tow. This is an indirect measure of the width of the *crustal accretion zone* (volcanics and magnetic plutonics). After the effects of crustal dilation by

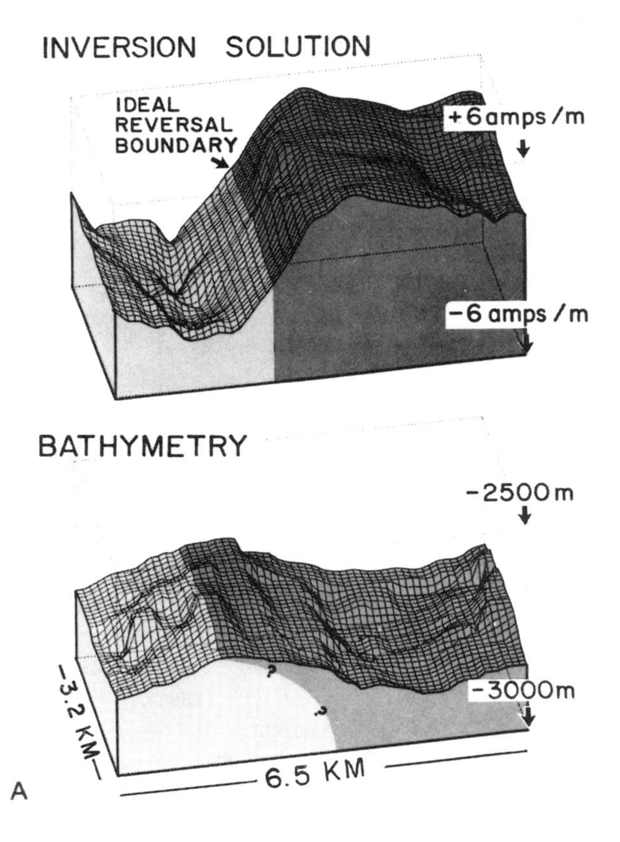

faulting and field reversal time are removed, we find that the half-width of the zone of crustal accretion is only 600–1000 m. Thus the zone of crustal accretion and the neovolcanic zone both now and circa 0.7 m.y. ago have been very stable in space and generally less than 2 km and 1 km wide respectively. (Macdonald et al 1980a, 1982b).

The remarkably neat picture just derived for magnetic anomalies and polarity transitions in the Pacific is reassuring, and yet puzzling in the light of complex magnetic results from 3 DSDP holes which penetrate deeper than 500 m into Atlantic Ocean basaltic crust (332B, 395A, 418A). These DSDP results show anomalous inclination and numerous reversals in a single hole. In most cases the 500 m section represented is totally inadequate for generating the measured magnetic anomaly (Hall & Robinson 1979). This contradicts the assumption derived largely from EPR anomalies that the magnetic source lies within the ~1 km thick volcanic layer (Huestis & Parker 1977, Atwater &

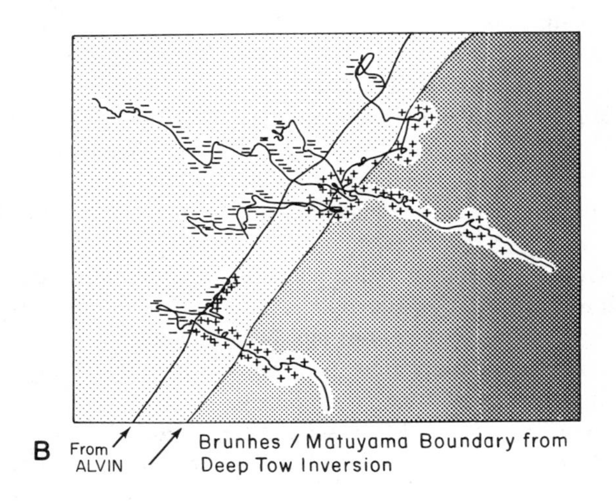

Figure 9 (*A*) *Top* Deep-tow magnetic inversion solution for crustal magnetization over a magnetic reversal boundary near the RISE area (from Macdonald et al 1982b). Notice how linear and uniformly narrow the transition boundary is. The transition width suggests that the half-width of the zone of crustal accretion was only 600–1000 m circa 0.7 m.y. ago. *Bottom* Corresponding (smoothed) bathymetry used in solution above. This is a typical abyssal hill, fault-bounded on the east side. The overlap zone of polarities marked by ? is based on ALVIN measurements shown in Figure 9*B*. (*B*) Magnetic polarity measurements made from ALVIN over the polarity transition shown in Figure 9*A*. Each symbol stands for one or more closely spaced mesurements. Underlying shading shows the inversion solution from Figure 9*A*. Note the ~500 m "spillover" of positive onto negative crust. This suggests a neovolcanic zone approximately 1000 m wide circa 0.7 m.y. ago, in excellent agreement with the width observed today from submersibles. Notice that on either side of this spillover zone, surface polarity is remarkably uniform.

Mudie 1973), and with the sharpness and clarity of the EPR magnetic stripe studied from ALVIN.

To reconcile the EPR and Atlantic results, I suggest that the crustal generating processes and resulting magnetic structure vary significantly with spreading rate (Macdonald et al 1982b). On the slow-spreading MAR, the major episodes of volcanism are likely to be infrequent (10^4 yr), the magma chamber is non-steady state, and the neovolcanic zone shifts or varies in width considerably. This sporadic, start-and-stop spreading process will contribute to a highly heterogeneous and complex crustal and magnetic structure. In addition, significant tilting of the crust may disrupt MAR crust (Hall & Robinson 1979). Models for both extreme tilting toward the spreading axis (Hall & Robinson 1979) and away from the axis (Verosub & Morres 1981) have been proposed. In some cases, extreme tilting of the crustal blocks may be sufficient to account for the non-dipole inclinations measured in Atlantic DSDP holes. For the fast-spreading EPR, more frequent volcanism (50–600 yr), a steady-state magma chamber, and a sharp, stable neovolcanic zone will create a less complex magnetic and crustal structure. This model is strongly supported by statistical studies of magnetic anomalies, which show that several reversals may be encountered in a single DSDP hole if the crustal accretion zone is 5–10 km wide (see Figure 5, Schouten & Denham 1979). Unfortunately most DSDP data is from the Atlantic, and most ALVIN magnetic data is from the Pacific. However, deep-tow and surface tow studies in both oceans verify that magnetic anomalies are far clearer and more lineated in the Pacific than in the Atlantic.

In addition, there is evidence that reversely magnetized rocks exist within the inner floor of the MAR (Ade-Hall et al 1973, Macdonald 1977, Johnson & Atwater 1977). This is quite startling, because the crust here should all be of positive polarity. Of the various possibilities, the most likely explanation for this is that blocks of older (>0.7 m.y.) crust have been left behind (Macdonald 1977, Atwater & Macdonald in preparation). Indeed, the sporadic tectonism within the MAR plate boundary zone renders approximately a 14% chance for old negative crust to become temporarily stranded near the axis (Macdonald 1977). The chances of this occurring drop off rapidly with spreading rate.

Another problem which arises is the rapid decay of the magnetic intensity of the volcanic layer away from the ridge axis. Intensities decrease to $1/e$ of their initial values in only 0.6 m.y. (Irving 1970, Macdonald 1977). This fact plus the DSDP results suggest that deep sources such as the gabbro section ("layer 3") carry a significant magnetic signal (Cande & Kent 1976, Harrison 1976, Blakely 1976). Magnetization of gabbros of 0.5–1.0 amp/m support this contention (Kent et al 1978, Day & Luyendyk 1981). On the other hand, the amplitudes of magnetic anomalies in old ocean basins still indicate a strong contribution from the volcanic layer, especially at fast spreading rates (Miller & Macdonald in preparation). It is still uncertain what percentage of the magnetic signal comes from different depths in the crust. This certainly varies with age, and may vary with spreading rate as well.

Two other magnetic curiosities from the MAR are worth mentioning. Oblique spreading patterns may be stable for most slow spreading ridges while an orthogonal pattern, as normally assumed, is preferred by intermediate to fast spreading centers (Atwater & Macdonald 1977). Asymmetric spreading with asymmetry up to a factor of 2 may persist for several m.y., but tends to reverse in sense so that over tens of m.y. the spreading is grossly symmetric (Macdonald 1977).

TOWARD A THREE-DIMENSIONAL MODEL OF SPREADING CENTERS

While it is tempting to think of a spreading center as a two-dimensional structure, there is evidence for considerable variation in the third dimension, along strike. For example, the neovolcanic zone is characterized by high-relief pillow lava constructions in some places and smooth sheet flows in others (Ballard et al 1978). Particularly on slow spreading ridges, the neovolcanic zone often has "gaps" in the sense that there is no central volcano and the crust on the axis is intensely fissured and faulted with no signs of volcanic activity in the last 50,000 years (Figure 3; e.g. AMAR rift, Ballard et al 1978). The neovolcanic zone may also be characterized by hydrothermal activity. It may be of the vigorous, high-temperature type (Spiess et al 1980), low temperature (Corliss et al 1979, Scott et al 1974), or dormant (Fehn et al 1977). Patterns of faulting also exhibit changes. For example, the MAR rift valley varies between a V-shaped valley with wide terraces and a narrow inner floor, and a U-shaped valley with narrow or no terraces and a wider inner floor (Figure 5). Magnetic anomalies also exhibit considerable variations along strike in clarity and linearity especially at slow spreading rates (compare Loncarevic & Parker 1971 with Macdonald 1977). These variations suggest episodicity in time. It is also possible that these episodes of tectonism, volcanism, and hydrothermal activity occur in some cyclic manner. This was suggested earlier for the sequencing of pillow lavas and sheet flows during volcanic eruptions (Figure 4; van Andel & Ballard 1979). Let us now consider a totally hypothetical cycle that can account for many of the observations.

Seafloor spreading results in a mass deficit along the axis which must be balanced by upwelling of material from the asthenosphere. Crustal volcanic and plutonic rocks will form by differentiation of these parent magmas in a shallow magma chamber. As seafloor spreading proceeds, a magma chamber is either created if it is non-steady state (e.g. MAR) or replenished if it is steady state (e.g. EPR).

Eventually, feeder dikes will break through to the surface and feed lava flows. During the initial stages of magma penetration to the surface, a shallow magma cupola may form. If so, it may help to stabilize the neovolcanic and dike intrusion zone (Figure 7). The first stages of volcanism will be fissure eruptions (as in Hawaii, Iceland, or Afar) in which lava erupts at a rapid rate, forming sheet flows. As the volcanic plumbing system develops, coupled with a possible decrease in lava flux, pillow lavas develop and build edifices upon the sheet flows (Figure 4). As new vents open, a complex intercalation of pillows and sheet flows develops. After 1–100 years the volcanism will wane and the last gasps of pillow lava will cap the volcanic carapace.

Hydrothermal activity may accompany volcanism and persist for some time after the volcanic episode. Continued faulting and fissuring in the off-axis tectonic zones (Figure 2) will allow cold seawater to penetrate to the base of the brittle crust to where ductile deformation dominates at approximately 600°C (Lister 1977). The mode of hydrothermal activity will depend on the degree of subsurface dilution of hydrothermal fluids with cold seawater. If the crust is intensely fissured, considerable mixing and dilution may occur at depth in the crust. High temperature activity and metallogenesis will not be evident on the seafloor, but may occur at depth within the crust. Diffuse, low temperature activity may be detectable on the seafloor. If the structure is such that little dilution occurs at depth, then pristine hydrothermal fluids may jet out of the volcanic carapace. The RISE area represents the latter stage, while the Galapagos and TAG (MAR 26°N) areas represent the former (Green et al 1981, Scott et al 1974). As cooling proceeds the axial magma cupola, and perhaps even the main chamber (at slow spreading rates), may freeze. A waning heat source combined with continued opening of the crust by faulting and fissuring (increasing subsurface mixing) will lower the temperature and vigor of hydrothermal circulation. The Galapagos spreading center may be just entering this phase since old abandoned smoker chimneys are observed a short distance off-axis, while present discharges are low temperature (22°C) (van Andel & Ballard 1979, Atwater personal communication). High-temperature (350°C) hydrothermal activity may last 10–100 years after volcanism wanes, while low-temperature (<20°C) activity may persist much longer. For example, ~20°C hydrothermal fluids are detected in the Galapagos mounds hydrothermal field in crust nearly 1 m.y. old (Williams et al 1979). At slow spreading rates, 10,000 years may pass until the next volcanic cycle, while at intermediate to fast rates, only 50–600 years of quiescence may intervene. Tectonism is likely to continue as indicated by the broad distribution of mid-ocean ridge earthquakes. Central volcanoes will either split or move as intact units away from the plate boundary. In addition to spreading, subsidence through faulting will occur so that the next volcanic episode will add to the thickness of the volcanic carapace.

The hypothetical cycle outlined above is a composite of ideas from van Andel & Ballard (1979), Macdonald et al (1980b), Crane & Ballard (1980), and N. Sleep (personal communication), as well as from hallway discussions with M. Mottl, T. Atwater, C. Hopson, and others at the Ocean Lithosphere Chapman Conference (1981). This cycle may not in fact be a clearly defined repetitive sequence, but a more random series of episodes. The crucial tests will be from analysis of field relationships seen from ALVIN, the DSDP holes, and in ophiolites.

Regardless of the existence of particular cycles, it appears that spreading rate plays an important role in the frequency of volcanic and associated hydrothermal episodes. As I pointed out earlier, the period between episodes may be roughly proportional to the square of the spreading rate. The frequency influences the manifestations of these episodes. At fast spreading rates, the increased continuity in time and the probability of a steady-state magma chamber produce a continuity along strike. The neovolcanic and tectonic zones are quite linear as are the resulting magnetic anomalies. High-temperature venting is more likely to occur. Three-dimensionality occurs primarily because of site-to-site variation in the recency of volcanism and the style of hydrothermal activity (high vs low temperature). This in turn may be affected by the presence or absence of a shallow magma cupola.

On slow spreading ridges, long period tectonic cycles may also occur. The valley may have a narrow inner floor and wide terraces (Figure 5, *bottom*) or a wide inner floor and narrow terraces (Figure 5, *top*). The time represented between the development of these two extreme structures is approximately 0.2–0.4 m.y. Clearly this is a much longer time scale than the volcanic episodes discussed earlier. Several episodes of volcanism will occur with intervening periods of down-faulting, quiescence, and subsequent burial during the next volcanic episode. When the inner floor is narrow, the neovolcanic zone may be narrow, restricted by the inner walls of the rift valley. As a result magnetic anomalies should be clearly recorded and have narrow polarity transitions. When the inner floor is wide, magnetic anomalies may be poorly recorded, as in parts of the Famous area (Macdonald 1977) and the MAR at 45°N (Loncarevic & Parker 1971). This model is supported by magnetic (Macdonald 1977), petrologic (Stakes et al in preparation), and structural data (Atwater 1979).

Another important concept in the three-dimensional behavior of spreading centers is that of propagating rifts. While this concept has been employed in several tectonic contexts (Bowin 1974, Shih & Molnar 1975), Hey has developed it into an important corollary of plate tectonics (Hey 1977, Hey et al 1980). It explains the westward propagation of the Galapagos spreading center, and quite spectacularly unravels the oblique magnetic anomaly offsets of the northeast Pacific (see Figure 2 of Hey et al 1980 for a summary of propagating rift kinematics). Oblique fracture zone patterns ("pseudofaults"), V-shaped trends in seafloor morphology, and occurrences of ferro-basalts and high amplitude magnetic anomalies appear to be related to these peripatetic rifts. This model also provides a mechanism for spreading centers to change azimuth in response to changes in stress directions. The rifts propagate at approximately 1–5 times the local spreading rate (Hey et al 1980, Crane 1979).

As well as creating and destroying plate boundaries on a large scale, rifts may also propagate between transform faults on a smaller scale. The tectonic, volcanic, and hydrothermal episodes outlined earlier may propagate back and forth along strike in the wake of a propagating crack between transform faults. This hypothesis remains to be tested.

Other more obvious perturbations to spreading centers in the third dimension are transform faults. Besides offsetting the spreading center, it appears that transform faults profoundly affect the creation of oceanic crust near ridge crest intersections. The cold, rigid boundary at the transform/ridge intersection appears to cause a decrease in the volcanic and plutonic budget (Fox et al 1980). This results in local crustal thinning and contributes to the topographic depression at ridge/transform intersections. Hydraulic head loss at the intersection may also contribute to the topographic low (Sleep & Biehler 1970). Seismic refraction results show that the resulting volcanic carapace and plutonic section is anomalously thin, approximately one half normal thicknesses (~2 km) (Fox et al 1980). As a result, faults and antithetic faults may often expose plutonic gabbros in the faulted intersection walls (Stroup & Fox 1981).

Morphologic data suggest that transform faults may influence the structure and generation of oceanic crust throughout the entire length of spreading centers that are at most 50 km long (Macdonald & Luyendyk 1977). This may be due to both thermal edge effects and increased head loss at the intersection. This would affect most of the Atlantic oceanic crust, where spreading segments average 50 km in length (Fox et al 1969). Transform spacing is wider on the EPR, so crustal thinning may not alter the structure of Pacific crust as extensively. This is yet another complexity in the third dimension that may render the slow-spreading Atlantic crust extremely heterogeneous relative to the Pacific.

Epilogue

In the process of writing this review, I have been impressed both by how much we have learned about the fine scale tectonic, volcanic, and hydrothermal processes of mid-ocean ridges, as well as by how many important controversial issues remain unresolved. For example, evidence from seismic, petrologic, and ophiolite field studies underscores the importance of an axial magma chamber, yet several key questions remain unanswered. What is the stratigraphic relationship of the magma chamber to the oceanic crust and upper mantle? What are the dimensions and shape of the chamber? At what spreading rate does the chamber cease to be steady state? Concerning axial hydrothermal activity, what is the temporal behavior of high temperature springs of the "black smoker" variety? How deep does hydrothermal activity penetrate? What are the water/rock ratios? What is the nature of hydrothermal activity and metallogenesis at slow spreading centers? Concerning magnetic anomalies, how stable (in time and in space) is the crustal generation process? How deep in the crust are magnetic sources significant? How can the magnetic heterogeneity observed in DSDP holes be reconciled with clearly recorded magnetic anomalies documented for much of the ocean floor? Concerning faulting, how deep does active faulting penetrate on mid-ocean ridges? Does the oceanic crust undergo extreme tilting in its tectonic evolution, and if so, is the degree of tilting spreading-rate dependent? How far away from the spreading center does faulting persist? What is the state of stress in the crust? Finally, do mid-ocean ridges undergo rhythmic cycles linking tectonic, volcanic, and hydrothermal processes, or is the ridge more chaotically episodic?

The level of excitement in this field is exemplified by the degree of controversy which brewed in the hallways at UCSB shortly after I dropped a first draft of this paper on the desks of the reviewers. The plausibility of cycles and of shallow magma cupolas was hotly debated. Strong evidence was presented for both ephemeral and steady-state magma chambers at slow spreading centers. Many other issues were raised. I hope that this preliminary attempt at a synthesis catalyzes debate in your hallways as well.

ACKNOWLEDGMENTS

This paper was improved by the careful reviews of Rachel Haymon, Tanya Atwater, Clifford Hopson, Bruce Luyendyk, Debra Stakes, and Steve Miller. My efforts in mid-ocean ridge research have been generously supported by the National Science Foundation and the Office of Naval Research. Dave Crouch and Ellie Dzuro drafted the figures and typed the text.

Literature Cited

Ade-Hall, J. M., Aumento, F., Ryall, P. J. C., Gerstein, R. E., Brooke, J., McKeown, D. L. 1973. The Mid-Atlantic ridge near 45°N., 21, Magnetic results from basalt drill cores from the Median Valley. *Can. J. Earth Sci.* 10:676–96

Anderson, R. N., Langseth, M. G., Sclater, J. G. 1977. The mechanisms of heat transfer through the floor of the Indian Ocean. *J. Geophys. Res.* 82:3391–409

Anderson, R. N., Noltimier, H. C. 1973. A model for the horst and graben structure of mid-ocean ridge crests based upon spreading velocity and basalt delivery to the oceanic crust. *Geophys. J. R. Astron. Soc.* 34:137–47

ARCYANA. 1975. Transform fault and rift valley from bathyscaph and diving saucer. *Science* 190:108–16

Atwater, T. M., 1979. Constraints from the Famous area concerning the structure of the oceanic section. In *Deep Drilling Results in the Atlantic Ocean: Ocean Crust,* ed. M. Talwani, C. G. Harrison, D. E. Hayes, 2:33–42. Am. Geophys. Union

Atwater, T. M., Macdonald, K. C. 1977. Slowly spreading ridge crests: are they perpendicualr to their transform faults? *Nature* 270:715–19

Atwater, T. M., Mudie, J. D. 1973. Detailed near-bottom geophysical study of the Gorda Rise. *J. Geophys. Res.* 78:8665–86

Ballard, R. D., Atwater, T., Stakes, D., Crane, K., Hopson, C. 1978. AMAR 78 preliminary results IV: AMAR rift valley—evidence for cycles in the evolution of rift valleys. *EOS* 59:1198 (Abstr.)

Ballard, R. D., Francheteau, J., Juteau, T., Rangin, C., Normark, W. 1981. East Pacific Rise at 21°N: The volcanic, tectonic and hydrothermal processes of the central axis. *Earth Planet. Sci. Lett.* In press

Ballard, R. D., Holcomb, R. T., van Andel, T. H. 1979. The Galapagos Rift at 86°W, 3, sheet flows, collapse pits, and lava lakes of the rift. *J. Geophys. Res.* 84:5407–22

Ballard, R. D., van Andel, T. H. 1977. Morphology and tectonics of the inner rift valley at lat. 36°50′N on the Mid-Atlantic Ridge. *Geol. Soc. Am. Bull.* 88:507–30

Bibee, L. D., Dorman, L. M., Johnson, S. H., Orcutt, J. A. 1981. Crustal structure of the East Pacific Rise at 10°S. *J. Geophys. Res.* Submitted for publication

Blakely, R. J. 1976. An age-dependent, two-layer model for marine magnetic anomalies. *Geophysics of the Pacific Ocean Basin and its Margin.* Geophys. Mongr. 18, Am. Geophys. Union, pp. 227–35

Blakely, R. J., Lynn, W. S. 1977. Reversal transition widths and fast spreading centers. *Earth Planet. Sci. Lett.* 33:321–30

Bowin, C. 1974. Migration of a pattern of plate motion. *Earth Planet. Sci. Lett.* 21:400–4

Bryan, W. B., Moore, J. G. 1977. Compositional variations of young basalts in the Mid-Atlantic ridge rift valley near lat. 36°49′N. *Geol. Soc. Am. Bull.* 88:556–70

Cande, S. C., Kent, D. V. 1976. Constraints imposed by the shape of marine magnetic anomalies on the magnetic source. *J. Geophys. Res.* 81:4157–62

Cann, J. R. 1974. A model for oceanic crustal structure developed. *Geophys. J. R. Astron. Soc.* 39:169–87

Christiansen, N. I., Salisbury, M. H. 1975. Structure and constitution of the lower oceanic crust. *Rev. Geophys. Space Phys.* 13:57–86

Corliss, J. B., Dymond, J., Gordon, L. I., Edmond, J. M., Von Herzen, R. P., Ballard, R. D., Green, K., Williams, D., Bainbridge, A., Crane, K., van Andel, T. H. 1979. Submarine thermal springs on the Galapagos Rift. *Science* 203:1073–83

Crane, K. 1979. The Galapagos rift at 86°W: Morphological waveforms; evidence of propagating rift. *J. Geophys. Res.* 84:6011–18

Crane, K., Ballard, R. 1980. The Galapagos Rift at 86°W, 4, Structure and morphology of hydrothermal fields and their relationship to the volcanic and tectonic processes of the rift valley. *J. Geophys. Res.* 85:1443–54

Crane, K., Normark, W. 1977. Hydrothermal activity and crustal structure of the East Pacific Rise at 21°N. *J. Geophys. Res.* 82: 5336–48

CYAMEX Team. 1981. First manned submersible dives on the East Pacific Rise at 21°N. (Project RITA): General Results. *Mar. Geophys. Res.* 4:345–79

Day, R., Luyendyk, B. P. 1981. Paleomagnetism of the Samail ophiolite, Oman II. First results from the Wadi Kadir gabbro section. *J. Geophys. Res.* In press

Deffeyes, K. S. 1970. The axial valley: A steady state feature in the terrain. In *Megatectonics of continents and oceans.* ed. J. Johnson, B. C. Smith, pp. 194–222, Brunswick, N. J: Rutgers Univ. Press

Dewey, J. F., Kidd, W. S. F. 1977. Geometry of plate accretion. *Geol. Soc. Am. Bull.* 88:960–68

Edmond, J. M. 1980. The chemistry of the 350°C. hot springs at 21°N on the East Pacific Rise. *EOS* 61:992

Edmond, J. M., Measures, C., McDuff, R. E., Chan, L. H., Collier, R., Grant, B., Corliss, J. B., Gordon, L. I. 1979. Ridge crest hydrothermal activity and the balances of the major and minor elements in the ocean: the Galapagos data. *Earth Planet. Sci. Lett.* 46:1–18

Fehn, V., Siegel, M. D., Robinson, G. R., Holland, H. D., Williams, D. L., Erickson, K. E., Green, A. J. 1977. Deep-water temperatures in the Famous area. *Geol. Soc. Am. Bull.* 88:488–94

Finkel, R. C., Macdougall, J. D., Chung, Y. C. 1980. Sulfide precipitates at 21°N. on the East Pacific Rise: ^{226}Ra, ^{210}Pb, and ^{210}Po. *Geophys. Res. Lett.* 7:685–88

Fowler, C. M. R. 1976. Crustal structure of the Mid-Atlantic Ridge crest at 37°N. *Geophys. J. R. Astron. Soc.* 47:459–91

Fox, P. J., Detrick. R. S., Purdy, G. M., 1980. Evidence for crustal thinning near fracture zones: Implications for ophiolites. *Ophiolites, Proceedings International Ophiolite Symposium,* ed. A. Panayiotou, Cyprus. Geol. Surv. Dept., Cyprus, Nicosia

Fox, P. J., Lowrie, A., Heezen, B. C. 1969. Oceanographer fracture zone. *Deep-Sea Res.* 16:59–66

Francis, T. J. G., Porter, I. T. 1973. Median valley seismology: The Mid-Atlantic Ridge near 45°N *Geophys. J. R. Astron. Soc.* 34:279–311

Francis, T. J. G., Porter, I. T., McGrath, J. R. 1977. Ocean bottom seismograph observations on the Mid-Atlantic Ridge near 37°N. *Geol. Soc. Am. Bull.* 88:664–77

Green, K. E., Von Herzen, R. P., Williams, D. L. 1981. The Galapagos Spreading Center at 86°W: A detailed geothermal field study. *J. Geophys. Res.* 86:979–86

Gregory, R. T., Taylor, H. P. 1981. An oxygen isotope profile in a section of cretaceous oceanic crust, Samail ophiolite, Oman: Evidence of $\delta^{18}0$ buffering of the oceans by deep (>5 km) seawater hydrothermal circulation on mid-ocean ridges. *J. Geophys. Res.* 86:2737–55

Hall, J. M. 1976. Major problems regarding the magnetization of oceanic crustal layer 2. *J. Geophys. Res.* 81:4223–30

Hall, J. M., Robinson, P. T. 1979. Deep crustal drilling in the North Atlantic Ocean. *Science* 204:573–86

Harrison, C. G. A. 1968. Formation of magnetic anomaly patterns by dyke injection. *J. Geophys. Res.* 73:2137–42

Harrison, C. G. A. 1976. Magnetization of the oceanic crust. *Geophys. J. R. Astron. Soc.* 47:257–84

Harrison, C. G. A., Stieltjes, L. 1977. Faulting within the Median Valley. *Tectonophysics* 38:137–44

Haymon, R., Kastner, M. 1981. Hot spring deposits on the East Pacific Rise at 21°N: Preliminary description of mineralogy and genesis. *Earth Planet. Sci. Lett.* 53:363–81

Heezen, B. C., Tharp, M., Ewing, M. 1959. The floors of the oceans, 1, the North Atlantic Ocean. *Geol. Soc. Am. Spec. Pap. 65.* 122 pp.

Heirtzler, J. R., Ballard, R. D. 1977. Submersible observations at the Hole 332B area. In *Initial Reports of the Deep Sea Drilling Project,* ed. F. Aumento, W. G. Melson et al 37:363–66

Hekinian, R., Moore, J. G., Bryan, W. B. 1976. Volcanic rocks and processes of the Mid-Atlantic Ridge rift valley near 36°49′N. *Contrib. Mineral. Petrol.* 58:83–110

Herron, T. J., Stoffa, P. L., Buhl, P. 1980. Magma chamber and mantle reflections—East Pacific Rise. *Geophys. Res. Lett.* 7:989–92

Hey, R. N. 1977. A new class of pseudofaults and their bearing on plate tectonics: A propagating rift model. *Earth Planet. Sci. Lett.* 37:321–25

Hey, R., Duennebier, F. K., Morgan, W. J. 1980. Propagating rifts on mid-ocean ridges. *J. Geophys. Res.* 85:3647–58

Houtz, R., Ewing, J. 1976. Upper crustal structure as a function of plate age. *J. Geophys. Res.* 81:2490–98

Huestis, S. P., Parker, R. L. 1977. Bounding the thickness of the oceanic magnetized layer. *J. Geophys. Res.* 82:5293–5303

Irving, E. 1970. The Mid-Atlantic Ridge at 45°N, 14, oxidation and magnetic properties of basalt; Review and discussion. *Can. J. Earth Sci.* 7:1528–38

Johnson, H. P., Atwater, T. M. 1977. Magnetic study of basalts from the Mid-Atlantic ridge. *Geo. Soc. Am. Bull.* 88:637–47

Juteau, T., Eissen, J. P., Francheteau, J., Needham, D., Choukroune, P., Rangin, C., Seguret, M., Ballard, R. D., Fox, P. J., Normark, W. R., Carranza, A., Cordoba, D., Guerrero, J. 1980. Homogeneous basalts from the East Pacific Rise at 21°N: Steady state magma reservoirs at moderately fast spreading centers. *Ocean. Acta* 3: 487–504

Keen, C. E., Tramontini, C. 1970. A seismic refraction survey on the Mid-Atlantic Ridge. *Geophys. J. R. Astron. Soc.* 20:473–91

Kennett, B. L. N. 1976. A comparison of travel time inversions. *Geophys. J. R. Astron. Soc.* 44:517–36

Kennett, B. L. N., Orcutt, J. A. 1976. A comparison of travel time inversions. *Geophys. J. R. Astron. Soc.* 81:4061–70

Kent, D. V., Honnorez, B. M., Opdyke, N. D., Fox, P. J. 1978. Magnetic properties of dredged oceanic gabbros and the source of marine magnetic anomalies. *Geophys. J. R. Astron. Soc.* 55:513–37

Kidd, R. G. W. 1977. A model for the process of formation of upper oceanic crust. *Geophys. J. R. Astron. Soc.* 50:149–83

Killingley, J. S., Berger, W. H., Macdonald, K. C., Newman, W. A. 1980. $^{18}0/^{16}0$ variations in deep-sea carbonate shells from the RISE hydrothermal field. *Nature.* 287:218–21

Klitgord, K. D., Huestis, S. P., Parker, R. L., Mudie, J. D. 1975. An analysis of near-bottom magnetic anomalies: Seafloor spreading, the magnetized layer, and the geomagnetic time scale. *Geophys. J. R. Astron. Soc.* 43:387–424

Klitgord, K. D., Mudie, J. D. 1974. The Galapagos spreading center: A near-bottom geo-

physical survey. *Geophys. J. R. Astron. Soc.* 38:563–86
Lachenbruch, A. H. 1973. A simple mechanical model for oceanic spreading centers. *J. Geophys. Res.* 78:3395–417
Lachenbruch, A. H. 1976. Dynamics of a passive spreading center. *J. Geophys. Res.* 81:1883–902
Larson, R. L. 1971. Near-bottom geophysical studies of the East Pacific Rise crest. *Geol. Soc. Am. Bull.* 82:823–42
Lewis, B. T. R. 1978. Evolution of ocean crust seismic velocities. *Ann. Rev. Earth Planet. Sci.* 6:377–404
Lilwall, R. C., Francis, T. J. G., Porter, I. T. 1977. Ocean bottom seismograph observations on the Mid-Atlantic Ridge near 45°N. *Geophys. J. R. Astron. Soc.* 51: 357–69
Lister, C. R. B. 1972. On the thermal balance of a mid-ocean ridge. *Geophys. J. R. Astron. Soc.* 26:515–35
Lister, C. R. B. 1977. Qualitative models of spreading-center processes, including hydrothermal penetration. *Tectonophysics* 37: 203–18
Lister, C. R. B. 1980. Heat flow and hydrothermal circulation. *Ann. Rev. Earth Planet. Sci.* 8:95–117
Loncarevic, B. D., Mason, C. S., Matthews, D. H. 1966. The Mid-Atlantic ridge near 45°N., 1, The median valley. *Can. J. Earth Sci.* 3:327–49
Loncarevic, B. D., Parker, R. L. 1971. The Mid-Atlantic ridge near 45°N., 17, Magnetic anomalies and seafloor spread. *Can. J. Earth Sci.* 8:883–98
Lonsdale, P. 1977. Structural geomorphology of a fast-spreading rise crest: The East Pacific Rise near 3°25′S. *Mar. Geophys. Res.* 3:251–93
Lowell, R. P. 1975. Circulation in fractures, hot springs, and convective heat transport on mid-ocean ridge crests. *Geophys. J. R. Astron. Soc.* 40:351–65
Luyendyk, B. P., Macdonald, K. C. 1976. Spreading center terms and concepts. *Geology* 4:369–70
Luyendyk, B. P., Macdonald, K. C. 1977. Physiography and structure of the inner floor of the Famous rift valley: Observations with a deep-towed instrument packages. *Geol. Soc. Am. Bull.* 88:648–63
Macdonald, K. C. 1977. Near-bottom magnetic anomalies, asymmetric spreading, oblique spreading and tectonics of the Mid-Atlantic Ridge near 37°N. *Geol. Soc. Am. Bull.* 88:541–55
Macdonald, K. C. 1982. The significance of splitting volcanoes on the East Pacific Rise. *Earth Planet. Sci. Lett.* Submitted for publication
Macdonald, K. C., Atwater, T. M. 1978a. Evolution of rifted ocean ridges. *Earth Planet. Sci. Lett.* 39:319–27
Macdonald, K. C., Atwater, T. M. 1978b. AMAR78, Preliminary results, 1, Evolution of the median rift *EOS* 59:1198 (Abstr.)
Macdonald, K. C., Atwater, T. M. 1982. Investigation of the Mid-Atlantic Ridge Rift Valley/Rift Mountain transition from a submersible: Evidence for significant crustal tilting. *J. Geophys. Res.* Submitted for publication
Macdonald, K. C., Becker, K., Spiess, F. N., Ballard, R. D. 1980b. Hydrothermal heat flux of the "black smoker" vents on the East Pacific Rise. *Earth Planet. Sci. Lett.* 48:1–7
Macdonald, K. C., Luyendyk, B. P., Mudie, J. D., Spiess, F. N. 1975. Near-bottom geophysical study of the Mid-Atlantic Ridge median valley near Lat. 37°N.: Preliminary observations. *Geology* 3:211–15
Macdonald, K. C., Luyendyk, B. P. 1977. Deep-tow studies of the structure of the Mid-Atlantic Ridge crest near Lat. 37°N. *Geol. Soc. Am. Bull.* 88:621–36
Macdonald, K. C., Luyendyk, B. P. 1981. The crest of the East Pacific Rise. *Sci. Am. 228:62–72*
Macdonald, K. C., Luyendyk, B. P., Atwater, T. M. 1982a. Investigation of faulting and abyssal hill formation on the flanks of the East Pacific Rise (21 N) using ALVIN. *Mar. Geophys. Res.* Submitted for publication
Macdonald, K. C., Miller, S. P., Huestis, S. P., Spiess, F. N. 1980a. Three-dimensional modelling of a magnetic reversal boundary from inversion of deep-tow measurements. *J. Geophys. Res.* 85: 3670–80
Macdonald, K. C., Miller, S. P., Luyendyk, B. P., Atwater, T. M., Shure, L. 1982b. Investigation of a Vine-Matthews magnetic lineation from a submersible: The source and character of marine magnetic anomalies. *J. Geophys. Res.* Submitted for publication
Macdonald, K. C., Mudie, J. D. 1974. Microearthquakes on the Galapagos Spreading Center and the seismicity of fast spreading ridges. *Geophys. J. R. Astron. Soc.* 36:245–57
Macdonald, K. C., Orcutt, J. A., McClain, J. S. 1980. Ocean bottom seismometer microearthquake studies of the RISE hydrothermal field *EOS* 61:1048 (Abstr.)
McClain, J. S., Lewis, B. T. R. 1980. A seismic experiment at the axis of the East Pacific Rise. *Marine Geol.* 35:147–69
Menard, H. W. 1967. Seafloor spreading, topography and the second layer. *Science* 157:923–24
Miller, S. P. 1977. The validity of the geological interpretations of marine magnetic anomalies. *Geophys. J. R. Astron. Soc.* 50:1–21
Moore, J. G., Fleming, H. S., Phillips, J. D.

1974. Preliminary model for extrusion and rifting at the axis of the Mid-Atlantic Ridge, 26°48′N. *Geology* 2:437–40

Needham, H. D., Francheteau, J. 1974. Some characteristics of the rift valley in the Atlantic Ocean near 36°48′N. *Earth Planet. Sci. Lett.* 22:29–43

Nelson, K. D. 1981. A simple thermal-mechanical model for mid-ocean ridge topographic variation. *Geophys. J. R. Astron. Soc.* 65:19–30

Nisbet, E. G., Fowler, C. M. R. 1978. The Mid-Atlantic Ridge at 37 and 45°N: Some geophysical and petrologic constraints. *Geophys. J. R. Astron. Soc.* 54:631–60

Normark, W. R. 1976. Delineation of the main extrusion zone of the East Pacific Rise at Lat. 21°N. *Geology* 4:681–85

Orcutt, J. A., Kennett, B. L. N., Dorman, L. M. 1976. Structure of the East Pacific Rise from an ocean bottom seismometer array. *Geophys. J. R. Astron. Soc.* 45:305–20

Orcutt, J. A., Kennett, B. L. N., Dorman, L. M., Prothero, W. A. 1975. Evidence for a low-velocity zone underlying a fast-spreading rise crest. *Nature* 256:475–76

Pallister, J. S., Hopson, C. A. 1981. Samail ophiolite plutonic suite: Field relations, phase variations, cryptic variation and layering, and a model of a spreading ridge magma chamber. *J. Geophys. Res.* 86: 2593–644

Parker, R. L., Huestis, S. P. 1974. The inversion of magnetic anomalies in the presence of topography. *J. Geophys. Res.* 79:1587–93

Poehls, K. 1974. Seismic refraction on the Mid-Atlantic Ridge at 37°N. *J. Geophys. Res.* 79:3370–73

Rea, D. K. 1975. Model for the formation of topographic features of the East Pacific Rise crest. *Geology* 3:77–80

Rea, D. K. 1978. Asymmetric seafloor spreading and a nontransform axis offset: The East Pacific Rise 20°S. survey area. *Geol. Soc. Am. Bull.* 89:836–44.

Reid, I. D., Jackson, H. R. 1981. Oceanic spreading rate and crustal thickness. *Nature* In press

Reid, I. D., Macdonald, K. C. 1973. Microearthquake study of the Mid-Atlantic Ridge near 37°N. using sonobuoys. *Nature* 246: 88–90

Reid, I. D., Orcutt, J. A., Prothero, W. A. 1977. Seismic evidence for a narrow zone of partial melting underlying the East Pacific Rise at 21°N. *Geol. Soc. Am. Bull.* 88: 678–82

Rhodes, J. M., Dungan, M. A. 1979. The evolution of ocean-floor basaltic magmas. See Atwater 1979, pp. 262–72

Rosendahl, B. R., Raitt, R. W., Dorman, L. M., Bibee, L. O., Hussong, D. M., Sutton, G. H. 1976. Evolution of oceanic crust, 1, A physical model of the East Pacific Rise crest derived from seismic refraction data. *J. Geophys. Res.* 81:5294–305

Schouten, H., Denham, C. R. 1979. Modeling the oceanic magnetic source layer. See Atwater 1979, pp. 151–59

Scott, M. R., Scott, R. B., Rona, P. A., Butler, L. W., Nalwalk, A. J. 1974. Rapidly accumulating manganese deposit from the median valley of the Mid-Atlantic Ridge. *Geophys. Res. Lett.* 1:355–58

Searle, R. C., Francis, T. J. G., Hilde, T. W. C., Somers, M. L., Revie, J., Jacobs, C. L., Saunders, M. R., Barrow, B. J., Bicknell, S. V. 1981. Gloria Side-scan Sonar in the East Pacific. *EOS* 62:121–22

Shih, J. S. F. 1980. *The nature and origin of fine-scale seafloor relief*. PhD thesis. Mass. Inst. Tech., Cambridge. 222 pp.

Shih, J., Molnar, P. 1975. Analysis and implications of the sequence of ridge jumps that eliminated the surveyor transform fault. *J. Geophys. Res.* 80:4815–22

Sleep, N. H. 1969. Sensitivity of heat flow and gravity to the mechanism of seafloor spreading. *J. Geophys. Res.* 74:542–49

Sleep, N. H. 1975. Formation of ocean crust: Some thermal constraints. *J. Geophys. Res.* 80:4037–42

Sleep, N. H. 1978. Thermal structure and kinematics of mid-oceanic ridge axes, some implications to basaltic volcanism. *Geophys. Res. Lett.* 5:426–28

Sleep, N. H., Biehler, S. 1970. Topography and tectonics at the intersections of fracture zones with central rifts. *J. Geophys. Res.* 75:2748–52

Sleep, N. H., Rosendahl, B. R. 1979. Topography and tectonics of mid-ocean ridge axes. *J. Geophys. Res.* 84:6831–39

Spiess, F. N., Macdonald, K. C., Atwater, T., Ballard, R., Carranza, A., Cordoba, D., Cox, C., Diaz Garcia, V. M., Francheteau, J., Guerrero, J., Hawkins, J., Haymon, R., Hessler, R., Juteau, T., Kastner, M., Larson, R., Luyendyk, B., MacDougall, J. D., Miller, S., Normark, W., Orcutt, J., Rangin, C. 1980. East Pacific Rise: Hot Springs and Geophysical Experiments. *Science* 207:1421–33

Spindel, R. C., Davis, S. B., Macdonald, K. C., Porter, R. P., Phillips, J. D. 1974. Microearthquake survey of the median valley of the Mid-Atlantic Ridge at 36°30′N. *Nature* 248:577–79

Stroup, J., Fox, P. J. 1981. Geological investigation of the Mid-Cayman Rise: Evidence for thin oceanic crust along the Mid-Cayman Rise. *J. Geol.* 89:101–15

Sykes, L. R. 1967. Mechanism of earthquakes and nature of faulting on the mid-oceanic ridge. *J. Geophys. Res.* 72:2131–53

Tapponnier, P., Francheteau, J. 1978. Necking of the lithosphere and the mechanics of slowly accreting plate boundaries. *J. Geophys. Res.* 83:3955–70

Turekian, K. K., Cochran, J. K. 1981. Growth rate determination of a vesicomyid clam from the Galapagos Spreading Center hydrothermal field using natural radionuclides. *Earth Planet. Sci. Lett.* In press

van Andel, T. H., Ballard, R. D. 1979. The Galapagos Rift at 86°W, 2. Volcanism, structure and evolution of the rift valley. *J. Geophys. Res.* 84:5390–406

van Andel, T. H., Bowin, C. O. 1968. Mid-Atlantic ridge between 22° and 23°N latitude and the tectonics of mid-ocean rises. *J. Geophys. Res.* 73:1279–98

Verosub, K. L., Moores, E. M. 1981. Tectonic rotations in extensional regimes and their paleomagnetic consequences for oceanic basalts. *J. Geophys. Res.* 86: 6335–50

Weiss, R. F., Lonsdale, P., Lupton, J. E., Bainbridge, A. E., Craig, H. 1977. Hydrothermal plumes in the Galapagos Rift. *Nature* 267:600–3

Whitmarsh, R. B. 1975. Axial intrusion zone beneath the median valley of the Mid-Atlantic Ridge at 37°N detected by explosion seismology. *Geophys. J. R. Astron. Soc.* 42:189–215

Williams, D., Von Herzen, R. P. 1974. Heat loss from the earth: New estimate. *Geology* 2:327–28

Williams, D. L., Green, K., van Andel, T. H., Von Herzen, R. P., Dymond, J. R., Crane, K. 1979. The hydrothermal mounds of the Galapagos Rift: Observations with DSRV ALVIN and detailed heat flow studies. *J. Geophys. Res.* 84:7467–84

Ann. Rev. Earth Planet. Sci. 1982. 10:191-220

PRE-MESOZOIC PALEOMAGNETISM AND PLATE TECTONICS

Rob Van der Voo

Department of Geological Sciences, University of Michigan, Ann Arbor, Michigan 48109

INTRODUCTION

Although the arguments perhaps did not convince everyone at the time, the paleomagnetic polar wander paths for Europe and North America plotted by Runcorn (1956) certainly convinced me as a young graduate student that "continental drift" (as we called it in those pre-plate-tectonic days) deserved serious attention. Then, throughout the 1960s, the geoscience world seemed busy documenting and refining the models of seafloor spreading and plate tectonics that governed the opening of today's oceans. As the number of publications espousing plate tectonics seemed to grow exponentially, an often tacit assumption was that the continental breakup was a unique event, and that Pangea was a quasi-primordial continental configuration. Ahead of his time, however, J. Tuzo Wilson (1966) queried in a now classical paper "Did the Atlantic close and then re-open?"

The 1973 Penrose Conference in Vail, Colorado, on pre-Mesozoic plate tectonics (Dewey & Spall 1975) showed that by then many earth scientists were preoccupied with proving that the "tacit assumption" was wrong and that Wilson was right. But compared to Mesozoic and later plate tectonics, the task of quantifying pre-Mesozoic continental movements is much more difficult, since there are no seafloor magnetic anomalies to work with and much of the potential evidence (e.g. ophiolites, diagnostic supracrustal sequences, high pressure–low temperature metamorphic rocks) has been destroyed by that ultimate plate tectonic process, the continent-continent collision, and by subsequent uplift and erosion. Nevertheless, a multitude of observations, facts, interpretations, reinterpretations, proposals, and hypotheses can now be found in the literature for virtually any pre-Mesozoic period and any geographic-

0084–6597/82/0515–0191$02.00

tectonic element. These publications, though important, are often confusing and mutually conflicting. I personally do not feel that Hallam (1979) overstated the problem when he ended his review ("A decade of plate tectonics") stating that "our best hope seems to lie with the paleomagnetists. . . ."

It is my purpose here to review the methods and some of the available paleomagnetic data relevant to Paleozoic and Precambrian plate motions. It must be evident that the question of whether plate tectonics was operative throughout pre-Mesozoic time or whether it evolved gradually is foremost in many people's minds. Answers to this question remain elusive and the paleomagnetic evidence for early or middle Proterozoic time is still controversial, as is explained later.

Data for the Paleozoic and latest Precambrian, on the other hand, provide us with very convincing evidence of pre-Mesozoic plate tectonics. Most of these data have become available in the last decade, and it is with some personal sense of excitement and gratification that I review them, since my coworkers, my graduate students, and I have been able to make some contributions to the subject. Although much paleomagnetic work still has to be done on Paleozoic rocks and many problems remain, the story is beginning to make sense.

Paleomagnetism is now a maturing subfield of Earth Science and, as is common in such cases, new insights and techniques have greatly improved the quality of its data. Although many of the studies of two decades ago have been redone or have been discarded as less reliable, we should pay tribute to the early workers whose efforts launched us toward today's vantage points. In the following, I first review the methods and criteria by which modern paleomagnetic results are commonly judged, and then present two chapters on Paleozoic and Precambrian results.

DATA SELECTION, METHODS, AND TECHNIQUES

In view of the nearly universal acceptance that moving continents and oceans are a reality, and the conclusion of Jurdy & Van der Voo (1975) that it is these movements of the lithospheric plates, rather than a moving polar axis (i.e. true polar wandering), that are responsible for the apparent polar wander paths constructed from paleomagnetic data, the most logical approach to a documentation of the past peregrinations of the plates would be a movie-like scenario with the pole being fixed. For most purposes, however, this is impractical and costly, although maps and atlases are regularly being produced (Briden et al 1974, 1981, Ziegler et al 1977, 1979, Scotese et al 1979). Apparent polar wander paths (APWPs) for the plates or continental blocks involved still constitute the most common documentation and visualization technique for paleomagnetic data. How then does one go about constructing an APWP?

Catalogues and lists containing nearly all published paleomagnetic poles exist for this purpose in books, international journals, and special issues (Irving 1964, McElhinny 1968a,b, 1969, 1970, 1972a,b, 1973, Hicken et al 1972, Irving & Hastie 1975, Irving et al 1976a,b,c, McElhinny & Cowley 1977, 1978, 1980). Pitfalls exist, however, for the uninitiated trying to attempt the construction of APWPs, despite a certain familiarity with the usual paleomagnetic textbooks (Irving 1964, Strangway 1970, Tarling 1971, McElhinny 1973). Many formations have been studied and restudied paleomagnetically; improved techniques, such as alternating-field, thermal, and chemical demagnetization, better statistical treatments, vector analysis, higher-sensitivity magnetometers, better age dating, and new insights in the acquisition mechanisms of remanent magnetizations (from depositional mechanisms to diagenesis and metamorphism), usually make later studies more reliable than earlier ones. Although calculation errors occur infrequently, they have to be checked for. A paleomagnetic pole is only valid for the limited area from which the samples were collected, unless continuity with and rigid attachment to neighboring areas is assured; thus, some geological insight is required. Certain poles are "anomalous" when compared to contemporaneous results from the same block (e.g. Harrison & Lindh 1982); sometimes the anomaly can be explained by unusual secular variation ("excursions") or by the inference that the field was recorded in the transitional stage during a polarity reversal, but often this remains at best an assumption.

It is clear, therefore, that selection criteria must be applied in APWP construction. This is a subjective process and only the fullest documentation (set criteria, poles accepted, poles rejected and on what basis) elevates an APWP to a scientific tool and guarantees repeatability of the analysis.

Modern selection criteria may vary in detail, but commonly include (e.g. Van der Voo & French 1974) (*a*) demonstrated stability of the magnetizations through demagnetization analysis and paleomagnetic tests (fold-, contact-, reversal-, or conglomerate tests, rock-magnetic experiments, identification of remanence carriers); (*b*) good structural control and provenance from an area that can be inferred as having belonged to the continental block in question since the time of the magnetization of the rocks; (*c*) a minimum number of samples and sites to average out secular variation and sampling or measurement errors, and statistically acceptable confidence limits; and (*d*) good control of the age of magnetization with a precision that is commensurate with the analysis goals.

The age control is perhaps one of the more important criteria, but—evidently—dating precision varies with age. For instance, it can and should be much better for the late Paleozoic than for the early Proterozoic. In addition, I need only recall the variations in the estimate for the radiometric age of the Cambrian-Precambrian boundary, commonly taken to be about 570 million years (Ma) but perhaps as late as 530 Ma (Charlot 1976, 1978), to illustrate the potential disparity between radiometric and stratigraphic ages. For this review, the Phanerozoic time scale of Van Eysinga (1975) has been used, supplemented by the time scale of McKerrow et al (1980) and an age of 540 Ma for the Precambrian/Cambrian boundary. For the constant for ^{87}Rb decay, I have used the following:

$$\lambda = 1.42 \times 10^{-11}\ \mathrm{yr}^{-1}.$$

For many Paleozoic periods, the major continental blocks have spotty paleomagnetic coverage, although the number of available poles has increased perhaps five- to tenfold during the last decade. For the Precambrian, the data base is adequate only for a gross outline of the questions and possible answers that will undoubtedly occupy paleomagneticians for the rest of this century. The reasons for this inadequacy can be easily understood when the increased uncertainty of age dating and the increasing lack of suitable rock formations with increasing age are considered.

An additional inherent paleomagnetic complexity occurs for time periods with sparse data coverage: the indeterminancy of whether or not a given result is one of normal or reversed polarity, i.e. whether to construct the APWP through pole A or through its antipole A′. In the absence of additional information, most paleomagneticians follow a conservative scheme of selecting the shortest distance, although unusual proposals have been made (e.g. Morris et al 1979) that seem to force APWPs to fit a certain preconceived notion.

Next to age, structural control is perhaps most important. For the Paleozoic it is possible to distinguish between cratons and mobile belts, but this distinction is gradually lost in the Precambrian. The major geographical entities (cratons) that enter my discussion for the Paleozoic are Laurentia (the North American craton including Greenland in a predrift position), Siberia, Baltica (the Scandinavian Baltic Shield and the Russian platform), and Gondwana in its predrift configuration (Smith & Hallam 1970) of Africa, South America, Antarctica, Australia, Madagascar, and India. Other important entities are more loosely defined in the discussion of the results below (e.g. Armorica, see Figure 1), or lack paleomagnetic data to a large extent (China in particular). Then there are smaller geographical units, such as displaced terranes or microplates, that I will define as need arises.

The paleomagnetism of mobile belts is a fascinating subfield and many creative uses of paleomagnetism can be found in the literature. In contrast to the APWPs of the major continental blocks, paleomagnetic data of the orogenic belts are subject to their own special sets of rules and constraints, but these fall outside the scope of this paper. A recent review on this topic is given by Van der Voo & Channell (1980).

PALEOZOIC PALEOMAGNETISM AND PLATE TECTONICS

The Paleozoic story is essentially that of the assembly of Pangea with most of the action taking place in the Atlantic domain. It has long been recognized that in gross outline an older (Caledonian) orogenic belt could have marked the collision of Baltica and Laurentia, followed in time by a younger (Appalachian-Hercynian-Uralian) orogeny when Gondwana and Siberia joined this earlier-formed nucleus (Figure 1). In detail, however, new developments have been proposed in the last few years that modify the overall scheme. For organizational purposes, it is best to proceed by discussing the sequence of events by period while going back in time, so as to build from what is known before describing the more speculative events earlier in the Paleozoic.

The Permotriassic

Pangea was mostly assembled during the Permotriassic, with possible exceptions being China and other parts of southeastern Asia for which there is very little paleomagnetic information. Although perhaps the best known continental configuration for this time is the Wegener-type fit of Bullard et al (1965), it has been noted that the Permotriassic paleomagnetic data require some modification of the fit between Gondwana and the northern continents, if the usual assumption of a geocentric dipole field is granted. One type of alternative fit (Walper & Rowett 1972, Van der Voo & French 1974, Van der

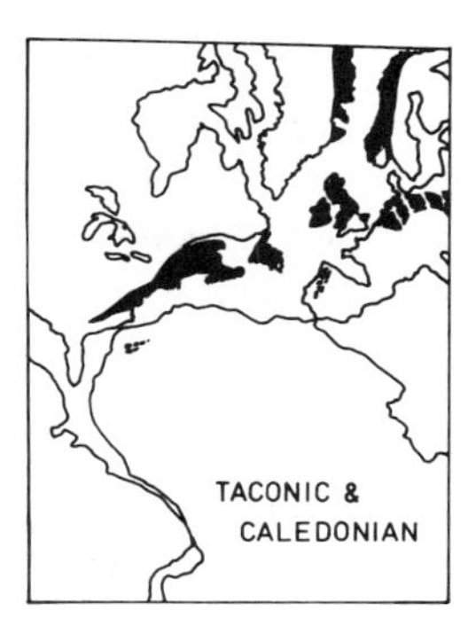

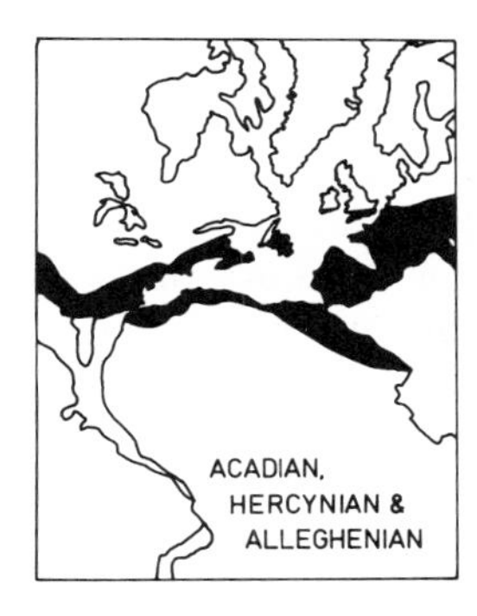

Figure 1 Pangea configuration of the Atlantic-bordering continents with early Paleozoic (Taconic, Caledonian) and late Paleozoic (Acadian, Hercynian-Alleghenian) orogenies in black. On the right, the possible maximum extent of the Armorica plate, as proposed by Van der Voo (1979), is indicated. This Armorica plate comprises, in a counterclockwise sense, Hercynian Europe with its older Precambrian Massifs, the London-Brabant Massif in Belgium and southern England, Wales, possibly the Avalonian terranes of northeastern North America (eastern Newfoundland, coastal Canadian Maritimes, eastern New England), and perhaps northernmost Morocco.

Voo et al 1976, Pilger 1978) closes the Gulf of Mexico by juxtaposition of the cratonic edges of southern North America and northern South America. This fit has been used for the configuration of Figure 1. Another alternative reconstruction, satisfying the paleomagnetic data equally well, was proposed by Irving (1977) and Morel & Irving (1981) and involves a position of Gondwana about 3500 km more to the east when compared to the other fits, such that the northwest coast of South America is adjacent to the eastern (Atlantic) seaboard of North America. This fit has been called the Pangea B fit by Irving (1977), in contrast to the Wegener-type Pangea A fit. To a first approximation, the difference between the two is in longitudes only; since the paleomagnetic method relies on axisymmetric dipole field models, it cannot resolve paleolongitudes. Most workers agree that the Atlantic ocean began opening from a Pangea A fit, and Irving (1977) and Morel & Irving (1981) have argued therefore for a Permotriassic transition from Pangea B to Pangea A involving a 3500 km megashear between Gondwana and the northern continents. Van der Voo (1981a) has argued that the model of Irving and Morel cannot easily be reconciled with the Permotriassic geology of the area of the hypothetical megashear (e.g. the Western Mediterranean, southern France, Spain, and Florida). Although both the Pangea B and the Van der Voo et al fit are paleomagnetically permissible, geological and paleogeographical constraints favor the latter.

Geological evidence and paleomagnetic data suggest that Siberia and Baltica were welded together during the Permian, although they may have been roughly adjacent from the Devonian onwards (Irving 1977).

The Carboniferous

The major phases of the Hercynian and Alleghenian orogenies in southern Europe, Morocco and the Mauritanides, the Appalachians, the Ouachita mountains, and the Venezuelan Andes mark the final collision of Gondwana with the northern continents (Laurussia). Gondwana and Laurussia approached each other between late Devonian and middle Carboniferous (Namurian) time: paleomagnetically determined paleolatitudes indicate that the intervening ocean, still about 3000 $\pm$ 700 km wide during the middle-to-late Devonian (Figure 2), was no more than 800 km wide in the Visean stage of the early Carboniferous (Lefort & Van der Voo 1981). It is difficult to estimate the precise timing of the first collisional contact between Laurussia and Gondwana, since paleomagnetic data do not provide the required resolution whereas structural information, e.g. the Hercynian orogenic phases of Stille (1924), does not necessarily enable us to distinguish subduction-related processes from collisional events. Lefort & Van der Voo (1981) have suggested that most likely the collision was a long-lasting process not unlike the prolonged impact of India upon Asia, which produced the Tertiary Himalayan mountain chain (Molnar & Tapponnier 1977, 1978). In recent years it has become clear, moreover, that the Gondwana-Laurussia collision caused an internal rearrangement of Laurussia. This rearrangement occurred along a sinistral megashear that followed the previous Caledonian zones of weakness from New England through Newfoundland and Scotland to Spitsbergen, according to the available Devonian and Lower Carboniferous paleomagnetic data (Kent & Opdyke 1978, 1979, Van der Voo et al 1979, Harland 1980, Van der Voo &

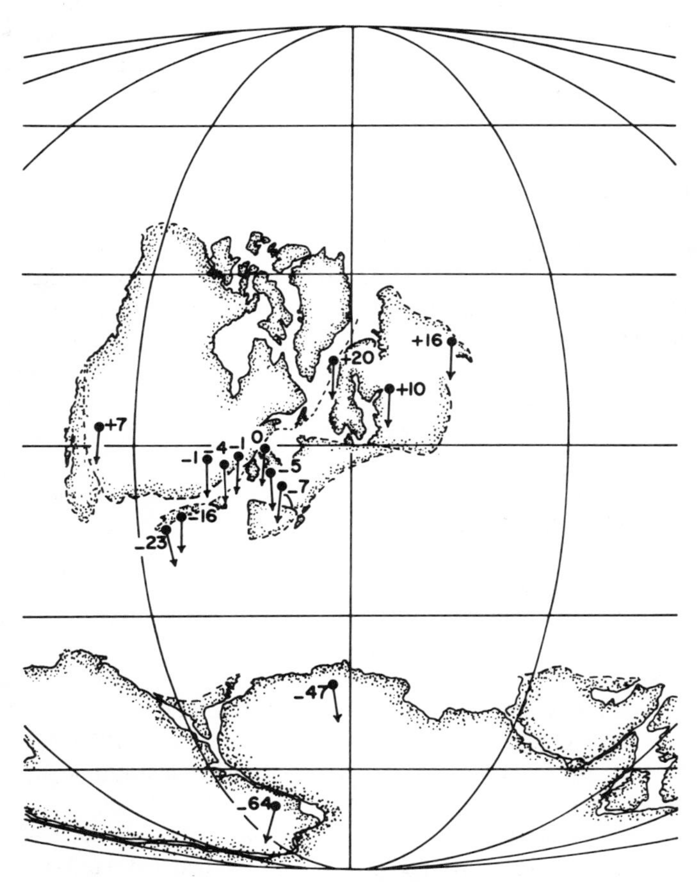

Figure 2 Paleogeographic map in Mollweide projection for the middle to late Devonian of the Atlantic-bordering continents, compiled on the basis of paleomagnetic data. Each plotted point represents the average declination (arrow) and paleolatitude (number, positive North and negative South paleolatitude) for a given region. The paleomagnetic poles reveal a small amount of apparent polar wander for this time (approximately 370 to 340 Ma), which accounts for small local deviations from the mean.

Scotese 1980, 1981, Van der Voo 1981b). The movements along this megashear are estimated to be between 1800 and 2100 km (Van der Voo 1981b) and are thought to have occurred predominantly during the late early and middle Carboniferous, since late Carboniferous (Stephanian) paleopoles from Europe and North America suggest that the movements had ended by that time. A comparative examination of Figures 2 and 1 will reveal the relative positions of Europe and North America before and after the megashear movements. Lefort & Van der Voo (1981) relate these sinistral movements, and those of presumably lesser magnitude along east-west dextral faults in northwest Africa, Hercynian Europe, and northeastern North America, to the collisional impact of the West African craton upon the broad mobile marginal belts of Laurussia, in analogy to the indentation models of Molnar & Tapponnier (1977).

The Middle to Late Devonian

The middle-to-late Devonian map of Figure 2 has already been mentioned. It should be noted that the position of Gondwana is based on very scant paleomagnetic data: one apparently reliable pole from Morocco (south of the Atlas Fault) and one less reliable result from the Picos and Passagim Series in Brazil (Creer 1970). No other (early or late) Devonian data pass modern reliability criteria for the cratonic areas of Gondwana. Eastern Australia's Devonian results cannot be used, since the real possibility exists that parts of the mobile Tasman belt were displaced with respect to the craton. Our Devonian paleopoles from Gondwana reassuringly fall on the track between Silurian and early Carboniferous poles, but nevertheless more data are badly needed.

The map of Figure 2, based on data tabulated elsewhere (Van der Voo et al 1980, Van der Voo & Scotese 1981), displays two other noteworthy results. First, late Devonian and older results from Maine and New Brunswick indicate that this area was located on the "European" side of the Carboniferous megashear, as first described by Kent & Opdyke (1978, 1979) and Spariosu & Kent (1980). Second, late Devonian and early Carboniferous results from France and Spain (Jones et al 1979, Duff 1979, De Bouvier et al 1979, Perroud & Bonhommet 1980, Bonhommet et al 1981) indicate that at this time these areas of Hercynian Europe were close to or connected with Baltica, and that the major ocean separating Baltica and Gondwana in the late Devonian was located to the south of the Armorican Massif in France and the Asturian Arc in Spain. If the Kulm deposition of late Devonian to early Carboniferous age near the Hercynian front marked the site of an ocean (Johnson 1973, 1974), this ocean must not have been very wide. The suture between Gondwana and Laurussia must, as a consequence, be sought farther south between the Ibero-Armorican Arc and the Sahara platform.

The Silurian and Early Devonian

For this period the paleomagnetic data are still partly ambiguous or even absent for some continental blocks. Consequently, one must rely to a large extent on geological information to build a framework into which the sparse paleomagnetic data can be fitted.

The latest Silurian marks the time when the last deep-water marine sedimentation took place in the Caledonian orogenic belt in Greenland, Spitsbergen, Norway, Great Britain and north-Central Europe; from structural information we know that the peak of the orogeny occurred then as well. A late orogenic to postorogenic molasse type sedimentation is seen throughout the belt and in adjacent areas, and is known as the Old Red Sandstone. For decades the area where this facies occurs has been called the Old Red Continent, which comprises the northern half of the Russian Platform, the Baltic Shield, Spitsbergen, Greenland, the Ardennes in Belgium, a perhaps questionable occurrence in Normandy (France), and northeastern North America as far south as the Catskill delta in New York and Pennsylvania. From this geological evidence it can be safely concluded that if the Caledonian orogeny resulted from continent-continent collision, then the collision occurred at the latest during late Silurian time.

The location of the Caledonian orogen forms a T-shaped pattern (Figure 1): besides the well-known belt through Greenland, Norway and Great Britain, there is increasing evidence for a branch which runs northwest-southeast from Great Britain, through the North Sea, the Netherlands, Belgium, northern Germany, to Poland (Zwart & Dornsiepen 1978, Ziegler 1978, 1981, Watson & Dunning 1979). Exposures of this Caledonian branch occur in the Ardennes and in the Holy Cross mountains of Poland; elsewhere the information is entirely from borehole data showing pre-Devonian deformation and radiometric ages.

These two branches of the Caledonian orogen outline the northwestern and southwestern margin of Baltica. Taken at face value, the belts could be construed as marking the collision of Baltica with the remainder of Europe and with Laurentia, but some other questions arise in this context. One of these pertains to the nature and timing of the pre-Alleghenian deformation in the northern, central, and southern Appalachians. To the southwest from Great Britain to Newfoundland and beyond in the assembly of Figure 2, the Caledonian orogeny (*sensu stricto*) is no longer seen. Instead the early to middle Devonian Acadian orogeny and the Middle to late Ordovician Taconic orogeny take its place along strike. From the late Devonian paleomagnetic results for France, it is clear that if Hercynian Europe was an independent plate called Armorica (Van der Voo 1979) in the early Paleozoic, then it must have collided with Laurentia before the late Devonian, i.e. during either the Taconic or the Acadian orogeny, whereas its collision with Baltica is most logically associated with the Caledonian branch from Great Britain to Poland.

One may well ask whether the occurrences of the Taconic (~ 440 Ma), the Caledonian (~ 415 Ma), and the Acadian (~ 380 Ma) orogenies are sufficiently distinct in time to assign separate collisions or other plate tectonic events to each, or whether the distinctions are even relevant; it may be that continent-continent collisions occurred obliquely so that the timing at one end is much earlier than at the other. If this was the case, perhaps all three continental units (Baltica, Laurentia, and Armorica) can be considered as having coalesced at essentially the "same" time.

In view of all of this, the relative scarcity of paleomagnetic data leaves the models somewhat unconstrained. Nevertheless, there are North American and European (mostly British) Silurian paleomagnetic poles that yield an interesting conclusion. Morris (1976) was the first to recognize that Ordovician and Silurian data from Great Britain and the U.S.A. indicated similar latitudinal positions for the two. Piper (1979) updated this analysis, and suggested some relative in situ rotations for the British Isles. Van der Voo (1981b) extended the analysis of the relative paleolatitudes to the time between middle Ordovician and late Carboniferous and concluded on the basis of the comparison (Table 1) that Great Britain and North America maintained a near-constant relative paleolatitude position from Ordovician through early Carboniferous time. Then in the late early and middle Carboniferous the previously mentioned sinistral megashear occurred.

Figure 3 displays the paleolatitude patterns as well as the declinational evidence for possible in situ rotations. The paleolatitudes of North America and western Europe (mostly Great Britain with a few results from Hercynian Europe) are compared as follows. The Atlantic Ocean is closed according to the fit by Bullard et al (1965). North American cratonic poles have been averaged and the mean paleopoles are used to predict a paleolatitude and a declination for all European sampling sites, taking into account the ages of the rocks at these sites. The differences ($\Delta\phi$) between observed and predicted paleolatitudes have been used to calculate the averages and standard deviations of Figure 3; similarly, differences (ΔD) between predicted and observed declinations are plotted as arrows, all as a function of Paleozoic time. One observes small declination deviations for postorogenic time and often large differences for Silurian and earlier time, indicating that local (in situ) rotations of sampled areas may have been caused by the Caledonian deformation in the mobile belt.

The paleolatitude differences are remarkably similar from Ordovician through early Carboniferous time and support the previously described Carboniferous megashear. Great Britain and Baltica were undoubtedly adjacent to North America in Devonian and late Paleozoic time since no deeper-water sediments are seen anywhere in this area; for Late Ordovician and Silurian time this cannot be ascertained because the paleomagnetic data do not provide any longitudinal information. If we assume Great Britain to be roughly contiguous with North America during the entire middle Paleozoic (allowing for some in situ block rotations), the near-constant average value of 15° for the paleolatitude differences indicates a paleoposition of Great Britain (south of the Great Glen Fault) to the east of New York State opposite the Catskill delta. The sparse paleomagnetic data for Hercynian Europe, principally from East Germany and Czechoslovakia, suggest continuity with Great Britain, although more data are needed. If, on the other hand, one wishes to have relative drift between Great Britain and North America during the late Ordovician and/or Silurian, the paleomagnetic analysis constrains the convergence to one with purely east-west motions.

The preceding does not settle the question of whether the collision between North America and Great Britain plus Hercynian Europe produced the Acadian (Kent 1980) or Taconic orogeny (Van der Voo 1979). The Ordovician geology of western Europe and the Appalachians induced me to favor the Taconic orogeny, but this forces the adoption of a rather ad hoc hypothesis for the Acadian orogeny, whereas in Kent's model the Taconic orogeny is left unexplained. The Acadian orogeny is characterized by abundant plutonic activity and often high-grade metamorphism. Besides the northern Appa-

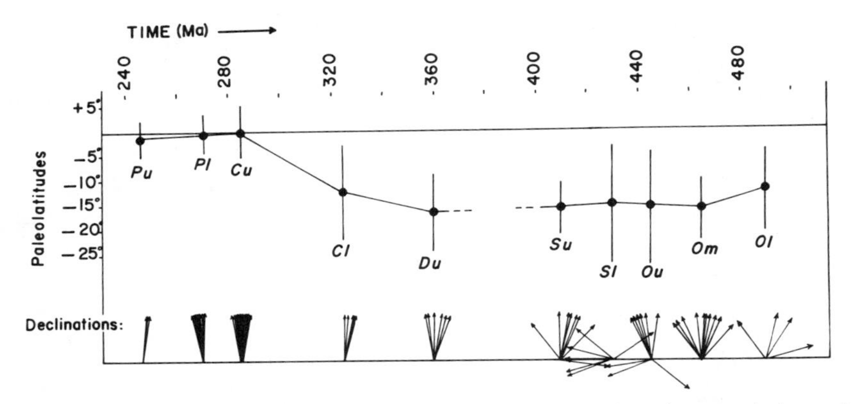

Figure 3 Paleolatitude and declination differences between Laurentian paleomagnetic data and those for western Europe (mostly Great Britain, south of the Great Glen Fault), plotted as a function of Paleozoic time, and with respect to the fit of Bullard et al (1965). See also Table 1. The consistent paleolatitude difference for times preceding the Late Carboniferous reflects the more southerly paleolatitude position of western Europe shown in Figure 2, whereas the declination deviations can be explained by local rotations of the sampling areas. Explanation of the ages: P is Permian, C is Carboniferous, D is Devonian, S is Silurian, O is Ordovician, u is upper, m is middle, and l is lower.

Table 1 Paleozoic data for cratonic North America and for western Europe[a]

Age group	$\Delta\phi \pm$ s. d.	North American pole position	North American entries	West European entries
Late Permian (Thuringian)	−2.0° ± 3.6°	51°N, 116°E	9.65; 11.58; 11.65; 13.47a; 13.47b	14.307/308; 12.110; 14.326
Early Permian (Autunian, Saxonian)	−0.7° ± 4.0°	45°N, 119°E	10.106; 13.50; 13.51; 13.52; 13.47c; 13.47d; P 1	Irving: 7.11; 7.13; 7.54; McE: 14.334; 8.87; 11.70; P 7; 14.317; 14.318; 14.310/5; P 8
Latest Carboniferous (Stephanian, Stephano-Autunian)	−0.1° ± 5.4°	41°N, 128°E	8.95; 8.96; 8.97; 8.99; 8.100; 8.88	14.324/5; 15.110; 14.336; P 9; 12.119; 10.107; 10.108; 10.109; 9.89; 9.90; 14.350; 11.77; 10.111; 11.71
Early Carboniferous (Tournaisian, Visean, Namurian)	−12.8° ± 9.7°	46°N, 123°E	10.119; P 2	14.353; 14.354; 15.125; 14.358; 8.118
Middle and late Devonian (Couvinian-Famennian)	−16.8° ± 7.7°	51°N, 116°E	16.157; 16.158; 16.159; P 3; 14.365; 14.366	14.359; 14.374; 16.162; P 10; 12.134; 14.380a
Late Silurian (Wenlock, Ludlovian)	−16.1° ± 5.3°	24°N, 115°E	see footnote below	14.379; 12.138; 12.139; 8.130; 14.383; 10.129; 14.377; 15.131

Early Silurian (Llandoverian)	$-15.3° \pm 11.6°$	24°N, 115°E	see footnote below	15.133; 14.385; 16.168; 16.167; 16.169; 16.165
Late Ordovician (Caradocian, Ashgillian)	$-15.9° \pm 11.7°$	31°N, 121°E	14.392; 16.173; 14.394; P 4; 14.396; 16.176; 16.177; 16.178	14.380b; 16.170; 16.172; 8.132; 14.386; 14.389; 15.140; 14.390; 14.391; 15.134
Middle Ordovician (late Arenig, Llanvirn, Llandeilo)	$-16.4° \pm 6.2°$	33°N, 147°E	P 5; P 6	14.400; 16.181; 15.136; 15.139; 14.407; 9.131; 16.179; 16.180; 11.80; 14.398; 14.399

[a] $\Delta\phi$ is the latitude difference between observed and predicted values as discussed in the text, with s. d. being the standard deviation about the mean; the entries for North America and western Europe are listed by their catalogue numbers from McElhinny's lists (1968a, b, 1969, 1970, 1972a, b) or McElhinny & Cowley (1977, 1978, 1980). Where indicated some entries come from the listing of Irving (1964). Poles more recent than these listings have been labelled P; references for these results are 1 (Diehl & Shive 1979), 2 (Kent & Opdyke 1979), 3 (Van der Voo et al 1979), 4 (Chapman Ridge pole from Watts & Van der Voo 1979), 5, 6 (Moccasin & Bays poles from Watts & Van der Voo 1979), 7 (Thorning & Abrahamsen 1980), 8 (Bylund 1974), 9 (Bylund 1974), 10 (Jones et al 1979). The North American mean paleopoles for the late and the early Silurian have been based on the Bloomsburg Formation, the Castanea Formation, the Rose Hill Formation, and the Wabash Limestones from Indiana (Wilkinson et al 1981).

lachians, a similar late Silurian–middle Devonian belt is seen in the southern part of the Armorican Massif in France, facing the interior of the Ibero-Armorican Arc (Cogné 1974, Peucat et al 1978), and perhaps farther east in the Massif Central. This Acadian belt could perhaps have formed the southern margin of the combined North American–European continent, facing the ocean that separated it from Gondwana. One of the rare pre-Mesozoic occurrences of blueschist metamorphism is found in a paired-metamorphic belt setting in Ile de Groix, France (Peucat et al 1978), and suggests that this margin could have been of Andean type with northward subduction (without collision) responsible for the Acadian features.

To summarize, two paleomagnetic models exist for the assembly of Laurentia, Baltica, and Armorica. In one (Kent 1980), Baltica and Laurentia collide first in the late Silurian, with Armorica joining them to produce the Acadian orogeny. In the other (Van der Voo 1979), Armorica and Laurentia collide first to produce the middle-to-late Ordovician Taconic orogeny, followed by a Caledonian collision of Baltica with the combined Laurentia/Armorica continent. Both models are paleomagnetically permissible and a definite choice cannot yet be made.

The Ordovician

The available paleopoles and paleogeographic data (e.g. Morel & Irving 1978, Ziegler et al 1979, Scotese et al 1979) indicate that North America was situated in equatorial latitudes throughout Paleozoic time, whereas Gondwana moved gradually northward over the southpole during the time between late Cambrian and early Mesozoic. Glacial markers of Ordovician age in the western Sahara (Schermerhorn 1971, Fairbridge 1969) and Ordovician paleopoles for its cratonic parts (path X of Morel & Irving (1978)) constrain the positions of Gondwana.

An uncertainty exists for the position of Baltica, although the available cratonic poles, all from the Russian platform, indicate near-equatorial positions (McElhinny 1973).

Although it is likely that Armorica was in similar latitudes as North America and Baltica by latest Ordovician to early Silurian times, an ambiguity exists for the early Ordovician. Both high-latitude and intermediate-to-low paleolatitude positions have been obtained from paleomagnetic studies and only a very high rate of apparent polar wander (i.e. drift with respect to the pole) can reconcile these data (e.g. Thomas & Briden 1976, Piper 1979, Perroud & Bonhommet 1981). The high-latitude results are geographically interspersed with the others, so most workers have treated the high-latitude results as anomalous (see Piper 1979), which implies that southern England and Wales, and presumably the rest of Armorica, were close to North American paleolatitudes during the Ordovician (see also Table 1). Piper (1978) has shown that early Ordovician results from southern England and Wales, when compared to those of Scotland south of the Great Glen Fault but north of the inferred Caledonian suture, suggest a north-south separation of some 6°, which is statistically insignificant. Paleontological data suggests that the east-west separation may have been considerable (McKerrow & Cocks 1976).

From the preceding, it must be clear that we can obtain rough estimates of the paleolatitude positions of the major tectonic elements in our analysis (Laurentia, Baltica, Gondwana, Armorica), but that the details are lacking. Again one must turn to other geological information to build a working hypothesis, which eventually must be tested with future paleomagnetic studies.

The main event in the Ordovician geological framework of North America is the Taconic orogeny. Its effects are seen to a varying degree along the ancient cratonic margin now located in the Appalachians between Alabama and Newfoundland (e.g. Hatcher 1972, Zen 1972, Williams 1979, Diecchio 1980, Rowlands 1980, Rowley 1980, Stephens 1980, Robinson & Hall 1980, Hatcher et al 1980, Thomas et al 1980, Tull 1980, Drake 1980, Haworth 1982). These effects include intense structural deformation, thrusting and obduction, and even metamorphism, but relatively little igneous activity occurred on the North American cratonic margin. Classically, the Taconic orogeny has been interpreted (see Williams 1979, Haworth 1982) as due to a collision of the North American craton with the Avalonian terrane (a microcontinent or displaced terrane in eastern Newfoundland, eastern Nova Scotia, and eastern Massachusetts) or with a central Newfoundland–New England island arc. The Avalon terrane is underlain by Pan-African type Precambrian crust. Most workers assumed subduction to be eastward, dipping under Avalon. Could it be that Avalon and Armorica were the same plate and that it was this ensemble rather than an island arc or narrow microcontinent that collided with Laurentia? In this context it is of interest to note the Ordovician events in Armorica: Ordovician calcalkaline granites and andesitic volcanism in England and Wales, in the Armorican Massif of France (Lefort 1977), and in Spain and Portugal (Priem et al 1966).

There is no paleomagnetic evidence to determine whether Avalon and Armorica were part of the same continental plate in Ordovician and earlier time. However, both areas have a Pan-African type (i.e. Avalonian, Cadomian, Arvonian; see Williams & Max 1980) basement. Latest Precambrian and early Paleozoic similarities of these areas have been noted repeatedly, but are not conclusive—paleomagnetic data are badly needed to substantiate this claim. Van der Voo (1979) has suggested that Armorica (including the Avalon terrane) collided with Laurentia during the Taconic orogeny, as discussed earlier, and further work is in progress that will support or refute this idea.

An area with strong Taconic overprinting as seen in radiometric ages (Amenta 1974, Grauert & Wagner 1975, Wagner & Crawford 1975, Foland & Muessig 1978) is the northern Appalachian Piedmont, which remains very enigmatic in the Paleozoic assembly of Pangea. If the northern Piedmont is allochthonous, just as its southern counterpart in South Carolina appears to be (Cook et al 1979), it could be of Laurentian, Gondwanan, or Armorican origin. Rao & Van der Voo (1980) and Brown & Van der Voo (1981) have found very steep inclinations, which imply a paleolocation very close to the Ordovician pole, in their northern Piedmont studies in Delaware and adjacent areas. This could suggest an African affinity for this area, since the Ordovician pole is thought to be located in the western Sahara.

The Cambrian and Latest Precambrian

Good paleomagnetic coverage is available for this time for Laurentia (Watts et al 1980a,b), Gondwana (McElhinny & Embleton 1976, Klootwijk 1980, Kröner et al 1980), and Armorica (Hagstrum et al 1980, Duff 1980, Morris 1980). For Baltica few poles are available (Poorter 1972, McElhinny 1973, Prasad & Sharma 1978). Taken at face value, the poles for Laurentia and Baltica indicate near-equatorial paleopositions, whereas a very large rate of apparent polar wander (implying alternating high-latitude and equatorial paleopositions) is indicated for any area of Gondwana and Armorica. In fact, Hagstrum et al (1980) have argued that the latter two may have nearly identical APWPs for the latest Precambrian and early to middle Cambrian (Figure 4), which would imply that the two areas were adjacent and moved together with respect to the pole. I was a coauthor of this study and am certainly in agreement with its conclusion. Nevertheless, I am fully aware of the uncertainties associated with Gondwana's and Armorica's APWPs, which may result for instance from incorrect dating of the magnetizations. Many of the rocks studied by Hagstrum et al are very well dated, but it remains possible that some have been remagnetized. At least three key poles, however, are based on paleomagnetic studies that have shown more than one ancient component of magnetization in the rocks; in these cases magnetite was indicated as the carrier of the magnetizations. Since in thin section the magnetites appeared to be primary, their magnetizations are most likely thermo-remanent magnetizations. Thus, the acquisition order of the components of magnetization could be established on the basis of the blocking temperatures. Further work is in progress on rocks from the Armorican Massif (Morris 1980, Perigo et al 1981, Van der Voo & Morris 1981) and so far the results fully corroborate the APWP of Hagstrum et al. Thus the concept of the Armorica plate has come about; while during the late Precambrian to middle Cambrian, Armorica moved with Gondwana, we have seen that in the late Devonian it was no longer part of Gondwana.

If a concensus exists about the Cambrian paleomagnetic data and the corresponding paleogeographic positions, it is that the major continental units (Laurentia, Baltica, and Gondwana) were all moving independently of one another and that they all straddled the equator in the late Cambrian. The APWPs suggest that if a supercontinent assembly existed before the Paleozoic Wilson cycle(s), then this supercontinent had already broken up by Cambrian

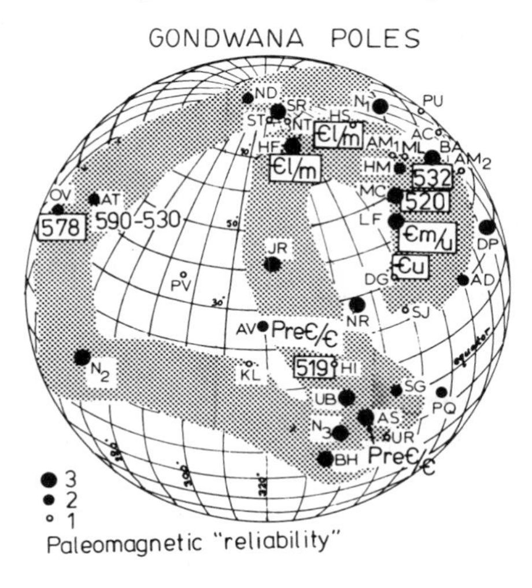

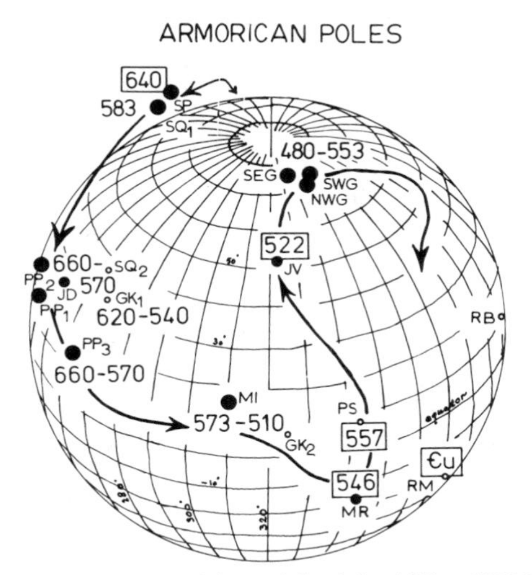

Figure 4 Paleopoles for the late Precambrian and Cambrian (650 to 500 Ma) for Gondwana and the Armorican Massif, with best-fitting APWPs from Hagstrum et al (1980).

times. Late Precambrian results from Gondwana (Kröner et al 1980) and Laurentia (Watts et al 1980b) are not similar either and suggest that one probably should look at Hadrynian APWPs in the interval between 1000 and 650 Ma for a possible match of the paths. Unfortunately, for this time there is only one continental unit (Gondwana) with sufficient paleomagnetic coverage; a lack of well dated and suitable North American rocks with ages between 900 and 650 Ma precludes immediate resolution of this question.

PRECAMBRIAN PALEOMAGNETISM AND PLATE TECTONICS

In the preceding chapter we have seen that paleomagnetism strongly supports Paleozoic plate motions, albeit with increasing lack of detail for the earlier periods of this era. For the Precambrian, the uncertainties increase again by an order of magnitude. Although the last decade has seen a tremendous increase in Precambrian paleomagnetic studies, the current state of knowledge about Precambrian APWPs does not yet permit the construction of plate tectonic models. Because of a lack of detail, it seems better to restrict the discussion to a more basic level: has paleomagnetism thus far demonstrated whether Precambrian plate motions actually occurred? I will address this question by describing the following examples: (*a*) the coherence (or lack thereof) of the African Shield in the Precambrian, (*b*) the Laurentian Shield's APWP, and (*c*) the comparison between Africa and Laurentia. For lack of detailed knowledge as well as lack of space, this chapter is not an exhaustive treatment of the subject. Many important topics will be ignored (e.g. the correlations between Siberia, Baltica, and Laurentia; a comparison of Africa with the rest of Gondwana; the question of the late Precambrian glaciations).

Inspection of Precambrian APWPs would a priori appear to give an affirmative answer to the question of whether or not plate motions occurred. Most Precambrian paths show a very significant motion of the continent with respect to the magnetic polar axis (Ullrich & Van der Voo 1981). It is, however, not at all clear whether a uniformitarian approach is justified: perhaps the continents were stationary while rapid *true* polar wander occurred. Even so, it can be seen at a glance that the APWPs of the two or three best studied continents are not at all similar. On the other hand, this is not the answer to the more basic question faced by paleomagneticians and tectonicians: even though relative motions possibly occurred, we would like to know whether the rules of *plate tectonic* motions applied. Did relative plate motions result in seafloor spreading and can we explain Precambrian orogenic belts by initial rifting, subduction, and eventual continent-continent collision?

If Precambrian mobile belts exist between older cratonic elements that did not move with respect to one another, the orogeny must have been ensialic, i.e. no oceanic crust was involved in the mobilization of the belt. The paleomagnetic technique is best applied to test the ideas about such belts if the ensemble of cratons has retained continuity since the mobilization of the intervening orogenic belt(s)—in such a case we know the temporal and spatial framework. Precambrian belts at the perimeter of a craton, e.g. the Grenville province in Laurentia, are unlikely to provide the resolution, because the "other side" has since drifted away and probably remains unknown. For these reasons, I next discuss the African and Laurentian Shields, which are in places bisected by Precambrian belts.

The African Shield

The Precambrian cratonic elements of Africa are shown in Figure 5 (from McElhinny & McWilliams 1977). The intervening mobile belts are Pan-African (*c*. 750 to 500 Ma). McElhinny and McWilliams have shown that all the paleopoles of the three cratons, Kalahari, Congo, and West Africa, fall on a common APWP at quasi-regular intervals. Figure 5 shows this for the paleopoles of the 2300–1900 Ma interval, but poles with ages between 1100 and 700 Ma (not shown) reveal a similar coherence for the Congo and Kalahari (including the Kaapvaal) cratons (McElhinny & McWilliams 1977). These results suggest, but do not prove, that the West African, Congo, and Kalahari cratons remained in roughly similar positions relative to one another throughout the Proterozoic and Phanerozoic, despite the fact that they are separated by intervening Pan-African belts, such as the Damara belt.

It is theoretically possible, of course, that the Congo and Kalahari cratons drifted widely apart, but that the new "Damaran" ocean in-between closed precisely where it had originally opened. APWPs for both the Congo and the Kalahari cratons based on densely distributed poles with ages between 750 and 500 Ma could prove or disprove this possibility, but suitable rocks are not available. Therefore, our main conclusion at this time is that there is no paleomagnetic support for any but an ensialic model of the Damaran orogeny.

Pan-African belts are widespread in Gondwana, and the above-mentioned conclusion for the Damara belt should not be applied dogmatically to the other belts. Recent work (Onstott & Hargraves 1981) and work in progress (e.g. McWilliams 1981) has suggested that relative motions are revealed by paleopoles from other cratons in South America and Australia.

The Laurentian Shield

The Precambrian poles for North America and Greenland (Laurentia) have been reviewed by Irving & McGlynn (1976) and Irving (1979). The Precambrian APWP for Laurentia is shown in Figure 6, based on Irving (1979)

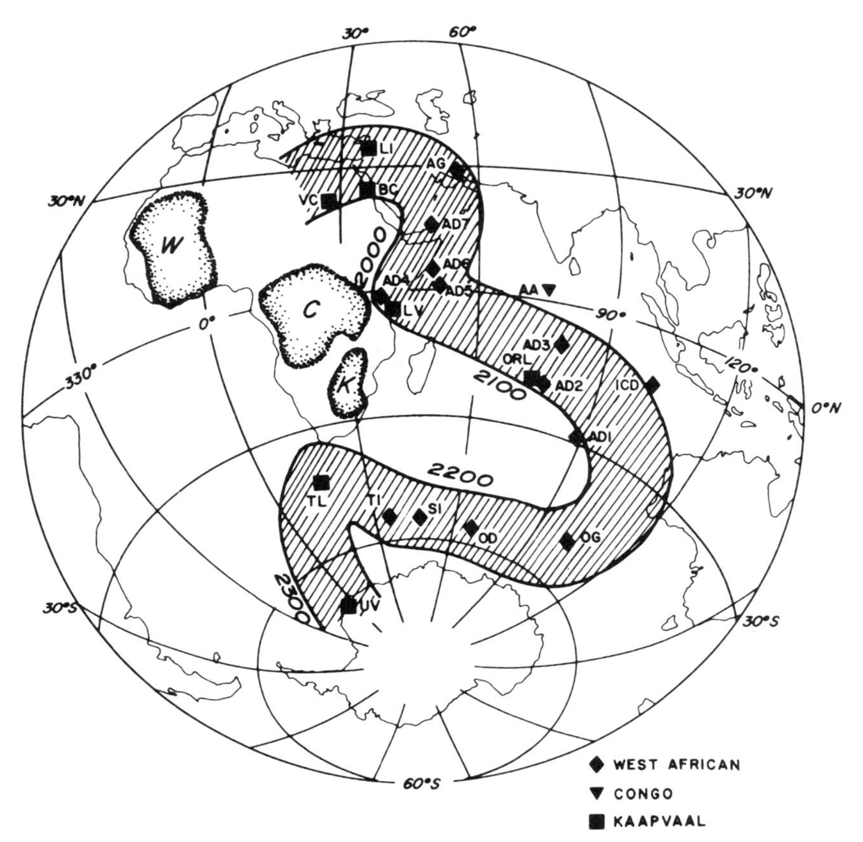

Figure 5 APWP for the African cratons (stippled) for 2300 to 1900 Ma, with individual poles indicated by different symbols (from McElhinny & McWilliams 1977). Reprinted by permission from the authors and from Elsevier Scientific Publishing Company.

with recent additions from Van der Voo (1980). The gaps in the path (650–900 Ma, 1450–1650 Ma, > 2600 Ma) reflect the lack of suitable rocks for those times. Probably the best documented segment of the path is the Keweenawan track between 1200 and 1000 Ma (Halls & Pesonen 1981), which is followed by the Grenville track with ages of approximately 1000–900 Ma based on cooling ages of Berger et al (1979). A now-historical debate ensued in the past decade about the interpretation of the Grenville track. On the one hand, it was thought that the Grenville paleopoles were different from those for the rest of Laurentia, thus implying relative motions (Irving et al 1972). On the other hand, the geochronologic data and the geologic setting of the Grenville and Superior provinces suggested that if the Grenville orogeny was due to relative motions and collision, then this collision occurred well before the acquisition

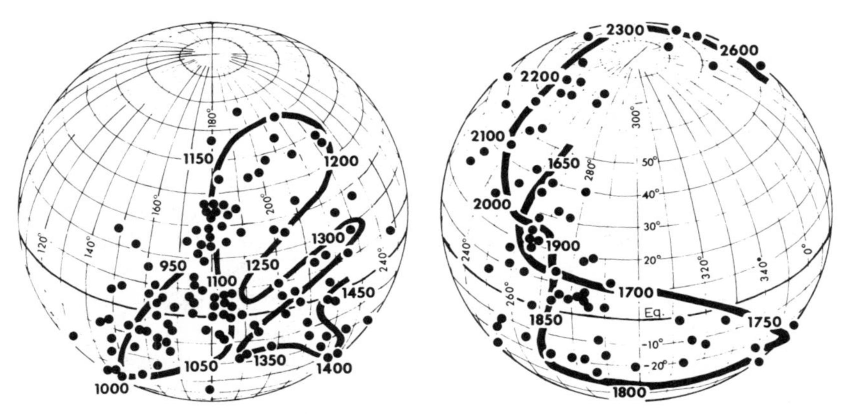

Figure 6 Laurentian APWP for 950 to 1450 Ma (*left*) and 1650 to 2600 Ma (*right*), plotted on identical spheres but centered at different longitudes (from Van der Voo 1980).

time of the very magnetizations that suggested the collision in the first place. With better age calibration of the resetting of the Grenville magnetizations, as well as the discovery of Grenville-type paleopoles from outside the Grenville province (Halls & Pesonen 1981, Watts 1981), the issue appears to have been settled. Most workers nowadays would incorporate the Grenville track into the Laurentian APWP. The orogeny may well have been due to a continent-continent collision, but again there are no paleomagnetic data to substantiate this idea.

There is a cluster of paleopoles with ages of about 1350–1450 Ma, that are for rocks from a great variety of provinces (Ozark mountains in Missouri, Beltian Supergroup in Montana and adjacent Canada, Arizona, Colorado, Ontario, Labrador). As was the case for Africa, these results suggest, but do not prove, that the Laurentian Shield existed more or less in its present form during middle Proterozoic times: coincidence between poles still allows relative movements along lines of latitude, whereas coincidence between APWP segments (i.e. a whole sequence of poles) implies no relative movements for the duration of the segments involved. Tracing the Laurentian APWP back from 1400 Ma to 2100 Ma, the paleopoles suggest that Laurentia was indeed a coherent unit, provided that the age assignments, as used by Irving (1979), are reasonable. Thus, the Hudsonian orogenic belts of the Laurentian Shield would best be interpreted as of ensialic origin, despite contrary proposals on the basis of geologic data alone (Gibb 1975, Burke et al 1976). An opposite viewpoint has also been presented (Cavanaugh & Seyfert 1977, Seyfert & Cavanaugh 1978) in a paleomagnetic analysis based in part on different age assignments and in part on the use of antipoles (compared to the poles used by Irving) for the Slave Province. Cavanaugh & Nairn (1980) have further examined this issue and their (revised) interpretation is shown in Figure 7. The differences between their paths and the simple path of Figure 6 (essentially that of Irving 1979) can be summarized as follows: (*a*) the tracks are roughly in similar places, which is not surprising since they are both based on a nearly identical set of paleopoles; (*b*) the ages between 1650 and 2500 Ma are quite different, as can be seen for instance in the segments through Brazil (2000 Ma in Figure 7 and 1750 Ma in Figure 6) or west of California (2400 Ma in Figure 7 and 2050 Ma in Figure 6); and (*c*) whereas Irving (1979) has a single APWP for the Superior and Slave provinces, Cavanaugh & Nairn (1980) have two separate tracks for the interval of 1750 to 2150 Ma. The latter would imply that a Wilson cycle may have operated in this interval, but that the two provinces were welded together again where they had previously drifted apart. The marked absence of poles between the age calibration points of 1750 and 2100 Ma for the track of the Superior Province (Figure 2 of Cavanaugh & Nairn 1980) raises the critical question, furthermore, of whether or not the path may in reality be more complex (and perhaps identical to that of the Slave Province), but that a lack of poles causes an apparent smoothing. I agree with Irving (1979) that as a working hypothesis, one path rather than two seems preferable. He concluded that "as more data accumulate one may be obliged to abandon the idea of a simple single path, and with it, the integrity of Laurentia, but that time is not yet."

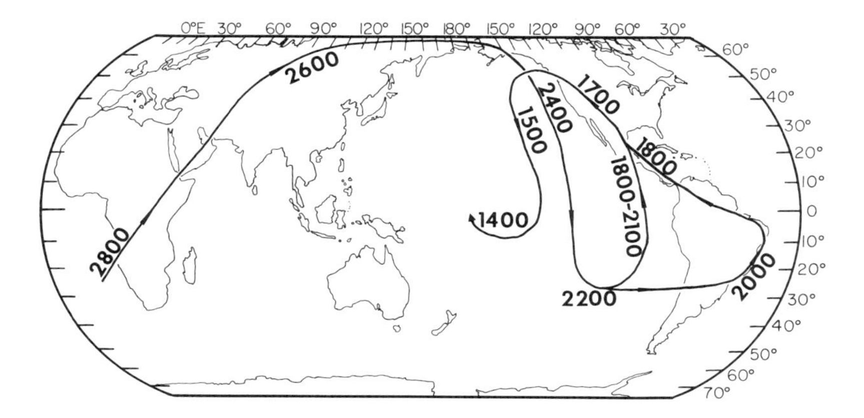

Figure 7 Summary of APWPs for Laurentia prior to 1400 Ma, from Cavanaugh & Nairn (1980), illustrating their interpretation of the data from the Superior and Slave provinces in terms of a Wilson cycle during the interval 1750 to 2150 Ma. Reprinted by permission from the authors and from Elsevier Scientific Publishing Company.

A Comparison Between Africa and Laurentia

For the Precambrian, Africa and Laurentia are by far the best-studied shields with over 60% of the world's Precambrian paleomagnetic results (Irving & Lapointe 1975). On the basis of these results, Piper (1974) has maintained that a common Proterozoic APWP could be constructed, implying that these two shields formed a single continent from about 2200 Ma to 1100 Ma. In this reconstruction, Laurentia is located to the northeast of Africa, so that the Colorado plateau would be adjacent to Arabia. In subsequent publications and discussions (e.g. Piper 1980), the analogy of segments of the APWPs has been further illustrated.

This idea has been strongly contested, however. Again the debate centers on ages, quality, and pole-versus-antipole arguments, as well as on the degree of smoothing versus complexity, i.e. loops and hairpins. This complex set of issues can be grasped somewhat from Figure 8 (from McGlynn et al 1975). As was the case for the Superior and Slave Provinces of Laurentia, one may

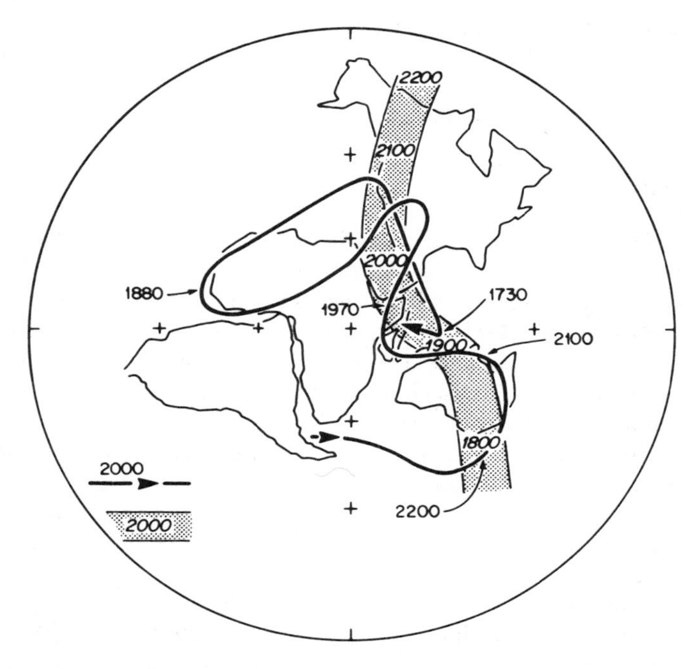

Figure 8 APWPs for the interval of 2200 to 1800 Ma from Africa and Laurentia (shaded), plotted according to Piper's (1974) proposal of a supercontinent assembly during this time. From McGlynn et al (1975); reprinted by permission from the authors and from Nature, Vol. 255, pp. 318–319. Copyright © 1975 by Macmillan Journals Limited.

wonder whether the straighter path is not just a function of having missed complexities due to lack of data. Whatever the answer to this question may be, I note that the ages of the African path (solid line in Figure 8) do not agree with the ages of either the Irving APWP (Figure 6) or the Cavanaugh & Nairn path (Figure 7). But since the latter two differed by up to 350 Ma, even that objection may perhaps be overcome.

A straightforward conclusion for this Precambrian chapter is clearly not possible. Several options exist: plate motion with ensialic orogenies, plate motion with seafloor spreading, a supercontinent assembly with substantial longevity but moving with respect to the pole, no motion but only true polar wander, or plate motions with transcurrent faults as the plate boundaries (e.g. Onstott & Hargraves 1981). As Briden (1981) wisely remarked, this last style of proposed motion exhausts the alternatives, thus ensuring that at least someone is right.

Most paleomagneticians not immediately involved in any of the controversies will take a conservative stance. While relative motions (with any of the above characteristics) between continents are possible and ad hoc models can be proposed that satisfy the paleomagnetic data, the answer to the basic question remains elusive: we have, at the time of writing, no undisputed (!) paleomagnetic (!) evidence for middle Proterozoic or earlier subduction, collision, spreading, rifting, or any other plate tectonic process.

SUMMARY

I have tried in this review to describe the current state of the paleomagnetic subdiscipline that deals with plate tectonic models in pre-Mesozoic time. As such this is a rather personal review, since different authors will adopt different reliability criteria and selection methods to weed out the bad data from the good. Many paleomagneticians, however, are beginning to agree on the most basic criteria: stability tests, such as demagnetization and field tests, provenance from a coherent unit or craton, sufficient samples and sites to average out secular variation and acceptable statistical parameters, and accurate age control with a precision commensurate with the analysis goals. With these criteria, the polar wander paths of the major continents (Laurentia, Baltica, Gondwana, etc) are beginning to be reasonably well defined for the Phanerozoic. Yet, there is a step-wise increase in the associated uncertainties of the APWPs before Carboniferous time, which undoubtedly reflects the problems inherent to orogenic overprinting of magnetizations, the lack of other quantitative data such as seafloor spreading anomalies, and a lack of suitable rock types. For the Precambrian there is yet another step-wise increase in the associated uncertainties, particularly reflecting the inaccuracies in the age determinations of the magnetizations.

For the Paleozoic, the available paleomagnetic data have been presented in the context of some plate tectonic models for the assembly of Pangea. Since this is a paleomagnetic review, I must add that other models exist and they are tacitly acknowledged; but since they are not based on paleomagnetic data and would not be supported by the available paleopoles, I have not included them.

For the Precambrian, my main conclusion is that plate motions may well have taken place, and that in fact the APWPs indicate significant movements with respect to the pole. In the context of plate tectonic processes, however, there is not yet any paleomagnetic evidence for subduction, seafloor spreading, rifting, or collision. Although several proposals exist in the literature for relative movements of the continents that imply such processes, the available paleomagnetic data of the best-studied continents, Africa and Laurentia, cannot yet be construed as supportive beyond doubt. Consequently, many of the intracontinental Proterozoic orogenic belts may have been ensialic, if one wishes to interpret these data in a conservative fashion.

ACKNOWLEDGMENTS

It is a pleasure to acknowledge the fruitful discussions with many of my colleagues and graduate students at the University of Michigan. In particular, the critical reading of the manuscript by Henry N. Pollack and William C. Kelly is appreciated. The manuscript is the result of paleomagnetic research funded by the National Science Foundation, Division of Earth Sciences, grants GA 38038, EAR 76–14996, and EAR 81–03031.

Literature Cited

Amenta, R. V. 1974. Multiple deformation and metamorphism from structural analysis in the eastern Pennsylvanian Piedmont. *Geol. Soc. Am. Bull.* 85:1647–60

Berger, G. W., York, D., Dunlop, D. J. 1979. Calibration of Grenvillian paleopoles by $^{40}Ar/^{39}Ar$ dating. *Nature* 277:46–48

Bonhommet, N., Cobbold, P. R., Perroud, H., Richardson, A. 1981. Paleomagnetism and cross-folding in a key area of the Asturian Arc (Spain). *J. Geophys. Res.* 86:1873–87

Briden, J. C. 1981. Precambrian orogenies and polar wandering. *Nature* 289:125–26

Briden, J. C., Drewry, G. E., Smith, A. G. 1974. Phanerozoic equal-area world maps. *J. Geol.* 82:555–74

Briden, J. C., Hurley, A. M., Smith, A. G. 1981. Paleomagnetism and Mesozoic-Cenozoic paleocontinental maps. *J. Geophys. Res.* 86. In press

Brown, P., Van der Voo, R. 1981. Paleomagnetic study of the Piedmont Province of northern Delaware. *EOS, Trans. Am. Geophys. Union* 62:265 (Abstr.)

Bullard, E. C., Everett, J., Smith, A. G. 1965. A symposium on Continental Drift. *Philos. Trans. R. Soc. London Ser. A* 258:41–51

Burke, K., Dewey, J. F., Kidd, W. S. F. 1976. Precambrian paleomagnetic results compatible with contemporary operation of the Wilson cycle. *Tectonophysics* 33:287–99

Bylund, G. 1974. Paleomagnetism of dykes along the southern margin of the Baltic Shield. *Geol. Foeren. Stockholm Foerh.* 96:231–35

Cavanaugh, M. D., Nairn, A. E. M. 1980. The role of the geologic province in Precambrian paleomagnetism. *Earth Sci. Rev.* 16:257–76

Cavanaugh, M. D., Seyfert, C. K. 1977. Apparent polar wander paths and the joining of the Superior and Slave provinces during early Proterozoic time. *Geology* 5:207–11

Charlot, R. 1976. The Precambrian of the Anti-Atlas (Morocco): a geochronological synthesis. *Precambrian Res.* 3:273–99

Charlot, R. 1978. *Caractérisation des événements éburnéens et panafricains dans l'Anti-Atlas marocain, apport de la méthode Rb-Sr*. Thèse de Doctorat. Univ. Rennes, France. 237 pp.

Cogné, J. 1974. Le Massif Armoricain. In *Géologie de la France,* ed. J. Debelmas, 1:106–61. Paris: Doin Editeurs. 296 pp.

Cook, F. A., Albaugh, D. S., Brown, L. D., Kaufman, S., Oliver, J. E., Hatcher, R. D. 1979. Thin-skinned tectonics in the crystalline southern Appalachians; COCORP seismic reflection profiling of the Blue Ridge and Piedmont. *Geology* 7:563–67

Creer, K. M. 1970. A review of paleomagnetism. *Earth Sci. Rev.* 6:369–466

De Bouvier, M. C., Bonhommet, N., Van der Voo, R. 1979. Paleomagnetism and K-A40 dating of dolerite dikes from the Armorican Massif, France. *EOS, Trans. Am. Geophys. Union* 60(7):220 (Abstr.)

Dewey, J. F., Spall, H. 1975. Penrose Conference Report: Pre-Mesozoic plate tectonics: how far back in Earth history can the Wilson cycle be extended? *Geology* 3:422–24

Diecchio, R. J. 1980. Stratigraphic and petrologic evidence for partial closure of the proto-Atlantic during the Taconic orogeny. *Geol. Soc. Am. Abstr. with Programs* 12(7):413 (Abstr.)

Diehl, J. F., Shive, P. N. 1979. Paleomagnetic studies of the Early Permian Ingelside Formation of northern Colorado. *Geophys. J. R. Astron. Soc.* 56:271–82

Drake, A. A. 1980. The Taconides, Acadides, and Alleghenides in the Central Appalachians. In *The Caledonides in the U.S.A.,* ed. D. R. Wones. Blacksburg: Dept. Geol. Sci., Va. Polytech. Inst./State Univ., Mem. 2, pp. 179–87

Duff, B. A. 1979. The palaeomagnetism of Cambro-Ordovician red beds, the Erquy spilite series, and the Trégastel-Ploumanac'h granite complex, Armorican Massif (France and the Channel Islands). *Geophys. J. R. Astron. Soc.* 59:345–65

Duff, B. A. 1980. The palaeomagnetism of Jersey volcanics and dykes, and the Lower Palaeozoic apparent polar wander path for Europe. *Geophys. J. R. Astron. Soc.* 60:355–75

Fairbridge, R. W. 1969. Early Paleozoic south pole in northwest Africa. *Geol. Soc. Am. Bull.* 80:113–14

Foland, K. A., Muessig, K. W. 1978. A Paleozoic age for some charnockite-anorthosite rocks. *Geology* 6:143–46

Gibb, R. A. 1975. Collision tectonics in the Canadian Shield? *Earth Planet Sci. Lett.* 27:378–82

Grauert, B., Wagner, M. E. 1975. Age of the granulite facies metamorphism of the Wilmington complex, Delaware-Pennsylvania Piedmont. *Am. J. Sci.* 275:683–91

Hagstrum, J. T., Van der Voo, R., Auvray, B., Bonhommet, N. 1980. Eocambrian-Cambrian paleomagnetism of the Armorican Massif, France. *Geophys. J. R. Astron. Soc.* 61:489–517

Hallam, A. 1979. A decade of plate tectonics. *Nature* 279:478

Halls, H. C., Pesonen, L. J. 1981. Paleomagnetism of Keweenawan rocks. *Geol. Soc. Am. Mem.* In press

Harland, W. B. 1980. Comment on "A paleomagnetic pole position from the folded Upper Devonian Catskill red beds, and its tectonic implications." *Geology* 8:258–59

Harrison, C. G. A., Lindh, T. 1982. A polar wander curve for North America during the Mesozoic and Cenozoic. *J. Geophys. Res.* Under review

Hatcher, R. D. 1972. Developmental model for the southern Appalachians. *Geol. Soc. Am. Bull.* 83:2735–60

Hatcher, R. D., Butler, J. R., Fullagar, P. D., Secor, D. T., Snoke, A. W. 1980. Geologic synthesis of the Tennessee-Carolinas-Northeast Georgia Southern Appalachians. See Drake 1980, pp. 83–90

Haworth, R. T. 1982. Appalachian development in light of paleomagnetically derived and geologically interpreted plate motions during the Early Paleozoic. *Can. J. Earth Sci.* Under review

Hicken, A., Irving, E., Law, L. K., Hastie, J. 1972. *Catalogue of Paleomagnetic Directions and Poles,* 45(1):1–135. Ottawa: Publ. Earth Phys. Branch, Dept. Energy, Mines, Resour.

Irving, E. 1964. *Paleomagnetism and Its Application to Geological and geophysical Problems*. New York: Wiley. 399 pp.

Irving, E. 1977. Drift of the major continental blocks since the Devonian. *Nature* 270: 304-9

Irving, E. 1979. Paleopoles and paleolatitudes of North America and speculations about displaced terrains. *Can. J. Earth Sci.* 16: 669–94

Irving, E., Hastie, J. 1975. *Catalogue of Paleomagnetic Directions and Poles, Second Issue: Precambrian Results 1957–1974*. Ottawa: Publ. Earth Phys. Branch, Geomagn. Ser. 3:1–42

Irving, E., Lapointe, P. L. 1975. Paleomagnetism of Precambrian rocks of Laurentia. *Geosci. Can.* 2(2):90–98

Irving, E., McGlynn, J. C. 1976. Proterozoic magnetostratigraphy and the tectonic evolution of Laurentia. *Phil. Trans. R. Soc. London Ser. A* 280:433–68

Irving, E., Park, J. K., Roy, J. L. 1972. Paleomagnetism and the origin of the Grenville front. *Nature Phys. Sci.* 236:344–56

Irving, E., Tanczyk, E., Hastie, J. 1976a.

Catalogue of Paleomagnetic Directions and Poles, Third Issue: Paleozoic Results 1949–1975. Ottawa: Publ. Earth Phys. Branch, Geomagn. Ser. 5:1–98

Irving, E., Tanczyk, E., Hastie, J. 1976b. *Catalogue of Paleomagnetic Directions and Poles, Fourth Issue: Mesozoic Results 1954–1975 and Results from Seamounts*. Ottawa: Publ. Earth Phys. Branch, Geomagn. Ser. 6:1–70

Irving, E., Tanczyk, E., Hastie, J. 1976c. *Catalogue of Paleomagnetic Directions and Poles, Fifth Issue: Cenozoic Results 1927–1975*. Ottawa: Publ. Earth Phys. Branch, Geomagn. Ser. 10:1–87

Johnson, G. A. L. 1973. Closing of the Carboniferous sea in western Europe. In *Implications of Continental Drift to the Earth Sciences*, ed. D. H. Tarling, S. K. Runcorn, 2: 845–50. London & New York: Academic. 1184 pp.

Johnson, G. A. L. 1974. Crustal margins and plate tectonics during the Carboniferous. *Comptes Rendus 7th International Congress Carboniferous Stratigraphy and Geology* 3:261–65

Jones, M., Van der Voo, R., Bonhommet, N. 1979. Late Devonian to early Carboniferous paleomagnetic poles from the Armorican Massif, France. *Geophys. J. R. Astron. Soc.* 58:287–308

Jurdy, D. M., Van der Voo, R. 1975. True polar wander since the Early Cretaceous. *Science* 187:1193–96

Kent, D. V. 1980. Formation of Euramerica in the Paleozoic. *EOS, Trans. Am. Geophys. Union* 61(17):220–21 (Abstr.)

Kent, D. V., Opdyke, N. D. 1978. Paleomagnetism of the Devonian Catskill red beds: evidence for motion of the coastal New England–Canadian Maritime region relative to cratonic North America. *J. Geophys. Res.* 83:4441–50

Kent, D. V., Opdyke, N. D. 1979. The Early Carboniferous paleomagnetic field for North America and its bearing on the tectonics of the northern Appalachians. *Earth Planet. Sci. Lett.* 44:365–72

Klootwijk, C. T. 1980. Early Palaeozoic palaeomagnetism in Australia. *Tectonophysics* 64:249–332

Kröner, A., McWilliams, M. O., Germs, G. J. B., Reid, A. B., Schalk, K. E. L. 1980. Paleomagnetism of Late Precambrian to early Paleozoic mixtite-bearing formations in Namibia (southwest Africa): the Nama group and Blaubeker Formation. *Am. J. Sci.* 280:942–68

Lefort, J. P. 1977. Possible 'Caledonian' subduction under the Domnonean domain, North Armorican area. *Geology* 5:523–26

Lefort, J. P., Van der Voo, R. 1981. A kinematic model for the collision and complete suturing between Gondwanaland and Laurussia in the Carboniferous. *J. Geol.* 89: 537–50

McElhinny, M. W. 1968a. Paleomagnetic directions and pole positions—VIII. *Geophys. J. R. Astron. Soc.* 15:409–30

McElhinny, M. W. 1968b. Paleomagnetic directions and pole positions—IX. *Geophys. J. R. Astron. Soc.* 16:207–24

McElhinny, M. W. 1969. Paleomagnetic directions and pole positions—X. *Geophys. J. R. Astron. Soc.* 19:305–27

McElhinny, M. W. 1970. Paleomagentic directions and pole positions—XI. *Geophys. J. R. Astron. Soc.* 20:417–29

McElhinny, M. W. 1972a. Paleomagnetic directions and pole positions—XII. *Geophys. J. R. Astron. Soc.* 27:237–57

McElhinny, M. W. 1972b. Paleomagnetic directions and pole positions—XIII. *Geophys. J. R. Astron. Soc.* 30:281–93

McElhinny, M. W. 1973. *Paleomagnetism and Plate Tectonics*. Cambridge: Cambridge Univ. Press. 358 pp.

McElhinny, M. W., Cowley, J. A. 1977. Paleomagnetic directions and pole positions—XIV. Pole numbers 14/1 to 14/574. *Geophys. J. R. Astron. Soc.* 49:313–56

McElhinny, M. W., Cowley, J. A. 1978. Paleomagnetic directions and pole positions—XV. Pole numbers 15/1 to 15/232. *Geophys. J. R. Astron Soc.* 52:259–76

McElhinny, M. W., Cowley, J. A. 1980. Paleomagnetic directions and pole positions—XVI. Pole numbers 16/1 to 16/296. *Geophys. J. R. Astron Soc.* 61:549–71

McElhinny, M. W., Embleton, B. J. J. 1976. Precambrian and Early Paleozoic palaeomagnetism in Australia. *Phil. Trans. R. Soc. London Ser. A* 280:417–31

McElhinny, M. W., McWilliams, M. O. 1977. Precambrian geodynamics—a paleomagnetic view. *Tectonophysics* 40:137–59

McGlynn, J. C., Irving, E., Bell, K., Pullaiah, G. 1975. Paleomagnetic poles and a Proterozoic supercontinent. *Nature* 255:318–19

McKerrow, W. S., Cocks, L. R. M. 1976. Progressive faunal migration across the Iapetus Ocean. *Nature* 263:304–5

McKerrow, W. S., Lambert, R. St. J., Chamberlain, V. E. 1980. The Ordovician, Silurian and Devonian time scales. *Earth Planet. Sci. Lett.* 51:1—8

McWilliams, M. O. 1981. Palaeomagnetism and Precambrian tectonic evolution of Gondwana. In *Precambrian Plate Tectonics*, ed. A. Kröner, pp. 649–87. Amsterdam: Elsevier

Molnar, P., Tapponnier, P. 1977. Relation of the tectonics of eastern China to the India-Eurasia collision: application of slip-line field theory to large-scale continental tectonics. *Geology* 5:212–16

Molnar, P., Tapponnier, P. 1978. Active tectonics of Tibet. *Geophys. Res.* 83:5361–75
Morel, P., Irving, E. 1978. Tentative paleocontinental maps for the Early Paleozoic and Proterozoic. *J. Geol.* 86:535–61
Morel, P., Irving, E. 1981. Paleomagnetism and the evolution of Pangea. *J. Geophys. Res.* 86:1858–72
Morris, W. A. 1976. Transcurrent motion determined paleomagnetically in the northern Appalachians and Caledonides and the Acadian orogeny. *Can. J. Earth Sci.* 13: 1236–43
Morris, W. A. 1980. A palaeomagnetic study of Cambrian red beds from Cartaret, Normandy, France. *Geophys. J. R. Astron. Soc.* 62:577–90
Morris, W. A., Schmidt, P. W., Roy, J. L. 1979. A graphical approach to polar paths: paleomagnetic cycles and global tectonics. *Phys. Earth Planet. Inter.* 19:85–99
Onstott, T. C., Hargraves, R. B. 1981. Proterozoic transcurrent tectonics: palaeomagnetic evidence from Venezuela and Africa. *Nature* 289:131–36
Perigo, R., Van der Voo, R., Auvray, B., Bonhommet, N. 1981. Paleomagnetism of Late Precambrian-Cambrian volcanics and intrusives from the Armorican Massif, France. *EOS, Trans. Am. Geophys. Union* 62:271 (Abstr.)
Perroud, H., Bonhommet, N. 1980. Paleomagnetism of the Ibero-Armorican Arc and plate tectonics implication for Hercynian orogeny in western Europe. *EOS, Trans. Am. Geophys. Union* 61(46):945 (Abstr.)
Perroud, H., Bonhommet, N. 1981. Palaeomagnetism of the Ibero-Armorican Arc and the Hercynian orogeny in Western Europe. *Nature*. 292:445-8
Peucat, J. J., Le Métour, J., Audren, C. 1978. Argument géochronologique en faveur de l'existence d'une double ceinture métamorphique d'âge siluro-dévonien en Bretagne méridionale. *Bull. Soc. Géol. France* 7 (XX-2):163–67
Pilger, R. H. 1978. A closed Gulf of Mexico, pre-Atlantic ocean plate reconstruction and the early rift history of the Gulf and North Atlantic. *Trans. Gulf Coast Assoc. Geol. Soc.* 28:385–93
Piper, J. D. A. 1974. Proterozoic crustal distribution, mobile belts and apparent polar movements. *Nature* 251:381–84
Piper, J. D. A. 1978. Palaeomagnetism and palaeogeography of the southern Uplands block in Ordovician times. *Scott. J. Geol.* 14:93–107
Piper, J. D. A. 1979. Aspects of Caledonian palaeomagnetism and their tectonic implications. *Earth Planet. Sci. Lett.* 44:176–92
Piper, J. D. A. 1980. Analogous Upper Proterozoic apparent polar wander loops. *Nature* 283:845–47
Poorter, R. P. E. 1972. Preliminary palaeomagnetic results from the Fen Carbonatite Complex, S. Norway. *Earth Planet. Sci. Lett.* 17:194–98
Prasad, S. N., Sharma, P. V. 1978. Palaeomagnetism of the Nexø sandstone from Bornholm Island, Denmark. *Geophys. J. R. Astron. Soc.* 54:669–80
Priem, H. N. A., Boelrijk, N. A. I. M., Verschure, R. H., Hebeda, E. H., Floor, P. 1966. Isotopic evidence for Upper Cambrian or Lower Ordovician granite emplacement in the Vigo area, northwestern Spain. *Geol. Mijnbouw* 45:36–40
Rao, K. V., Van der Voo, R. 1980. Paleomagnetism of a Paleozoic anorthosite from the Appalachian Piedmont, northern Delaware: possible tectonic implications. *Earth Planet. Sci. Lett.* 47:113–20
Robinson, D., Hall, L. M. 1980. Tectonic synthesis of southern New England. See Drake 1980, pp. 73–82.
Rowlands, D. 1980. Age of slaty cleavage in the Martinsburg Formation: evidence from the Beemerville area, northwestern New Jersey. *Geol. Soc. Am. Abstr. with Programs* 12(7):512 (Abstr.)
Rowley, D. B. 1980. Along-strike variations in style of volcanic arc-continental margin collision during the Taconic orogeny. *Geol. Soc. Am. Abstr. with Programs* 12(7):512 (Abstr.)
Runcorn, S. K. 1956. Palaeomagnetic comparisons between Europe and North America. *Geol. Assoc. Can. Proc.* 8:77–85
Schermerhorn, L. J. G. 1971. Upper Ordovician glaciation in northwest Africa? Discussion. *Geol. Soc. Am. Bull.* 82: 265–68
Scotese, C. R., Bambach, R. K., Barton, C., Van der Voo, R., Ziegler, A. M. 1979. Paleozoic base maps. *J. Geol.* 87:217–77
Seyfert, C. K., Cavanaugh, M. D. 1978. Reply to comments on "Apparent Polar wander paths and the joining of the Superior and Slave provinces during early Proterozoic time" by J. L. Roy and others. *Geology* 6:133–35
Smith, A. G., Hallam, A. 1970. A fit of the southern continents. *Nature* 225:139–44
Spariosu, D. J., Kent, D. V. 1980. Paleomagnetic results from northern Maine and their bearing on displaced terrains. *EOS, Trans. Am. Geophys. Union* 61:220 (Abstr.)
Stephens, G. C. 1980. Middle Ordovician sedimentation—a key to Taconic events in the central Appalachians. *Geol. Soc. Am. Abstr. with Programs* 12(7):529 (Abstr.)
Stille, H. 1924. *Grundfragen der Vergleichenden Tektonik*. Berlin: Borntraeger. 443 pp.
Strangway, D. W. 1970. *History of the Earth's*

Magnetic Field. New York: McGraw-Hill. 168 pp.
Tarling, D. H. 1971. *Principles and Applications of Palaeomagnetism*. London: Chapman & Hall. 164 pp.
Thomas, C., Briden, J. C. 1976. Anomalous geomagnetic field during the Late Ordovician. *Nature* 259:380–82
Thomas, W. A., Tull, J. F., Bearce, D. N., Russell, G., Odom, A. L. 1980. Geologic synthesis of the southernmost Appalachians, Alabama and Georgia. See Drake 1980, pp. 91–97
Thorning, L., Abrahamsen, N. 1980. Palaeomagnetism of multiple intrusion dykes in Bohuslän, SW Sweden. *Geophys. J. R. Astron. Soc.* 60:163–86
Tull, J. F. 1980. Overview of the sequence and timing of deformational events in the southern Appalachians: evidence from the crystalline rocks North Carolina to Alabama. See Drake 1980, pp. 167–77
Ullrich, L., Van der Voo, R. 1981. Minimum continental velocities with respect to the pole since the Archean. *Tectonophysics* 74:17–27
Van der Voo, R. 1979. Paleozoic assembly of Pangea: a new plate tectonic model for the Taconic, Caledonian, and Hercynian orogenies. *EOS, Trans. Am. Geophys. Union* 60(18):241 (Abstr.)
Van der Voo, R. 1980. Precambrian paleomagnetism and tectonics. In *The Primitive Earth Revisited, A Symposium,* ed. M. H. Hickman, pp. 75–85. Oxford, Ohio: Dept. Geol., Miami Univ. 103 pp.
Van der Voo, R. 1981a. A paleomagnetic comparison of various reconstructions of the Atlantic-bordering continents which have implications for the origin of the Gulf of Mexico. In *The Origin of the Gulf of Mexico and the Early Opening of the Central North Atlantic Ocean,* ed. R. H. Pilger, 2:1–5. Houston: Houston Geol. Soc. Contin. Educ. Ser. 108 pp.
Van der Voo, R. 1981b. The position of Great Britain with respect to the North American craton in the Paleozoic. *EOS, Trans. American Geophys. Union* 62:264 (Abstr.)
Van der Voo, R., Channell, J. E. T. 1980. Paleomagnetism in orogenic belts. *Rev. Geophys. Space Phys.* 18:455–81
Van der Voo, R., French, R. B. 1974. Apparent polar wander for the Atlantic-bordering continents: Late Carboniferous to Eocene. *Earth Sci. Rev.* 10:99–119
Van der Voo, R., Morris, W. A. 1981. A short note on Early Cambrian paleomagnetism from Normandy, France. *Geophys. J. R. Astron. Soc.* In press
Van der Voo, R., Scotese, C. R. 1980. Great Glen Fault: 2000 km sinistral displacement during the Carboniferous. *EOS, Trans. Am. Geophys. Union* 61(17):220 (Abstr.)
Van der Voo, R., Scotese, C. R. 1981. Paleomagnetic evidence for a large (*C*. 2000 km) sinistral offset along the Great Glen Fault during the Carboniferous. *Geology*. 9:583–89
Van der Voo, R., Mauk, F. J., French, R. B. 1976. Permian-Triassic continental configurations and the origin of the Gulf of Mexico. *Geology* 4:177–80
Van der Voo, R., French, A. N., French, R. B. 1979. A paleomagnetic pole position from the folded Upper Devonian Catskill red beds, and its tectonic implications. *Geology* 7:345–48
Van der Voo, R., Briden, J. C., Duff, B. A. 1980. Late Precambrian and Paleozoic paleomagnetism of the Atlantic-bordering continents. *Proc. 26th Int. Geol. Cong., Paris. Colloque C-6,* pp. 203–12
Van Eysinga, F. W. B. 1975. *A geological time table,* 3rd ed., Amsterdam: Elsevier
Wagner, M. E., Crawford, M. L. 1975. Polymetamorphism of the Precambrian Baltimore Gneiss in southeastern Pennsylvania. *Am. J. Sci.* 275:653–82
Walper, J. L., Rowett, C. L. 1972. Plate tectonics and the origin of the Caribbean and the Gulf of Mexico. *Trans. Gulf Coast Assoc. Geol. Soc.* 22:105–16
Watson, J., Dunning, F. W. 1979. Basement-cover relations in the British Caledonides. In *The Caledonides of the British Isles—Reviewed,* ed. A. L. Harris, C. H. Holland, B. E. Leake, pp. 67–91. Edinburgh: Scottish Acad. Press. 768 pp.
Watts, D. R. 1981. Paleomagnetism of the Fond-du-Lac Formation and the Eileen and Middle River sections with implications for Keweenawan tectonics and the Grenville problem. *Can. J. Earth Sci.* 18:829–41
Watts, D. R., Van der Voo, R. 1979. Paleomagnetic results from the Ordovician Moccasin, Bays, and Chapman Ridge formations of the Valley and Ridge province, eastern Tennessee. *J. Geophys. Res.* 84:645–55
Watts, D. R., Van der Voo, R., Reeve, S. C. 1980a. Cambrian paleomagnetism of the Llano Uplift, Texas. *J. Geophys. Res.* 85:5316–30
Watts, D. R., Van der Voo, R., French, R. B. 1980b. Paleomagnetic investigation of the Cambrian Waynesboro and Rome formations of the Valley and Ridge province of the Appalachian mountains. *J. Geophys. Res.* 85:5331–43
Wilkinson, B. H., Van der Voo, R., McCabe, C. 1981. Paleomagnetism of Silurian Reef limestones in Ohio and Indiana. *EOS, Trans. Am. Geophys. Union* 62:271–72 (Abstr.)
Williams, H. 1979. Appalachian orogen in Canada. *Can. J. Earth Sci.* 16:792–807

Williams, H., Max, M. D. 1980. Zonal subdivision and regional correlation in the Appalachian-Caledonian Orogen. See Drake 1980, pp. 57–62

Wilson, J. T. 1966. Did the Atlantic close and then re-open? *Nature* 211:676–81

Zen, E. 1972. The Taconide zone and the Taconic orogeny in the western part of the northern Appalachian orogen. *Geol. Soc. Am. Spec. Pap.* 135. 72 pp.

Ziegler, A. M., Hansen, K. S., Johnson, M. E., Kelly, M. A., Scotese, C. R., Van der Voo, R. 1977. Silurian continental distributions, paleogeography, climatology, and biogeography. *Tectonophysics* 40:13–51

Ziegler, A. M., Scotese, C. R., McKerrow, W. S., Johnson, M. E., Bambach, R. K. 1979. Paleozoic paleogeography. *Ann. Rev. Earth Planet. Sci.* 7:473–502

Ziegler, P. 1978. Northwestern Europe: tectonics and basement development. *Geol. Mijnbouw* 57:589–626

Ziegler, P. 1981. Evolution of sedimentary basins in northwest Europe. *Proc. Conf. Petrol. Geol. Cont. Shelf NW Eur.*, pp. 3–39. London: Inst. Petroleum. 389 pp.

Zwart, H. J. Dornsiepen, V. F. 1978. The tectonic framework of Central and Western Europe. *Geol. Mijnbouw* 57:627–54

Ann. Rev. Earth Planet. Sci. 1982. 10:221-33

THE ROLE OF PERFECTLY MOBILE COMPONENTS IN METAMORPHISM

Douglas Rumble, III

Geophysical Laboratory, Carnegie Institution of Washington, Washington, D.C., 20008

INTRODUCTION

The concept of perfectly mobile components was introduced to petrologic literature by D. S. Korzhinskii (1936, 1950). Korzhinskii noticed that in metasomatic rocks the content of certain components was more or less fixed throughout the metasomatic process, but that the content of other components, either volatile ones such as H_2O and CO_2 or those with appreciable solubility in pore fluid, changed greatly during metasomatism (compare Shaw 1956). Components of the first type were designated "inert" and of the second type "perfectly mobile" (in English translation). The terms "perfectly mobile" and "inert" were redefined by Korzhinskii in the context of his thermodynamic theory of open systems, the result being that the words lost their literal meaning and acquired an esoteric, technical significance. The redefinition was unfortunate as it provides an example of how the use of common words in multiple senses can lead to misunderstanding. The terminology and concepts have been widely used, discussed, and criticized in petrologic studies of metamorphic and metasomatic rocks.

The purpose of this paper is to review the historical development of the concepts of "inert" and "perfectly mobile" components. Problems that have arisen in the application of the concepts to understanding rocks are discussed. The concepts are then evaluated in the light of current research in metamorphic petrology.

0084–6597/82/0515–0221$02.00

DEFINITIONS AND HISTORICAL DEVELOPMENT

Korzhinskii (1959, p. 17) defined inert and perfectly mobile components as follows:

> Thus, we call those components inert, whose masses or molar amounts (i.e., extensive parameters) are equilibrium factors of the system. The "perfectly mobile" components are those whose chemical potentials, activities, and concentrations in one of the phases or partial vapor pressures (i.e., intensive parameters) are factors of equilibrium in the given system.

By way of further explanation he states regarding inert components (Korzhinskii 1959, p. 16) that the equilibrium factor for a component is its mass

> in the case of components for which the exchange between the system and the external medium is difficult, so that in the attainment of equilibrium the mass of the component in the system has the decisive role, while its chemical potential, as in a closed system, is a dependent parameter. Such components with limited mobility, as well as immobile components, we shall call "inert," as if they resisted movement.

Additional explanation is given in the following quotation (Korzhinskii 1959, p. 17).

> In the equilibrium processes each component may be either inert or perfectly mobile, but may not be intermediate between the two because the number of factors of equilibrium is limited and may include either the mass of a component or its chemical potential. In some processes a gradual change of mass, i.e., a certain mobility, is possible even for inert components . . . As for the perfectly mobile components, it is assumed that their masses change without any difficulty as soon as the equality between their chemical potentials and those of the external medium is destroyed, as if their masses possessed no inertia. Naturally, real systems only approximate the perfectly mobile condition, just as in nature we find only approximations to the state of equilibrium.

Thompson (1955, p. 66) evidently accepted Korzhinskii's definition stating:

> Thermodynamically, this means that we must regard a rock or petrologic "system" as *open* to certain mobile components, notably water and carbon dioxide. The field of stability of a mineral containing a mobile component is then dependent not only upon temperature and pressure but also upon the chemical potential (partial molar free energy) of the mobile component in the immediate environment. In a completely closed system the chemical potential of any component is determined by the pressure, temperature, and bulk composition. If a system is open to a certain component, however, its chemical potential is independent of temperature and pressure, owing to the possibility of transfer of the mobile component between a given system and its environment.

A change in terminology was proposed by Zen (1963, p. 930) who suggested using the phrases "initial value component" and "boundary value component" instead of the terms "inert" and "perfectly mobile" components, respectively. The reason given for the change was "to bring the terminology more into line with those used in analogous potential problems such as heat flow. . ."

The thermodynamic treatment of open systems by Korzhinskii (1959), and, to a lesser extent that of Thompson (1959), was criticized by Weill & Fyfe (1964, 1967). The latter writers concluded (*a*) that Korzhinskii's (1959) derivation of a thermodynamic potential function for open systems contributed nothing fundamentally new to petrology; (*b*) that Gibbs' phase rule could not be applied to metasomatic systems that were in an overall state of disequilibrium; and (*c*) that the concept of perfectly mobile components breaks down if it is applied across more than one zone boundary in a sequence of metasomatic mineral zones.

The criticism by Weill & Fyfe (1964, 1967) was answered by Korzhinskii (1966, 1967) and Thompson (1970). In reply to point (*a*), it was noted that the thermodynamic potential function for open systems has led to new phase diagrams for representing mineral assemblages (i.e. the projection of Thompson 1957); and isothermal, isobaric μ_i vs μ_j diagrams (Korzhinskii 1959, pp. 80–135) that are widely used in current research (Burt 1981).

The version of the phase rule propounded by Weill & Fyfe (1964) and their choice of components of minerals was opposed by Korzhinskii (1966, 1967) and Thompson (1970). Weill & Fyfe (1964, pp. 569–571) advocated choosing the components of an assemblage as identical to the compositions of the minerals present in the assemblage. The consequences of this choice are stated as follows:

> The application of the phase rule to petrologic systems simply allows us to detect possible divariant equilibrium ($F = 2$), "(where F is the number of degrees of freedom)" possible univariant equilibrium ($F = 1$), possible invariant equilibrium ($F = 0$), and, above all, disequilibrium ($F < 0$) . . . This straightforward application of the phase rule will always yield all the information which the phase rule is capable of. It is possible to state the phase rule so as to incorporate additional knowledge of the system such as compositional variations of some phases, or actual processes in the systems . . . but since this information must be fed into these phase rules before they are applied we cannot expect to wring more information out of them.

The quoted remarks of Weill & Fyfe have the attractive appearance of logical rigor but there is little else to recommend them. Apart from the fact that their choice of components does not correspond to that of Gibbs (1961, pp. 63–64), their restrictive concept of the phase rule drastically limits its usefulness in the study of naturally occurring mineral assemblages. The task of deducing the conditions of formation of metamorphic and metasomatic rocks is a difficult one under the best of circumstances. Information from all the fields of geology, petrology, and mineralogy is required in order to achieve definitive results. It would be impractical to deliberately discard the data of crystal chemistry and experimental petrology when choosing the components of minerals. If the variance of natural assemblages is limited to a maximum of 2 (cf Turner 1968, Table 2-2, p. 57), then what is to be made of a small outcrop in which are exposed different metasedimentary beds containing the same mineral assemblage, but in which the minerals vary systematically in composition according to whether the beds are more or less magnesian, calcic, or manganiferous? (cf Rumble 1978).

The third critical point of Weill & Fyfe (1964, p. 574) concerning the changing character of mobile components across metasomatic mineral zones has been discussed in several works. Vidale (1969) emphasized that a sequence of metasomatic zones typically consists of layers of higher variance assemblages separated by contact surfaces along which lower variance assemblages are found (cf A. B. Thompson 1975). It follows that the number of possible perfectly mobile components appears to decrease at the contact surfaces where lower variance assemblages occur and increase within higher variance assemblages. In order to correctly deduce the character of the components, whether perfectly mobile or inert, it is necessary to consider all of the metasomatic zones and their contact surfaces in relation to one another (Vidale & Hewitt 1973, Joesten 1974, p. 897).

Recognizing the problem of giving common words a technical definition, Thompson advocated dropping the terms "perfectly mobile" and "inert". He states (Thompson 1970, p. 543):

> For convenience we shall designate as K-components those components for which the chemical potentials are fixed by some medium that lies outside what we have selected as our thermodynamic system, or, in other words, components for which the chemical potential is externally controlled. We shall designate all other components as J-components. In certain petrologic applications what we shall call K-components and J-components correspond in a sense to the "perfectly mobile" and "inert" components, respectively, of Korzhinskii (1936, 1959). In other petrologic applications a specified component may be either a K-component or a J-component depending on what we choose to include within our thermodynamic system. In this last instance "mobility," in the sense in which the concept appears in diffusion theory, is not relevant to the problem.

Thompson (1970 p. 544) suggested a method for distinguishing J- from K-components in mineral assemblages. The first step in differentiating the two types is to classify the components of an assemblage as to whether they are buffered or not. Buffered components are those whose compositions can be expressed as a stoichiometric relation between the measured chemical compositions of some or all of the minerals in an assemblage. Nonbuffered components cannot be so expressed. The stoichiometric relation can be determined graphically or by inspection in simple systems, or by linear algebraic methods in complex systems. Thompson (1970) showed that if a given component is always a buffered component in different mineral assemblages, then that component is a J-component. In contrast, the observation that a component is rarely or never buffered by different mineral assemblages is consistent with the classification of that component as a K-component.

The definitions of "perfectly mobile" and "inert" have suffered a certain amount of confusion due to vagaries of translation. The phrase "perfectly mobile" has been translated as "entirely active" or "completely active" Korzhinskii 1964, p. 1716). The term "perfectly inert" is used by Korzhinskii (1968, p. 226) instead of "inert" for a component involved in a metasomatic process whose content does not change. According to Fonteilles (1978, p. 177), perfectly inert components are those "whose content or, rather, the ratio of whose contents, does not vary detectably in the course of a reaction which, for other components, is manifestly of metasomatic character" (translation by the writer).

DISCUSSION OF DEFINITIONS AND CONCEPTS

The concepts of "perfectly mobile" and "inert" components were conceived when it was noticed that the content of some chemical constituents of rocks subjected to metasomatic or metamorphic processes changed as a consequence of the process, but that other constituents did not change. The definitions of the two types of components are only indirectly related to the original observations of variations in the chemical content of rocks during metamorphic and metasomatic processes. The definitions as they now stand are based on the thermodynamic analysis of open systems by Korzhinskii (1959) and Thompson (1955). Use of the definitions by a petrologist does not lead to a descriptive classification of components so much as to a commitment to the genetic theory of Korzhinskii and Thompson. For this reason, the suggestion by Thompson (1970) to classify the components of an assemblage as buffered or non-buffered, a purely descriptive classification, is most welcome.

The definitions of "inert" and "perfectly mobile" components depart in a number of ways from customary English or more technical petrologic usage of the words "inert" and "mobile." The term "inert" is usually used to refer to parts of a physical or chemical system that do not interact in any way with other parts of the system (e.g. the walls of a crucible). In the definition of Korzhinskii and Thompson, however, inert components react chemically with each other and with mobile components at discrete locations in a rock, but do not change in the amount present.

Study of chemical analyses of a suite of progressively metamorphosed or metasomatized rocks leads to the conclusion that some components change more than others, i.e. they are more mobile; in metamorphic rocks, for example, it is reasonable to conclude that H_2O is more mobile than Na_2O (Shaw 1956). The Korzhinskii-Thompson definition excludes the possibility of components of intermediate character. In their definition, a given component in a mineral assemblage is either perfectly mobile or inert. Thompson's

(1970) decision to use the phrases "K-components" and "J-components" and abandon the terms "perfectly mobile" and "inert" helps to alleviate the misunderstanding caused by assigning a specialized, technical meaning to commonly used words.

The discrepancy between the literal meaning of the word "mobile" and the definition of the phrase "perfectly mobile" is well illustrated by considering rocks which buffer the volatile components of metamorphic fluids. In such rocks either the whole mineral assemblage or a subset of its minerals constitutes a divariant buffer with respect to some volatile component (see review, above, of Thompson 1970). The assemblage hematite-magnetite, for example, with compositions of pure Fe_2O_3 and Fe_3O_4 is a divariant buffer for the component O_2. Misunderstanding arises because a divariant assemblage, containing components unlikely to be perfectly mobile, can be, in fact, an open system. This paradox can be explained by an example. Suppose that the assemblage hematite-magnetite is subjected to progressive isothermal, isobaric reduction by infiltration of an aqueous fluid at an f_{O_2} lower than that in equilibrium with the assemblage. The hypothetical example is an open system in which O_2 and H_2O (and H_2, as well) are literally mobile and the chemical potentials of O_2 and H_2O are fixed by an external reservoir; therefore, the volatile components are perfectly mobile. In this example, however, the component O_2 is buffered by the mineral assemblage. Now let small, representative samples of the model rock be removed at regular intervals throughout progressive reduction. Chemical analysis of the samples would show a continuous increase in FeO/Fe_2O_3, and it would be reasonable to conclude that the system was open to O_2. In contrast, petrographic examination of the samples would reveal the persistence of a divariant buffer assemblage and, therefore, the probable absence of perfectly mobile components. Only if the reduction reaction proceeded to completion so that all hematite was consumed would it be possible to classify O_2 as a possible perfectly mobile component. It is to be emphasized that components cannot be classified as perfectly mobile or inert merely on the basis of counting phases and components in a single rock specimen. Not only is it necessary to examine a suite of rocks involved in a metamorphic or metasomatic process, but it is also necessary to know something about the geologic and recrystallization history of the rock suite.

One of the difficulties that arises in classifying the components of rocks as perfectly mobile or inert (alternatively, K or J) is that it is easier to prove that a component is not perfectly mobile than to prove that it is. The asymmetry in proof comes about because the criteria used to classify components as perfectly mobile are logically necessary but not sufficient. All that need be shown to prove that a component is not perfectly mobile is the existence of a number of divariant buffer assemblages in a succession of rocks, or the existence of gradients in the chemical potential of a given component between different mineral assemblages. In contrast, the absence of divariant buffers and chemical potential gradients is consistent with classifying components as perfectly mobile, but their absence does not definitely prove the classification.

CLASSIFICATION OF COMPONENTS OF MINERAL ASSEMBLAGES

The classification of the components of a mineral assemblage as perfectly mobile or inert involves a number of key steps. A perfectly mobile component is one that is in equilibrium with a given mineral assemblage and also in equilibrium with an external reservoir. The first and most essential step in classification is to determine whether or not a group of contiguous assemblages satisfies the criteria for the attainment of chemical equilibrium. Among the items of evidence that must be considered in assessing equilibration are the following: (*a*) geologic history; (*b*) textures and fabrics; (*c*) chemical homogeneity of grains of a given mineral in a given assemblage; (*d*) partitioning of components between coexisting minerals; and (*e*) disposition of tie lines between minerals. Collection of such a body of data is a major effort because it requires field work, petrographic study of specimens, and chemical analyses of minerals. Note that even if the assemblages satisfy all of the criteria, the criteria are logically necessary but not sufficient to prove the attainment of equilibrium (Zen 1963). If the criteria for attainment of equilibrium are satisfied, it is justified to proceed to classify components as buffered or nonbuffered. If the criteria are not satisfied, however, it is necessary to deduce the recrystallization history of the assemblages in order to understand their behavior as open systems.

The next step in the classification of components is to learn which components are buffered and which are not. Greenwood (1967a) has presented a linear algebraic method of testing for buffered components in complex systems. For components that are not buffered it is necessary to test thermodynamically for the existence of chemical potential gradients between different mineral assemblages (Rumble 1976).

Once the components have been classified as buffered or nonbuffered, and as having chemical potential gradients or not, it remains to decide which ones are J- or K-components. In the example given above of the reduction of a hematite-magnetite assemblage, it was pointed out that a component behaving as a perfectly mobile one, may, nevertheless, be recorded as a buffered component by an assemblage in which equilibration with the external reservoir has not been completed. Therefore, the final decision on the classification of a component requires knowledge of the recrystallization history of the assemblages. In many rocks it is impossible to reconstruct a sufficiently detailed recrystallization history so that a definite classification can be made. Such a disappointing conclusion is not unusual in the study of ancient rocks, where subsequent events often erase evidence of earlier processes.

The reader may question whether it is worth the exercise to arrive at a possibly indefinite conclusion. The work done in establishing which components are buffered, however, will not be wasted. Ferry (1980) has shown that the progress of divariant buffer reactions, as measured by petrographic modal analyses, can be used to determine how much fluid has moved through a given volume of an assemblage during metamorphism.

CASE STUDIES OF METAMORPHIC ROCKS

A number of case studies of perfectly mobile and inert components in regionally metamorphosed rocks have appeared. Albee (1965) used a graphical projection method developed by Thompson (1957) to demonstrate that analyzed mineral assemblages were consistent with the hypothesis that H_2O was a component that equilibrated with an external reservoir during metamorphism. It was also shown that the oxygen isotope composition of minerals of a given type separated from the rocks were uniform in $\delta^{18}O$, a result that confirms the conclusion that the mineral assemblages could have been in equilibrium with an external reservoir (Taylor et al 1963).

A linear algebraic method (Greenwood 1967a) was employed by Pigage (1976) and Fletcher & Greenwood (1979) to test analyzed mineral assemblages for the presence of divariant buffers. Pigage (1976) found assemblages that were buffers with respect to H_2O to be widely distributed. In contrast, Fletcher & Greenwood (1979) reported that the majority of assemblages studied by them were incapable of buffering the chemical potential of H_2O.

Rumble (1978), using a thermodynamic approach, showed that differences in the chemical potentials of the components H_2O, H_2, and O_2 existed between the beds of a metamorphosed quartzite. Oxygen isotope analyses revealed that quartz separated from different beds varies over a range of 2.5‰, a result that supports the conclusion that the assemblages could not have been in equilibrium with an external reservoir.

In a recent study by Rumble et al (1981), the presence of buffer assemblages and the existence of chemical potential gradients for the components H_2O and CO_2 was demonstrated. Nevertheless, quartz separated from different assemblages is homogeneous in its oxygen isotopic composition despite premetamorphic $\delta^{18}O$ differences of 10‰. The oxygen isotope data, as well as mineralogic evidence of fluid-rock ratios greater than 1.0, suggests that the oxygen-bearing species H_2O and CO_2 behaved as perfectly mobile components during metamorphism, but that the buffer capacity of mineral assemblages was so great that the buffer reactions did not proceed to completion (cf Albee 1965, p. 299).

The component H_2O is likely to behave as a K-component during metamorphism. The results of the case studies cited above, however, emphasize that local mineral assemblages may have great buffer capacity with respect to K-components and, thus, obscure the nature of such components. The classification of components must take into account not only information derived from phase equilibrium studies but also stable isotope data and the recrystallization-devolatization history of rocks.

An important impact of the concept of perfectly mobile components on the study of metamorphic petrology has been to focus interest on the mechanisms of equilibration between fluids and rocks. In order for a rock to equilibrate at an externally imposed value of μ_{H_2O}, for example, it may be necessary for pre-existing minerals to be destroyed and their place taken by new minerals. Oxygen isotope equilibration between a rock and an external source of fluid, however, merely requires the exchange of oxygen isotopes between minerals in the rock and an oxygen bearing species, such as H_2O, present in fluid flowing through the rock.

The consideration of fluid species as possible K-components has led to the study of processes whereby rocks lose their volatile constituents as a consequence of metamorphism. Fluid flow into and through fissures in which $P_{fluid} < P_{lithostatic}$ has been considered by Thompson (1955). Evidence of fluid flow parallel to schistosity and bedding has been presented by Ferry (1979) and Rumble et al (1981).

PERFECTLY MOBILE COMPONENTS AND METASOMATIC ROCKS

The concepts of perfectly mobile and inert components have been used in a number of studies of metasomatic rocks formed during either contact or regional metamorphism. Joesten (1974, pp. 896–97) made an important observation about the relationship between the designation of components as perfectly mobile and knowledge of the recrystallization history of metasomatic zones. He stated:

> Understanding of the growth history of the nodules allows the determination for each local assemblage of the number of components whose chemical potentials are determined by the composition of the phases in the local assemblage and the number of those whose chemical potentials are determined by conditions external to the local system. It must be emphasized, however, that this number can be determined only on the basis of knowledge of the history of growth of the nodules. It cannot be determined by enumeration of phases in each local assemblage without an assumption of the path leading from the initial to the present state of the system.

An exciting recent development in the study of metasomatic rocks has been the utilization of theories of diffusion, infiltration, and irreversible thermodynamics to build mathematical models of the evolution of metasomatic mineral zones. Brady (1977) has discussed the relationship between diffusing components, i.e. components moving with respect to an inert marker, and K-components. In a three-component system with one diffusing component, that component is by definition a K-component because the local equilibrium in planar volume elements perpendicular to the direction of diffusion depends on conditions external to the local system (Brady 1977, p. 115). In a multi-component system of n-components, there may well be n diffusing components, but there can only be a maximum of $n - 1$ K-components (Brady 1977, p. 119).

Recent theoretical and model studies of metasomatism scarcely mention the terms "perfectly mobile" and "inert" components (see Fisher 1973, Fletcher & Hofmann 1974, Weare et al 1976, Frantz & Mao 1976, 1979, Joesten 1977). Indeed, the only concept that has survived explicitly in these models from the work of Korzhinskii and Thompson is that of local equilibrium (Fisher & Elliott 1974). It would be incorrect to assume that because the concepts of perfectly mobile and inert components are not discussed explicitly in recent model studies of metasomatism the work of Korzhinskii and Thompson has been rejected. The general predictions of Korzhinskii (1959) and Thompson (1959) regarding the mineralogical composition and spatial distribution of metasomatic zones have been confirmed by model studies. Mathematically computed metasomatic zones show a succession of layers containing assemblages with variance equal to 3 or higher, separated by contact surfaces across which there are abrupt discontinuities in bulk chemical and modal composition.

The concepts of perfectly mobile and inert components have fallen into disuse because it is unnecessary to consider them in building specific numerical models of metasomatism. What is required in model studies is the choice of appropriate values for such parameters as diffusivity, porosity, and permeability. The act of choosing these values ultimately determines which components will behave as K-components and which will not.

Statements such as that of Korzhinskii (1959, p. 17) that perfectly mobile components equilibrate with an external reservoir immediately "as if their masses possessed no inertia" are at odds with the goals of model builders. This statement makes no sense in the context of numerical models of metasomatism because it describes an ideal state of practically unattainable equilibrium. Surely, a prime motive behind model studies is to achieve a more realistic understanding of metasomatism by treating explicitly the impediments to equilibration.

The J- vs K-component classification scheme presents a problem for model studies because of its either/or nature. At equilibrium, either the mass of a component or its chemical potential (but not both) is an equilibrium factor of the system (Korzhinskii 1959). In a realistic model system, however, both mass and chemical potential exert a controlling influence on the outcome of the attempt to equilibrate. The chemical potential of a component imposes a condition toward which a system tends to equilibrate, whereas the mass of a component determines the inertia that must be overcome in order to attain equilibrium.

CONCLUSION

The concepts of perfectly mobile and inert components have had an important impact in metamorphic petrology. Greenwood (1967b, p. 542) has stated that the work of Korzhinskii (1959), Thompson, (1959), and Zen (1961) "produced a sharpened awareness of the critical role that can be played by the composition of the pore fluid in a rock." There has been vigorous discussion and widespread use of the terms in published literature. The concept of perfectly mobile components focused attention on the mechanisms of equilibration between fluids and rocks. Of particular importance was the recognition that rocks have a great capacity to buffer fluid composition. Studies of the reaction progress of buffer reactions are now leading to quantitative estimates of fluid-rock ratios during metamorphism. Recent numerical simulation studies of metasomatism confirm the general features of the analyses of Korzhinskii and Thompson, but Korzhinskii and Thompson's concepts of perfectly mobile and inert components have fallen into disuse because they are not required in building mathematical models.

It is not a simple matter to apply the concepts and definitions of perfectly mobile and inert components to rocks. Misunderstanding is caused by the discrepancy between the literal and technical meaning of the terms. The nature of components may be obscured by the buffer capacity of mineral assemblages. Equilibrium of local assemblages with an external reservoir is an idealized concept and is probably never fully achieved in nature. To apply the concepts and definitions objectively, moreover, requires a great deal of investigation, including petrographic study of textures and fabrics, chemical and stable isotopic analyses of minerals, and reconstruction of the geologic and recrystallization history of the rocks in question. For these reasons, it is understandable that not every researcher would choose to use the concepts and definitions of perfectly mobile and inert components. In defense of the concepts, however, it should be pointed out that there are no simple, easy methods for studying metamorphic and metasomatic rocks. The investigation of rocks that may have been open systems during recrystallization is inherently one of the most difficult tasks faced by petrologists.

ACKNOWLEDGMENTS

I am very grateful to A. L. Albee, P. M. Bell, J. B. Brady, J. M. Ferry, G. W. Fisher, J. D. Frantz, T. C. Hoering, F. S. Spear and H. S. Yoder, Jr., for their critical comments on this paper.

Literature Cited

Albee, A. L. 1965. Phase equilibria in three assemblages of kyanite-zone pelitic schists, Lincoln Mountain quadrangle, central Vermont. *J. Petrol.* 6:246–301

Brady, J. B. 1977. Metasomatic zones in metamorphic rocks. *Geochim. Cosmochim. Acta* 41:113–25

Burt, D. M. 1981. Acidity-salinity diagrams—application to greisen and porphyry deposits. *Econ. Geol.* 76:832–43

Ferry, J. M. 1979. A map of chemical potential differences within an outcrop. *Am. Mineral.* 64:966–85

Ferry, J. M. 1980. A case study of the amount and distribution of heat and fluid during metamorphism. *Contrib. Mineral. Petrol.* 71:373–85

Fisher, G. W. 1973. Nonequilibrium thermodynamics as a model for diffusion-controlled metamorphic processes. *Am. J. Sci.* 273:897–924

Fisher, G. W., Elliott, D. 1974. Criteria for quasi-steady diffusion and local equilibrium in metamorphism. In *Geochemical Transport and Kinetcs,* ed. A. W. Hoffman, B. J. Giletti, H. S. Yoder, Jr., R. A. Yund., pp. 243–59. Washington: Carnegie Inst. Publ. 634. 353 pp.

Fletcher, C. J. N., Greenwood, H. J. 1979. Metamorphism and structure of Penfold Creek area near Quesnel Lake, British Columbia. *J. Petrol.* 20:743–94

Fletcher, R. C., Hofmann, A. W. 1974. Simple models of diffusion and combined diffusion-infiltration metasomatism. See Fisher & Elliott 1974, pp. 243–59

Fonteilles, M. 1978. Les mechanismes de la metasomatose. *Bull. Mineral* 101:166–94

Frantz, J. D., Mao, H. K. 1976. Bimetasomatism resulting from intergranular diffusion: I. A theoretical model for monomineralic reaction zone sequences. *Am. J. Sci.* 276:817–40

Frantz, J. D., Mao, H. K. 1979. Bimetasomatism resulting from intergranular diffusion: II. Prediction of multimineralic zone sequences. *Am. J. Sci.* 279:302–23

Gibbs, J. W. 1906. *The Scientific Papers of J. W. Gibbs,* Vol. 1. New York: Dover. 434pp. (Reprinted 1961)

Greenwood, H. J. 1967a. The N-dimensional tie-line problem. *Geochim. Cosmochim. Acta* 31:465–90

Greenwood, H. J. 1967b. Mineral equilibria in the system $MgO–SiO_2–H_2O–CO_2$. In *Researches in Geochemistry,* ed. P. H. Abelson, 2:542–67. New York: Wiley. 663 pp.

Joesten, R. 1974. Local equilibrium and metasomatic growth of zoned calc-silicate nodules from a contact aureole, Christmas Mtns., Big Bend region, Texas. *Am. J. Sci.* 174:876–901.

Joesten, R. 1977. Evolution of mineral assemblage zoning in diffusion metasomatism. *Geochim. Cosmochim. Acta* 41: 649–70

Korzhinskii, D. S. 1936. Mobility and inertness of components in metasomatosis. *Izv. Akad. Nauk. SSSR, Ser. Geol., No. 1*, pp. 35–65. English translation in *Source Book in Geology 1900–1950,* ed. K. F. Mather, pp. 290–303. Cambridge: Harvard. 1967

Korzhinskii, D. S. 1950. Phase rule and geochemical mobility of elements. *18th Int. Geol. Congr. (Great Britain) Report, Part 2,* pp. 50–65

Korzhinskii, D. S. 1959. *Physicochemical Basis of the Analysis of the Paragenesis of Minerals.* New York: Consultants Bureau. 142 pp.

Korzhinskii, D. S. 1964. An outline of metasomatic processes, parts 1–3. *Int. Geol. Rev.* 6: 1713–34, 1920–52, 2169–98

Korzhinskii, D. S. 1966. On thermodynamics of open systems and the phase rule (a reply to D. F. Weill and W. S. Fyfe). *Geochim. Cosmochim. Acta* 30:829–35.

Korzhinskii, D. S. 1967. On thermodynamics of open systems and the phase rule (a reply to the second critical paper of D. F. Weill and W. S. Fyfe). *Geochim. Cosmochin. Acta* 31:1177–80

Korzhinskii, D. S. 1968. The theory of metasomatic zoning. *Mineral. Deposita* 3:222–31

Pigage, L. C. 1976. Metamorphism of the Settler schist, southwest of Yale, British Columbia. *Can. J. Earth Sci.* 13:405–21

Rumble, D. 1976. The use of mineral solid solutions to measure chemical potential gradients in rocks. *Am. Mineral.* 61:1167–74

Rumble, D. 1978. Mineralogy, petrology, and oxygen isotopic geochemistry of the Clough Formation, Black Mountain, New Hampshire, USA *J. Petrol.* 19:317–40

Rumble, D., Ferry, J. M., Hoering, T. C., Boucot, A. J. 1981. Fluid flow during metamorphism at the Beaver Brook fossil locality, New Hampshire. *Am. J. Sci.* In press

Shaw, D. M. 1956. Geochemistry of pelitic rocks. Part III: major elements and general geochemistry. *Geol. Soc. Am. Bull.* 67:919–34

Taylor, H. P. Jr., Albee, A. L., Epstein, S. 1963. $^{18}O/^{16}O$ ratios of coexisting minerals in three assemblages of kyanite-zone pelitic schist. *J. Geol.* 71:513–22

Thompson, A. B. 1975. Calc-silicate diffusion zones between marble and pelitic schist. *J. Petrol.* 16:314–46

Thompson, J. B. Jr. 1955. The thermodynamic basis for the mineral facies concept. *Am. J. Sci.* 253:65–103

Thompson, J. B. Jr. 1957. The graphical analysis of mineral assemblages in pelitic schists. *Am. Mineral.* 42:842–58

Thompson, J. B. Jr. 1959. Local equilibrium in metasomatic processes. In *Researches in Geochemistry,* ed. P. H. Abelson, 1:427–57. New York: John Wiley

Thompson, J. B. Jr. 1970. Geochemical reaction and open systems. *Geochim. Cosmochim. Acta* 34:529–51

Turner, F. J. 1968. *Metamorphic Petrology.* New York: McGraw-Hill. 403 pp.

Vidale, R. 1969. Metasomatism in a chemical gradient and the formation of calc-silicate bands. *Am. J. Sci.* 267:857–74

Vidale, R. J., Hewitt, D. A. 1973. "Mobile" components in the formation of calc-silicate bands. *Am. Mineral.* 58:991–97

Weare, J. H., Stephens, J. R., Eugster, H. P. 1976. Diffusion metasomatism and mineral reaction zones: general principles and application to feldspar alteration. *Am. J. Sci.* 276:767–816

Weill, D. F., Fyfe, W. S. 1964. A discussion of the Korzhinskii and Thompson treatment of thermodynamic equilibrium in open systems. *Geochim. Cosmochim. Acta* 28:565–76

Weill, D. F., Fyfe, W. S. 1967. On equilibrium thermodynamics of open systems and the phase rule (a reply to D. S. Korzhinskii). *Geochim. Cosmochim. Acta* 31:1167–76

Zen, E.-A. 1961. The zeolite facies: an interpretation. *Am. J. Sci.* 259:401–9

Zen, E.-A. 1963. Components, phases, and criteria of chemical equilibrium in rocks. *Am. J. Sci.* 261:929–42

Ann. Rev. Earth Planet. Sci. 1982. 10:235-56

EARTHQUAKE PREDICTION

Ziro Suzuki

Geophysical Institute, Tohoku University, Sendai, Japan

INTRODUCTION

Systematic research directly oriented to earthquake prediction originated around 1965 in four countries: the USA, Japan, USSR, and China. In 1962 a group of Japanese seismologists published a report (Tsuboi et al 1962), which is sometimes called the "blueprint of earthquake prediction research," on the progress to date and plans for further development. The Japanese national program for earthquake prediction started in 1965 in response to the report. The first step of the Chinese national project was printed in 1966 on the occasion of the Xingtai earthquake (Bolt 1974). American scientists proposed a ten-year plan for research on earthquake prediction (Press et al 1965) in 1965, although the actual start of the Earthquake Hazards Reduction Program (Wallace 1974) was postponed until 1973. A similar project began in the USSR around 1965 (Savarensky 1968).The International Commission on Earthquake Prediction was set up in 1967 within the International Association of Seismology and Physics of the Earth's Interior (IASPEI) of the International Union of Geodesy and Geophysics (IUGG). Since then numerous reports have been published in this field, a high percentage of them by geophysicists in the four countries. More than ten international symposia have been held in various parts of the world under the sponsorship of many organizations. A comprehensive review of prediction-oriented studies before 1975 was given by Rikitake (1976) and a brief review of recent American work is given by Ward (1979).

A general survey of these studies indicates that the research in this field has progressed tremendously in this decade. Nevertheless the present state of the art is very chaotic, or at least seems more confusing than in the past. A remarkable variety of earthquake precursors have been reported so far. Some reported precursors seem very strange and open to doubt. Even excluding these ambiguous cases, no general and definite way to successful earthquake prediction is clear. No panacea is suggested even from the experiences in

0084-6597/82/0515-0235$02.00

successful predictions. Presentations at international meetings (Sidorenko et al 1979, Ku 1979) and other personal communications indicate that a similar state of chaos exists in the USSR and China, where predictive alarms have been successfully issued several times.

The aim of this paper is to present a critical review of recent prediction studies mainly those subsequent to Rikitake's (1976) textbook. Most recent papers describe the successful finding of some forerunning phenomena, but very few papers have discussed nonexistence of a precursor or a false prediction based on some method. If this balance is correct, we should now have a useful way for prediction. Therefore, this implies that there have been many unsuccessful cases. In this review paper, an emphasis is laid on the negative cases to elucidate the actual situation and to show the types of difficulties encountered.

Various techniques are available as possible devices for earthquake prediction. Geological studies provide the locations of active faults or foldings that might cause large earthquakes in the future. Geodetic and seismological observations may be the basic way to success. Geoelectric and geomagnetic means have also been reported to detect precursory variations. Geochemical studies, such as those on emanation of radon or other isotopic elements, color and other qualities of ground water and water level in wells have been demonstrated to be useful. Anomalous behavior of animals or plants have been claimed as precursors. Some papers have argued that even certain meteorological phenomena or emission of radio waves can show forerunning anomalies for impending earthquakes. Some of these phenomena can be explained on physical bases rather easily while others are hard to interpret.

GEOLOGICAL STUDIES

The location of an earthquake is closely related to geologically active zones and geological knowledge gives us information on potential locations of earthquakes. Geological and/or structural maps have been made for most areas of the world, but many are inadequate for the purpose of earthquake prediction. The accuracy in predicting the location of earthquake depends much on the social conditions in the concerned region. A high precision is required in populated or developed areas and exhaustive and detailed geological knowledge is necessary in such cases. Geological information at present is not fully satisfactory from this point of view. Recently some geophysical and geochemical phenomena were shown to be very useful for the determination of the exact location of a fault (e.g. Wakita et al, 1980a). The joint use of geology, geophysics, and geochemistry promises more reliable data not only for the location but also for history of past movements and the activity of faults.

There is no fixed standard for grading a fault concerning its potential for causing an earthquake. The recognition of active faults, especially of minor ones, depends on the subjective judgment of the individual researcher, and a map of faults in one area cannot necessarily be directly correlated with that in a neighboring area made by a second geologist. Matsuda (1978) proposed a method of grading according to the long-term average of the slip rate during the Quaternary. This idea may be useful in Japan because about 80% of its major destructive earthquakes occurred within 5 km from a fault of high activity, as shown on a recent map of active faults compiled with a uniform standard (Research Group for Active Faults 1980). However, as is well known, some parts of the San Andreas fault in California have frequently shown aseismic creeps of large amount (e.g. Slater 1978). The method is clearly not applicable in such cases. Moreover, large earthquakes did not always occur on the major fault in a region. For an example, the San Fernando earthquake in southern California in 1971 took place not on the main San Andreas fault but on a rather minor one that had not been recognized as active before the occurrence (Wentforth & Yerkes 1971). Even in Japan the inverse of the earlier statement indicates that 20% of the big earthquakes occurred comparatively far from the known active faults.

Geological studies may supply information on time as well as on place. Estimates of average recurrence time of earthquake occurrence can be obtained from the past history of fault movement, coastal terrace data, and other information (e.g. Matsuda et al 1978). Recently, trenches cut across fault zones have been used as a means for recognizing prehistoric movements (e.g. Sieh 1978). The recurrence time from geological research is a rough average of time intervals between two successive events and it is not always a sufficiently accurate indicator of the time of impending earthquake even for long-term prediction. New techniques for age determination beyond the limit of the ^{14}C method will give more precise data for prehistoric earthquakes. However, the time scale in geology is usually very long and quite different from the time scale in human life.

GEODETIC RESULTS

Earth crustal deformation can be detected by various methods: repeated surveys of leveling, triangulation, trilateration by means of geodimeter observation of sea level by tide gauge, and continuous measurement by strainmeter or tiltmeter. Gravity measurement gives the information on vertical movement. Recently space techniques, such as very long baseline interferometry (VLBI), have become available (e.g. Whitney et al 1976). The above techniques measure strain, but the determination of in situ stress has been achieved in this decade by several different techniques (e.g. McGarr & Gay 1978, US Geological Survey 1978a).

The most beautiful and convincing geodetic precursor was detected by repeated leveling surveys before the Niigata earthquake, 1964, in central Japan (Tsubokawa et al 1964, Dambara 1973). Judging from the spacial and temporal variations shown in Figure 1, the pre-seismic land uplift and sudden subsidence are plausibly considered to be associated with the occurrence of the earthquake.

Anomalous crustal movement found by various kinds of measurements have been claimed as earthquake precursors in many regions of the world. Suyehiro (1978) compiled a list of these reports for the Japanese earthquakes based on research by Y. Suzuki (unpublished). The list is reproduced in Table 1 with some modifications. It contains 33 cases and, excluding old events, 29 post-dated the Kwanto earthquake in 1923, which was an epoch for the development of seismological observation in Japan. On the other hand, 86 big earthquakes caused damage in Japan from 1923 to 1976 (Rika-nenpyo 1981), and 22 of these damaging events are included in Table 1. This means that some anomalous geodetic phenomenon was reported for about 26% of destructive earthquakes. This figure is a minimum because such measurements had not been carried out in the vicinity of all these earthquakes. Even taking these considerations into account, it is questionable whether or not all cases of big earthquakes have been preceded by some anomalous deformation of considerable size.

Table 1 contains a microearthquake case with magnitude smaller than 3 around the Yamasaki fault in southwestern Japan. Strain measurement stations are located within the seismically active area. According to Oike (1978) some

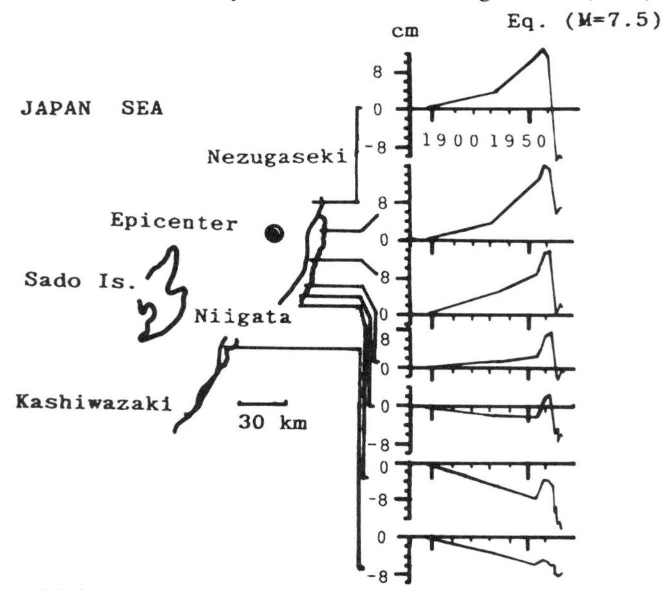

Figure 1 Crustal deformations before the Niigata earthquake, Japan (Dambara 1973).

anomaly in strain precedes increased activity of microearthquakes with an average distance from the geodetic station of about 10 km. Dambara (1966) presented a formula for the relation between the size of the area where anomalous crustal movements were observed and the magnitude of the earthquake associated with it. Although the basis of this relation includes many co-seismic data, it is sometimes assumed to be valid also for preseismic movement. This relation indicates that the logarithm of the radius of the area is approximately proportional to one half the magnitude. Based on this relationship, any event with magnitude 7 or more should be accompanied by crustal movement in an area whose radius is more than a hundred times that in the microearthquake case. It implies that the precursory anomaly should have been found more frequently than can be seen from the results in Table 1 indicate, taking into consideration the number of large earthquakes and the density of observation in Japan. Oike (1978) suggests that heavy rainfall excites fault movement, which increases microearthquake activity. If this is correct, it might be possible to assume that the mechanism in the microearthquake case is different from other cases of larger events.

Theoretically, when the hypocentral region is in the state of dilatancy a large change in the amplitude of earth tide, which reflects the stress state in the region, is expected before a big earthquake (Beaumont & Berger 1974). Such an anomaly has been observed in a few cases (Nishimura 1950, Latynina & Rizaeva 1976, Mikumo et al 1978), but other papers (e.g. Earthquake Research Institute 1975) reported no change before some large events.

Another problem is that the mode of appearance of precursory crustal movement differs from one case to another. In fact, no regular relationship between time of appearance, magnitude of earthqauke, epicentral distance of station, and other factors can be inferred from Table 1. The reason may be partly attributed to scanty data but the difficulty remains when a large amount of other data are included. There have been several cases where no anomaly was detected at one station, while an anomalous change was observed at a nearby station (e.g. Japan Meteorological Agency 1980).

Nonregularity is also seen in the type of precursory anomaly. Sometimes a gradual change of creep type was reported as a feature of the earthquake-preparing stage (e.g. Thatcher 1976). In other cases, the appearance or disappearance of a sudden change of step type on the strain record was reported as a preseismic signal (e.g. Japan Meteorological Agency 1980). Almost every type of change has been suggested as a possible precursor. Some papers (e.g. Geodetic Survey Brigade 1977) claimed that the differences indicated spatial or temporal character such that gradual and abrupt changes corresponded to long-term and imminent precursors respectively. However, other cases have shown that this is not always true.

Furthermore, nonseismic crustal movements have been observed in many regions. Aseismic creep has been observed frequently along the San Andreas

Table 1 List of reported crustal movements prior to large earthquakes in Japan (after Suyehiro (1978) with modification by Z. Suzuki)

	Date			Location					
Name	Year	Month	Day	Lat. (N)	Long. (E)	Mag.	Obs. pt. (Distance:km)	Time of appearance*	Mean of observation
Noshiro	1964	6	19	40.2	140.2	7.0	Oomorishitahama (17)	2 months	Eye observation
West-Tsugaru	1793	2	8	40.7	140.0	6.9	Ajigasawa (19)	Several hours	Eye observation
Sado	1802	12	9	37.8	138.4	6.6	Ogiminato (10)	4 hours	Eye observation
Hamada	1872	3	14	34.8	132.0	7.1	Hamadaura (13)	20 months	Eye observation
Kwanto	1923	9	1	35.2	139.3	7.9	Aburatsubo (22)	10 years	Sea level
							Mitaka (40)	4 years	Base line
							Tokyo (48)	1 month, 8 hours	Tiltmeter
North-Tango	1927	3	7	35.6	135.1	7.5	Sannotsu (15)	2 ~ 3 hours	Eye observation
Sekigahara	1927	10	27	37.5	138.8	5.3	BM 3755–3760 (7)	(1894–1927.7)	Levelling
North-Izu	1930	11	26	35.1	139.0	7.0	BM 9333–9332 (13)	7 months	Levelling
Tottori	1943	9	10	35.5	134.2	7.4	Ikuno (68)	6 hours	Tiltmeter
Tonankai	1944	12	7	33.7	136.2	8.0	Kakegawa (200)	10 years	Levelling
							Kakegawa (200)	several hours	Levelling
Mikawa	1945	1	13	34.7	137.0	7.1	Sengen (10)	4 ~ 5 years	Sea level
							Nishiura (19)	4 ~ 5 years	Sea level
							Maeshiba (32)	4 ~ 5 years	Sea level
Nankai	1946	12	21	33.0	135.6	8.1	Kii and Shikoku (60 ~ 300)	30 years	Levelling
							Muroto-Misaki (129)	11 years	Levelling
							Uwajima (276)	5 ~ 6 years	Sea level
							Tosashimizu (242)	4 ~ 5 years	Sea level
Tokachi-oki	1952	3	4	42.2	143.9	8.1	Hachinohe (244)	5 years	Sea level
Daishoji-oki	1952	3	7	36.5	136.2	6.8	Ogoya (43)	3 months, 8 days	Tiltmeter
Yoshino	1952	7	18	34.5	135.8	7.0	Oosakayama (79)	10 months	Strainmeter
							Yura (87)	2 weeks	Tiltmeter

Futatsui	1955	10	19	40.3	140.2	5.7	BM 5856–5857 (12)	(1942–1949)	Levelling
Oodaigahara	1960	12	26	34.2	136.2	6.0	Kii (40 ~ 100)	a few weeks	Strainmeter, tiltmeter
Nagaoka	1961	2	2	37.5	138.8	5.2	BM 3759 (3)	(1958–1961)	Levelling
Hyuga-nada	1961	2	27	31.6	131.9	7.0	Hosojima (90)	4 years	Sea level
							Makimine (115)	12 days	Tiltmeter
North-Mino	1961	8	19	36.0	136.8	7.0	Katsuyama-Oono (27)	(1949–1961)	Levelling
Niigata	1964	6	16	38.4	139.2	7.5	Niigata (30 ~ 80)	10 years, 4 ~ 5 years	Levelling
							Maze (80)	6 ~ 7 years, 4 years	
							Nezugaseki (37)	6 ~ 7 years, 1 ~ 2 years	Sea level
Matsushiro	1965~	8	3~	36.5	138.3	<4.5	Matsushiro (<10)	2 hours	Tiltmeter
Asazumi	1967	9	14	36.4	138.2	5.1	BM 5090–5128 (2 ~ 22)	4 months	Levelling
Central Gifu	1969	9	9	35.8	137.1	6.6	Inuyama (50)	300 days, 50 days, several hours	Strainmeter, tiltmeter
							Kamitakara (63)	8 ~ 9 months	Strainmeter, tiltmeter
							Tsukechi (35)	1 year	Trilateration
Southeastern-Akita	1970	10	16	39.2	140.7	6.2	BM 5540 ~ 5556 (8 ~ 20)	14 ~ 4 years	Levelling
							Nibetsu (79)	60 ~ 70 days	Tiltmeter
Atumihanto-oki	1971	1	5	34.4	137.2	6.1	Inuyama (104)	250 days	Strainmeter, tiltmeter
Nemurohanto-oki	1973	6	17	43.0	146.0	7.4	Erimo (258)	1 year, 1 month	Strainmeter, tiltmeter
Central-Wakayama	1973	11	25	33.9	135.4	5.9	Kishu-kozan (56)	several hours	Strainmeter
Izuhanto-oki	1974	5	9	34.6	138.8	6.9	Fujigawa (80)	7 months, 2 months	Strainmeter
South-Aichi	1975	11	12	34.6	137.4	4.3	Toyohashi (15)	3 days	Strainmeter
Yamasaki-fault	1975	12	14	35.0	134.5	<3	Yasutomi (<10)	5 days	Strainmeter
East-Yamanshi	1976	6	16	35.5	139.0	5.5	Shizuoka (83)	2 months	Strainmeter
							Fujigawa (56)	6 months	Strainmeter, tiltmeter
Hamamatsu	1976	12	27	34.7	137.8	3.5	Toyohashi (29)	2 days	Strainmeter

*( ) stands for the variation during indicated period.

fault in California, as stated previously. There are two other typical examples of movements that are not associated with earthquake occurrence. One is in the Kawasaki region in central Japan. The observed uplift is seen in Figure 2 (Geographical Survey Institute 1976, 1977). If this is an earthquake precursor, the forthcoming earthquake would be about magnitude of 6.5 based on Dambara's (1966) formula. Since this region is very close to Tokyo, the observation caused considerable consternation among local inhabitants. After many observations of various kinds, the Coordinating Committee for Earthquake Prediction, Japan, finally concluded that this was not a preseismic indication. Another example is the large-scale uplift around Palmdale in southern California found by Castle et al (1976). No big earthquake has occurred in this region so far and even the real existence of the uplift is now open to argument (Rundle & McNutt 1981).

It is natural to expect that some crustal movement would precede earthquakes and nobody can deny the usefulness of geodetic observations for successful prediction. However, the situation is far too complicated for a straightforward explanation. Complex geological underground structure and some other complicated conditions might control the appearance of geodetic precursors. More dense and precise measurement is necessary to unravel the confusion.

SEISMOLOGICAL RESEARCH

Seismological observation naturally has given a variety of fundamental information on earthquake prediction and quite a number of studies have been made in this discipline. These studies can be classified into several categories. Statistics on past big earthquakes have been utilized for earthquake prediction. Certain featural patterns of seismic activity have been reported before a big event (e.g. Keilis-Borok et al 1980). Temporal change in seismic wave veloc-

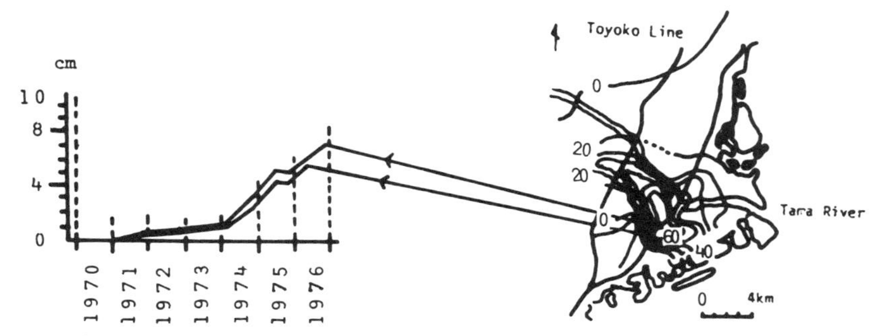

Figure 2 Ground uplift around Kawasaki, Japan (compiled from Geographical Survey Institute, Japan, 1976, 1977).

ity, source mechanism, source parameter, and other factors have been discussed.

The probability of earthquake occurrence in a certain area within a certain period of time can be statistically estimated from past data. The theoretical basis and many tests along this line are described in detail in Rikitake's (1976) book. Some researchers (e.g. Kawasumi 1970) claim a tendency for periodical occurrence and argue for a triggering mechanism (e.g. Tamrazyan 1971). An extreme-value scheme has been used to estimate the maximum possible earthquake in a region (e.g. Shakal & Willis 1972). A similar approach is to use a truncated function for the relation between earthquake magnitude and frequency of occurrence (e.g. Cosentino et al 1977).

In general, however, the present statistical results are not satisfactory for the practical purpose of earthquake prediction, because some studies treated too little data or too wide a region as one block. A sufficiently large data base is essential to obtain an accurate statistical result. China has historical records for more than 2700 years and Japan has recently found many old documents on historical earthquakes resulting in the increase of documented number of old earthquakes. In this decade seismological station networks have been developed in many countries and a great increase in observable events, especially small earthquakes, has occurred, though the period of observation is rather short. It is very helpful, therefore, to find a successful way to use these data on small events. If a statistical relation between precursor appearance and occurrence of earthquake is found, it will give additional information. However, it is necessary for this purpose to solve the problem of irregularity in appearance of precursor.

Several patterns of seismic activity have been cited as preseismic features. The seismic gap, which means a state of low activity in the epicentral region prior to a big earthquake, has been most frequently reported. A conference on this approach was held in 1978. The proceedings were published by the US Geological Survey (1978b) and a comprehensive review of the approach was given by McCann et al (1980). There have been several reports on precursory earthquake swarms (e.g. Evison 1977), as well as on the so-called doughnut pattern (Moge 1969)—high activity surrounding a seismic gap. Neither of these precursors are as common as a seismic gap. Foreshock activity has been clearly detected in some cases (e.g. Wu et al 1976). According to Jones & Molnar (1976), about 44% of big-shallow earthquakes were preceded by foreshocks. These preseismic patterns of seismic activity were briefly reviewed by Kanamori (1981). Besides these, a regular migration of epicenters has been shown in a few exceptional cases, for example, in the North Anatolian fault zone of Turkey (Toksöz et al 1978). Keilis-Borok et al (1980) tried to make a quantitative prediction based on a combination of some patterns. Yasamashina & Miura (1980) suggested that the differences among earthquake magnitudes in a swarm could be used as a probabilistic measure for impending earthquake.

The problem with precursory seismic patterns lies also in the complexity of their appearance. For example, a seismic gap is evident in Figure 3*A*, which represents the space-time plot of earthquakes before the Oaxaca, Mexico, earthquake in 1978. The foreshock activity is also clear, although no precursory swarm or doughnut pattern is seen. On the other hand, a similar space-time plots (Figure 3*B*) for the Alaskan, 1964, and Rat Isand, Aleutian, 1965, earthquakes do not show such a feature. In fact the preseismic activity increased before the major events.

Another problem is the definition of foreschock, swarm, and other such terms. Although the areas, time duration, smallest magnitude, and some other factors should be fixed for comparative discussion, there are no established standards for these terms. In some extreme cases, a slight change in the adopted value of a factor causes a different result. When the general reliability of a conclusion about a seismic pattern is claimed, some evidence for the validity of the adopted definition should be indicated (US Geological Survey 1978b).

The variation in seismic-wave velocity is one of the most discussed items in prediction-oriented seismological research. After Aggarwal et al (1973) demonstrated a precursory change of velocity at Blue Mountain Lake, New York, as in some Russian cases (e. g. Semyenov 1969), many papers followed reporting similar results in various parts of the world. Figure 4*A* gives a Chinese case, for example (Feng 1975). At first this method appeared to be generally successful.

Temporal variation of the difference between travel times and a standard table was also studied for this purpose (e.g. Wyss & Holcomb 1973). However, later research (e.g. Wesson et al 1977) questioned these results. In particular, the analysis of explosion studies (e.g. McEvilly & Johnson 1974), which usually give more accurate results than those from natural earthquakes, has cast doubt on the reliability of this precursor. A negative example is the result of explosion studies in Japan. Observations have been conducted many times with exactly the same observation system for the special purpose of detecting temporal variation in travel time. The result did not show any significant change in travel time before the Izu-oshima earthquake in January, 1978, although the paths to some stations certainly penetrate the hypocentral region (Geological Survey of Japan, unpublished; Figure 4*B*). For the same type of faulting, such as strike-slip, and sometimes even for the same event, conclusions by various authors are different. A list of conflicting examples has been compiled by Dung et al (1979). A possible conclusion may be that the situation differs from one event to another and/or that the variation is not as large as reported initially.

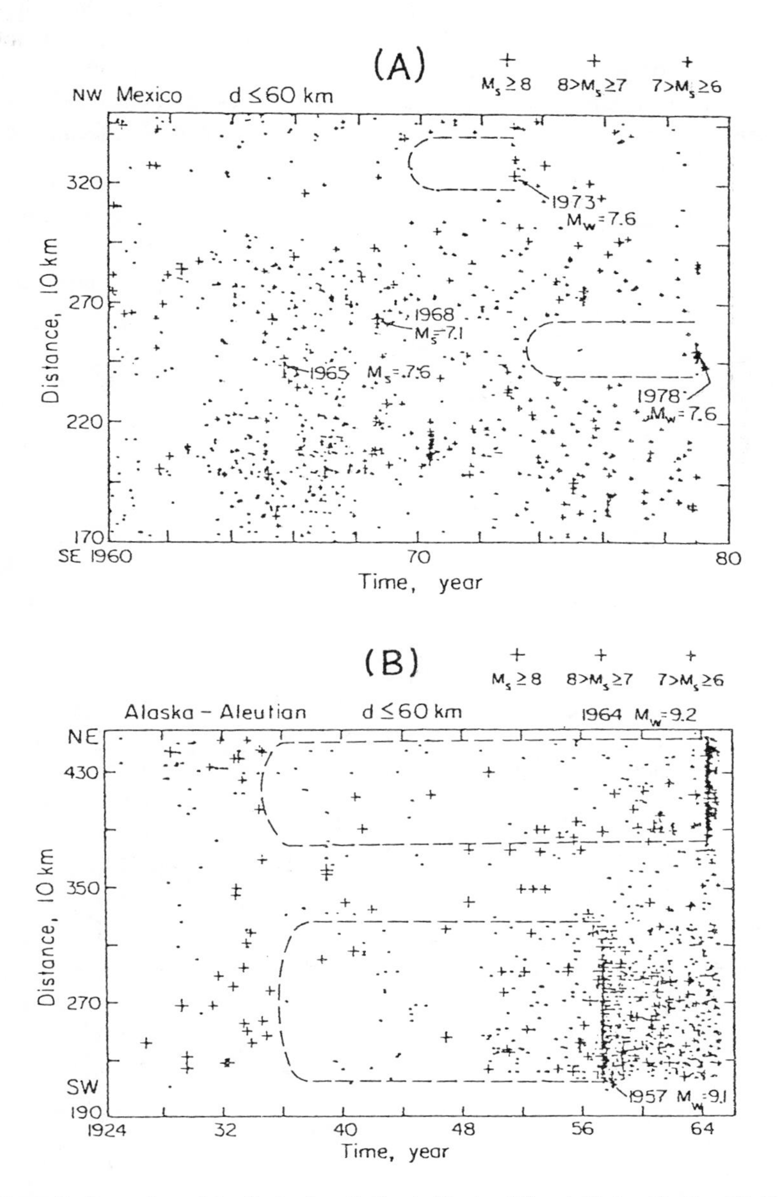

Figure 3 Space-time plots of seismic activities in Mexico (*A*) and Alaska-Aleutian (*B*) (Kanamori 1981).

A systematic change in source mechanism (e.g. Engdahl & Kisslinger 1978) or in source parameter, such as stress drop (Saito et al 1981), has reportedly shown a premonitory change. Though this line of study has not been thoroughly tested, such changes are surely not a very common feature before every big event. A general survey of many studies shows that no single seismological precursor appears to be useful as a general predictive technique.

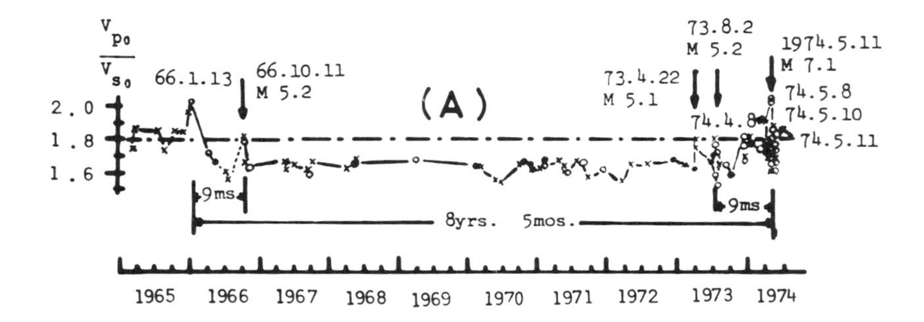

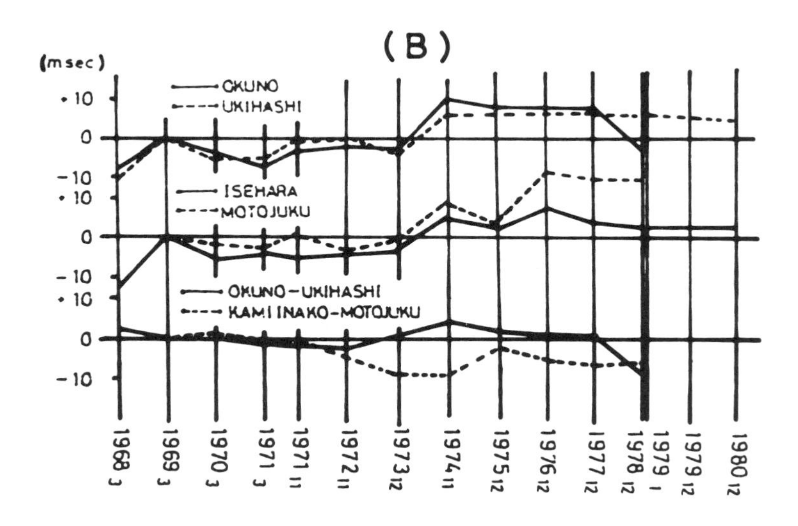

Figure 4 Variations in seismic-wave velocity before the Haicheng, China earthquake (*A*) (Feng 1975) and the result of special experiments in Japan (*B*) (Geological Survey, Japan, unpublished).

GEOMAGNETISM AND GEOELECTRICITY

Variations in geomagnetic fields have been reported to be associated with earthquakes. Rikitake (1976) lists 26 such reports made before 1972. Nine later reports during 1973–1978 were shown in a similar table by Fujita & Mizuno (1980). It should be noted, however, that these cases are not all preseismic variations, but include co-seismic changes, some where the exact times are not known because of intermittent observations, and some where only a general correlation between geomagnetic and seismic activities was found. Older data are not always trustworthy (e.g. Johnston et al 1975) but possible precursory variation has been claimed in about half of the 12 listed cases after 1970.

The situation with geomagnetic precursors is similar to the geodetic one, that is, too few cases compared to the number of strong earthquakes in the same time period, and no regularity among magnitude, distance, and amount of variation. In some cases, secular variation has been argued to be in association with seismic activity and, in other cases, short period variation, such as geomagnetic pulsation, was reported to show a precursory signal. Furthermore, some papers (e.g. Johnston 1978) disclosed that these anomalies were found not only before big seismic events but also before large aseismic fault creep.

In general, detection of preseismic anomalies involves a problem of noise due to other natural or artificial causes. The use of a tranfer function can reduce the noise of a geomagnetic field to approximately one half of the level obtained by simple differential technique. Even then, the noise level is still very high, even for a densely spaced network (Poehls & Jackson 1978). This implies that the reliable detection of a precursory magnetic field anomaly by simple instrumentation may not be easy, especially for moderate-size earthquakes.

Geoelectric precursors have been reported many times. Most of the old reports are based on the observatrion of natural earth-current or self-potential. More recently, ground resistivity has been measured, sometimes by sending artificial current into ground to improve the signal/noise ratio. Rikitake & Yamazaki (1978) reviewed resistivity measurement at Aburatsubo, 60 km south of Tokyo, Japan from the view point of earthquake prediction. The observations frequently showed co-seismic change of step shape with a regular relationship among magnitude of earthquake, distance from epicenter, and amplitude of co-seismic step. They also mentioned that a precursory variation has been observed in 21 cases of 30 where co-seismic steps were recorded. According to Mazzella & Morrison (1974), 24% of earthquakes occurring near Melendy Ranch along the southern San Andreas fault, California, were preceded by resistivity changes. However, the same instrumentation as that at Aburatsubo did not show such successful results at other stations. Another complex example is the 1976 Tangshan earthquake, northeastern China. A resistivity anomaly was recorded at some stations. Even at a distant station about 80 km from the epicenter, an anomaly of 17 Ω-m was detected during the four days prior to the earthquake, as shown in Figure 5 (Noritomi 1978). However, no anomalous change was observed at the closest station to the epicenter.

It is reasonable to assume that the resistivity change is a reflection of the strain at the observation point. Theoretical estimates of piezo-electricity, based on a dislocation model of source and the simultaneous observation of strain and resistivity, reveal that the successfully observed variation at the San Andreas fault zone is 10^4 times bigger than the theoretically expected value (Bufe et al 1973). Therefore, the success at some stations may be partially the result of a special property of the rocks at the site (Yamazaki 1974).

GEOCHEMICAL APPROACH

Wakita (1978) listed 113 Japanese earthquakes, including historical ones, which were accompanied by some geochemical anomalies, though most of these anomalies were co-seismic phenomena. Most of these cases are changes in level of underground water at a spring or in a well, because it can be readily observed even by nongeologists. At present there are many groups of volunteers for water level measurement, as can be seen by the proceedings of a US Geological Survey conference (1978c). Recently, scientifically conducted ob-

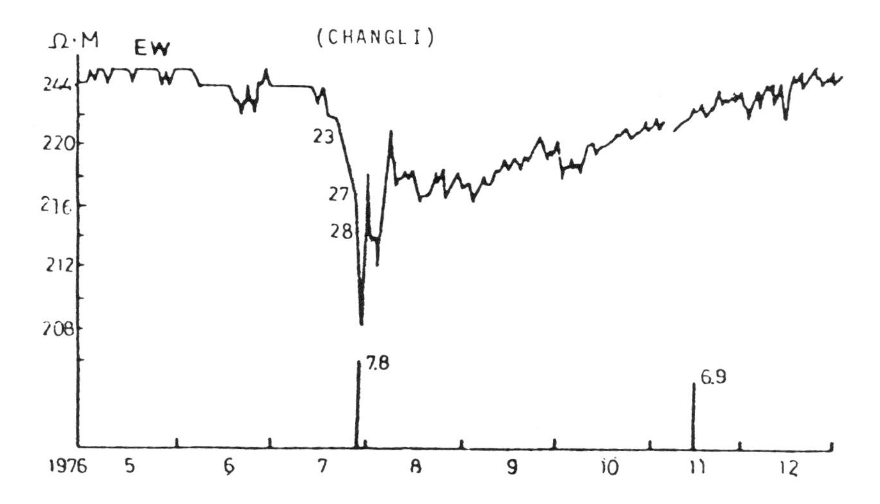

Figure 5 Resistivity change before the Tangshan earthquake, China (Noritomi 1978).

servations have also been carried out (e.g. Wakita 1978). Not many such changes are persuasively connected with earthquake occurrence. The geographical distribution of wells that report premonitoring variation shows little regularity. Water level certainly somehow reflects the strain-state of ground and some wells may work as a sensitive strainmeter. However, the percentage of such sensitive wells is not high. According to a Chinese authority (personal communication), who has a long experience of managing amateurs' reports in a province of China, the percentage is as low as 0.5% and, moreover, the sensitivity depends on the location of the epicenter. Accumulation of reliable data is necessary for further advancement. Color, muddiness, and other properties of underground water have been reported as to indicate forerunning change, but these reports are even more confusing than those concerning water level.

Ulmov (1968) demonstrated that radon concentration within underground water at Tashkent, USSR, has shown a precursory increase before major earthquakes. Since then, geochemistry has been introduced into prediction research. In the mid-1960s, China began measuring Rn with the intent of detecting earthquakes. Systematic study of Rn originated in Japan in 1973 and American observation began in 1975 (King 1978). The history of Rn research is shorter than that of other precursors.

Radon concentration is the most frequently observed item among various isotopic schemes and, for a recent example, a successful result was reported in the case of Izu-oshima earthquake, 1978, in Japan (Wakita et al 1980b) as seen in Figure 6. To summarize many reports, preseismic variation in Rn has been detected usually within a distance of 300 km from epicenter, but in some special cases, it has been found even at 600 km. Amplitude of the change amounted to 20–100% and a variety of anomaly shapes are documented. The appearance is neither in all cases nor at all places like other precursors, one of the reasons being the difference in some characteristics of the wells from which the ground water is sampled.

Besides Rn, many chemical elements (such as Cl) and ratios of various isotopes (such as $^{2}H/^{1}H$) have been studied in relation to prediction and some of them were reported as possible forerunning indicators. For instance, Sugisaki & Shichi (1978) claimed that the ratios of He/Ar and N^2/Ar in fault gases are sensitive precursors. The evaluation of these techniques must be left for future examination.

OTHER PHENOMENA

Other miscellaneous phenomena have been suggested as premonitors of earthquakes. Some of them even occur aboveground, such as the previously men-

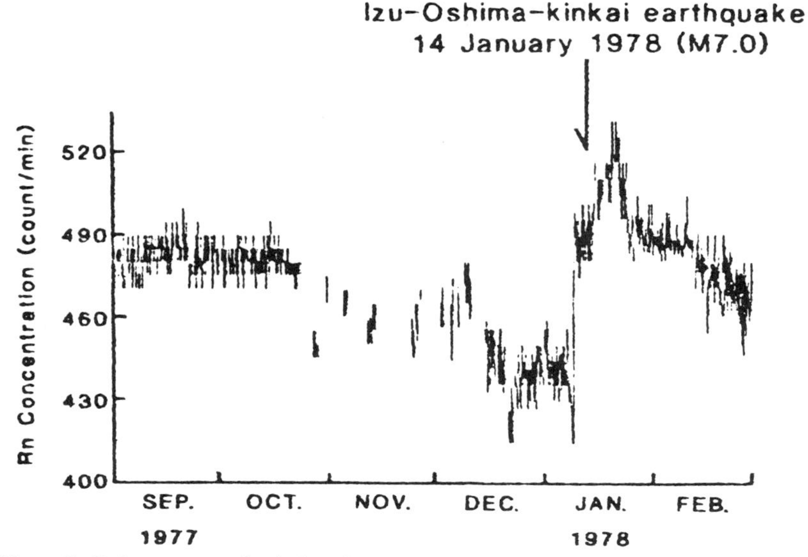

Figure 6 Radon concentration before the Izu-oshima earthquake, Japan (Wakita et al 1980a).

tioned example of rainfall. Perhaps the abnormal behavior of animals is the most widely known. The Chinese report on animal behavior as a precursor (e.g. Chu 1976) has been widely circulated and sensationalized by the press. The circumstances as well as possible explanations for this problem are found in the proceedings of two conferences convened by the US Geological Survey (1976, 1980a). The compilatioin of such reports (e.g. Rikitake 1978) indicates that almost all animals have reportedly shown some type of forerunning anomaly. It is difficult to scientifically analyze this problem because no statistics exist about the appearance and nonappearance of the phenomenon. Two recent questionnaires circulated after the 1978 Izu-oshima and Miyagiken-oki earthquakes in Japan (Rikitake 1978, Rikitake & Suzuki 1979) may give a rough idea on this point. The total number of no answer and no anomaly responses amounted to 77 and 93% respectively. Some of the answers reporting anomalies may have been affected by the reporters' later awareness of earthquake occurrence. In any case, the biological behavior must be more complicated than natural physical phenomena.

EMPIRICAL, THEORETICAL, AND EXPERIMENTAL BASES

For prediction, the three elements of magnitude, time, and location of forthcoming earthquake have to be specified. Relations between magnitude and areal size of precursor appearance have been proposed not only for the geodetic phenomena previously described but for other precursors as well. A relationship between magnitude and precursory time has been also suggested. A detailed description of these empirical relationships is given in Rikitake's (1976) book. Estimates of the three elements can be made using these empirical formulas, but since they are obtained from fairly scattered data, the accuracy of any estimate is not high enough for practical purposes. The prediction of time is most difficult since there exists cases that clearly do not fit the empirical relationship between precursor interval and earthquake magnitude.

The general mechanism of earthquake occurrence, especially for interplate earthquakes of large magnitude, can be explained fairly well by the idea of plate tectonics (e.g. Isacks et al 1968). The interpretation of precursor appearance has been commonly based on dilatancy pheonomenon, which means the opening of microcracks before a main fracture. Models of dry (e.g. Brady 1974) and wet (e.g. Scholz et al 1973) dilatancy have been proposed, different in their consideration of pore fluid. Both models can interpret observed facts and future research will determine which is superior. Different interpretations have been suggested for a specific precursor. Piezomagnetism has been used as an explanation for seismomagnetism, (e.g. Shamsi & Stacey 1969) but Mizutani & Ishido (1976) recently proposed an explanation based on the electrokinetic effect induced by moving water in a dilatant region.

Interpretations for differences in the modes of precursor appearances have been suggested by many authors. As an interesting example, Winkler & Nur (1978) demonstrated that the most significant anomaly in seismic wave velocity occurs only within the uppermost few kilometers of the Earth's crust and the anomaly is not always likely to be detected in seismic observation. Another example is the explanation of various modes of seismic patterns from the idea of the asperity model (Kanamori 1981), which assumes a heterogeneous distribution of rock strength in the hypocentral region. Further developments in rock fracture experimentation will undoubtedly give more detailed understanding of precursor appearance.

SOCIAL SCIENCES

The importance of the social sciences in prediction research has increased in recent years as accurate prediction has become increasingly possible. The US National Academy of Sciences (1975) published a report by a panel on earthquake prediction and public policy that recommended several concrete research items. In 1979 UNESCO held an international synmposium on earthquake prediction which concerned both natural and social sciences, and two conferences on communication problems were convened by the US Geological Survey (1978d, 1980b).

Most work so far has been in the field of communication and the psychological responses of inhabitants to earthquake alarm. The issue of prediction has sometimes had a strong impact on society and erroneous communication has often occurred. Such a situation was recently seen in Peru (US National Earthquake Prediction Evaluation Council 1981). The studies have usually been done by questionnaires based on either an assumed scenario (Hass & Mileti 1978) or the actual occurrence of some anomalous phenomena observed by many people (e.g. Turner et al 1979). In a few papers socio-economic and political consequences were also discussed.

The Earthquake Hazards Reduction Act was enacted in 1977 in the United States and a Large-Scale Earthquake Countermeasures Act was put into effect in 1978 in Japan. A jurisprudential study of earthquake law has become a matter of practical necessity. Earthquake prediction naturally influences the economic state of society but very little research has been done in this area despite such a recommendation by the US National Academy of Sciences (1975).

CONCLUDING REMARKS

The chaotic state of earthquake prediction research may be attributed to several reasons. First, reported precursors probably include many phenomena not really associated with earthquakes. It is particularly true because the usual way to search for a precursor is to try to find an anomaly by using a priori knowledge of earthquake occurrence (a method ironically called post-prediction). The recognition of a real precursor should be made with critial evaluation on two points; whether or not the observed phenomenon is really anomalous and whether or not it is really connected with the earthquake. Some past studies appear to have been too hasty in trying to achieve successful results.

The complex mode of precursor appearance is also a problem. This is probably due partially to regional characteristics of both hypocentral areas and observation sites. The physical process controlling the appearance should be pursued in more detail. In other words, under what conditions do what kind of precursors appear at an observable magnitude. For the elucidation of this problem, the accumulation of many case histories with an abundance of reliable data is required.

Probably the best strategy is as follows: First, possible dangerous places are selected based on geodetic and/or seismological information. This may be called long-term prediction. Then intensified observations are carried out in these regions to watch for temporal variation of various phenomena and to find some systematic appearance of precursors. This method will serve to accumulate reliable data as well as give a reliable foundation of official issuance of an alarm. Such procedures have been actually adopted in some areas such as southern California or central Japan.

A review of prediction-oriented research produces the conclusion that no omnipotent method for successful prediction is known at present and further research in the various approaches must be carried out before prediction is practically available. From this point of view, the idea of international cooperative research in earthquake prediction, which is now undertaken by IASPEI and UNESCO, is highly promising.

Literature Cited

Aggarwal, Y. P., Sykes, L. R., Armbruster, J., Shar, M. L. 1973. Premonitory changes in seismic velocities and prediction of earthquakes. *Nature* 241:101–104

Beaumont, C., Berger, J. 1974. Earthquake prediction: modification of the earth tilts and strains by dilatancy. *Geophys. J.* 39: 111-121

Bolt, B. A. 1974. Earthquake studies in the People's Republic of China. *EOS* 55: 108–17

Brady, B. T., 1974. Theory of earthquakes, 1. A scale independent theory of rock failure. *Pageoph* 112:701–725

Bufe, C. G., Bakun, W. H., Tocher, D. 1973. Geophysical studies in the San Andreas fault zone at the Stone Canyon Observatory, California. *Proc. Conf. Tectonic Probl. San Andreas Fault Syst.*, ed. R. L. Kovach, A. Nur, pp. 86–93, Stanford Univ. Publ.

Castle, R. O., Church, J. P., Elliott, M. R. 1976. A seismic uplift in southern California. *Science* 192:251–53

Chu, F. M. 1976. An outline of prediction and forecast of Haicheng earthquake of M = 7.3: In *Proceedings of the Lectures by the Seismological Delegation of the People's Republic of China* (In Japanese), Seism. Soc. Japan., trans. by Jet Propulsion Laboratory, Calif. Inst. Tech., pp. 11–17

Cosentino, P., Ficarra, V., Luzio, D. 1977. Truncated experimental frequency-magnitude relation in earthquake statistics. *Bull. Seismol. Soc. Am.* 67:1615–23

Dambara, T. 1966. Vertical movements of the earth's crust in relation to the Matsushiro earthquake. *J. Geod. Soc. Jpn.* 12:18–45 (In Japanese)

Dambara, T. 1973. Crustal movetants before, at, and after the Niigata earthquake. *Rep. Coord. Comm. Earthquake Predict* 9:93–6 (In Japanese)

Dung, S. S., Ge, H. C., Lo, Y. L., Hsu C. Y., Wang, F. C. 1979. Earthquake prediction on the basis of V_P/V_S variations—a case history. *The Observational Basis for Earthquake Prediction*, ed. Z. Suzuki, F. F. Evison, *Phys. Earth Planet. Inter.* 18:303–8

Earthquake Research Institute, Tokyo Univ. 1975. Changes in tidal factors during the 1974 Izu-hanto-oki earthquake by means of an Askania tidal gravimeter. *Rep. Coord. Comm. Earthquake Predict.* 13:67–8 (In Japanese)

Engdahl, E. R., Kisslinger, C. 1978. Seismological precursors to a magnitude 5 earthquake in the central Aleutian islands. In *Earthquake Precursors*, ed. C. Kisslinger, Z. Suzuki, pp. 243–50, Tokyo: Cent. Acad. Publ., Japan, and Japan Sci. Soc. Press. 296 pp. (Ext. abstr.)

Evison, F. F. 1977. The precursory earthquake swarm. *Phys. Earth Planet. Inter.* 15:19–23

Feng, D. Y. 1975. Anomalies of seismic velocity ratio before the Tangshan-Daguan earthquake (M = 7.1) on May 11, 1974. *Acta Geophys. Sin.* 18:235–39 (In Chinese), English transl. in *Chinese Geophysics*, Am. Geophys. Union 1:47–53

Fujita, N., Mizuno, H. 1980. Geomagnetism and earthquake. In *Earthquake Prediction, I, Geomagnetic and Geoelectric Approaches*, ed. T. Rikitake, pp. 1–50, Tokyo: Japan Sci. Soc. Press. 186 pp. (In Japanese)

Geodetic Survey Brigade for Earthquake Research, National Seismological Bureau, China. 1977. Ground surface deformation of the Haicheng earthquake of magnitude 7.3. *Acta Geophys. Sin.* 20:251–63 (In Chinese), English transl. in *Chinese Geophysics*, Am. Geophys. Union 1:139–55

Geographical Survey Institute, Japan. 1976. Vertical movements in the lower area of Tamagawa river. *Rep. Coord. Comm. Earthquake Predict.* 15:37–40 (In Japanese)

Geographical Survey Institute, Japan. 1977.

Vertical movements in the lower area of Tamagawa river (2). *Rep. Coord. Comm. Earthquake Predict*. 18:27–28 (In Japanese)
Hass, J. E., Mileti, D. S. 1978. Socioeconomic and political consequences of earthquake prediction. See Engdahl & Kisslinger 1978, pp. 283–93
Isacks. B., Oliver, J. E., Sykes, L. R. 1968. Seismology and the new global tectonics. *J. Geophys. Res*. 73:5855–99
Japan Meteorological Agency. 1980. Continuous observation of crustal deformation by the borehole strainometers along Tokai coast. *Rep. Coord. Comm. Earthquake Predict*. 23:85–8 (In Japanese)
Johnston, M. J. S. 1978. Local magnetic field variations and stress changes near a slip discontinuity on the San Andreas fault. *J. Geomagn. Geoelectr*. 30:511–22
Johnston, M. J. S., Myren, G. D., O'Hara, N. W., Rodgers, G. H. 1975. A possible seismomagnetic observation on the Garlock fault, California. *Bull. Seismol. Soc. Am*. 65:1129–32
Jones, L., Molnar, P. 1976. Frequency of foreshocks. *Nature* 262:677–79
Kanamori, H. 1981. The nature of seismicity patterns before large earthquakes. *Earthquake Prediction: An International Review*, Maurice Ewing Ser. 4, ed. D. W. Simpson, P. G. Richards, Am. Geophys. Union, pp. 1–19
Kawasumi, H. 1970. Proofs of 69-year periodicity and imminence of destructive earthquakes in southern Kwanto district and problems in the countermeasures thereof. *Chigaku Zassi* 79:115–38 (In Japanese)
Keilis-Borok, V. I., Knopoff, L., Rotvain, I. M., Sidorenko, T. M. 1980. Bursts of seismiticity as long-term precursors of strong earthquakes. *J. Geophys. Res*. 85:803–11
King, C. Y. 1978. Radon emanation on San Andreas fault. *Nature* 271:516–19
Ku, K. 1979 *Scientific research and administration of earthquake prediction in China*. Presented at ICG/IASPEI Symposium Earthquake Predict., Canberra
Latynina, L. A., Rizaeva, S. D. 1976. On tidal-strain variations before earthquakes. *Tectonophysics* 31:121–27
Matsuda, T. 1978. Estimation of future destructive earthquakes from active faults on land of Japan. See Engdahl & Kisslinger 1978, pp. 251–60
Matsuda, T., Ota, Y., Ando, M., Yonekura, N. 1978. Fault mechanism and recurrence time of major earthquakes in southern Kanto district, Japan, as deduced from coastal terrace data. *Bull. Geol. Soc. Am*. 89:1610–18
Mazzella, A., Morrison, H. F. 1974. Electrical resistivity variations associated with earthquakes on the San Andreas fault. *Science* 185:855–57
McCann, W., Nishenko, R. S. P., Sykes, L. R., Kraus, J. 1980. Seismic gaps and plate tectonics: seismic potential for major boundaries. *Pageoph* 117:1087–1147
McEvilly, T. V., Johnson, L. R. 1974. Stability of P and S velocities from central California quarry blasts. *Bull. Seismol. Soc. Am*. 64:343–53
McGarr, A., Gay, N. C. 1978. State of stress in the Earth's crust. *Ann Rev. Earth Planet. Sci*. 6:405–36
Mikumo, T., Kato, M., Doi, H., Wada, Y., Tanaka, T., Shichi, R., Yamamoto, A. 1978. Possibility of temporal variation in Earth tidal-strain amplitudes associated with major earthquake. See Engdahl & Kisslinger 1978, pp. 123–36
Mizutani, H., Ishido, T. 1976. A new interpretation of magnetic field variation associated with the Matsushiro earthquakes. *J. Geomagn. Geoelectr*. 28:179–88
Moge, K. 1969. Some features of recent seismic activity in and near Japan, (2) Activity before and after great earthquakes. *Bull. Earthquake Res. Inst. Tokyo Univ*. 47: 393–417
Nishimura, E. 1950. On earth tides. *Trans. Am. Geophys. Union* 31:357–76
Noritomi, K. 1978. Application of precursory geoelectric and geomagnetic phenomena to earthquake prediction in China. *Chinese Geophysics*, Am. Geophys. Union, 1:377–91
Oike, K. 1978. Seismic activities and crustal movements at the Yamasaki fault and surrounding region in southwest Japan. See Engdahl & Kisslinger 1978, pp. 31–41
Poehls, K. A., Jackson, D. D. 1978. Tectonomagnetic event detection using empirical transfer function. *J. Geophys. Res*. 83:4933–40
Press, F., Benioff, H., Forsch, R. A., Griggs, D. T., Handin, J., Hanson, R. E., Hess, H. H., Housner, G. W., Munk, W. H., Orowan, E., Pakiser, L. C. Jr., Sutton, G., Tocher, D. 1965. *Earthquake Prediction: A Proposal for a Ten Year Program of Research*, Washington, D. C: Office Sci. Tech. 134 pp.
Research Group for Active fault. 1980. *Active Fault in Japan, Tokyo*, Tokyo Univ. Press. 363 pp. (In Japanese)
Rika-nenpyo. 1981. *Rika-nenpyo (data book)*. Tokyo; Maruzen. 855 pp. (In Japanese)
Rikitake, T. 1976. *Earthquake Prediction*, Amsterdam: Elsevier. 375 pp.
Rikitake, T. 1978. Anomalous animal behavior preceding the 1978 earthquake near Izuoshima Island. *Rep. Coord. Comm. Earthquake Predict*. 20:67–76 (In Japanese)
Rikitake, T., Suzuki, M. 1979. Anomalous animal behavior preceding the 1978 Miyagi-

ken Oki earthquake. *Rep. Coord. Comm. Earthquake Predict*. 21:28–38 (In Japanese)
Rikitake, T., Yamazaki, Y. 1978. Precursory and coseismic changes in ground resistivity. See Engdahl & Kisslinger 1978, pp. 161–73
Rundle, J. B., McNutt, M. 1981. Southern California uplift—is it or isn't it? *EOS* 62:10
Saito, K., Masuda, T., Suzuki, Z. 1981. A precursory change of stress pattern before the 1978 Miyagi-oki earthquake. *Rep. Res. Group Disaster Prev. Sci. Tohoku Area*. 17:88–91 (In Japanese)
Savarensky, E. F. 1968. On the prediction of earthquakes. *Tectonophysics* 6:17–27
Scholz, C. H., Sykes, L. R., Aggarwal, Y. P. 1973. Earthquake prediction: a physical basis. *Science* 181:803–10
Semyenov, A. N. 1969. Variations in the travel time of traverse and longitudinal waves before violent earthquakes. *Izv. Acad. Sci. USSR (Phys. Solid Earth)* 4:245–48 (English transl.)
Shakal, A. F., Willis, D. E. 1972. Estimated earthquake probabilities in the north circum-Pacific area. *Bull. Seismol. Soc. Am.* 62: 1397–1410
Shamsi, S., Stacey, F. D. 1969. Dislocation models and seismomagnetic calculations for California 1906 and Alaska 1964 earthquakes. *Bull. Seismol. Soc. Am.* 59: 1435–48
Sidorenko, A. V., Sadovsky, A. M., Nersesov, I. L. 1979. *Soviet experience of prediction of earthquakes in the USSR*. Presented at UNESCO Symposium on Earthquake Predict., Paris
Sieh, K. 1978. Slip along the San Andreas fault associated with the great 1857 earthquake. *Bull. Seismol. Soc. Am.* 68: 1241–1448
Slater, L. E. 1978. Crustal deformation and aseismic fault slip near Hollister, California. *Proc. Conf. 7th, Stress and strain measurements related to earthquake prediction,* Open-file report 79–370, pp. 502–20, Menlo Park, Calif., U.S.G.S., 651 pp.
Sugisaki, R., Shichi, R. 1978. Precursory changes in He/Ar and N_2/Ar ratios of fault gases prior to earthquakes. *Zisin, Ser. 2,* 31:195–206 (In Japanese)
Suyehiro, S. 1978. Continuous observation of crustal deformation. In *Methods for Earthquake Prediction,* ed. T. Asada, pp. 117–45, Tokyo Univ. Press. 264 pp. (In Japanese)
Tamrazyan, G. P. 1971. On the synodic age of destructive earthquakes in Japan. *Zisin, Ser. 2,* 24:67–68 (In Japanese)
Thatcher, W. 1976. Episodic strain accumulation in southern California. *Science* 194: 691–95
Toksöz, M. N., Shakal, A. F., Michael, A. J. 1978. Space-time migration of earthquakes along the North Anatolian fault zone and seismic gaps. See US Geological Survey 1978b, pp. 829–56
Tsuboi, C., Wadati, K., Hagiwara, T. 1962. *Prediction of earthquakes—progress to date and plans for further development. (Report of Earthquake prediction Research Group, Japan),* Earthquake Res. Inst., Univ. Tokyo, 21 pp.
Tsubokawa, I., Ogawa, Y., Hayashi, T. 1964. Crustal movements before and after the Niigata earthquake. *J. Geod. Soc, Jpn* 10: 165–71
Turner, R. H., Nigg, J. M., Paz, D. H., Young, B. S. 1979. *Earthquake Threat—The Human Response in Southern California,* Los Angeles: Univ. Calif. 152 pp.
Ulmov, V. I. 1968. On the way to prognosis of earthquakes. *Zemlya i Vseiennaya, Acad. Sci. USSR* 3:23–30 (In Russian)
US Geological Survey. 1976. *Proc. Conf. I, Abnormal animal behavior prior to earthquakes, I.* U.S.G.S., Menlo Park, Calif. 429 pp.
US Geological Survey. 1978a. *Proc. Conf. VII, Stress and strain measurements related to earthquake prediction,* Open-file report 79–370, U.S.G.S., Menlo Park, Calif. 651 pp.
US Geological Survey. 1978b. *Proc. Conf. VI, Methodology for identifying seismic gaps and soon-to break gaps,* Open-file-report 78–834, U.S.G.S., Menlo Park, Calif. 923 pp.
US Geological Survey. 1978c. *Proc. Conf. IV, The use of volunteers in the earthquake hazards reduction program,* Open-file report 78–336, U.S.G.S., Menlo Park, Calif. 273 pp.
US Geological Survey. 1978d. *Proc. Conf. V, Communicating earthquake hazard reduction information,* Open-file report 78–993, U.S.G.S., Menlo Park, Calif. 426 pp.
US Geological Survey. 1980a. *Proc. Conf. XI, Abnormal animal behavior prior to earthquakes, II,* Open-file report 80–453, U.S.G.S., Menlo Park, Calif. 237 pp.
US Geological Survey. 1980b. *Proc. Conf. XII, Earthquake prediction information,* Open-file report 80–834, U.S.G.S., Menlo Park, Calif. 328 pp.
US National Academy of Sciences. 1975. *Earthquake prediction and public policy,* Washington, D.C.: Nat. Acad. Sci. 142 pp.
US National Earthquake Prediction Evaluation Council. 198l. Official statement. *EOS* 62:129
Wakita, H. 1978. Variation in water level and chemical composition of underground water. In *Methods for earthquake prediction,* ed. T. Asada, pp. 146–66, Tokyo Univ. Press. 264 pp. (In Japanese)
Wakita, H., Nakamura, Y., Notsu, K., Nog

uchi, M., Asada, T. 1980a. Radon anomaly: a possible precursor of the 1978 Izu-oshima kinkai earthquake. *Science* 207:882–83

Wakita, H., Nakamura, Y., Kita, I., Fujii, N., Notsu, K. 1980b. Hydrogen release: new indicator of fault activity. *Science* 210: 188–90

Wallace, R. E. 1974. Goals, strategy and task of EHRP. *US Geol. Surv. Circ. No. 701,* 26 pp.

Ward, P. L. 1979. Earthquake prediction. *Rev. Geophys. Space Phys.* 17:343–53

Wentforth, C. M., Yerkes, R. F. 1971. Geologic setting and activity of faults in the San Fernando area, California. In *The San Fernando Earthquake of February 9, 1971.* pp 6–16, Washington D.C: US GPO. 254 pp.

Wesson, R. L., Robinson, R., Bufe, C. G., Ellsworth, W. L., Pfluke, J. H., Steppe, J. A., Seekings, L. C. 1977. Search for seismic forerunners to earthquakes in central California. *Tectonophysics* 42:111–26

Whitney, A. R., Rogers, A. E. E., Hinteregger, H. F., Knight, C. A., Levine, J. I., Lippincott, S., Clark, T. A., Shapiro, I. I., Robertson, D. S. 1976. A very-long-baseline interferometer system for geodetic applications. *Radio Sci.* 11:421–32

Winkler, K. W., Nur, A. 1978. Depth constraints on dilatancy-induced velocity anomalies. See Engdahl & Kisslinger 1978, pp. 231–41

Wu, K. T., Yue, M. S., Wu, H. Y., Chao, S. L., Chen, H. T., Huang, W. Q., Tien, K. Y., Lu, S. D. 1976. Certain characteristics of the Haicheng earthquake (M = 7.3) sequence. *Acta Geophys. Sin.* 19:295–305 (In Chinese), English trans. in *Chinese Geophysics,* Am. Geophys. Union 1:289–308

Wyss, M., Holcomb, D. J. 1973. Earthquake prediction based on station residuals. *Nature* 245:139–40

Yamashina, K., Miura, R. 1980. The M = 3.9 earthquake sequence of May 1978 in eastern Shimane, Japan—seismic process and possibility on its prediction. *Bull. Earthquake Res. Inst. Tohoku Univ.* 55:621–33

Yamazaki, Y. 1974. Coseismic resistivity steps. *Tectonophysics* 22:159–71

Ann. Rev. Earth Planet. Sci. 1982. 10:257-95

INTERIORS OF THE GIANT PLANETS[1]

D. J. Stevenson

Division of Geological and Planetary Sciences, California Institute of Technology, Pasadena, California 91125

1. INTRODUCTION

From our position as inhabitants of a rather insignificant rock orbiting close in to the Sun, there is an inevitable tendency to think of the giant planets (Jupiter, Saturn, Uranus, and Neptune) as being qualitatively similar. One of the major advances in our understanding of the giant planets in recent years has been the realization that this supposed similarity is superficial. With our previously blurred vision replaced by the focused spotlight of flyby spacecraft, and with recent theoretical and experimental advances in the properties of materials at high pressure, the individuality of these planets has emerged. Jupiter and Saturn, once thought to be very similar, now emerge as having substantially different compositions, evolutions, and structures. Uranus and Neptune still appear to be similar because our vision is still blurred (flybys not having taken place yet), but previous experience suggests that we should not be surprised if important differences exist.

The challenge confronting the theoretician is to extract a coherence and a pattern from this emerging diversity. This is a daunting challenge since the corresponding problem for the terrestrial planets remains unsolved. In some respects, the giant planet problem is better posed. (For example, we possess moment of inertia estimates for all the giant planets, whereas the values for Mercury and Venus remain undetermined.) One purpose of this review is to demonstrate that existing observational and theoretical constraints are sufficient to restrict severely the range of acceptable internal models. It is possible to set up a limited inverse problem in which models are suitably simplified to the extent that the number of unknowns is matched to the number

[1] Contribution number 3659 from the Division of Geological and Planetary Sciences, California Institute of Technology, Pasadena, CA 91125

0084-6597/82/0515-0257$02.00

of independent observables. Existing models are nevertheless deficient and questionable in several respects, and this review does not attempt to avoid that fact.

Interior models, together with careful and concise statements of their assumptions and uncertainties, play an essential role in any assessment of solar system formation and evolution. Since the giant planets comprise about 99.5% of the planetary mass, any satisfactory theory for solar system formation must be consistent with the inferences reported here. No theory currently exists which simultaneously achieves this and explains the terrestrial planet systematics. This is *the* major challenge in theoretical planetary science.

The planetary models rest on two foundations: planetary observations and high pressure physics. The observations which constrain the interior are described in Section 2. The relevant high pressure physics are described in Section 3. Both are undergoing continuous and necessary improvement, and readers of this review should be aware of the potential obsolescence of some of the material presented here. In Section 4, the procedures for constructing both present day ("static") and evolutionary models are described. The individual planets are then discussed, leading to a summary that identifies those things that are well understood, those things that have well-developed hypotheses or models but are still tentative, and those aspects that remain unexplained or unexplored.

2. THE OBSERVATIONAL BASIS

2.1 *Mass, Radius, Rotation Rate, and Gravity Field*

The external gravity field of a spherically symmetric planet conveys only one piece of information: the planetary mass. Fortunately, planets rotate and are therefore oblate. The resulting deviations in the gravitational potential from spherical symmetry convey partial information on the mass distribution within the planet.

If hydrostatic equilibrium strictly applies, then the external gravitational potential Φ of a uniformly rotating body can be expanded in even Legendre polynomials:

$$\Phi = -\frac{GM}{r}\left[1 - \sum_{n=1}^{\infty}\left(\frac{R_e}{r}\right)^{2n} J_{2n}P_{2n}(\cos\theta)\right], \tag{1}$$

where $\nabla^2\Phi = 0$, G is the gravitational constant, M is the planetary mass, R_e is the equatorial radius, θ is the colatitude (the angle between the rotation axis and the radial vector $\mathbf{r}$), P_{2n} are the Legendre polynomials, and the dimensionless numbers J_{2n} are known as the gravitational moments. The assumption of hydrostatic equilibrium is a good one because these planets are primarily fluid and because dynamic motions (such as convection) deep within their interiors are much slower than rotation velocities and are driven by very small density contrasts. (This can only be convincingly demonstrated after interior models are constructed.) The gravitational potential in the corotating frame, $\Phi - \frac{1}{2}\Omega^2 r^2 \sin^2\theta$ (where Ω is the planetary angular rotation), should be constant on a constant pressure surface of the planet. Equating equatorial to polar corotating-frame potentials gives a relationship for the oblateness $\epsilon \equiv (R_e - R_p)/R_e$, where R_p is the polar radius:

$$\epsilon \simeq \frac{1}{2}\left(3J_2 + \alpha\right)\left(1 + \frac{3}{2}J_2\right) + \frac{5}{8}J_4,$$

$$\alpha \equiv \frac{\Omega^2 s_0^3}{GM} \simeq \frac{\Omega^2 R_e^3 (1 - \epsilon)}{GM}, \tag{2}$$

where α is a dimensionless measure of the rotation rate and s_0 is the equivalent planetary radius (defined such that $\frac{4}{3}\pi s_0^3$ is the actual planetary volume). Table 1 lists the values of planetary mass, optically observed oblateness ϵ_0, and s_0.

The average density $\bar{\rho} \equiv M/(\frac{4}{3}\pi s_0^3)$ is also tabulated and is the single most important constraint on internal composition. In Section 4, it is shown that the $\bar{\rho}$ for Jupiter and Saturn imply that hydrogen is the major constituent, whereas Uranus and Neptune require more dense constituents.

The value of J_2 and an approximate value of J_4 can be obtained from observations of natural satellite orbits or from the Doppler shift of S-band radio signals returned from flyby spacecraft. A special case is Uranus, where the best estimates of J_2 and J_4 are obtained from the observed precessions of elliptical rings. Pioneer 10 and 11 data for Jupiter have not only provided accurate J_2 and J_4 values but a possible detection of $J_6 = (3 \pm 5) \times 10^{-5}$ and stringent upper bounds on non-hydrostatic components of Φ (Null 1976). Table 1 lists all the current best values of J_2 and J_4.

Interpretation of the gravitational moments requires very accurate determinations of rotation rates. The rotation rate of Jupiter is taken to be the magnetic field rotation rate, which is tied to the deep interior. The near axisymmetry of the Saturnian magnetic field prevented a rotation rate determination by Pioneer 11, but the detection of modulated radio noise from Saturn by Voyager I has led to a magnetically defined rotation period for that planet also (Desch & Kaiser 1981). Neither Uranus nor Neptune have well determined rotation periods. The best estimate for Uranus is 15.5 ± 1.2 hours, indirectly obtained from J_2, the measured oblateness of the planet, and the assumption of hydrostatic equilibrium (using Equation 2). Direct "measurements" of the Uranian rotation period (based on temporal variations in the light curve or doppler linewidths) range from 10.8 hours (Moore & Menzel 1930) to 24 hours (Hayes & Belton 1977, Slavsky & Smith 1980).

Table 1 Planetary Data

	Jupiter	Saturn	Uranus	Neptune
Mass (Earth = 1)	318.05 (Duncombe et al 1974)	95.147 (Allen 1973)	14.58 (± 0.1) (Klepcynski et al 1971)	17.23 (± 0.08)
Equivalent radius (10^9 cm) (P = 1 bar level)	6.98 ± 0.001 (calculated from Hubbard et al 1980)	5.83 ± 0.003	2.55 ± 0.02 (Elliot et al 1979)	2.45 ± 0.03 (Freeman & Lyngå 1970)
Average density (g.cm^{-3})	1.334 ± 0.006	0.69 ± 0.01	1.26 ± 0.07	1.67 ± 0.1
J_2 J_4	$(14733 \pm 4) \times 10^{-6}$ $(-587 \pm 7) \times 10^{-6}$ (Null 1976)	$(16479 \pm 18) \times 10^{-6}$ $-(937 \pm 38) \times 10^{-6}$ (Null et al 1981)	$(3354 \pm 5) \times 10^{-6}$ $\|J_4\| \lesssim 3 \times 10^{-5}$ (Elliot et al 1981)	$(41 \pm 4) \times 10^{-4}$ — (Peale 1973)
Observed oblateness	0.065 ± 0.001 (Hubbard 1977)	0.088 ± 0.008 (Gehrels et al 1980)	0.024 ± 0.003 (Elliot et al 1981)	0.026 ± 0.018 (Freeman & Lyngå 1970)
Hydrostatic oblateness (Equation 2)	0.065 ± 0.0005	0.096 ± 0.0015	No accurate independent measure	?
Rotation period	$9^h\ 55^m\ 29.7^s$ (Berge & Gulkis 1976)	$10^h\ 39.4^m$ (Desch & Kaiser 1981)	15.6^h (± 1.2) (Elliot et al 1981)	$17\text{–}18^h$? (see text)
Density moment q_2	0.38 ± 0.005	0.34 ± 0.01	0.24 ± 0.03	0.2 ± 0.05?

Temperature (K) at 10^5 Pa (1 bar) (see text)	170±20	135±15	75–80?	70–75?
Excess luminosity (watts) (Hubbard 1980)	$(4\pm1)\times10^{17}$	$(1.3\pm0.3)\times10^{17}$	$\lesssim1.5\times10^{15}$	$(2\pm1)\times10^{15}$
Dipole magnetic field (Gauss–R^3_{planet}) (see text)	4.2	0.21	$\lesssim1$	$\lesssim1$

Estimates for Neptune range from 11 hours (Munch & Hippelein 1980) to 22 hours (Hayes & Belton 1977) with a value around 17–18 hours appearing to be most likely (Smith & Slavsky 1980, Brown et al 1980).

The tabulated rotation rates, J_2 and J_4 can be substituted in Equation (2) to yield a hydrostatic oblateness ϵ_h for comparison with the observed value ϵ_0. In the two cases, Jupiter and Saturn, where a meaningful comparison can be made, agreement is excellent and the hydrostatic assumption is vindicated.

Even with exact hydrostatic equilibrium, the interpretation of the J_{2n} is not simple. The following discussion illustrates the basic ideas, but readers interested in the details should consult Hubbard & Slattery (1976) or Zharkov & Trubitsyn (1978). The fundamental equation for the gravitational potential is

$$\Phi = -G\int \frac{\rho(\mathbf{r}')\mathrm{d}^3\mathbf{r}'}{|\mathbf{r} - \mathbf{r}'|}. \tag{3}$$

Using the spherical harmonic expansion of $|\mathbf{r} - \mathbf{r}'|^{-1}$ and comparing equations (1) and (3) leads to the identification

$$J_{2n} = \frac{-1}{MR_e^{2n}(4n + 1)^{1/2}} \int \mathrm{d}^3r\, P_{2n}(\cos\theta) r^{2n} \rho(\mathbf{r}). \tag{4}$$

Since the Legendre polynomials are orthogonal, it is clear that J_{2n} depends on that part of $\rho(\mathbf{r})$ which has a P_{2n} latitudinal variation. The strong radial weighting factor r^{2n} implies that the outer regions of the planet play an important role. This suggests that J_{2n} should be related to the density moment q_{2n}, defined by

$$q_{2n} \equiv \frac{1}{MR_e^{2n}} \int_0^{s_o} 4\pi s^{2n+2} \rho(s)\, \mathrm{d}s, \tag{5}$$

where the equivalent radius s labels equipotential (equal density) surfaces in an oblate body. In fact, there is no simple algebraic relationship, but rather a complicated nonlinear integro-differential relationship between any particular gravitational moment and all the q_{2n}. Nevertheless, J_2 is primarily sensitive to q_2. For example, if the equipotential surfaces had approximately the same shape throughout the planet then $r = s[1 - \frac{2}{3}\epsilon P_2(\cos\,\theta)]$ is an approximate equation for the equipotential fo equivalent radius s. Substituting this into equation (5) yields $J_2 = \frac{2}{3} q_2 \epsilon$. From equation (3) and omitting higher order terms,

$$q_2 = \frac{J_2}{J_2 + \frac{1}{3}\alpha}. \tag{6}$$

Substitution of the appropriate values for Jupiter into this approximate formula yields $q_2 = 0.33$ whereas the "actual" value for the best models (Section 5) is

0.38–0.39. For comparison; $q_2 = 0.6$ for a uniform density sphere, $q_2 = 0.496$ for the Earth, and $q_2 = 1 - 6/\pi^2 \simeq 0.391$ for a hydrostatic sphere in which the pressure $P \propto \rho^2$ at each point (of interest because this approximates the equation of state of dense hydrogen-helium mixtures—see Section 3). Detailed modeling shows that q_2 and J_2 are strongly correlated even though equation (6) is not quantitatively valid (primarily because J_4 is not negligible). For a simple model consisting of a high density core surrounded by an envelope in which $p \propto \rho^2$, the value of J_2 implies estimates of q_2 (Table 1) for which the ratio of core mass to total mass is small ($\lesssim 10\%$) for Jupiter, larger ($\sim 20\%$) for Saturn, and larger still ($\sim 50\%$) for Uranus and Neptune. Detailed models (Sections 5–7) confirm this preliminary assessment.

In contrast, there is no correspondingly close correlation between J_4 and q_4. In fact, J_4 depends more sensitively on the outer regions than does q_4. Hubbard (1974a) has developed an approximate theory in which J_4 is primarily determined by the properties of the outer shell, defined as the region exterior to $r = R_p$ (i.e., the equatorial bulge). In this region, the density is very sensitive to temperature (unlike the degenerate, deep interior). It follows that J_4 can be used as a probe of the thermal structure (or to refine the envelope composition if the thermal structure is well constrained by other considerations). Although J_4 is correlated with J_2, it is sensitive to different aspects of a planetary model and is thus an important, independent constraint. It has no terrestrial counterpart (because J_4 is nonhydrostatic in terrestrial planets). Interpretation and calculation of J_4 have now reached a high level of sophistication (Hubbard et al 1980).

Higher order moments are neither available nor would they be particularly useful (at least in the context of hydrostatic theory). In practice,the value of J_6 is essentially determined by J_2 and J_4.

2.2 *The Atmospheres*

There is no direct relationship between the temperature or composition of a terrestrial planetary atmosphere and the temperature or composition of that planet's interior, so it is not immediately apparent why such a relationship should be expected for the giant planets. The relationship exists because hydrogen, the dominant constituent in each of the giant planet atmospheres, is supercritical at the temperatures of interest (i.e. there is no gas-liquid or gas-solid phase transition in the outer regions). In other words, these planets have bottomless atmospheres.

The atmosphere of Jupiter appears to be close to "cosmic" in composition (Table 2). The predominance of hydrogen is evident from scaleheight determinations (e.g. Elliot et al 1974) and the inversion of ground-based IR data (Orton 1975). Helium, the next most abundant element in the Universe, is inferred from an analysis of pressure-induced absorption of IR caused by

Table 2 Atmospheric abundances (mass fraction)

	Jupiter	Saturn	Uranus	Neptune	Cosmic (Ross & Aller 1976)
H	0.81 ± 0.04	0.89 ± 0.02	$\gtrsim 0.5$	$\gtrsim 0.5$	0.71 ± 0.05
He	0.19 ± 0.04 (Gautier et al 1981)	0.11 ± 0.02 (Hanel et al 1981)	?	?	0.26 ± 0.05
H_2O	Detected	Undetected	Undetected	Undetected	0.014
CH_4	~ 0.01 (Smith & Greene 1980)	~ 0.01	0.05-0.5 (Wallace 1980)	0.05?	0.007
NH_3	Undersaturated? (Tokunaga et al 1980)	Detected	$\lesssim 1 \times 10^{-5}$	Undetected (see text)	0.0015
D (Hubbard & MacFarlane 1981)	$(10 \pm 3) \times 10^{-5}$	$(7 \pm 4) \times 10^{-5}$	$(8 \pm 4) \times 10^{-5}$	Unmeasured	$(4 \pm 2) \times 10^{-5}$

collisions of H_2 molecules with He atoms (Gautier et al 1981). Water is expected to be the next most abundant molecule, but is observed in only small amounts because it condenses out to form clouds at a level 5×10^5–10^6 Pa (5–10 bar) pressure, well below optical depth unity. Ammonia abundances are similarly modified by the formation of clouds and by photochemistry (Tokunaga et al 1980). Methane and deuterium are detected at "cosmic" levels although methane may be enhanced by as much as a factor of two. Many nonequilibrium species are also detected (e.g. carbon monoxide), but these are presumably a consequence of photochemical processes and have no bearing on the planetary interior. Inversion of the infrared spectrum (Orton 1975, Hanel et al 1979) suggests an adiabatic atmosphere at pressures exceeding about half a bar, with a temperature of $T = 170 \pm 20$ K at $P = 10^5$ Pa. This is an important boundary condition for interior models. The inferred temperature at levels as deep as one bar is somewhat model dependent, and a recent analysis of Pioneer data (Hunten et al 1980) suggests a temperature of 156 K. The error bar quoted above is generous and intended to encompass the model-dependence of the analyses. The inferred existence of an adiabat is profoundly important because it suggests a convective atmosphere (as in the Earth's troposphere). This is further supported by the global energy balance, which indicates that Jupiter emits almost twice as much energy as it absorbs from the Sun (see Hubbard 1980 for a review of giant planet global energy balances). The implied internal energy source of about 4×10^{17} W requires convective transport from the deep interior (see Section 5). It is also a crucial constraint on the thermal structure and evolution of the interior.

The atmosphere of Saturn is also predominantly hydrogen (Table 2), but preliminary analysis of the Voyager I infrared data suggests that the helium abundance is less than the Jupiter or cosmic values (Hanel et al 1981). If this observation is verified then it has profound implications for the structure and evolution (Section 6). Water has not been detected and is not likely to be detected because of the very low vapor pressures at the low temperatures prevailing at observable levels. Ammonia is present but at an appropriately reduced vapor pressure because of lower temperatures. Methane and deuterium (as HD) appear to be present at roughly cosmic levels, although there might be significant differences between Jupiter and Saturn in the CH_4 abundance. Inversions of the infrared data (Orton and Ingersoll 1980, Hanel et al 1981) are consistent with an adiabatic structure at levels deeper than ~ 0.5 bars and a temperature $T = 135 \pm 15$ K at $P = 10^5$ Pa. Saturn emits over twice as much energy as it absorbs from the Sun, corresponding to an internal energy source of about 1.3×10^{17} W. Although this is a comparable source per unit mass to Jupiter's source, it is unexpectedly large per unit gravitational energy of the planet (a more meaningful comparison since gravitational energy in some form is the ultimate source of the thermal energy). The likely explanation for both the atmospheric helium depletion and the high heat flow is ongoing differentiation of helium from hydrogen (Section 6).

The atmosphere of Uranus is predominantly hydrogen, with a helium abundance that is not well constrainted but consistent with the cosmic abundance (Courtin et al 1978). Water is, of course, undetectable (the temperature at optical depth unity being $\sim$ 70 K) but the inferred nondetection of NH_3 in the microwave observations (Gulkis et al 1978) is surprising and requires explanation. The simplest interpretation is a 100-fold depletion of NH_3 relative to cosmic abundance, but an alternative explanation is the presence of sufficient H_2S to incorporate essentially all the NH_3 as NH_4SH clouds (Prinn & Lewis 1973). The models discussed in Section 7 suggest a possible scenario for substantial NH_3 depletion. Methane is observed and may be enriched relative to cosmic abundance. Theoretical models for the atmospheric thermal structure also find best agreement with observations for substantial methane enhancements (Wallace 1980). Deuterium (as HD) has also been detected, but at levels consistent with cosmic abundance. The interpretation of this observation is unclear (Hubbard & MacFarland 1981). The temperature at $P = 10^5$ Pa is probably 75–80 K (Wallace 1980) but is sensitive to modeling. There is no assurance that the atmosphere is adiabatic at greater depth, although radio brightness temperature observations do indicate that the temperature increases as one goes deeper (Newburn & Gulkis 1973). The effective temperature of Uranus is indistinguishable from the equilibrium insolation temperature so only an upper bound on the internal heat source of $\sim 1.5 \times 10^{15}$ W is possible.

The atmosphere of Neptune has received much less attention. The atmosphere is primarily H_2 (Newburn & Gulkis 1973) but may have an enhanced CH_4 abundance (Owen & Cess 1975). No other constituents have been detected. Unlike Uranus, the global energy balance clearly indicates that about twice as much energy is emitted as is received from the Sun. The great distance of Neptune from the Sun implies that this is a relatively modest internal energy source (compared to Jupiter or Saturn) of about 2×10^{15} W, although still much larger per unit mass than the Earth. The temperature at $P = 10^5$ Pa is model-dependent but probably 70–75 K (Hubbard & MacFarlane 1980). Radio brightness temperature measurements indicate greater temperatures at depth (Newburn & Gulkis 1973).

2.3 *Magnetic Fields*

The only known mechanism for sustaining a large, global planetary magnetic field is the hydromagnetic dynamo process, which requires a large fluid, conducting region in nonuniform motion. The inference of such a region from external magnetic field measurements is an important constraint on the thermal and dynamic state of the deep interior (Smoluchowski 1979).

Jupiter possesses a large and complex magnetic field. The dominant field contribution for the external observer is the dipole of magnitude 4.2 Gauss–R_J^3 and a tilt of $\sim$ 10° to the rotation axis (Smith et al 1976). However, the higher order (multipole) terms are so large than an extrapolation to deep below the atmosphere would lead to these terms being comparable to the dipole at a depth $\sim$ 20,000 km (Elphic & Russell 1978). This is plausibly a measure of the size of Jupiter's conducting core (Section 5). No secular variation has been convincingly detected for Jupiter yet, although there is a suggestion that the field models from successive flybys might be significantly different (Hide & Malin 1979).

Saturn possesses a much smaller and much less complex field and is well represented by a dipole of magnitude 0.21 Gauss–R_S^3, aligned to within $\sim$ 1° of the rotation axis (Smith et al 1980, Ness et al 1981). The smallness and relative simplicity of the field suggest a very deep source of dynamo generation, consistent with a small conducting core (Section 6). The small tilt of the dipole is *not* explainable by the depth of the source region, but may be explainable by the ongoing downward differentiation of helium (Stevenson 1980, 1981a).

There has been a possible detection of radio bursts at 0.5 MHz from Uranus (Brown 1976), but the presence of a magnetic field has not been clearly demonstrated. An upper bound of $\sim$ 1 Gauss has been suggested for the Uranian field (Kavanaugh 1975), but since this is based on scaling from Jupiter, it is not reliable. No evidence exists for a Neptunian magnetic field and only a comparable upper bound $\sim$ 1 Gauss has been suggested (Kavanaugh 1975).

2.4 *Satellite Systems*

The decreasing trend in density, as one proceeds outward in the Jupiter system from the ice-free Io to the ice-rich Callisto, is plausibly related to the thermal environment in which the Galilean satellites formed. One possibility is that these satellites formed in the presence of a young Jupiter that was too luminous for ice to be in radiative equilibrium in the inner region. A more likely possibility (Section 5) is that the forming Jupiter was surrounded by a dense, opaque, adiabatic nebula out of which the satellite-forming matter condensed. In this case, the newly forming Jupiter does not have to be highly luminous to ensure temperatures as high as 240 K at the distance of Ganymede. In any event, an explanation of the Galilean satellite system is an integral part of understanding the structure and evolution of Jupiter. The recent discovery of very high heat flow and volcanic activity for Io provided an additional unexpected constraint on the interior of Jupiter, because the orbital evolution and tidal heating of Io require that the tidal dissipation factor Q for Jupiter is $\lesssim 10^6$ (Greenberg 1981, Yoder & Peale 1981). A value of $Q \sim 10^6$ is not readily explained by any simple, fluid model (Hubbard 1974b, Goldreich & Nicholson 1977) but might be marginally explainable by a model involving irreversible entropy production as fluid is cycled through a first order phase transition (Stevenson, in preparation).

Saturn possesses only one large satellite, Titan, and there is no clear trend of densities in the extensive satellite system. The presence of ice or ice-covered particles in the rings and the low densities of the innermost satellites (Mimas has a density of 1.2 ± 0.1 g/cm^3, Smith et al 1981) suggests low temperatures in the inner Saturnian environment at formation. This might be misleading, however, because there is no guarantee that 95% of the satellite mass (Titan) is cogenetic with the remaining 5% (all the other satellites). Limitations on the orbital evolution of the Saturnian satellites imposes a lower bound on the Q for Saturn of $\sim 10^5$ (Goldreich & Soter 1966).

Uranus possesses an extensive system of narrow rings and at least five satellites of unknown density. The close proximity of the satellite orbits to the equatorial plane indicates that they formed after the events responsible for the unusual Uranian axis tilt of 98° (Greenberg 1975). The tidal Q of Uranus must exceed $\sim 10^5$ (Goldreich & Soter 1966). This implies that there is no solid surface within a few thousand kilometers of the observable atmosphere.

Neptune possesses at least two satellites, but the retrograde and highly inclined orbit of the large satellite Triton suggests a system that is very different from the other giant planets. In this regard, it is interesting to note that the ratio of total satellite mass to primary mass is comparable for Jupiter, Saturn, and Uranus but over a factor of two larger for Neptune.

3. HIGH PRESSURE PHYSICS

A typical internal pressure $\overline{P}$ for a planet is about $\overline{\rho q R}$ where $\overline{q} \simeq GM/R^2$. It follows that $\overline{P}$ is about 2.5 TPa in Jupiter, 400 GPa in Saturn, and 300 GPa in Uranus and Neptune. (One GPa is 10^9 N/m^2, equivalent to 10 kilobars. One TPa $\equiv 10^3$ GPa.) For comparison, the atomic unit of pressure, e^2/a_0^4, is 29.4 TPa, where e is the electron charge and a_0 is the first Bohr radius. A more relevant pressure might be $\Delta E/V$ where ΔE is a typical electronic energy $\sim$ a few electron volts (e.g. the band gap in a typical insulator) and V is the volume per atom or molecule in the material. For $\Delta E = 1$ eV and $V = 10a_0^3$, $\Delta E/V \sim 100$ GPa. A pressure of the order of 100 GPa is thus likely to substantially modify the electronic structure of a material, because the internal energy change in achieving this pressure is comparable to typical electronic energies. The immediate conclusion is that the materials deep within a giant planet may behave very differently from their low pressure forms. The most important problem in the high pressure physics of giant planets is to identify all relevant phase transitions and develop thermodynamic models of the high pressure phases of cosmically abundant materials. Furthermore, it is shown below that these planets have sufficiently high internal temperatures such that at least the "gas" (H_2, He) and "ice" (H_2O, NH_3, CH_4) components are in the fluid phase. The required thermodynamic modeling thus involves consideration of primarily fluid phases encompassing the entire range from ideal gas to dense, Coulomb plasma.

The various likely constituents are discussed in order of cosmic abundance. Although it may not yet be obvious to the reader, hydrogen predominates in Jupiter and Saturn and therefore merits most attention. It is convenient to discuss pure compositions before dealing with the far more complicated problem of cosmic mixtures.

3.1 *Hydrogen*

The low pressure, low temperature form of hydrogen is molecular because of the existence of a strongly bound (covalent) diatomic state. Other monovalent elements (e.g., the alkali metals) also possess diatomic states but are not normally found in this form because the cohesive energy of the metallic state is larger than the binding energy of the diatomic state. In hydrogen, the inequality is reversed. However, the monatomic state can be achieved by either high temperatures or high pressures. The high temperature molecular dissociation (and eventually ionization) are well-understood phenomena requiring thermal energies of the order of electronic energies (except at extremely low densities). The high pressure monatomic form of hydrogen, called metallic hydrogen, has not yet been convincingly detected in laboratory experiments. Its existence is not in doubt, at least from a theoretical standpoint, because of the Pauli exclusion principle: there must exist some sufficiently high density (and corresponding pressure) above which a bound, diatomic state becomes impossible because the kinetic energy of a localized wave function would exceed the negative (essentially Coulombic) energy of the bound state. The crucial point here is that the kinetic energy scales as $\rho^{2/3}$, where ρ is the electron density, whereas Coulombic terms scale as $\rho^{1/3}$. It is for this reason that every element or compound must become metallic at sufficiently high pressure. The quantification of this general principle turns out to be rather difficult.

Three types of high pressure data exist: shock wave, isentropic, and static. Shock wave data for hydrogen (van Thiel et al 1974, Nellis & Mitchell unpublished) exist up to $P \sim 100$ GPa, lower than the pressure at which metallic hydrogen is expected ($\gtrsim 200$ GPa) but the temperatures achieved ($\sim 10^4$ K) are very similar to the actual temperatures in Jupiter and Saturn at 100 GPa. Isentropic compression experiments (Grigor'ev at al 1972, Hawke et al 1972) achieve higher pressures but with too low accuracy for constraining adequately the equation of state or for detection of a molecular-to-metallic transition. Electrical conductivity measurements during isentropic compression indicate a dramatic increase in conductivity at $P \simeq 200$ GPa (Hawke at al 1978), perhaps the best evidence for this transition. Most static data for H_2 is limited to $P \lesssim 2.5$ GPa (Stewart 1956, Anderson & Swenson 1974) but recent diamond cell anvil experiments have provided data at much higher pressures, including the interesting and significant result that the intramolecular vibrational frequency of H_2 decreases as P increases above 30 GPa (Sharma et al 1980). This suggests that the molecule is becoming "softer" and less well bound. However, the best and most relevant pressure-density determinations to 10 GPa $\lesssim P \lesssim$ 100 GPa continue to be those obtained from shock wave data (Ross 1974).

Theoretical models for molecular hydrogen are usually based on a pair potential approach, in which the interaction energy of an assemblage of H_2 molecules is approximated as the sum of pairwise-additive intermolecular potential energies:

$$U_{\text{int}} = \langle \sum_{i<j} \varphi(r_{ij}) \rangle, \tag{7}$$

where φ is the potential, i and j label molecules separated by a distance r_{ij} and the brackets denote an ensemble average. It has also been assumed that the relative angular orientation of the molecules can be averaged to yield a spherical potential that depends only on the distance between molecules. None of the assumptions implicit in this formulation is rigorously justified, especially the neglect of nonpairwise additive effects (Ree & Bender 1974). However, the existing data do not warrant a more sophisticated approach, at least for giant planet models, and it is sufficient to find a choice of φ that is compatible with the data (Ross 1974) and which has a functional form suggested by first principles calculations (McMahan et al 1974, Ree & Bender 1979). The form usually chosen is (in atomic units):

$$\varphi(r) = Ae^{-\alpha r} - \left(\frac{13}{r^6} + \frac{116}{r^8}\right) \exp\left(\frac{-400}{r^6}\right), \tag{8}$$

where the attractive part is a truncated van der Waals contribution. Several possible choices of A and α are consistent with the data.

Three approaches have been used by planetary modelers in formulating the thermodynamics of H_2. One approach (Zharkov & Trubitsyn 1978) treats the system essentially as a Debye solid. This must be regarded as an unsatisfactory procedure for modeling a *fluid* phase, the more relevant phase at the temperatures of interest. In the second approach, Hubbard and coworkers (Slattery & Hubbard 1976, Hubbard & MacFarlane 1980) use Monte Carlo simulations of the fluid at a number of points in temperature-density space to provide the basis of a parametric formulation of the thermodynamics. This approach has the advantage that it requires no assumptions concerning the molecular distribution. However, the Monte Carlo technique is less flexible and more time consuming than the third technique, which is based on liquid perturbation theory. This approach was used by Ross (1974) in his analysis of shock wave data and by Stevenson & Salpeter (1976) in models of Jupiter. In all approaches, it is necessary to include corrections for molecular rotation, vibration, and dissociation.

A brief description of liquid perturbation theory seems warranted here because of its wide applicability and suitability. The essential idea is to formulate an approximate Helmholtz free energy by assuming that the molecular *distribution* (but *not* the interactions) can be approximated by that of a hard sphere fluid (i.e. an assemblage of perfectly rigid billiard balls) in which the diameter of the equivalent hard sphere is a function of temperature and density and is chosen by varying its value to minimize the Helmholtz free energy (Barker & Henderson 1976). The free energy and configuration of a hard sphere liquid are well known so the variational calculation is easy to perform. For each choice of φ that is consistent with the shock wave and other data, the free energy $F(\rho, T)$ can be determined, from which any thermodynamic parameter used in planetary modeling can be calculated. The range of acceptable φ translates into an uncertainty in interior models and in the transition to the metallic state.

Metallic hydrogen is much better understood because of its very simple structure: protons immersed in an approximately uniform, degenerate electron gas. The basic interactions are exactly known, although the details of the electronic response involve the subtleties of many-body theory and ultimately limit the accuracy of current theoretical descriptions to $\sim 1\%$ at the lowest pressures ($\sim$ 200 GPa), improving to $\sim 0.3\%$ at 5 TPa. The major contributions to the energy of metallic H are the zero temperature energy of a uniform electron gas E_{eg} and the electrostatic energy of the interaction of this gas with an assemblage of protons, E_{es}:

$$E_{eg} \simeq \frac{1.105}{r_s^2} - \frac{0.458}{r_s} - 0.0575 + 0.0155 \ln r_s,$$

$$E_{es} \simeq \frac{-1.8}{r_s}, \tag{9}$$

in atomic units (this part is common to all alkali metals; Heine & Weaire 1970). The dimensionless parameter r_s is defined by $\frac{4}{3}\pi r_s^3 a_0^3 = n^{-1}$ where n is the electron number density. (In pure metallic hydrogen, the mass density is $\rho \equiv 2.696/r_s^3$ g.cm^{-3}.) In the deep interiors of Jupiter and Saturn, $r_s \sim 1$. The last two terms in E_{eg} are an approximate form for the correlation energy; other approximate forms are possible (Hedin & Lindqvist 1971).

Three kinds of corrections to Equation (8) are necessary for a complete theory. First, the constant in E_{es} is not exactly 1.8 but depends on the configuration of the protons. Second, the electron gas is nonuniform because of the protons; this leads to a "band structure" energy, which can be thought of as the sum of a structure-independent term (the piling up of electronic charge around each proton) and a structure-dependent term (the screened interactions between protons immersed in a nonlinear dielectric). Third, finite temperature corrections for the electron gas and both zero point and finite temperature contributions from the protonic motion are required. The latter are calculated for the fluid state by either machine simulation (Hubbard & Slattery 1971) or by liquid perturbation theory (Stevenson 1975a). Machine simulations (Monte Carlo or molecular dynamics) are well developed for metallic hydrogen because of the close relationship to the classical one-component plasma problem (Pollock & Hansen 1973, Slattery et al 1980). The hard sphere model would seem inappropriate for the liquid perturbation theory of metallic hydrogen, but it is an adequate approximation because of the strongly repulsive nature of the screened proton-proton interaction (Stevenson & Ashcroft 1974). A much more complete discussion of metallic hydrogen than is possible here can be found in Ross & Shishkevish (1977) or Ross & McMahan (1976).

One might suppose that the transition pressure between molecular and metallic hydrogen could be established by calculating the Gibbs free energies of the phases and determining where they become equal. There are three problems with this. The first is that the Gibbs energies are very similar over a range of pressures. This makes the identification of the transition pressure exceedingly difficult *even* if the energies of the two phases are well determined! The second problem concerns the nature of the transition. It is not known whether the transition is first order at $T = 0$ K, nor is it known whether the molecular phase exists as a well-defined, undissociated insulating phase at all pressures up to the transition pressure. It is conceivable, for example, that a conducting yet diatomic phase exists in an intermediate pressure range. Recent density functional calculations for H_2 suggest that the molecular-metallic transition may not be simple (Chakravarty et al 1980). The third problem is that even if the transition is first order at absolute zero, it may be continuous at the temperatures prevailing in Jupiter and Saturn. This is a controversial point (Kerley 1972, Aviram et al 1976, Stevenson & Salpeter 1977a, Franck 1980) for which there is no resolution yet in sight. The nature of the transition plays a very important role in the interior models and this current *qualitative* uncertainty is more serious than the quantitative uncertainty. Current theoretical estimates for the transition pressure are in the range 200–400 GPa but it must be stressed that these are based on the *assumption* that the Gibbs energies construction is meaningful (Stevenson & Salpeter 1977a).

The high pressure transport properties are more difficult to calculate than the thermodynamic properties. Like all dense, insulating fluids molecular hydrogen has a thermal diffusivity $\sim 10^{-2}$ cm^2/s for which conductive transport of heat is negligible over the age of the solar system. (All the transport properties discussed here are extensively reviewed in Stevenson & Salpeter 1977a.) The radiative opacity is not known at high pressures, but all plausible theoretical estimates suggest that radiative heat transport can be important in the deep atmosphere but not in the deep interior. (In fact, minor constituents such as water are the major sources of opacity in the wavelength region ~ 2000 cm^{-1} just below the water clouds in Jupiter or Saturn.) The thermal conductivity of liquid metallic hydrogen is about a factor of three greater than that of room temperature copper. Even so, it is too small by a factor ~ 10 to transport the observed heat flow out of the deep interior of Jupiter or Saturn if the temperature gradient is stable (i.e. subadiabatic). The inability of microscopic processes (conduction, radiation) to transport the observed heat flow for a temperature gradient that is convectively stable implies that the dominant means of heat transport must be convection. Only a very small superadiabaticity is required to drive the required convective heat flux, implying that the temperature profile is essentially adiabatic except possibly in boundary layers or at phase transitions (Salpeter & Stevenson 1976). The kinematic viscosities of both fluid molecular and fluid metallic hydrogen are $\sim 10^{-2}$ cm^2/s, too small to be of importance in large-scale fluid dynamic processes.

Figure 1 shows the phase diagram of hydrogen. The high pressure melting curve for H_2 is estimated from the hard sphere criterion, which states that the packing fraction (i.e. fraction of volume occupied) for the equivalent hard sphere fluid is 0.45 (Barker & Henderson 1976). This criterion fails at $P \lesssim 10$ GPa (Diatschenko & Chu 1981) but should be valid at higher pressures. The melting curve of metallic hydrogen is the *classical* result of Pollock & Hansen

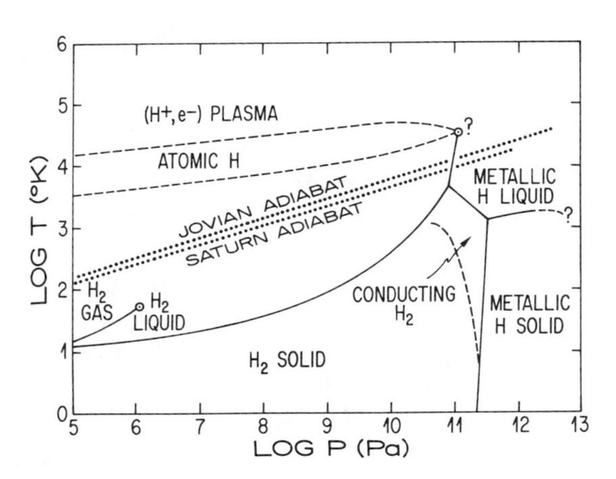

Figure 1 Phase diagram of hydrogen. Solid lines indicate first order phase transitions (except that the line ending in a question mark and separating fluid H_2 from fluid metallic H is uncertain). The conducting H_2 region is hypothetical. The dotted adiabats for Jupiter and Saturn are lines of constant entropy fixed by the atmospheric temperature at 10^5 Pa (1 bar) given in Table 1.

(1973)—allowance for quantum effects might lower the temperature. The molecular-metallic transition is placed at the "best guess" value of 300 GPa. Uncertain features of the phase diagram include the hypothetical first order character of the fluid molecular-metallic transition (terminated by a critical point) and the existence of conducting H_2. Estimated adiabats for the giant planets are superimposed for the pressure region in each planet in which hydrogen dominates. The adiabat is a line of constant entropy determined by the model free energy of liquid perturbation theory and chosen to satisfy the atmospheric boundary condition (Table 1). These adiabats confirm the supercritical ("bottomless atmosphere") natures of the outer regions of the giant planets, at least with respect to hydrogen.

Figure 2 shows the pressure-density relationship for hydrogen along an adiabat appropriate to Jupiter. An interesting feature is the fortuitous similarity to $P \propto \rho^2$, discussed further in Section 4.

3.2 *Helium and Hydrogen-Helium Mixtures*

Remarkably little is known about the properties of helium at high pressure. There have been no shock wave experiments and only very limited static compression studies (Besson & Pinceaux 1979, Mills et al 1980). Since helium is the most difficult element to ionize and the most difficult substance to metallize (see review by Stevenson & Salpeter 1977a), a simple pair potential should be a good approximation, at least for a molecular environment (Trubitsyn 1967, Silver 1980). However, helium is likely to be present in the giant planets primarily as a minor constituent in a hydrogen-helium mixture, so it is much more important to understand and model the mixture.

The molecular mixture has been modeled by both Monte Carlo (Slattery & Hubbard 1976) and liquid perturbation theory (Stevenson & Salpeter 1976, 1977a) techniques. In the latter calculation, the important H_2–He interaction was taken from Shafer & Gordon (1973), and all the interactions were taken to have the same functional form as Equation (12). Volume additivity was found to be approximately satisfied, i.e.

$$\frac{1}{\rho(P)} = \frac{x_H}{\rho_{H_2}(P)} + \frac{x_{He}}{\rho_{He}(P)}, \tag{10}$$

where ρ, ρ_{H_2}, and ρ_{He} are the densities of the mixture, pure H_2 and pure He, respectively, at pressure P; x_H and x_{He} are the mass fractions of hydrogen and helium. Helium has limited solubility in hydrogen at low temperatures ($T \sim 10^2$ K for $P \sim 1$ GPa) and liquid perturbation theory is able to reproduce this experimentally observed behavior (Streett 1973) to modest accuracy, a very severe test of the correctness of the chosen potentials. The theoretical calculations indicate that helium is completely soluble in molecular hydrogen at the pressures and temperatures encountered along the adiabats of the giant planets.

Two approaches are possible in the metallic hydrogen regime. The simpler approach is to consider a model of protons and alpha particles immersed in an electron gas. This has been studied by both machine simulation (Hubbard & Slattery 1971, Hansen & Vieillefosse 1976, Pollock & Alder 1977) and by liquid perturbation theory (Stevenson 1975a). The latter calculation included terms of third order in the electron-ion interaction (to allow for the rather severe perturbation that the α-particles impose on the electron gas). It was

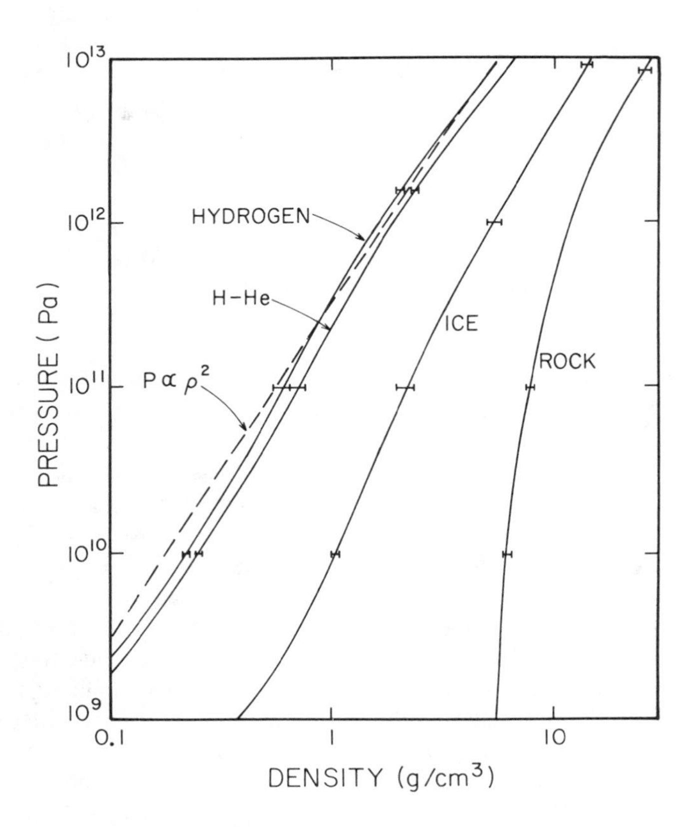

Figure 2 Typical isentropes relevant to the giant planets. The hydrogen and hydrogen-helium (25% helium by mass) isentropes pass through $T = 170$ K at $P = 10^5$ Pa (appropriate to Jupiter). The molecular-metallic hydrogen transition has been smoothed but may be discontinuous. The dashed line is the best fitting curve of the form $P = K\rho^2$ for pure hydrogen, indicating the usefulness of this simple analytic approximation. The isentropes of "ice" and "rock" correspond to the mixtures used by Hubbard & MacFarlane (1980) and are chosen to be appropriate for Uranus (i.e. $T \simeq 2000$ K at $P = 2 \times 10^{10}$ Pa for ice, $T \simeq 7000$ K at $P = 6 \times 10^{11}$ Pa for rock). Error bars indicate the uncertainties.

found that the mixture has significant volume nonadditivity: the alloy occupies less volume than the equation analogous to (14) would predict. The assumption of volume additivity would lead one to overestimate the amount of helium in the deep interior of Jupiter by 10–20% (Stevenson & Salpeter 1976). Even more significantly, Stevenson (1975a) found that helium has limited solubility in metallic hydrogen even at $T \sim 10^4$ K, the relevant temperature for the interior of Jupiter or Saturn. This limited solubility was confirmed by the subsequent machine simulations (Hansen & Vieillefosse 1976, Pollock & Alder 1977). It could be aruged that these calculations are not relevant for the "low" pressures encountered in Jupiter or Saturn because the helium atoms cannot be considered to be pressure-ionized. However, a pseudopotential calculation (Stevenson 1979), which treated the helium atoms as neutral entities immersed in an electron gas, showed that the limited solubility of helium is even more pronounced at low pressure. These essentially first principles calculations provide the foundation for the interpretation of Saturn given in Section 6.

Figure 2 shows the pressure-density relationship for a cosmic hydrogen-helium mixture and an adiabat corresponding to Jupiter. As in pure hydrogen, $P \propto \rho^2$ is a good first approximation for the dense regions.

3.3 *The Ices*

The compounds H_2O, CH_4 and NH_3 are known collectively as "ices" and are relatively minor constituents of Jupiter and Saturn but very important for Uranus and Neptune. Previous equations of state for the ices relied heavily on Thomas-Fermi-Dirac or Quantum Statistical methods (Zharkov & Trubitsyn 1978), but recent shock wave data from Livermore have exposed the weaknesses of these techniques and provided a much improved data base for planetary modeling (Mitchell & Nellis 1979, Nellis et al 1980, Nellis & Mitchell, unpublished).

Water is the most important of the ices and also probably the most difficult to model theoretically (Ree 1981). However, the electrical conductivity measurements (Hamann & Linton 1966, Mitchell et al 1980) indicate that the conductivity rises to a plateau value $\sim 20\ (\Omega\text{-cm})^{-1}$ at $P \gtrsim 20$ GPa under shock compression, a value similar to that of ionic melts. This provides motivation for a model in which water disssociates to form an ionic melt $H_3O^+OH^-$, which is isoelectronic with $NH_4^+F^-$. The advantage of this model is that it is much easier to quantify than the complex hydrogen bonding of low pressure water. Stevenson & Fishbein (1981) show that this model is consistent with both the pressure-density behavior and the measured temperatures (Lyzenga 1980) observed under shock compression. These calculations together with scaling of existing water-argon data (Lentz & Franck 1969) also suggest limited solubility of water in hydrogen. However, the water abundance is too low and the temperatures are too high for this to be important in Jupiter or Saturn. In contrast, the colder and ice-rich Uranus and Neptune may have ionic water oceans at $P \gtrsim 20$ GPa because of this limited solubility.

The shock compression data for methane can be interpreted as indicating dissociation to elemental carbon (diamond or metal) and molecular hydrogen at $P \gtrsim 10$ GPa and $T \gtrsim 10^3$ K (Ree 1979, Nellis et al 1980). This may be a premature conclusion for two reasons. First, the data only indicate volume additivity of carbon and hydrogen; they do not demonstrate dissociation directly. Second, and more important, carbon in a hydrogen-rich environment (H:C $\sim 10^3$:1) will be driven toward an associated state with hydrogen because of the law of mass action. This latter statement is true even if CH_4 does not exist as a bound state. The energy favoring a mixed state over a state in which the carbon forms diamond is $\sim kT \ln x$ where $x \simeq [H]/[C]$. This energy is *large* ($\sim$ 5 to 10 eV in the deep interior of Jupiter or Saturn; smaller in Uranus or Neptune). Methane does not readily form ions and is not likely to partition into the hypothetical ionic ocean of Uranus and Neptune, but will instead concentrate into the outer envelope, consistent with the tentatively observed atmospheric enhancement (Table 2).

Ammonia readily forms NH_4^+ ions and is expected to partition into any ionic phase such as the water ocean. It was once thought that ammonia and hydrogen could form an ammonium metal (NH_4^+ ions immersed in a degenerate electron gas), but energy calculations (Stevenson 1975b) show that this is not possible. Ammonia also has a high electrical conductivity under shock compression (Mitchell et al 1980), indicating a tendency to dissociate.

The finite temperature equations of state for the ices are summarized by Hubbard & MacFarlane (1980). More work needs to be done in this area, especially on the behavior of H_2O–H_2 mixtures, before the behavior and disposition of ices in the giant planets can be said to be even qualitatively understood. Figure 2 shows a pressure-density isentrope for a cosmic ice mixture and temperatures appropriate to Uranus or Neptune, assuming volume additivity.

3.4 *Rock*

This refers to all the remaining constituents: primarily magnesium, silicon, iron, and whatever oxygen these elements incorporate at high pressures. Neither the composition nor the equation of state for a given composition are well known for the rock component. This is probably not a serious deficiency of the planetary models, compared with other uncertainties, because the rock component is a relatively minor fraction. The partitioning of "rock" into "gas" and "ice" is unknown. (It is important to know, for example, the solubility of iron in metallic hydrogen.) Some of these issues are currently under study. For the present, the equations of state tabulated by Zharkov &Trubitsyn (1978) are adequate, and the particular mix of constituents chosen by Hubbard & MacFarlane (1980) for Uranus and Neptune is plausible. Figure 2 shows the resulting isentrope (or isotherm, since thermal corrections are small).

4. CONSTRUCTION OF MODELS

4.1 *Static Models*

The construction of a static planetary model is much easier than the formulation of the input physics (especially the equation of state). "Static" means that the heat flow and corresponding thermal profile are taken as given rather than as planetary properties to be determined. The ingredients of static models are

1. The equation of hydrostatic equilibrium, including the effect of rotation:

$$\frac{\mathrm{d}p}{\mathrm{d}s} = -\frac{GM(s)}{s^2}\rho(s) + \frac{2}{3}\Omega^2 s\rho(s) + \mathrm{O}(\Omega^4), \tag{11}$$

   where $M(s)$ is the mass within equivalent radius s and Ω is the planetary rotation rate, assumed constant.
2. The equations of state $p(\rho, T, \{x_i\})$, where $x_i(s)$ denotes the fractional abundance of constituent i.
3. The temperature profile $T(\rho)$ which, in almost all the models discussed here, is assumed to be adiabatic because of the inability of microscopic processes (conduction, radiation) to transport the observed heat flow from the interior. (This is not at all certain for Uranus.)
4. The theory of planetary figures, which relates the internal density distribution to the observable gravitational moments J_{2n}.

Before attempting to construct models of specific planets, it is of interest to consider the properties of generic planets. Figure 3 shows the mass-radius relationship for cold ($T = 0$ K) bodies of hydrogen, a cosmic hydrogen-helium mixture, a cosmic ice mixture, and "rock"; the relationship can also be seen for isentropic hydrogen and hydrogen-helium bodies for a specific entropy corresponding to either Jupiter or Saturn. From the superimposed positions of the giant planets, several conclusions are immediately apparent. First, the dominant constituent of Jupiter and Saturn (but not of Uranus and Neptune) must be hydrogen. No other material is of sufficiently low density. (Since a highly superadiabatic structure is highly unstable, models in which the higher intrinsic density of heavier elements is offset by much higher temperatures are unphysical.) It is also apparent that Saturn departs more from a uniform cosmic mixture than does Jupiter. This is most easily seen by considering the isentropic models. The radius of a nonrotating body in which $P = K\rho^2$ is

$(\pi K/2G)^{1/2}$, *independent* of mass (a special property of $P \propto \rho^2$). Thus, the fact that Saturn is smaller than Jupiter is an immediate indication of an intrinsically denser constitution (despite the much lower actual average density). It is also apparent from Figure 3 that Uranus and Neptune are likely to be ice-rich.

The conventional procedure in constructing static models of the giant planets is to hypothesize a layered planet: a core of rock, possibly a layer of ice, and then an envelope of cosmic or near-cosmic composition (primarily hydrogen and helium). In the absence of any evolutionary or solubility considerations, this approach is strictly ad hoc. However, it is sufficiently simple that the number of unknowns can be commensurate with the number of independent constraints. Knowledge of $\bar{\rho}$, J_2, J_4, and an accurate atmospheric bound-

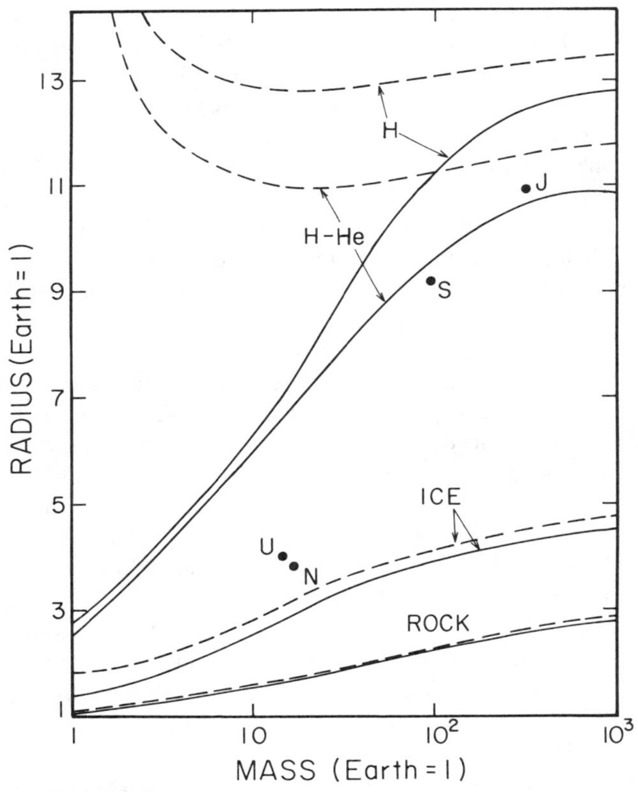

Figure 3 The mass-radius relationship for self-gravitating bodies of the same compositions as in Figure 2. The solid lines are for cold matter ($T = 0$ K); the dashed lines correspond to the isentropes of Figure 2. The insensitivity of radius or mass for hydrogen and hydrogen-helium is a consequence of the approximate validity of $P \propto \rho^2$ (see text for discussion). The positions of the giant planets are labelled by J, S, U, and N.

ary condition are sufficient, in principle, to determine these layers. In practice, there is always ambiguity concerning the relative amounts of rock and ice, and modelers frequently resort to a cosmogonic prejudice concerning the relative abundances of these components incorporated during accretion. Other uncertainties (such as the helium abundance) also limit the extent to which the data can be "inverted" into a planetary model. Fortunately, evolutionary models provide additional constraints on the range of acceptable models.

4.2 *Evolutionary Models*

The internal heat source of each of the giant planets (except possibly Uranus) is too large to be explained by natural radioactivity in a chondritic rock component. The temperature is too low for fusion, even of deuterium (Grossman & Graboske 1973) and the present-day accretion rate of interplanetary material onto these planets is negligible. The only plausible energy source is gravitational—either in the form of primordial heat generated during the collapse leading to planetary formation, or in the form of ongoing differentiation of heavy material from light material. These are characterized as homogeneous evolution and heterogeneous evolution, respectively. Heterogeneous scenarios may also involve latent heat effects (any first order phase transition in a multicomponent system will involve both thermal and compositional changes) and may even involve partial *upward* redistribution of heavy material (i.e. thermal convection may do gravitational work).

Two ideas of giant planet formation are currently advocated. In the giant, gaseous protoplanet scenario favored by Cameron (1978), the solar nebula directly undergoes fragmentation because of gravitational instabilities. According to the planetesimal scenario, first discussed in detail by Perri & Cameron (1974) but subsequently improved by Hayashi and coworkers (Mizuno et al 1978, Mizuno 1980), the giant planets first develop in a similar way to that generally advocated for the terrestrial planets (e.g. Wetherill 1980) by the accumulation of a rock/ice core, until the surrounding solar composition envelope cannot satisfy hydrostatic equilibrium and hydrodynamic collapse is initiated. A striking feature of Mizuno's models is that this collapse always occurs for a core $\sim$ 10 Earth masses, similar to the core sizes of the present giant planets (Sections 5–7). The important point for our present considerations, however, is that either scenario yields substantially higher initial internal termperatures than the present day internal temperatures (Bodenheimer et al 1980), at least for Jupiter and Saturn. This simplifies the analysis of homogeneous evolution and enables one to show that the present heat outflow is insensitive to the initial states.

This important conclusion for a homogeneous evolution can be demonstrated as follows. To a good approximation, the luminosity L is given by the rate of change of internal thermal energy:

$$L \equiv 4\pi R^2 \sigma (T_e^4 - T_0^4) \simeq -\frac{\mathrm{d}}{\mathrm{d}t}[M\bar{C}_v T_i], \tag{12}$$

where α is Stefan-Boltzmann's constant, T_e is the effective temperature, T_0 is the equilibrium effective temperature in the absence of an internal heat source (nonzero because of the presence of the Sun), $\bar{c}_v$ is the average specific heat per gram, and T_i is an appropriately defined average internal temperature. This equation is discussed further by Hubbard (1980). Throughout most of the evolution, R is essentially constant because the planet consists mostly of degenerate matter (i.e. $\alpha T << 1$, where α is the coefficient of thermal expansion). Since the planet is essentially adiabatic, $T_i \propto T_e$. (If the opacity of the atmosphere is constant during the evolution, then the proportionality constant depends only on M and R.) It follows that

$$\tau = \frac{M\bar{C}_v \vartheta}{4\pi R^2 \sigma} \int_{T_{e0}}^{T_{ei}} \frac{\mathrm{d}T}{T^4 - T_0^4}, \tag{13}$$

where $\vartheta = T_i/T_e$. and τ is the elapsed time for the planet to cool from an initial effective temperature T_{ei} to its present value T_{e0}. Then the T^{-4} dependence of the integrand for $T >> T_0$ ensures that the choice of the upper limit is unimportant if $T_{ei} \gtrsim 2T_{e0}$ (in fact, it can be replaced by ∞). Indeed, Equation (13) can be replaced by the simple approximate solution

$$\tau \simeq \frac{(0.25)(\text{Present heat content})}{(\text{Present excess luminosity})}. \tag{14}$$

Planets which evolve homogeneously should have $\tau \simeq 4.5 \times 10^9$ years, since there is no reason to suspect that the age of a giant planet differs greatly from the ages of meteorites or terrestrial planets.

No similarly simple results are possible for heterogeneous evolutions. However, gravitational differentiation is potentially a much larger energy source than the heat content. For example,

$$kT_i \simeq \frac{1}{20}\frac{GMm_p}{R} \tag{15}$$

for Jupiter ($T_i \sim 10^4$ K, m_p is the proton mass). A redistribution of helium, for example, can imply a change in the planetary gravitational energy that is up to several times larger than the total thermal energy. This is important for Saturn (Section 6).

5. JUPITER

The most recent analyses of the Jovian interior are those of Hubbard and coworkers (Hubbard & Slattery 1976, Slattery 1977, Hubbard et al 1980),

Stevenson & Salpeter (1976), and Zharkov & Trubitsyn (1978). All these models evaluate the gravity field to at least third order (J_6) which is a minimal requirement for comparing theory with the accurately observed J_2 and J_4. The models of Hubbard et al (1980) are the most sophisticated in their treatment of the gravity field and the equation of state, but make very limited excursions in parameter space. Their models are discussed in detail here not only because they represent the state-of-the-art, but also because they demonstrate both the strengths and the weaknesses of current Jupiter models. The models consist of three layers (rock, ice, gas) but in practice the rock-ice region can be lumped into a single core. There are then two main unknowns to be determined: the core mass M_c and the helium mass fraction Y of the homogeneous envelope. (The value of Y is commonly allowed to be variable in models because of the large uncertainty in the "cosmic" value; see Table 2.) There are three observables to be satisfied ($\bar{\rho}$, J_2, J_4) so no compatible solution is guaranteed unless some additional parameter is varied. Changes in the temperature at 10^5 Pa or in the abundance of ice or rock in the envelope are both similar in effect to changing Y. Hubbard et al chose instead to vary the equation of state in the dense molecular hydrogen region ($0.3 \lesssim \rho \lesssim 1.4$ g.cm^{-3}) where it is least well known. They were then able to obtain a model consistent with all observables in which $M_c \simeq 30\, M_E$ ($1M_E \equiv$ one Earth mass) and $Y \simeq 0.14$. Another model with a different equation of state had $M_c \simeq 20\, M_E$ and $Y \simeq 0.20$ but the magnitude of J_4 was too large by $\sim 8\%$ (compared with the observational error of $\sim 1.2\%$). Although the former of these models is more "correct" from the point of view of satisfying observational constraints, it is not necessarily the "best" model because it uses an equation of state that is marginally acceptable but deviates substantially from the form that is most preferable based on shock wave data. This highlights the major problem that continues to confront giant planet modeling: insufficient information on the equation of state of hydrogen and hydrogen-helium mixtures. Small errors in the theoretical model for hydrogen propagate into large errors in M_c and Y. A value of $Y = 0.14$ is substantially lower than any current estimate of cosmic abundance and only marginally consistent with the IRIS (Infared-imaging spectrometer) observations (Gautier et al 1981) from Voyager.

The other published models referenced above include models in which all the data are satisfied and Y is a more plausible value (~ 0.2 to 0.3). It is not clear whether these earlier models with a larger Y were found because of a more extensive parameter search or because of deficiencies in their input physics. It *is* clear that more modeling is needed. Meanwhile, it is best to emphasize those aspects of the various models that are common to all groups involved in these calculations.

Figure 4 shows the characteristics of a "typical" Jupiter model, actually a composite picture of existing published models. (Tabulation of a particular model has been purposely avoided here because nonexperts tend to take such tabulations too seriously.) A guided tour from the outside inward follows: The atmosphere could be essentially cosmic in composition (although models can be constructed with enhancements of rock or ice in the envelope—at the expense of reducing the helium abundance). As one proceeds downward, the temperature rises rapidly in accordance with an adiabat, approximately $T \propto \rho^{0.45}$. Already, at a depth of only 700 km below the observable cloud deck, the temperature has reached 2000 K. No phase transitions are encountered (except those associated with the cloud formation of minor constituents). The fluid becomes progressively nonideal until eventually the pressure from intermolecular interactions exceeds the thermal pressure (at $\rho \sim 0.05$ to 0.1 g.cm^{-3}, $T \sim 3000$ K). This dense, molecular fluid is undergoing convection with convective velocities $V_c \sim 0.1$ cm/s (Hubbard & Smoluchowski 1973). Eventually at $P \sim 200$ GPa ($\rho \simeq 1$ g.cm^{-3} and $T \simeq 10^4$ K) the molecular hydrogen transforms into the monatomic, metallic fluid state. This could be an abrupt transition, in which case discontinuities in specific entropy and minor constituent abundances (including helium) must occur, and convection across the interface between the phases is inhibited (Salpeter & Stevenson 1976, Stevenson & Salpeter 1977b). Alternatively, the transition may be gradual with no discontinuities of any kind. This region, at 75–80% of Jupiter's radius, presumably represents the outer boundary of the dynamo generation of the Jovian magnetic field, although some generation in the lowermost,

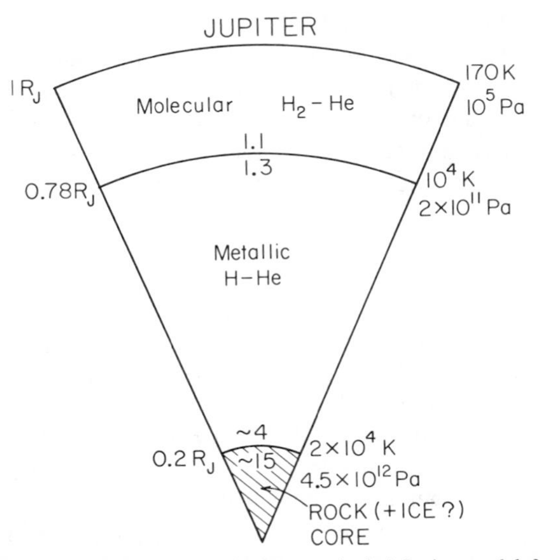

Figure 4 Schematic representation of a typical (no particular) Jupiter model. Numbers adjacent to boundaries are densities in g.cm^{-3}.

semiconducting part of the molecular region is conceivable (Smoluchowski 1975). Proceeding deeper through the fluid, convective, metallic hydrogen-helium region, pressures rise by over an order of magnitude eventually reaching ~ 4.5 TPa (at $\rho \sim 4.5$ g.cm^{-3}, $T \simeq 2 \times 10^4$ K) at the boundary of the rock (and ice?) core. This core is a common feature of all models and is required by J_2 (i.e. by the moment of inertia). However, its size is very uncertain. Most recent models have $10\ M_E \lesssim M_c \lesssim 30\ M_E$. The state of the matter in this core is also very uncertain; it is not clear whether it is fluid or solid. A major puzzle is to understand why this core does not dissolve in the metallic hydrogen above. Thermal convection can redistribute part of this heavy material but a primordial core could persist (Stevenson 1981b). Perhaps a core was required to initiate Jupiter formation (Mizuno 1980) and was then partially disseminated by convection. A model with a partially disseminated core would also be capable of explaining J_2. Any substantial core is so dense that the pressure drop across it is very large (despite the reduced gravitational acceleration near the center) and the central pressure may exceed 10 TPa. The central temperature is not well established, nor is it important. The temperature at the metallic H–He/core boundary of $\sim 2 \times 10^4$ K *is* well determined to within 10–15%, provided the entire planet above this level is isentropic (Hubbard 1973).

A model of this general form is also consistent with a formation scenario leading to high internal temperatures and to conditions appropriate for the formation of the Galilean satellites with their observed density trend (Graboske et al 1975; Pollack & Reynolds 1974). Subsequent homogeneous cooling of the interior leads to the present day heat outflow after an elapsed time (Equation 13) of $\tau = 5 \pm 1.3 \times 10^9$ years (Hubbard 1980, Stevenson 1980), consistent with the age of the solar system. Consequently, there is no reason at present to invoke gravitational differentiation, such as the downward displacement of helium (Smoluchowski 1967, Salpeter 1973).

6. SATURN

In contrast to Jupiter, there exist no Saturn models at present that are consistent with all the observables. The problem is most evident in the large heat output: existing models (Slattery, 1977, Hubbard et al 1980, Zharkov & Trubitsyn 1978) when applied to Equation (13) predict $\tau = 2.8 \pm 1.2 \times 10^9$ years (Stevenson 1980), almost certainly less than the age of the solar system. The insufficiency of homogenous cooling had been suspected in earlier calculations (Pollack et al 1977, Stevenson & Salpeter 1977b) using ground-based observations. Evidently, Saturn is emitting more energy than can be explained by the loss of primordial heat. The excess heat output can be explained by the insolubility and downward migration of helium in the metallic region. Downward migration of helium was first proposed (for Jupiter) by Smoluchowski (1967) and in a substantially modified but more applicable version by Salpeter (1973). Detailed dynamics (Stevenson & Salpeter 1977b) and specific application to Saturn (Stevenson 1980) followed. This explanation is supported by the observed depletion of helium in Saturn's atmosphere (Table 2). No detailed models currently exist which incorporate differentiation. However, Figure 5 shows the essential idea. After formation, Saturn was qualitatively similar to Jupiter and possessed a core surrounded by a homogeneous, primarily hydrogen-helium envelope. As Saturn cooled, a time was eventually reached when the adiabat intercepted the saturation solubility curve for helium (indicated by the dash-dot line in Figure 5). This might have occurred after about 2×10^9 years. The uncertainty in the theoretical solubility estimates indicated by the stippled area, prevents an a priori estimate for the time at which differentiation commenced. Rather, the estimate of 2×10^9 years is based on the measured heat flow (see Stevenson 1980). At this stage, helium raindrops

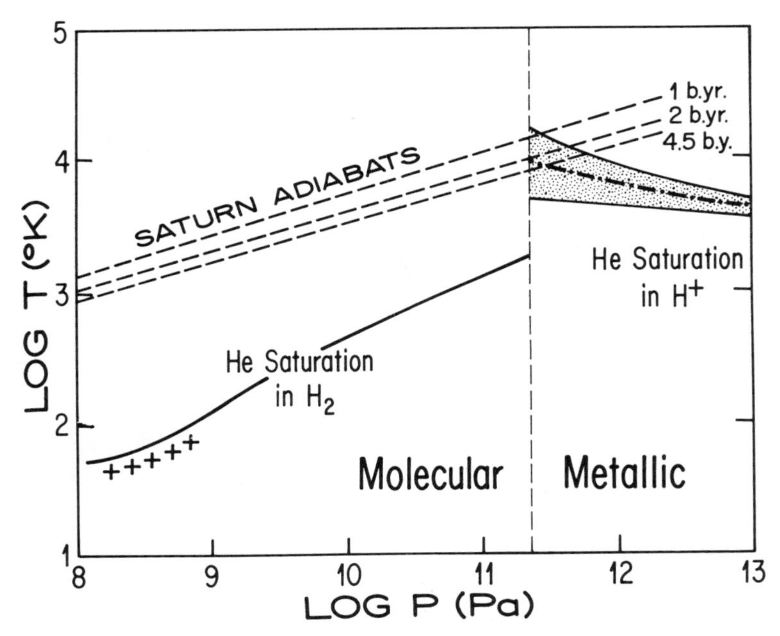

Figure 5 Saturation temperature of helium for a cosmic mixture as a function of pressure. At lower temperatures than the solid or dash-dot lines, helium droplets nucleate. The stippled region represents the theoretical uncertainty for helium solubility in metallic hydrogen. Crosses are experimental results (Streett 1973). The dashed lines represent three Saturnian adiabats of different ages as Saturn cools down. At ~ 2 billion years after formation of the planet, the adiabat begins to intercept the dash-dot line and helium raindrops form.

must form. They grow to ~ 1 cm in radius and sink under the action of gravity, releasing gravitational energy as heat because of the small-scale viscous dissipation. Since the solubility is greater at deeper levels, these raindrops must eventually redissolve.

Figure 6 shows the main features of the preferred differentiated model. The observed Saturnian heat flow implies that the outer envelope be depleted in helium by about a factor of two relative to cosmic abundance, consistent with the IRIS observations (Hanel et al 1981).

Although existing tabulated Saturn models do not incorporate differentiation, it is useful to examine the models of Hubbard et al (1980), since they represent the state-of-the-art, and some of their features will survive the incorporation of differentiation effects. As in the Jupiter models, M_c, Y, and the equation of state of dense molecular hydrogen are adjustable. The lower accuracy of J_4 for Saturn allows a greater range of acceptable models. The same equation of state that yielded $M_c \simeq 20\ M_E$ and $Y \simeq 0.20$ for Jupiter provides an acceptable model for Saturn if $M_c \simeq 18.5\ M_E$ and $Y \simeq 0.19$. It is important to stress, however, that the equation of state for the most dense

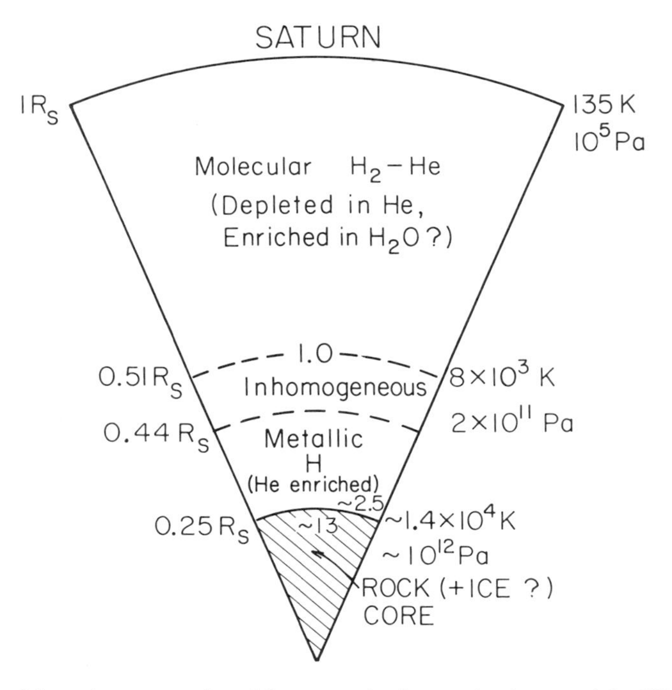

Figure 6 Schematic representation of the present day Saturn, showing a partially differentiated structure because of downward helium migration. Numbers adjacent to boundaries are densities in g.cm^{-3}.

molecular hydrogen is relevant to different regions of these planets (this region being much deeper in Saturn). This complicates comparisons of the two planets. The similarity in the values of Y may also be misleading (and is, in fact, inconsistent with the atmospheric observations). For example, Saturn's envelope may be enriched in ices (especially water) and this could be misinterpreted as helium in models such as Hubbard et al (1980) where no enhancement of heavy material in the envelope is allowed.

These models, together with a semiquantitative understanding of the differentiation, suggest the following guided tour of the interior: The outermost region is colder than Jupiter by $\sim$ 20% at the same pressure level, depleted in helium by about a factor of two, and possibly enriched in heavier constituents (especially water). Proceeding inward, the temperature rises rapidly (as in Jupiter) and no first order transitions are encountered. The fluid becomes highly nonideal at $\rho \sim 0.05$ to 0.1 g.cm^{-3} and eventually transforms to the metallic phase at a similar pressure and density to Jupiter's transition region (but at a *lower* temperature). This transition occurs at $\sim$ 50% of Saturn's radius, much deeper than the transition within Jupiter. Unlike Jupiter, the temperature is low enough at this level for helium raindrops to form. The region immediately below the molecular-metallic transition must therefore follow the phase boundary defining the pressure and temperature-dependent solubility of helium (Stevenson & Salpeter 1977b), which implies a *stable* composition gradient. Large-scale convective overturn is strongly inhibited and dynamo generation of a magnetic field is not possible despite the high electrical conductivity of the fluid. This inhomogeneous rain-forming region is perhaps $\sim$ 5000 km thick and is bounded below by a helium-enriched region, uniformly mixed, in which large-scale convection and dynamo generation occur. The great depth of this region ensures that the externally observed magnetic field is small and nearly dipolar. Furthermore, differential rotation in the intermediate, stably stratified region may explain the small angle of tilt of the dipole (Stevenson 1980, 1981a). This conclusion follows from the theoretical fact that differentiation rotation strongly attenuates non-axisymmetric components of the poloidal field (e.g. Moffatt 1978). Proceeding deeper still, the central core $\sim 20\, M_E$ is encountered at a pressure $\sim$ 1 TPa and temperature $\sim$ 12,000 K. The state and composition of this core is uncertain, and it is likely (as in Jupiter) that some fraction of this core has been mixed upwards by convection.

The similarity of core sizes for Jupiter and Saturn is consistent with the formation scenario of Mizuno (1980) involving hydrodynamic collapse onto a core. Conservation of angular momentum during this collapse is expected to provide a gaseous disk from which the satellite system forms. However, the absence of a systematic density trend among the Saturnian satellites prevents any simple comparison between the environments of the newly forming Jupiter and Saturn.

7. URANUS AND NEPTUNE

It is appropriate to discuss Uranus and Neptune in one section, not because they are necessarily very similar but because the current data base is insufficient to clearly delineate their differences. Models of Uranus and Neptune are thus still essentially generic rather than highly specific. Four different kinds of models can be envisaged: (I) All constituents uniformly mixed. (II) Rock core, ice and gas mixed in an envelope. (III) Mixed rock and ice core, surrounded by a gas envelope. (IV) A three-layer model (rock core, ice layer, gas envelope). Intermediate cases are also conceivable. Type I can be immediately excluded because it has an excessive moment of inertia. Type III models have been constructed by Zharkov & Trubitsyn (1978), but it is unlikely that an ice-rock region could remain uniformly mixed because internal heating would cause the ice to migrate upwards. Type II models have been constructed (Podolak & Reynolds 1980) but have too low a moment of inertia, at least for the Uranus rotation rate and J_2 inferred from ring precessions (Elliot et al 1981). Type IV models have been calculated by both Hubbard & MacFarlane (1980) and Podolak & Reynolds (1980) and these models are rather similar. The three-layer models for Uranus tend to have a slightly lower moment of inertia than observation suggests, but this could be readily corrected by allowing part of the ice layer to be mixed in with the envelope. Approximate theoretical calculations for the solubility of water in hydrogen suggest that this is likely (Stevenson & Fishbein 1981). The lack of an accurate rotation rate for Neptune precludes a clear choice of model type; the most that can be said at present is that the three-layer model is satisfactory for both planets.

An interesting and significant clue to the preferred type of model is obtained by considering the thermal evolutions (Hubbard 1980). It is found that both planets should emit more than their observed heat flows if they cool homogeneously from an initial hot state. One possible explanation is that they were never hot, but this is difficult to reconcile with the Mizuno (1980) scenario, which is otherwise so successful. A more likely explanation is that the planets began with three very well separated layers of rock, ice, and gas (with little ice in the outer envelope) and that subsequent convection redistributed some of the heavier ice *upward*. The work done by thermal convection necessarily diminishes the available excess luminosity. Clearly, gravitational differentiation can increase the heat flow (as in Saturn), whereas homogenization of an initially differentiated structure will decrease the heat flow (as in Uranus and Neptune). The difference arises because the helium in Saturn was initially uniformly mixed with the hydrogen whereas the ices in Uranus and Neptune were probably incorporated as comet-like planetesimals onto a core that was subsequently overlain by hydrogen and helium.

Figure 7 shows a three-layer model for Uranus. (Neptune could be similar.) Proceeding inwards below the observable atmosphere, temperatures rise rapidly along an adiabat. No first order phase transitions are encountered, except a possibly limited solubility of water in hydrogen that may prevail even at several thousand degrees. This outer envelope is mostly hydrogen and helium but may be enriched in all the ices, especially CH_4, which is not likely to partition into the ocean below (see Section 3). At a level corresponding to ~ 70% of the radius (where $P \sim 20$ GPa, $\rho \sim 0.4$ g.cm^{-3}, $T \sim 2000$–2500 K) an abrupt transition occurs to an ionic ocean of $H_3O^+OH^-$ (with dissolved NH_3). The temperature is well above the melting point of water (~ 1000 K at that pressure) and the fluid has a density $\rho \sim 1.3$ g.cm^{-3}. This ocean is likely to be convective and extends to much deeper levels (to within ~ 30% of the center by radius, where $P \sim 600$ GPa, $\rho \sim 4$ to 5 g.cm^{-3}, $T \sim 7000$ K) where the electrical conductivity may be high enough to allow dynamo generation (Stevenson 1978). The innermost 30% by radius is a rock core $M_c \sim 4\ M_E$ which may be partly solid and may have differentiated into an iron core-silicate mantle structure similar to the Earth.

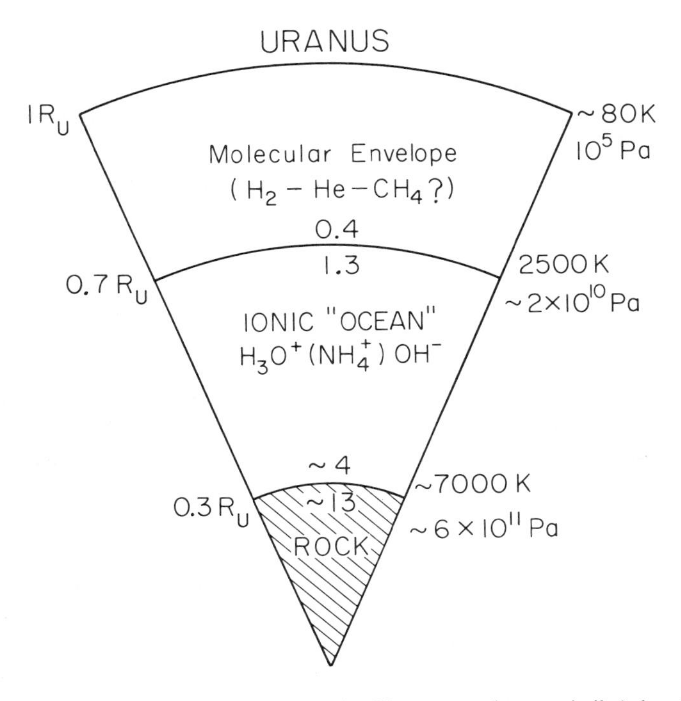

Figure 7 Schematic representation of Uranus (but Neptune may be very similar), based primarily on Hubbard & MacFarlane (1980). Numbers adjacent to boundaries are densities in g.cm^{-3}.

Dynamo generation may occur in the iron portion of this core (Torbett & Smoluchowski 1980). Both Uranus and Neptune have regions in which the pressure exceeds the transition pressure from molecular to metallic hydrogen. However, these regions are occupied by ice-rich or rock-rich material so there is little likelihood that metallic hydrogen is present anywhere in these bodies. The extent to which hydrogen might alloy with the ice or rock at extreme pressures is not known.

8. SUMMARY AND CONCLUSIONS

In this review, I have stressed the essential and complementary roles of accurate planetary observations and high pressure physics in constraining the structure and behavior of giant planetary interiors. The models can only be as good as the input physics and data. Existing models are still "simple" in the sense that they make ad hoc assumptions for the layering and distribution of constituents. Although the compatibility of these assumptions with the data can be demonstrated within the context of an "inversion," in reality it is necessary to understand the phase diagram of a multicomponent cosmic mixture at high pressures and temperatures. Until this understanding is achieved and can be synthesized with the thermal and dynamic history of the planet, the models will continue to have an ad hoc flavor to them. Caveat emptor!

The following reasonably firm conclusions are not tainted by the suggested ad hoc flavor of modeling exercises:

1. Hydrogen and helium are in approximately cosmic ratio on average and together form the dominant component of Jupiter ($\gtrsim 90\%$ by mass) and Saturn ($\sim 80\%$).
2. All the giant planets possess central concentrations of heavy elements (rock and/or ice) of roughly ten or twenty Earth masses. This represents a small deviation from a purely cosmic composition for Jupiter, a much larger deviation for Saturn, and an even larger deviation for Uranus and Neptune.
3. Jupiter and Saturn have extensive adiabatic regions and central temperatures of order 2×10^4 K and 1×10^4 K, respectively.
4. The internal heat flow of Jupiter is explainable as the gradual loss of primordial heat generated during the initial gravitational collapse that formed the planet. This loss is mediated by the atmosphere.
5. The internal heat flow of Saturn is partly a consequence of gravitational differentiation, involving the downward migration of helium raindrops. The high heat flow, observed low atmospheric helium abundance, and properties of the magnetic field all support this interpretation. The energy source is mediated by the temperature-dependent solubility of helium in metallic hydrogen. The interior of Saturn is thereby *qualitatively* different from Jupiter.

The following conclusions are less firm but are strongly indicated:

1. The outer envelopes of Jupiter and Saturn are likely to be enriched in heavier constituents (especially water) relative to cosmic abundance, and the enrichment in Saturn is likely to be greater than that in Jupiter.
2. Three-layer models are most likely for Uranus and Neptune, with the gas and ice layers being approximately adiabatic. The "ice" layer should form an ocean with an abrupt upper surface.
3. The heat flows from Uranus and Neptune are lower than homogeneous cooling would predict, and this is most probably a consequence of upward convective transport ("dredging") of some of the heavier constituents into the gaseous envelope.
4. Uranus and Neptune probably possess internally generated magnetic fields, although their external fields may be rather small (0.01–0.1 Gauss) because of the depth at which the field is generated.

The following information is badly needed for substantial advances in our understanding of giant planetary interiors:

1. The nature of the molecular-metallic hydrogen transition. (Over what temperature range, if any, is it a first order phase transition?)
2. The thermodynamics of molecular hydrogen and H_2–He mixtures at $\rho \gtrsim 0.1$ g.cm^{-3}, to an accuracy of a few percent. (Current accuracy is lower, especially at the highest densities.)
3. A better understanding of the behavior of ices, expecially water, including the solubility of hydrogen in the ices (and vice versa). The most important pressure range is 20–500 GPa, although both lower and higher pressures are also of interest.
4. Improved determinations of atmospheric compositions and thermal states, especially the He/H ratio.
5. Improved determination of J_4 for Saturn, and the first determination of J_4 values for Uranus and Neptune.
6. Accurate rotation rates for Uranus and Neptune.

Ongoing high pressure work should help with 2 and 3, but rapid progress with 1 seems unlikely. The mid-1980s should see a substantial improvement in the observational data base with Galileo (an atmospheric probe into Jupiter) and, hopefully, Voyager II at Uranus. Ground-based or orbital observations together with analysis of existing spacecraft data should help with 4–6. Progress is gradual but encouraging, and the importance of this work to the fundamental issues of solar system origin and evolution justifies a concerted effort.

Literature Cited

Allen, C. W. 1973. *Astrophysical Quantities* London: Athlone

Anderson, M. S., Swenson, C. A. 1974. Experimental compressions for normal hydrogen and normal deuterium to 25 kbar at 4.2 K. *Physical Review* 10B:5184–91

Aviram, I., Goshen, S., Rosenfeld, Y., Thieberger, R. 1976. Comments on pressure dissociation of H_2. *J. Chem. Phys.* 65:846–47

Barker, J. A., Henderson, D. 1976. What is "liquid"? Understanding the states of matter. *Rev. Mod. Phys.* 48:587–671

Berge, G. L., Gulkis, S. 1976. Earth-based radio observations of Jupiter: Millimeter to meter wavelengths. In *Jupiter*, ed. T. Gehrels, pp. 621–92, Tucson: Univ. Ariz. Press

Besson, J. M., Pinceaux, J. P. 1979. Melting of helium at room temperature and high pressure. *Science* 206:1073–75

Bodenheimer, P., Grossman, A. S., DeCampli, W. M., Marcy, G., Pollack, J. B. 1980. Calculations of the evolution of the Giant Planets. *Icarus* 41:293–308

Brown, L. W. 1976. Possible radio emission from Uranus at 0.5 MHz. *Astrophys. J. Lett.* 207:209–12

Brown, R. H., Cruikshank, D. P., Tokunaga, A. T. 1980. The rotation period of Neptune. *Bull. Am. Astron. Soc.* 12:704–5

Cameron, A. G. W. 1978. Physics of the primitive solar accretion disc. *Moon Planets* 18:5–40

Chakravarty, S., Rose, J. H., Wood, D. M., Ashcroft, N. W. 1980. Molecular and metallic hydrogen: A unified density function approach. In *High Pressure Science and Technology*, ed. B. Voder, P. Marteau, pp. 591–97. Oxford: Pergamon

Courtin, R., Gautier, D., Lacombe, A. 1978. On the thermal structure of Uranus from infrared measurements. *Astron. Astrophys* 63:97–101

Desch, M. D., Kaiser, M. L. 1981. Voyager measurement of the rotation period of Saturn's magnetic field. *Geophys. Res. Lett.* 8:253–56

Diatschenko, V., Chu, C. W. 1981. Melting of normal hydrogen under high pressures between 20 and 300 K. *Science* 212:1393–94

Duncombe, R., Klepczynski, W. J., Seidelmann, P. K. 1974. The masses of the planets, satellites and asteroids. *Fund. Cosmic Phys.* 1:119–65

Elliot, J. L., Wasserman, L. H., Veverka, J., Sagan, C., Liller, W. 1974. The occultation of Beta Scorpii by Jupiter II. The hydrogen-helium abundance in the Jovian atmosphere. *Astrophys. J.* 190:719–29

Elliot, J. L., Dunham, E., Mink, D. 1979. The radius and ellipticity of Uranus from its occultations of SAO 158687. *Bull. Am. Astron. Soc.* 11:568

Elliot, J. L., French, R. G., Frogel, J. A., Elias, J. H., Mink, D., Liller, W. 1981. Orbits of nine Uranian rings. *Astron. J.* 86:444–55

Elphic, R. C., Russell, C. T. 1978. On the apparent source depth of planetary magnetic fields. *Geophys. Res. Lett.* 5:211–14

Franck, S. 1980. On the dielectric-metal transition in hydrogen. *Ann. Phys.* 37:349–56

Freeman, K. C., Lyngå, G. 1970. Data for Neptune from occultation observations. *Astrophys. J.* 160:767–80

Gautier, D., Conrath, B., Flasar, M., Hanel, R., Kunde, V., Chedin, A., Scott, N. 1981. The helium abundance of Jupiter from Voyager. *J. Geophys. Res.* 86:8713–20

Gehrels, T., Baker, L. R., Beshore, E., Blenman, C., Burke, J. J., Castillo, N. D., Coffeen, D. L., DaCosta, B., Degewij, J., Doose, L. R., Esposito, L., Fountain, J. W., Gotobed, J., Kenknight, C. E., Kingston, R., McLaughlin, G., McMillan, R., Murphy, R., Smith, P. H., Stoll, C. P., Strickland, R. N., Tomasko, M. G., Wijesinghe, M. P. 1980. Imaging photopolarimetry on Pioneer Saturn. *Science* 207:434–39

Goldreich, P., Nicholson, P. D. 1977. Turbulent viscosity and Jupiter's tidal Q. *Icarus* 30:301–4

Goldreich, P., Soter, S. 1966. Q in the solar system. *Icarus* 5:375–89

Graboske, H. C. Jr., Pollack, J. B., Grossman, A. S., Olness, R. J. 1975. The structure and evolution of Jupiter: The fluid contraction stage. *Astrophys. J.* 199:265–81

Greenberg, R. 1975. The dynamics of Uranus' satellites. *Icarus* 24:325–32

Greenberg, R. 1981. Oribital evolution of the Galilean satellites. In *Satellites of Jupiter*, ed. T. Gehrels. Tucson: Univ. Ariz. Press

Grigor'ev, F. V., Kormer, S. B., Mikhailova, O. L., Tolochko, A-P., Urlin, V. D. 1972. Experimental determination of the compressibility of hydrogen at densities 0.5–2.0 g/cm^3. *JETP Lett.* 16:201–4

Grossman, A. S., Graboske, H. C. Jr. 1973. Evolution of low mass stars. V. Minimum mass for the deuterium main sequence. *Astrophys. J.* 180:195–98

Gulkis, S., Janssen, M. A., Olsen, E. T. 1978. Evidence for depletion of ammonia in the Uranus atmosphere. *Icarus* 34:10–19

Hamann, S. D., Linton, M. 1966. Electrical conductivity of water in shock compression. *Trans. Faraday Soc.* 62:2234–41

Hanel, R., Conrath, B., Flasar, M., Kunde, V., Lowman, P., Maguire, W., Pearl, J., Pirraglia, J., Samuelson, R., Gautier, D., Gierasch, P., Kumar, S., Ponnamperuma,

C. 1979. Infrared observations of the Jovian system from Voyager I. *Science* 204:972–76
Hanel, R., Conrath, B., Flasar, F. M., Kunde, V., Maguire, W., Pearl, J., Pirraglia, J., Samuelson, R., Herath, L., Allison, M., Cruikshank, D., Gautier, D., Gierasch, P., Horn, L., Koppany, R., Ponnamperuma, C. 1981. Infrared observations of the Saturnian system from Voyager I. *Science*. 212:192–200
Hansen, J-P., Vieillefosse, P. 1976. Equation of state of the classical two-component plasma. *Phys. Rev. Lett* 37:391–93
Hawke, R. S., Burgess, T. J., Duerre, D. E., Huebel, J. G., Keeler, R. N., Klapper, H., Wallace, W. C. 1978. Observations of electrical conductivity of isentropically compressed hydrogen at megabar pressures. *Phys. Rev. Lett.* 41:994–97
Hawke, R. S., Duerre, D. E., Huebel, J. G., Keller, R. N., Klapper, H. 1972. Isentropic compression of fused quartz and liquid hydrogen to several Mbar. *Phys. Earth Planetary Inter*. 6:44–47
Hayes, S. H., Belton, M. J. S. 1977. The rotation periods of Uranus and Neptune. *Icarus* 32:383–401
Hedin, L., Lindqvist, B. I. 1971. Explicit local exchange-correlation potentials. *J. Phys. C* 4:2064–83
Heine, V., Weaire, D. 1970. Pseudopotential theory of cohesion and structure. *Solid State Phys*. 24:249–63
Hide, R., Malin, S. R. C. 1979. The size of Jupiter's electrically conducting fluid core. *Nature* 280:42–43
Hubbard, W. B. 1973. Observational constraint on the structure of hydrogen planets. *Astrophys. J.* 182:L35–L38
Hubbard, W. B. 1974a. Inversion of gravity data for giant planets. *Icarus* 21:157–65
Hubbard, W. B. 1974b. Tides in the giant planets. *Icarus* 23:42–50
Hubbard, W. B. 1977. de Sitter's theory flattens Jupiter. *Icarus* 30:311–13
Hubbard, W. B. 1980. Intrinsic luminosities of the Jovian planets. *Rev. Geophys. Space Phys*. 18:1–9
Hubbard, W. B., MacFarlane, J. J. 1980. Structure and evolution of Uranus and Neptune. *J. Geophys. Res*. 85:225–34
Hubbard, W. B., MacFarlane, J. J. 1981. Theoretical predictions of deuterium abundances in the Jovian planets. *Icarus* 44:676–82
Hubbard, W. B., Slattery, W. L. 1971. Statistical mechanics of light elements at high pressure I. *Astrophys. J.* 168:131–39
Hubbard, W. B., Slattery, W. L. 1976. Interior structure of Jupiter: Theory of gravity sounding. In *Jupiter,* ed. T. Gehrels, pp. 176–94. Tucson: Univ. Arizona Press
Hubbard, W. B., Smoluchowski, R. 1973. Structure of Jupiter and Saturn. *Space Sci. Rev*. 14:599–662
Hubbard, W. B., MacFarlane, J. J., Anderson, J. D., Null, G. W., Biller, E. D. 1980. Interior structure of Saturn inferred from Pioneer 11 gravity data. *J. Geophys. Res*. 85:5909–16
Hunten, D. M., Tomasko, M., Wallace, L. 1980. Low-altitude thermal structure of Jupiter in the region 0.1–5 bars. *Icarus* 43:143–52
Kavanaugh, L. 1975. Synchrotron radio emission from Uranus and Neptune. *Icarus* 25:116–70
Kerley, G. I. 1972. Equation of state and phase diagram of dense hydrogen. *Phys. Earth Planet. Inter*. 6:78–82
Klepcynski, W. J., Seidelmann, P. K., Duncombe, R. L. 1971. The masses of the principal planets. *Celestial Mech*. 4:253–72
Lentz, H., Franck, E. U. 1969. Das system wasser-argon bei hohen drucken und temperaturen. *Ber. Bunsenges. Phys. Chem.* 73:28–35
Lyzenga, G. 1980. *Shock temperatures of materials: Experiments and applications to the high pressure equation of state*. PhD thesis. Calif. Inst. Technol. 208 pp. (Unpublished)
McMahan, A. K., Beck, H., Krumhansl, J. A. 1974. Short range interaction between hydrogen molecules. *Phys. Rev.* 9A: 1852–64
Mills, R. L., Liebenberg, D. H., Bronson, J. C. 1980. Equation of state and melting properties of ^{4}He from measurements to 20 kbar. *Phys. Rev. B* 2:5137–48
Mitchell, A. C., Nellis, W. J. 1979. Water hugoniot measurements in the range 30–220 GPa. In *High Pressure Science and Technology,* ed. K. D. Timmerhaus, M. S. Barber, pp. 428–33. New York: Plenum
Mitchell, A. C., Kovel, M. I., Nellis, W. J., Keller, R. N. 1980. Electrical conductivity of shocked water and ammonia. In *High Pressure Science and Technology,* ed. B. Vodar, P. L. Marteau, pp. 1048–53. Oxford: Pergamon
Mizuno, H. 1980. Formation of the giant planets. *Prog. Theor. Phys*. 64:544–57
Mizuno, H., Nagazawa, K., Hayashi, C. 1978. Instability of a gaseous envelope surrounding a planetary core and formation of the giant planets. *Prog. Theor. Phys.* 60:699–710
Moffatt, H. K. 1978 *Magnetic Field Generation in Electrically Conducting Fluids,* p. 70. Cambridge Univ. Press
Moore, J. H., Menzel, D. H. 1930. The rotation of Uranus. *Publ. Astron. Soc. Pac.* 42:330–335
Munch, G., Hippelein, H. 1980. The effects of seeing on the reflected spectrum of Uranus and Neptune. *Astron. Astrophys*. 81:189–97

Nellis, W. J., Mitchell, A. C., Ross, M., van Thiel, M. 1980. Shock compression of liquid methane and the principle of corresponding states. In *High Pressure Science and Technology,* ed. B. Vodar, P. L. Marteau, pp. 1043–47. Oxford: Pergamon

Ness, N. F., Acuna, M. H., Lepping, R. P., Connerney, J.E.P., Behannon, K.W., Burlaga, L. F., Neubauer, F. M. 1981. Magnetic field studies by Voyager I. *Science* 212:211–17

Newburn, R. L. Jr., Gulkis, S. 1973. A survey of the outer planets. *Space Sci. Rev.* 14:179–271

Null, G. W. 1976. Gravity field of Jupiter and its satellites from Pioneer 10 and Pioneer 11 tracking data. *Astron. J.* 81:1153–61

Null, G. W., Lau, E. L., Biller, E. D., Anderson, J. D. 1981. Saturn gravity results obtained from Pioneer 11 tracking data and earth-based Saturn satellite data. *Astron. J.* 86:456–68

Orton, G. 1975. The thermal structure of the Jovian atmosphere. *Icarus* 26:125–41

Orton, G., Ingersoll, A. P. 1980. Saturn's atmospheric temperature structure and heat budget. *J. Geophys. Res.* 85:5871–81

Owen, T., Cess, R. D. 1975. Methane absorption in the visible spectra of the outer planets and Titan. *Astrophys. J. Lett.* 197:L37–L40

Peale, S. J. 1973. The gravitational fields of the major planets. *Space Sci. Rev.* 14:412–23

Perri, F., Cameron, A. G. W. 1974. Hydrodynamic instability of the solar nebula in the presence of a planetary core. *Icarus* 22:416–425

Podolak, M., Reynolds, R. T. 1981. On the structure and composition of Uranus and Neptune. *Icarus* 46:40–50

Pollack, J. B., Reynolds, R. T. 1974. Implications of Jupiter's early contraction history for the composition of the Galilean satellites. *Icarus* 21:248–53

Pollack, J. B., Grossman, A. S., Moore, R., Graboske, H. C. Jr. 1977. A calculation of Saturn's gravitational contraction history. *Icarus* 30:111–28

Pollock, E. L., Alder, B. J. 1977. Phase separation for a dense fluid mixture of nuclei. *Phys. Rev. A* 15:1263–68

Pollock, E. L., Hansen, J-P. 1973. Statistical mechanics of dense ionized matter. *Phys. Rev. A* 8:3110–3112

Prinn, R. G., Lewis, J. S. 1973. Uranus atmosphere: structure and composition. *Astrophys. J.* 179:333–42

Ree, F. H. 1979. Systematics of high-pressure and high-temperature behavior of hydrocarbons. *J. Chem. Phys.* 70:974-83

Ree, F. H. 1981. Molecular interaction of dense water at high temperature. Preprint

Ree, F. H., Bender, C. F. 1974. Non-additive interaction in molecular hydrogen at high pressure. *Phys. Rev. Lett.* 32:85–88

Ree, F. H., Bender, C. F. 1979. Repulsive intermolecular potential between two H_2 molecules. *J. Chem. Phys.* 71:5362–75 Erratum: *J. Chem. Phys.* 73:4712

Ross, J. H., Aller, L. 1976. The chemical composition of the Sun. *Science* 191:1223–29

Ross, M. 1974. A theoretical analysis of the shock compression experiments of the liquid hydrogen isotopes and a prediction of the metallic transition. *J. Chem. Phys.* 60:3634–44

Ross, M., McMahan, A. K. 1976. Comparison of theoretical models for metallic hydrogen. *Phys. Rev. B* 13:5154–57

Ross, M., Shishkevish, C. 1977. Molecular and metallic hydrogen. *Defense Advanced Research Projects Agency, R-2056-ARPA*

Salpeter, E. E. 1973. On convection and gravitational layering in Jupiter and in stars of low mass. *Astrophys. J. Lett.* 181:83–86

Salpeter, E. E., Stevenson, D. J. 1976. Heat transport in a stratified two-phase fluid. *Phys. Fluids* 19:502–9

Shafer, R., Gordon, R. G. 1973. Quantum scattering theory of rotational relaxation in H_2-He mixtures. *J. Chem. Phys.* 58:876–86

Sharma, S. K., Mao, H. K., Bell, P. M. 1980. Raman measurements of H_2 in the pressure range 0.2-630 kbar at room temperature. *Phys. Rev. Lett.* 44:886–88

Silver, D. M. 1980. Interaction energy between two ground state helium atoms using many-body perturbation theory. *Phys. Rev. A* 21:1106–17

Slattery, W. L. 1977. The structure of the planets Jupiter and Saturn. *Icarus* 32:58–72

Slattery, W. L., Hubbard, W. B. 1976. Thermodynamics of a solar mixture of molecular H_2 and He at high pressure. *Icarus* 29:187–92

Slattery, W. L., Doolen, G. D., DeWitt, H. E. 1980. Improved equation of state for the classical OCP. *Phys. Rev. B* 21:2087–95

Slavsky, D. B., Smith, H. J. 1980. The rotation period of Uranus. *Bull. Am. Astron. Soc.* 12:704

Smith, B. A. et al. 1981. Encounter with Saturn: Voyager I imaging science results. *Science* 212:163–91

Smith, D. W., Greene, T. F. 1980 Galilean satellites eclipse studies. III. Jovian methane abundance. *Icarus* 44:134–41

Smith, E. J., Davis, L. Jr., Jones, D. E. 1976. Jupiter's magnetic field and magnetosphere. In *Jupiter,* ed. T. Gehrels, pp. 788–829. Tucson: Univ Arizona Press

Smith, E. J., Davis, L. Jr., Jones, D. E., Coleman, D. J. Jr., Colburn, D. S., Dyal, P., Sonnet, C. P. 1980. Saturn's magnetosphere and its interaction with the solar wind. *J. Geophys. Res.* 85:5655–74

Smith, H. J., Slavsky, D. B. 1980. Further

evidence for the longer rotation period of Neptune. *Bull. Am. Astron. Soc.* 12:704

Smoluchowski, R. 1967. Internal structure and energy emission of Jupiter. *Nature* 215:691–95

Smoluchowski, R. 1975. Jupiter's molecular hydrogen layer and the magnetic field. *Astrophys. J. Lett.* 200:119–21

Smoluchowski, R. 1979. Origin of the magnetic fields in the giant planets. *Phys. Earth Planet. Inter.* 20:247–54

Stevenson, D. J. 1975a. Thermodynamics and phase separation of dense fully-ionized hydrogen-helium fluid mixtures. *Phys. Rev. B* 12:3999–4007

Stevenson, D. J. 1975b. Does metallic ammonium exist? *Nature* 258:222–23

Stevenson D. J. 1978. The outer planets and their satellites. In *The Origin of the Solar System,* ed. S. F. Dermott, pp. 395–431. New York: John Wiley

Stevenson, D. J. 1979. Solubility of helium in metallic hydrogen. *J. Phys. F: Metal Physics* 9:791–800

Stevenson, D. J. 1980. Saturn's luminosity and magnetism. *Science* 208:746–48

Stevenson, D. J. 1981a. Reducing the non-axisymmetry of a planetary dynamo and an application to Saturn. *Geophys. Astrophys. Fluid Dyn.* In press

Stevenson, D. J. 1981b. Formation of the giant planets. *Planet. Space Sci.* Submitted for publication

Stevenson, D. J., Ashcroft, N. W. 1974. Conduction in fully ionized liquid metals. *Phys. Rev.* 9(A):782–89

Stevenson, D. J., Fishbein, E. 1981. The behavior of water in the giant planets. *Lunar Planet. Sci.* 12:1040–42 (Abstr.)

Stevenson, D. J., Salpeter, E. E. 1976. Interior models of Jupiter. In *Jupiter,* ed. T. Gehrels, pp. 85–112. Tucson: Univ. Arizona Press

Stevenson, D. J., Salpeter, E. E. 1977a. The phase diagram and transport properties for hydrogen-helium fluid planets. *Astrophys. J. Suppl.* 35:221–37

Stevenson, D. J., Salpeter, E. E. 1977b. The dynamics and helium distribution in hydrogen-helium fluid planets. *Astrophys. J. Suppl.* 35:239–61

Stewart, J. W. 1956. Compression of solidified gases to 20,000 kg/cm^2 at low temperatures. *J. Phys. Chem. Solids* 1:146–58

Streett, W. B. 1973. Phase equilibria in molecular H_2-He mixtures at high pressures. *Astrophys. J.* 186:1107–25

Tokunaga, A. T., Knacke, R. F., Ridgway, S. T. 1980. High spatial and spectral resolution 10 μm observations of Jupiter. *Icarus* 44:93–101

Torbett, M., Smoluchowski, R. 1980. Hydromagnetic dynamos in the cores of Uranus and Neptune. *Nature* 286:237–39

Trubitsyn, V. P. 1967. Equation of state of solid helium at high pressures. *Sov. Phys. Solid State* 8:2593–98

van Thiel, M., Hord, B. L., Gust, W. H., Mitchell, A. C., D'Addario, M., Boutwell, K., Wilbarger, E., Barrett, B. 1974. Shock compression of deuterium to 900 kbar. *Phys. Earth Planet. Inter.* 9:57–77

Wallace, L. 1980. The structure of the Uranus atmosphere. *Icarus* 43:231–259

Wetherill, G. W. 1980. Formation of the terrestrial planets. *Ann. Rev. Astron. Astrophys.* 18:77–113

Yoder, C. F., Peale, S. J. 1981. The tides of Io. *Icarus* 47:1–35

Zharkov, V. N., Trubitsyn, V. P. 1978. *Physics of Planetary Interiors* Tucson: Pachart. 388 pp.

Ann. Rev. Earth Planet. Sci. 1982. 10:297-326

HALLEY'S COMET[1]

Ray L. Newburn, Jr. and Donald K. Yeomans

Jet Propulsion Laboratory, California Institute of Technology, Pasadena, California 91109

INTRODUCTION

Periodic Comet Halley (P/Halley) is an historic object that has had enormous impact on men's minds throughout the centuries. Ask virtually anyone to name a comet, and if you get an answer at all, the answer will be "Halley!" Yet, should the answerer turn questioner and demand facts about Halley, an embarrassing situation can develop. Our "facts" are largely qualitative, representative of the state of astronomy in 1910.

In this review, we begin by covering the one truly quantitative aspect possible for P/Halley, its motion, in a step-by-step historical development. Then, following a brief look at the meteoroid streams associated with Halley, we discuss the observations of 1910 in the dual context of the state of cometary astronomy then and now. We derive what facts we can from those observations and extend them by analogy with comets observed recently. Finally, we consider what should be expected of the Halley return of 1985–86.

PERIODIC COMET HALLEY MOVES THROUGH HISTORY

Since 240 B.C., Chinese observers have documented a nearly unbroken record of scientifically useful observations of Comet Halley. Subsequent to the probable 240 B.C. apparition of Comet Halley, only the 164 B.C. apparition went unrecorded by the Chinese and with the exception of occasional Korean and Japanese observations, useful observations of Comet Halley made outside of China were virtually nonexistent for over a millennium thereafter. Beginning with the cometary observations of the Florentine physician and astronomer Paolo Toscanelli (1397–1482), quantitative and accurate cometary positions were available for use by Western astronomers (Celoria 1921). However, the necessary theory for representing a comet's motion was not available until the publication of Newton's *Principia* in 1687. It is ironic that Kepler (1619) actually used the 1607 observations of Comet Halley to demonstrate that comets move on straight line trajectories! Newton himself began his work on the comet of 1680 by trying to represent its motion by a straight line, but he later recognized its path as very nearly parabolic with the sun located at one focus. In his *Principia,* Newton (1687) outlined a semi-analytic orbit determination theory and used the comet of 1680 as an example. While Newton never utilized the method again on another cometary orbit, Edmond Halley began what he termed "a prodigious deal of calculation" and applied Newton's method to determine parabolic orbits for 24 well observed comets (Halley 1705). Struck by the similarity in the orbital elements for comets observed in 1531, 1607 and 1682, Halley suggested that these three apparitions were due to the same comet, and that it might be expected to return again in 1758. Halley's subsequent calculations indicated that a close approach to Jupiter in 1681 would cause an increase in the length of the next period. Halley then revised his prediction for the comet's return to late 1758 or early 1759 (Halley 1749). Lalande (1765) pointed out that a postperihelion 1683 approach to Jupiter decreased the comet's orbital period by a similar amount so that Halley's accurate prediction was a bit fortuitous. However, Halley rightly deserves credit for the first successful prediction of a cometary return.

With the acknowledged help of Lalande and the unacknowledged help of Madame Lepaute, Clairaut (1758) used a modified version of his analytic lunar theory to compute direct and indirect perturbations of Jupiter and Saturn upon Comet Halley over the interval 1531–1759. Only the perturbative effects upon the comet's orbital period were computed. Noting that calculations over the intervals 1531–1607 and 1607–1682 predicted the 1682 perihelion passage time to within one month, Clairaut stated that his mid-April 1759 prediction should be good to similar accuracy. The actual time of perihelion passage in 1759 was March 13.1. (Unless otherwise stated, all times are given in U.T.) Beginning with Clairaut's work in 1758, all subsequent work to 1910 on the perturbed motion of Comet Halley was based upon the variation of elements technique (Lagrange 1783). The various works differed only in how many perturbing planets were included, how many orbital elements were allowed to vary, and how many times per revolution the reference ellipse was rectified by adding the perturbations in elements. Until after the 1910 apparition, no attempt was made to link the observations of two or more apparitions of Comet Halley in one orbit.

The first work undertaken for the 1835 return of Comet Halley predicted a perihelion passage time of November 17.15, 1835, just 0.71 day later than the actual perihelion time (Damoiseau 1820). Damoiseau had computed the perturbative effects of Jupiter, Saturn, and Uranus on Comet Halley over the interval 1682–1835. However, Damoiseau's accurate prediction was fortuitous, and he subsequently added the perturbative effects of the Earth to his calculations and revised his prediction to November 4.81 (Damoiseau 1829). De Pontécoulant considered the perturbative effects of Jupiter, Saturn, and Uranus on the comet's motion over the 1682–1835 interval, as well as the Earth's perturbative effects near the 1759 perihelion passage. His several predictions for the 1835 perihelion passage time were, successively, November 7.5, November 13.1, November 10.8, and November 12.9 (de Pontécoulant 1830, 1834, 1835). In a rather complete and rigorous study of the comet's motion, Rosenberger (1830a, b) recomputed an orbit for the 1759 and 1682 apparitions and then went on to compute the effect on all the orbital elements from the perturbations of the seven known planets over the 1682–1835 interval (Rosenberger 1834, 1835). Assuming the comet's motion was unaffected by a resisting medium, Rosenberger's prediction for the 1835 perihelion passage time was November 12.0. We note here that de Pontécoulant's and Rosenberger's final perihelion passage time predictions were early by 3.5 and 4.4 days, respectively. As will be shown in the next section, this is just what would be expected, since the predictions did not allow for the so-called nongravitational effects. Lehmann (1835) also investigated the motion of Comet Halley over the interval 1607–1835. Perturbations of Jupiter, Saturn, and Uranus were taken into account, but his perihelion passage prediction of November 26.73 was too late by over 10 days.

The work leading up to the 1910 return of Comet Halley began with Angström's empirical attempt to fit a power series to the previous times of perihelion passage of Comet Halley. His series had a mean period of 76.93 years and two inequalities of amplitude 1.5 and 2.3 years with corresponding periods of 2650 and 782 years (Angström 1862). Although the calculated perihelion passage times in the past were all accurate to within a year, the first predicted perihelion passage time (1913.1) was in error by 2.8 years. De Pontécoulant (1864) took into account the perturbative effects of Jupiter, Saturn, and Uranus and predicted a 1910 perihelion passage time of May 24.36. Cowell & Crommelin began their work with preliminary calculations to see if de Pontécoulant's prediction was approximately correct (Cowell & Crommelin 1907a, b, c, 1908c). Their computations utilized the variation of elements technique and included perturbations by Venus, Earth, Jupiter, Saturn, Uranus, and Neptune. Pending an accurate redetermination of the Jupiter and Saturn perturbations from 1759–1835, Cowell & Crommelin predicted a 1910 preihelion passage time of April 8.5. They began a new study on the motion of Comet Halley by using numerical integration, whereby the perturbed rectangular coordinates are obtained directly at each time step (Cowell & Crommelin 1910). They included the perturbations of Venus through

Neptune and used a time step that varied from 2 to 256 days. Their computations were initiated in 1835 and run backward to 1759 and forward to 1910. The backward integration was terminated 230 days before reaching perihelion passage time, and the forward integration was terminated 108 days prior to the 1910 perihelion passage. The comet was then brought to perihelion in 1759 and 1910 under the assumption of undisturbed two-body motion. Noting that the computed perihelion passage time in 1759 required a correction of −0.55 days, the predicted perihelion passage time in 1910 was adjusted by a similar amount, the final prediction for 1910 then being April 17.11. The 1909 recovery of the comet revealed that their prediction required a correction of +3 days and Cowell & Crommelin (1910) revised their work by reducing the time steps by one half, carrying an additional decimal place and correcting certain errors in the previous work. The postrecovery prediction for the 1910 perihelion passage time was revised to April 17.51, and they concluded that at least two days of the remaining discordance was due to causes other than calculation errors or errors in the adopted positions and masses of the planets. Although Zadunaisky (1966) claimed the 1909–11 observations of Comet Halley were best satisfied by separate orbits for the pre- and postperihelion observations, Brady (1967) and Yeomans (1977a) successfully represented the 1909–11 observations with one orbit.

Similar to Angström's empirical attempt to predict the 1910 perihelion passage time, Kamienski (1962) used an empirical technique to predict the next perihelion passage time as 1986.88—a result that will be in error by 9 months. Brady & Carpenter (1967) used a Cowell numerical integration technique with all planetary perturbations in an attempt to link the observations of the 1835 and 1910 returns. Although a least squares differential correction on the observations of these two returns was unsuccessful, they did fit the observations of these two apparitions tolerably well, using an iterative trial and error adjustment of the initial conditions. They predicted a perihelion passage time of February 5.3678, 1986.

COMET HALLEY'S MOTION AND NONGRAVITATIONAL FORCES

Michielsen (1968) first pointed out that the perihelion passage time predictions of Comet Halley that had been based upon strictly gravitational perturbation calculations have required corrections of +4.4 days over the past seven revolutions. Using data from several more apparitions, Kiang (1971) determined a mean correction of +4.1 days. Brady & Carpenter (1971) continued their study of Comet Halley's motion by adding an empirical secular term in the cometary equations of motion. Although the empirical term had the unrealistic effect of decreasing the solar attraction with time, the device did allow an orbit to be fitted to the observations of the last four returns. As a differential correction again proved unsuccessful, they used the iterative technique of their previous work. Their resultant orbit was run forward in time to predict a 1986 perihelion passage time of February 9.3947. By analyzing the residuals between the past observed and computed times of perihelion passage, Brady (1972) tried to explain the residual trends as due to the perturbative effects of a massive trans-Plutonian planet traveling in an orbit whose inclination is 120 degrees. This hypothesis has been shown untenable both on observational and theoretical grounds (Klemola & Harlan 1972, Seidelmann et al 1972, Goldreich & Ward 1972). Kiang (1973) showed the residual trends to be an inherent property of the idealized Sun-Jupiter-Comet model.

Beginning with the work of Bessel (1835, 1836b) on the 1835 apparition of Comet Halley, it became recognized that comets may undergo substantial perturbations due to reactive forces or rocket-like effects acting upon the cometary nucleus itself. Whipple (1950, 1951) put these so-called nongravitational effects on a firm theoretical framework when he introduced his icy-conglomerate model for a cometary nucleus. In large part, Whipple introduced this nucleus model to explain the obvious nongravitational perturbations affecting the motion of periodic Comet Encke. In an effort to accurately represent the motions of many short period comets, Marsden (1968, 1969) began to model the nongravitational forces with a semi-empirical term in the cometary equations of motion. Marsden et al (1973) then revised the nongravitational force model so that the mathematical nongravitational force terms represented an empirical fit to a theoretical plot of water-snow vaporization flux versus heliocentric distance. The cometary equations of motion are written

$$\frac{\mathrm{d}^2\mathbf{r}}{\mathrm{d}t^2} = -\mu\frac{\mathbf{r}}{r^3} + \frac{\partial R}{\partial \mathbf{r}} + A_1 g(r)\hat{\mathbf{r}} + A_2 g(r)\hat{\mathbf{T}},$$

where

$$g(r) = \alpha(r/r_0)^{-m}[1 + (r/r_0)^n]^{-k}.$$

The acceleration is given in astronomical units per (ephemeris day)^2, μ is the product of the gravitational constant and the solar mass, while R is the planetary disturbing function. The scale distance r_0 is the heliocentric distance where reradiation of solar energy begins to dominate the use of this energy for vaporizing the comet's nuclear ices. For water ice, $r_0 = 2.808$ AU and the normalizing constant $\alpha = 0.111262$. The exponents m, n, k equal 2.15, 5.093, and 4.6142, respectively. The nongravitational acceleration is represented by a radial term, $A_1 g(r)$, and a transverse term, $A_2 g(r)$, in the equations of motion. The radial unit vector ($\hat{\mathbf{r}}$) is defined outward along the radius vector, while the transverse unit vector ($\hat{\mathbf{T}}$) is directed normal to $\hat{\mathbf{r}}$ in the orbit plane and in the direction of the comet's motion. An acceleration component normal to the orbit plane has been found to have an undetectable effect upon the orbital motion of short-period comets. While the nongravitational acceleration term $g(r)$ was originally established for water ice, Marsden et al (1973) have shown that if the Bond albedo in the visible range is assumed equal to the infrared albedo of the cometary ices, then the scale distance r_0 is inversely proportional to the square of the vaporization heat of the volatile substance. The vaporization heat (L) in calories per mole is related to the scale distance r_0 in AU by $r_0 = 4.0 \times 10^8/L^2$. A scale distance of $r_0 = 2.8$ corresponds to the vaporization heat of water ice.

Using 885 observations of Comet Halley over the 1607–1911 interval, Yeomans (1977a, b) investigated the nongravitational effects acting upon this comet. The most successful nongravitational force model was found to be consistent with the outgassing rocket effect of a water-ice nucleus, and these forces are time independent for nearly a millennium. If the icy-conglomerate model is correct for Comet Halley, the positive sign of the nongravitational parameter, A_2, implies the comet is rotating in a direct sense and the ratio of A_2/A_1 implies a small lag angle ($<4°$) between the subsolar meridian and the direction of maximum mass ejection. Yeomans (1977a) integrated the motion of Comet Halley back to 837 and forward to 2061 and predicted a 1986 perihelion passage time of February 9.66.

Attempts to numerically integrate the motion of Comet Halley backward over long periods of time must include the effects of nongravitational perturbations, and the computed motion must be constrained using the ancient Chinese observations. Brady & Carpenter (1971) made an effort to satisfy only the first criterion while Chang's (1978) integration satisfied neither. Using a variation of elements integration and successively more approximate perturbation techniques, Cowell & Crommelin (1907d, 1908a, b, d, e) carried the motion of the comet back to 239 B.C. By 239 B.C., their integration was in error by nearly 1.5 years in the predicted time of perihelion passage, and they adopted a perihelion passage time of May 15, 240 B.C., not from their integration but directly from the ancient observations themselves. Using a more sophisticated version of the variation of elements technique, Kiang (1971) traced the motion of Comet Halley from 1682 to 240 B.C. Observations were used directly to determine the perihelion passage times and the remaining five orbital elements were allowed to vary under the perturbative influence of all nine planets. Hasegawa (1979) also empirically determined perihelion passage times of Comet Halley. For each apparition from 1378 back to 240 B.C., Hasegawa computed several ephemerides using Kiang's (1971) orbital elements, except for the perihelion passage times, which were chosen to make the best fit with the observations. Earlier attempts to investigate or identify ancient apparitions of Comet Halley are outlined by Yeomans & Kiang (1981).

Yeomans & Kiang (1981) began with an orbit based upon the 1759, 1682, and 1607 observations of Comet Halley and numerically integrated the comet's motion back to 1404 B.C. Planetary and nongravitational perturbations were taken into account at each half-day integration step. In nine cases, the perihelion passage times calculated by Kiang (1971) from Chinese observations were redetermined and the unusually accurate observed perihelion passage times in 837, 374 and 141 were used to constrain the computed motion of the comet. The dynamic model, including terms for nongravitational forces, successfully represented all the existing quantitative Chinese observations of Comet Halley. This model assumed the comet's nongravitational forces remained constant with time. Hence, it seems that the transverse and radial nongravitational parameters have been constant from 1910 back at least to 87 B.C., implying that the comet's spin axis is fixed in space without noticeable precessional motion. Also implied is the relative constancy, over two millennia, of Comet Halley's ability to outgas. This result is consistent with the comet's nearly constant intrinsic brightness over roughly the same interval (Broughton 1979).

METEOR SHOWERS ASSOCIATED WITH P/HALLEY

Though the orbital periods of the May η-Aquarids and the October Orionid meteor shower particles are considerably less than Comet Halley's orbital period, the remaining orbital elements are sufficiently alike to allow a probable identification of these two meteor streams with the parent Comet Halley. Both meteor streams supply annual meteor showers with an average hourly rate of 10–20, but neither stream has ever been responsible for an outstanding display.

The early work on the Orionid and η-Aquarid streams is detailed in Olivier (1925) and Lovell (1954). More recently, Hajduk (1970, 1980) confirms the association of these two streams with Comet Halley. He suggests that the Orionid stream density varies with a period of 5–15 years and that stream filaments with diameters on the order of 10^6 km run parallel to the central orbital path. The η-Aquarid meteor stream showed very similar structural features with a central core of about 0.08 AU, roughly half the core radius of the Orionid stream. To determine whether enhanced meteor shower activity accompanies the parent comet's return, Yeomans (1977a) predicted possible shower maximum dates of October 24.2, 1985, and May 8.5, 1986, for the respective Orionid and η-Aquarid meteors.

PHYSICAL PROPERTIES OF P/HALLEY

The Observations

Any attempt to discuss the physical properties of P/Halley is frustrated to a great extent by the simple fact that the comet has not been seen since 1911. At that time, virtually all observations were either visual or photographic. Relative photometery was well developed but absolute photometry of faint extended sources certainly was not. The first commercial panchromatic plates became available in 1906, and there are a few spectra of Halley extending to the red slightly beyond Hα. There was no spectrophotometry at any wavelength, however. Therefore, nearly all information about Halley that cannot be derived from the position of something on a photographic plate is at best semiquantitative or a model result obtained by analogy with other comets in some way similar to Halley.

VISUAL OBSERVATIONS Visual observations of comets in 1910 or now usually consist of values for the total magnitude of the head, the apparent coma diameter, length and position angle of the tail or tails, and drawings of any detail near the nucleus such as jets and shells. The total magnitude should be determined by comparing an out-of-focus image of the comet with out-of-focus comparison stars using the smallest possible aperture and magnification. Even so, the apparent visual magnitude determined is a function of the aperture of the instrument used, and aperture corrections must be made. A complete study of these problems has been made by Meisel & Morris (1976). Unfortunately, several different methods of making visual estimates of comet brightness have been used, and observers in 1910 often did not indicate which method they used or even the type and size of instrument in use. The apparent visual size of the coma is an extremely sensitive function of the sky brightness, of air mass (distance from the horizon), and of the dark adaptation and intrinsic sensitivity of the eye of the observer, since the gaseous component of the coma has no sharp edges. Tail length measurements present a similar problem. The position angle of the nearly straight ion tails can give important information on the state of the solar wind, but dust tails are curved, and one must define the position angle that has been measured for them. If observations are made from near the plane of the comet orbit, the tails lie on top of each other as seen projected against the sky, the angle between an ion tail and the solar radius vector cannot be measured, and the dust tail has no apparent curvature. Unfortunately, this was the case with P/Halley in 1910.

In 1835, professional astronomers were all artists to some extent. The size and angles of well defined features were measured and beautiful detailed scale drawings rendered. (See, for example, the Halley studies of Bessel 1836a and Struve 1839.) The telescopes were small in 1835, however. Struve used the world's largest refractor, the Great Fraunhofer Refractor at Dorpat, which had an aperture of about 28 cm. In 1910, telescopes had improved tremendously, and both the 100 cm Yerkes refractor and the 150 cm Mt. Wilson reflector were among the many fine instruments used to study Halley. Photography had largely replaced visual studies, however, and many photographs were exposed to bring out detail in the faint tails, thereby overexposing structures near the nucleus. Meanwhile, the old facility with visual work had been lost in the new generation of astronomers. The 1910 apparition produced much of interest to those concerned with the behavior of ion tails but a tantalizingly small amount of information on coma structure. The visual studies of 1910 (e.g. Wood 1910, Barnard 1914) were, if anything, inferior to those of 1835.

Amazingly, some visual observations of P/Halley were made with spectroscopes. W. H. Wright made visual spectroscopic observations on the Lick Observatory 30 cm refractor, along with spectrographic plates on that instrument and with a quartz spectrograph on the 90 cm Crossley reflector (Bobrovnikoff 1931).

The light curve of P/Halley The most important single result of visual observations in 1909–11 is the light curve, the plot of brightness versus heliocentric distance, for P/Halley. There is a standard cometary brightness formula:

$$m = m_0 + 5 \log \Delta + 2.5n \log r,$$

where m = magnitude (visual)
m_0 = absolute magnitude (visual)
Δ = geocentric distance in AU
r = heliocentric distance in AU
n = brightness parameter.

An asteroidal type body will follow an inverse square law ($n = 2$) except for phase effects or changes caused by irregularities in shape and albedo. Since one component of cometary brightness is sunlight scattered from solids, a phase term is sometimes included for comets, too. Quite often, however, a simple least squares fit is made to the expression given, solving for the constants m_0 and n. Morris & Green (1981) have recently taken data collected by Bobrovnikoff from 32 observers and rederived these constants for Halley pre- and postperihelion. Their results were

	Preperihelion	Postperihelion
m_0	5.51 ± 0.06	4.94 ± 0.06
n	4.29 ± 0.09	3.04 ± 0.06
Δr	3.35–0.59 AU	0.59–5.00 AU

Their quoted errors are probable errors. The Δr is the range of heliocentric distances covered by the observations.

The only real advantage of the power law other than simplicity is that it offers an easy comparison with the asteroidal law. There is evidence of some considerable difference between pre- and postperihelion behavior of Halley in the great difference in n. When actually plotted, individual points show an enormous scatter, especially postperihelion. Much of this undoubtedly is caused by great variations in the apparent coma being measured by different persons with different instruments against different sky backgrounds, especially when Comet Halley approached so near to Earth. At closest approach, 10^5 km was more than one-quarter degree.

In 1977, Yeomans produced a light curve for P/Halley that has been widely used in recent studies. It is shown as Figure 1. Yeomans selected the results of only a few experienced observers who all used visually corrected refractors over most or all of the apparition, and most of the scatter in points on the light curve disappeared. What unexpectedly remained was an apparent decrease in brightness between perihelion and 1 AU postperihelion. This distance was covered in an interval of 40 days, during which the geocentric distance changed from 1.21 AU to 0.15 AU and back to 0.40 AU, and the elongation was less than 42° for all but the last seven days. In other words, observers were attempting to measure the brightness of an object of large angular size (the coma) having low surface brightness in its fuzzy outer parts, changing in size, near to the Sun, and low in the sky. The smallest values of brightness relative to those expected are those near 0.85 AU when the comet was closest to Earth and nearest to the Sun in the sky. In our opinion, the dip should not be taken seriously.

The coma There are two major contributions to the visible light from a cometary coma: scattered light from dust grains, and resonance fluorescence of the C_2 Swan bands. Removal processes for these contributors to coma visibility, other than nearly isotropic outflow, are radiation pressure for the dust and photo-dissociation and ionization for the gas. Initially, the surface brightness of the coma should fall off almost linearly, then more rapidly as dust and C_2 are removed. While there is a limit to the nucleus distance reached by dust particles of any given size (unless given added "boost" by an outburst), there is no sharp edge to a cometary coma.

Figure 2 is Yeomans' compilation of visual coma diameters reported from 1909–11 for P/Halley. No attempt was made to apply aperture or focal length corrections, or to allow for any other systematic effect. The coma diameters are of some value in modeling as an indication to how much of the coma a visual brightness estimate refers.

The tails Spectacular naked eye tails are produced by comets that are intrinsically bright, come near to Earth, and have good geometry, so that the tails are not seen too foreshortened. Halley is relatively bright and passed very

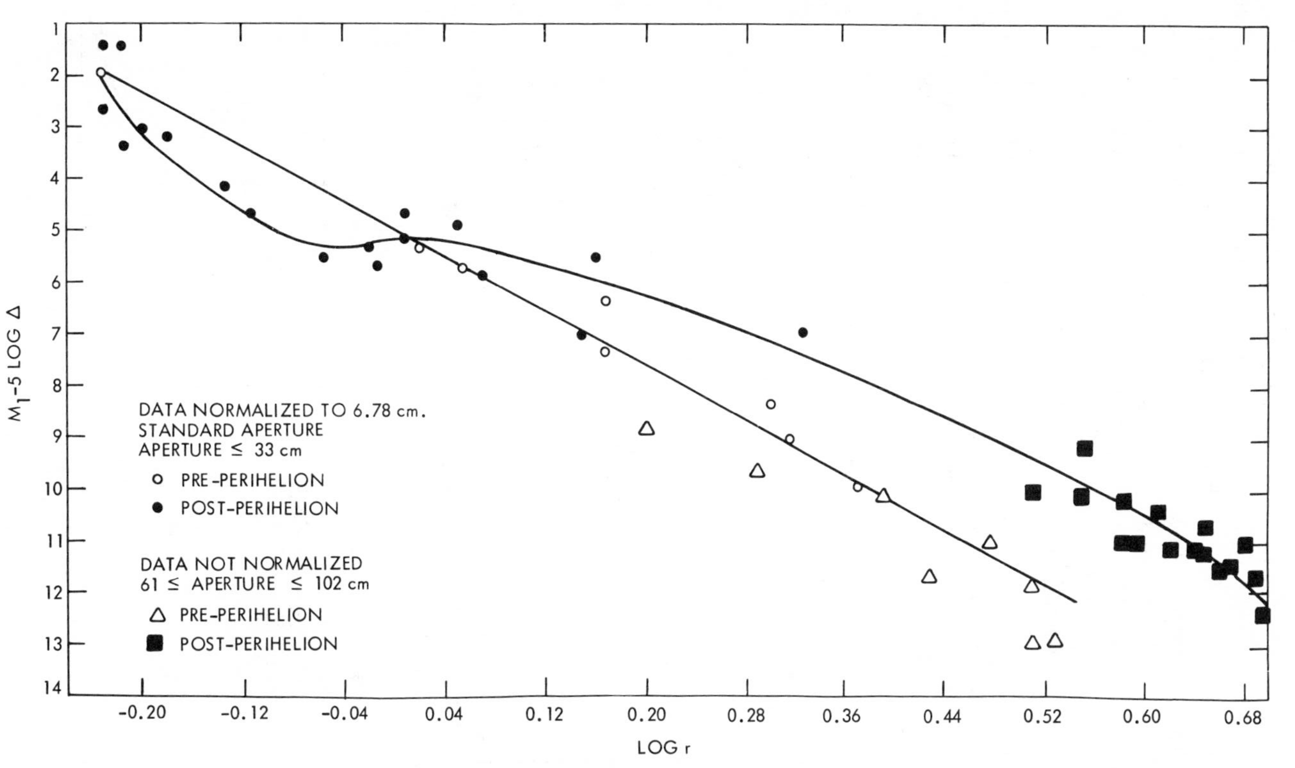

Figure 1 Comet Halley total magnitude estimates, 1910 visual estimates only. *r* is heliocentric distance, Δ is geocentric distance.

close to Earth in 1910. Earth lay near the plane of Halley's orbit at the time, so even the dust tail appeared narrow rather than as a fan of light, but the angular length was enormous. Halley actually passed through a phase angle of 90° twice in May, and Barnard (1914) claims its visible length exceeded 120°. On May 19, the phase angle was virtually 180° and Earth may have passed through part of a tail. For a brief period then, the tails were seen in both the morning and the evening skies (Barnard 1914, Wood 1910). Naked eye estimates of tail lengths collected by Yeomans are shown in Figure 3.

DIRECT PHOTOGRAPHS A single, poor photographic image of Comet Donati obtained on a wet plate by Usherwood in 1858 was apparently the first photograph of a comet. Useful pictures were not obtained until silver bromide dry plates became available as the result of experiments during the 1870s.

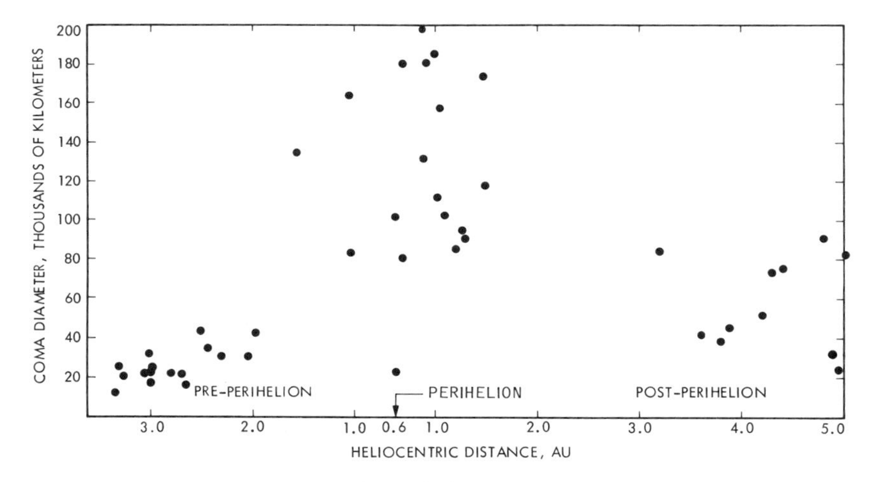

Figure 2 Comet Halley coma diameters.

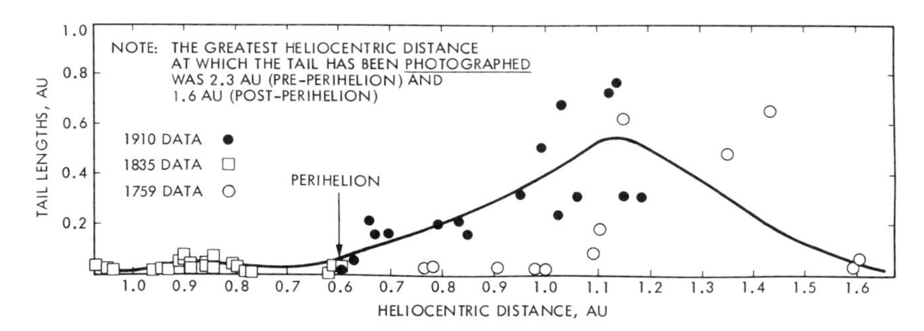

Figure 3 Comet Halley tail lengths.

Beginning with Comet Tebbutt in 1881, increasing use was made of photography in studying comets, and by 1910 it was a well-developed technique used universally by astronomers (de Vaucouleurs 1961).

P/Halley was recovered photographically by Wolf at Heidelberg on September 11, 1909, using a 75 cm reflector. Two prerecovery images were found later, the earlier from Helwan on August 24. In mid-September, P/Halley was 3.43 AU from the sun, of 15th magnitude visually, and already showed a coma some 7 arc seconds in diameter. The last photograph certainly showing Halley was taken May 30, 1911, at Lowell Observatory. The comet was 5.28 AU from the sun, and Giclas (private communication) estimates its photographic magnitude at about 18.0. During the previous five days, Giclas says it had faded by more than a magnitude, so the comet clearly was still more than a bare, inactive nucleus at that time. Curtis suspected "a small, hazy patch of utmost faintness" on a Crossley plate taken June 15 might be Halley (Bobrovnikoff 1931).

During some 21 months of Halley study, more than 1500 plates were obtained at observatories all over the world (Comstock et al 1915). Many were taken with fast, wide field lenses to produce good images of the entire tail. Newtonian foci of large reflectors were used to bring out detail in the tail and outer coma. Occasionally, photographs were taken that did not overexpose the inner coma, and these show fascinating jets and shell structure.

The coma Comstock et al (1915) list all the plates reported to them, making it obvious that there are three series having length, good quality, and good scale. The first is the Lick Observatory series at 535 cm focal length, which were augmented by a few outstanding plates from Mt. Wilson Observatory at 750 cm focal length and finally discussed in detail by Bobrovnikoff (1931). The second is the Cordoba Observatory series at 343 cm focal length, which has been discussed by Perrine (1934) in a source not widely available. The third is the Helwan Observatory series at 350 cm focal length, which was presented rather inadequately in another source difficult to obtain (Knox-Shaw 1911). Rahe, Brandt, and Donn are currently preparing a detailed Halley Atlas from original 1910 plates. It should be available in 1982.

Most old, short-period comets exhibit considerable asymmetry in their comae. In the older literature, these comets are often described as having short, fan-shaped tails, when in fact the "tails" point sunward and are just highly asymmetric comae (Sekanina 1979). Isophotes of P/Halley are symmetric and nearly circular (e.g. Högnar & Richter 1980) and similar to those of Comet Bennett 1970II (Rahe et al 1976). On Halley photographs having good scale that are not overexposed near the nucleus and on drawings both in 1835 and 1910, jet activity is quite prominent. This is also the case for Comet Bennett (Larson & Minton 1972).

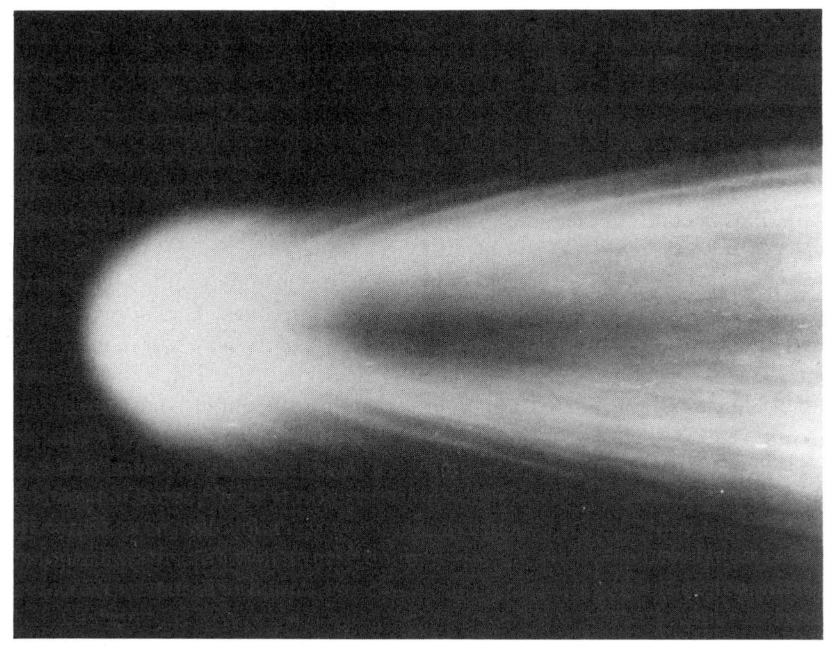

Figure 4 Head of Comet Halley, May 8, 1910, using 150 cm reflector. Courtesy of the Mt. Wilson and Las Campanas Observatories.

The tails All of the photographs of P/Halley showing significant detail in the tails were taken between mid-April and early July of 1910. An excellent example of the region near the head is shown in Figure 4. During this period, the distance of Halley from Earth decreased from 1.4 AU to 0.15 AU and then increased back to 1.6 AU, while its heliocentric distance changed from that near perihelion (0.587 AU on April 20) to 1.5 AU. The comet crossed the plane of the Earth's orbit on May 19. Thus, throughout this period of outstanding tail observations, the Earth lay near the plane of Halley's orbit and the dust and ion tails were superimposed as projected on the sky. One photograph taken on May 6, 1910, showing the two tails separated, perhaps by unusual solar wind conditions, was discovered in the Lowell Observatory collection by the Halley Atlas authors.

A general sequence of tail pictures taken during the months of most significant activity is shown in Figure 5. The sequence of pictures in Bobrovnikoff's (1931) monograph shows the development of what is now called an ion tail disconnection event. Figure 6 illustrates one state of this development. Such events are not uncommon in well-developed comets and may be caused by the passage of a sector boundary in the interplanetary magnetic field

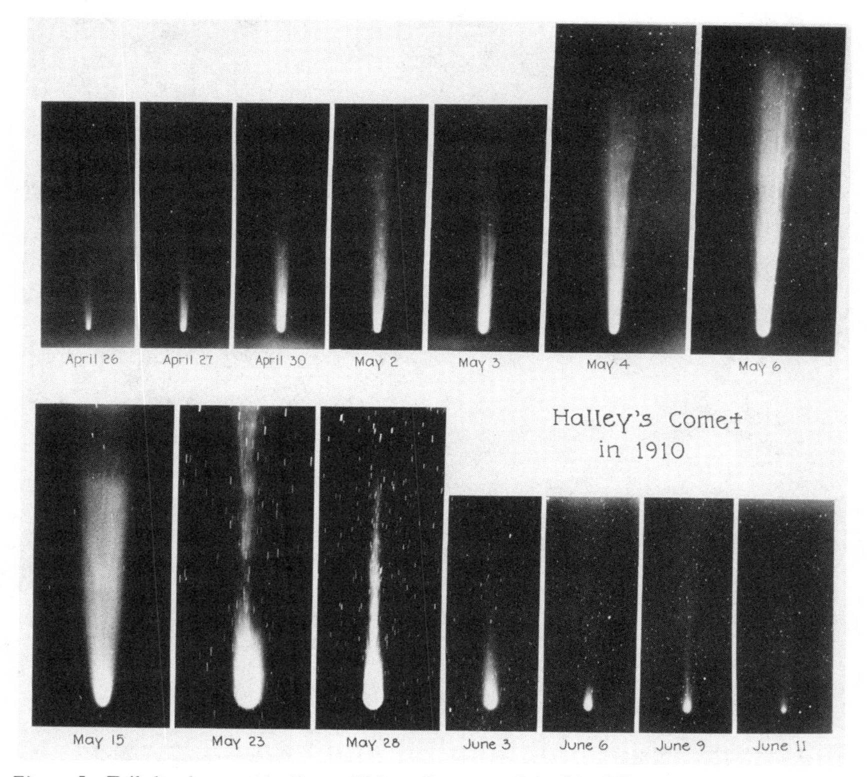

Figure 5 Tail development in Comet Haley. Courtesy of the Mt. Wilson and Las Campanas Observatories.

(Niedner & Brandt 1978, 1979). Another well-known disconnection event in Halley's history occured on May 13, 1910 (see Figure 7). The excellent photographic coverage, especially during May and early June, makes possible detailed studies of ion tail morphology, although faint detail is sometimes obscured by the dust tail.

SPECTROGRAMS The first successful photographic spectrum of a comet was obtained by Huggins in 1881 of Comet Tebbutt. For the following half-century or more, objective prism spectra were taken fairly systematically. The more difficult-to-obtain slit spectra were taken rather sporadically, because it was felt that there was no great need for high spectral resolution or quantitative photometric measurement. The interest was principally in identifying the molecules present, since a theoretical understanding of molecular band structure and line strengths was not possible until the appropriate parts of quantum mechanics were developed beginning in the late 1920s.

Figure 6 Comet Halley on June 6, 1910. Photograph by E. E. Barnard. Courtesy of the Yerkes Observatory.

The first spectrogram of P/Halley was taken in a three hour exposure on October 22, 1909, with an objective prism on the 90 cm Crossley reflector at Lick Observatory. This was followed by many more spectra, both objective prism and slit type, over the next year at Lick and elsewhere. A systematic study of 77 spectra of Halley, largely from Lick and Mt. Wilson Observatories, was finally published by Bobrovnikoff (1931) after 21 years had passed. Altogether, 23 papers on the Halley spectrum were published before World War II. A complete list of these will be found in Bobrovnikoff (1942). Since that time, new technology applied to the study of recent comets has dominated cometary research.

The emission spectrum of P/Halley The first three hour spectrographic exposure of Halley on Oct. 22, 1909, showed a faint uniform continuum as its only prominent feature, but faint CN and C_2 were suspected, and the C_3 4050 Å group (then called C+H or Raffety bands) were there faintly (Bobrovnikoff 1931). Actually, it is doubtful that C_2 could have been seen when Halley was still 2.95 AU from the Sun, since it has not been seen at such a great distance in any recent comet using the most modern equipment. By early February 1910, Halley was 1.6 AU from the Sun and the CN and (0-1) C_2 bands were

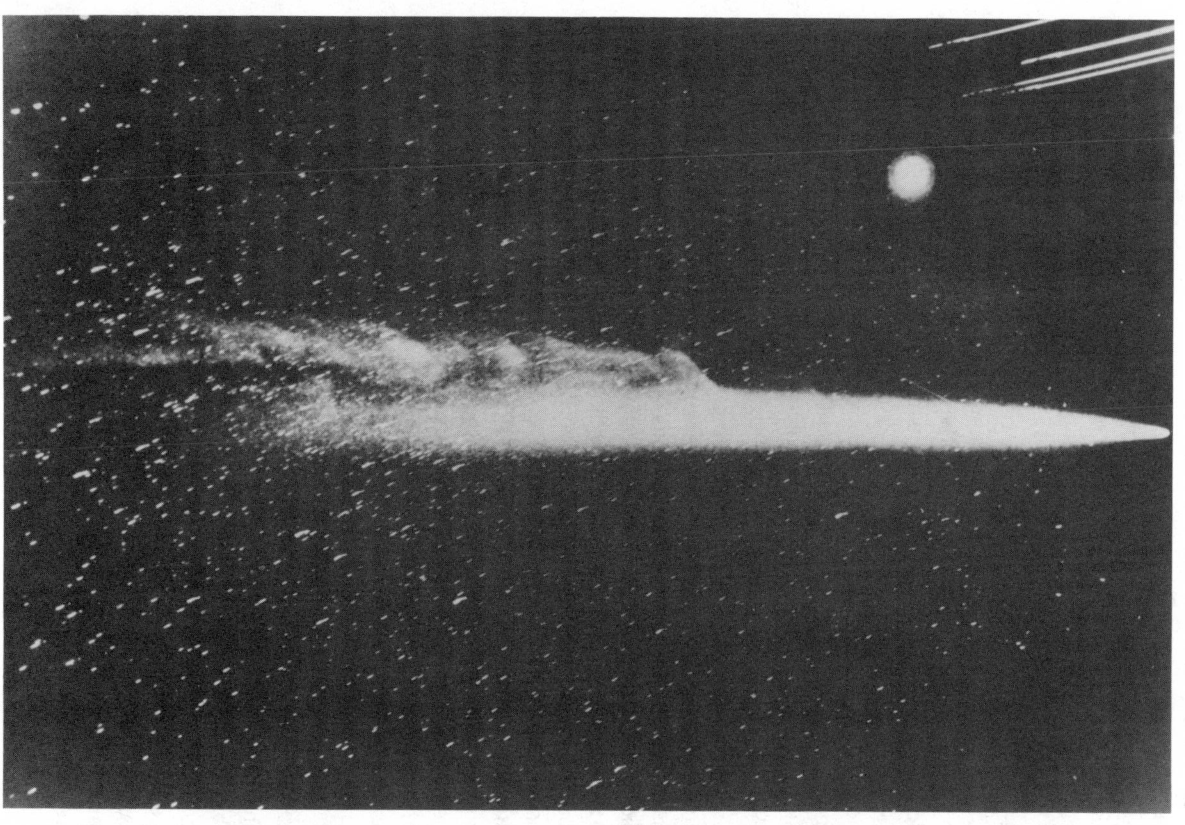

Figure 7 Comet Halley on May 13, 1910; Planet Venus is seen above the comet. Courtesy of the Lowell Observatory.

comparable in apparent strength. Thereafter, the C_2 band was generally reported as the stronger until late June when Halley was at 1.4 AU post-perihelion, after which CN again dominated. The C_3 group more or less paralleled CN in behavior (Bobrovnikoff 1931). This nonquantitative description of the behavior of the three most prominent blue spectral features in the head of P/Halley (or most comets) is quite normal.

Without question the (0-0) and (0-1) bands of CN, the C_3 group, and the (2-0), (1-0), (0-0), and (0-1) bands of C_2 were observed in the head of P/Halley. Also claimed in less convincing fashion were the (0-2) band of CN and the (0-2) and (0-3) bands of C_2. The CH molecule was observed as were the Na-D lines. Other proposed identifications remain dubious. In the tail of Halley, CO^+ was certainly present in its (1-0), (2-0), and (3-0) bands, which showed considerable fluctuation in their relative strengths from place to place. The molecule N_2^+ was observed in the tail on two nights (Bobrovnikoff 1931). These species are all that one would expect to see in P/Halley given the instruments available in 1910. Halley seems to have been normal in every way.

The continuum of P/Halley The combination of plate sensitivity variation with wavelength and no density-to-intensity conversion or calibrated standards makes any comment on the continuous spectrum of P/Halley both difficult and hazardous. The claim that Halley shifted from a "violet-type" continuum to a "solar-type" continuum when near the sun is almost certainly unwarranted and is probably the product of a poorly located continuum level on low resolution,uncalibrated plates as the C_2 bands changed intensity. In fact, although contrary to Bobrovnikoff's (1931) comments, we see no convincing evidence that the intrinsic reflection spectrum of P/Halley, obtained by dividing the actual Halley continuum by that of the sun, would be significantly different from that of other typical, short-period comets observed in recent years, i.e. reddish with no obvious detailed structure. Halley may be different, but the published results do not show this.

Derived Results

The derivation of any sort of numerical results from the nonquantitative observations that have been described is an uncertain thing at best. Nevertheless, many calculations have been made in recent years, because space probes are being designed for flight to P/Halley. Usually, nominal values and extreme values are supplied, the latter being the product of some sort of sum-of-negative tolerances calculation. These contain a great deal of intuition and opinion based upon work on other comets, and all results should be treated with great caution.

THE NUCLEUS No cometary nucleus has ever been resolved in a telescope. The sizes measured for "the nucleus" of Halley and other comets quoted in descriptive literature refer to the "photometric nucleus", a much larger structure than the true nucleus. The photometric nucleus perhaps may be a sharp-edged icy halo or a dust shell. It varies in size, and in some comets is not present at all. Therefore, any attempt to derive the size of the true nucleus must be based upon its photometric properties and not direct measurement. Similarly, no comet has ever caused a perceptible gravitational perturbation of another body, so its mass must be an implied one within limits set by other factors. Similar statements could be made about all the other properties of the nucleus, such as rotation, axial inclination, shape, and thermal properties.

The size of P/Halley The light curve of P/Halley is that of an active comet. Attributing those magnitudes strictly to light reflected from the nucleus would only set a very poor, extremely large upper limit on nucleus size. Until recently, the only reasonable size limits were set using Comet Bennett as a slightly brighter analog of Halley and using the analysis of Sekanina (1976) for Bennett. Newburn's (1979a) result from this approach gave Halley a 5 km diameter with 1 km and 16 km very extreme lower and upper limits. The search already begun to recover Halley (described below) has not yet been successful, but this negative result is nevertheless the first useful result of the new apparition of 1986. Belton, Butcher, Yeomans, and Newburn, for example, found that Halley could not have been brighter than about magnitude 24.1 in visible light on December 9, 1980, assuming Yeomans' ephemeris is correct. Even with a very low geometric albedo (0.1), the nucleus of Halley must then have had a radius of less than about 6-1/2 km.

The mass of P/Halley The mass of comets has generally been approximated by assuming a density and a model radius. The only other general possibility to consider is use of the nongravitational force terms in a comet's motion. Given the mass flux emitted throughout an apparition, axial inclination, and distribution of activity over the nucleus surface, the mass could be calculated from the nongravitational motion. None of these are known for Halley with any confidence except the motion.

Assuming Halley's nucleus to be poorly compacted with a bulk density of 1 gm cm^{-3} and a nominal 2.5 km radius, its mass is 6.5×10^{16} g. Extreme models of size and density could take the mass roughly two orders of magnitude higher or lower. It is no wonder then that comets have had no perceptible effect upon the motion of 10^{26} g bodies, such as the Galilean satellites of Jupiter, even in close approaches to them. (P/Lexell and P/Brooks 2 have actually passed through the Jovian satellite system.)

Rotation period and axial inclination Whipple (1978) has successfully applied his "zero date method" to determine rotation periods for a number of comets beginning with Comet Donati. Applied to P/Halley, the technique suggests a rotation period of $10^h\ 19^m$, with direction in the same sense as the revolution, and the axis nearly normal to the orbit plane (Whipple 1980). The direct rotation of Comet Halley's nucleus was also evident from Yeomans' (1977a) analysis of the comet's nongravitational forces. Other approaches to the rotation and inclination problem have been reviewed by Sekanina (1981), but no such results are available as yet for P/Halley.

Composition All evidence for the composition of any cometary nucleus is indirect. There are only the compositions of parts of the dust and gas components of the coma obtained by spectrophotometry to suggest the nature of their source, the nucleus. For P/Halley, even that evidence is strictly qualitative, as discussed earlier. In a recent study of spectra of 84 comets, Donn (1977) placed P/Halley in a class of comets having medium intrinsic continuum to emission intensity. In a crude, preliminary attempt to quantify Donn's classification, Newburn (1979a) derived a value of about 0.5 as the mass ratio of solids to gas emitted from a nucleus that results in a comet being placed in the medium category. Assumptions involved in this work are discussed in the modeling by analogy section. This does not mean the makeup of the nucleus as a whole is half volatiles and half nonvolatiles, even at the surface. Boulders cannot be blown off the surface even in Halley's weak gravity, while volatiles may well be depleted near the surface as compared to the interior.

The emission spectrum of P/Halley appears "normal" for a fairly active comet. By this it is meant that the spectrum is not almost pure CO^+ as was that of Comet Humason 1962VIII or pure continuum as was that of Comet Bowell 1980b, but rather exhibits all the usual emission features. There is good evidence that the dominant parent molecule in old, short-period comets is water, even where appropriate spectral data are not available, just from the constants in the nongravitational force expressions (Marsden et al 1973). Setting the value of the scale distance r_0 equal to that for water ice in the nongravitational expression for P/Halley gives the smallest residuals in fitting Halley positions, as discussed earlier (Yeomans 1977a). Yet in Comet Bennett, which is often used as the best recent analog of Halley, Delsemme & Combi (1976) have given evidence that CO_2 had an abundance of 20% that of H_2O. The [OI] line 6300 Å used for this study was too far to the red to observe in 1910 (and too mixed-up with Earth airglow for even nonquantitative work). It requires three apparitions to measure r_0 for a comet, so scale length has not been determined for Bennett. Most modeling of P/Halley has therefore been done assuming H_2O dominates the volatiles, but that there is a total of 20% of all "other things," which have an average molecular weight of 44 amu. One extreme model assumes pure water, and another assumes 40% "other things." The "other things" may include CO_2 as a parent for CO^+, HCN as a parent for CN, NH_3 as a parent for NH and NH_2 (neither actually observed in Halley, since the first was too far to the ultraviolet and the second too far to the red), and various hydrocarbons as parents for C_2, C_3, and CH. Many chemical reactions can occur in the inner coma, so in fact some or even most of the daughter fragments observed in visible light may not be simple photoproducts of original parent molecules present in a cometary nucleus. A summary of reasonably certain knowledge of the composition of Halley's nucleus can only conclude that there must be solids of unknown composition and roughly equal amounts by mass of volatiles dominated by water ice.

THE COMA Almost nothing quantitative has been derived directly from 1910 observations about the Halley coma. Because of the interest in flying spacecraft to P/Halley, a few ideas currently are being considered for derivation of such results. For example, isophotes near the nucleus on plates having good scale should give a measure of the departure from isotropy in the coma and general activity over the surface of the nucleus. To the extent that the characteristic curve for the old emulsions can be derived (perhaps from background stars of measured plate density and sky intensity), the iso-density traces can be turned into iso-intensity traces. There will always remain minor uncertainties, such as that caused by changes in the characteristic curve with wavelength, since the color balance of comets and stars will differ, but these are unimportant given the present lack of any quantitative information.

THE TAIL The Bessel-Bredikhin mechanical theory of cometary tails was already well developed by 1910. This theory states that all cometary forms and motion are the product of particles from the cometary nucleus subject to the attraction of solar gravity and the repulsion of some other central force also varying inversely as the square of solar distance (Bobrovnikoff 1951). (This, in fact, is essentially the case for dust tails, which are made up of small particles normally raised from the nucleus by aerodynamic drag forces and then forced antisunward by solar radiation pressure.) Therefore, many measures of the motion of any identifiable structure in Halley's tail were made in an attempt to gain quantitative understanding of the strength of the force and the nature of the particles being accelerated. Unfortunately, most of the structure in Halley's tail is in fact in the ion tail and not subject to the simple mechanical theory. Study of the dust tail would not be easy even today because of both the overlying ion tail and the edge-on geometry.

At least one attempt was made to measure the actual surface brightness of the tail in both relative and absolute units. This work by Schwarzschild & Kron (1911) was outstanding for the period, and they even suggested that "in the tails of comets we are concerned with fluorescent or resonance radiation excited by solar radiation," which is certainly the case for the CO^+ light making the major contribution to ion tail visibility on their blue sensitive plates. A recalibration of their photometry is planned as part of the photometric model for Halley spacecraft imaging systems.

Modeling by Analogy

Throughout the sections on existing observations of P/Halley and results derived from those observations, great emphasis was laid on the lack of quantitative results, and comparison was often drawn between the qualitative similarities of P/Halley and Comet Bennett. When estimates of the coma environment of Halley were needed by spacecraft designers, they were initially given models of Bennett. When interest increased in a possible flight to other comets as well, such as P/Tempel 2 or P/Encke, Newburn (1979a, b) developed a semiempirical theory of the dust and gas environment of any cometary coma for which a visible light curve was available. Complete details of this work are now available (Newburn 1981).

THEORY OF A SEMI-EMPIRICAL MODEL OF COMETARY COMAE The visible light from any normal comet as seen by a dark adapted human eye is more than 90% reflected sunlight and C_2 fluorescence. The basis of the general model is a photometric equation with terms for each of these quantities, as a function of the comet's hydrogen production, set equal to the comet's brightness in appropriate units. The theory assumes that the C_2 seen in visible light has a constant mixing ratio relative to hydrogen in all comets. It is calibrated in a few recent comets by comparing the hydrogen production, as measured by its $L\alpha$ resonance line, to the visible light. The relative contribution to that visible light from dust and gas is taken from modern photometry for comets of the same Donn class (Donn 1977, Newburn 1979a, b, 1981).

The semiempirical theory has many weaknesses. The origin of cometary C_2 is uncertain, and it occasionally seems to vary in abundance relative to CN by as much as a factor of 10. In the majority of comets, the C_2 abundance varies with heliocentric distance, roughly as the square of the H abundance, so an uncertainty of a factor of 10 in C_2 introduces an uncertainty of a factor of 3.2 in H. The theory assumes all hydrogen comes from water and, therefore, that the production rate of water is exactly half that of hydrogen. The relative contribution of gas and dust to the visible light is assumed the same for Halley as for one or two modern comets whose spectra appeared similar to Halley. It is assumed that the distribution function for particle sizes is the same as for comets such as Bennett. There are valid reasons for all of the assumptions and approximations within the framework of knowledge of a few comets observed recently. Given that the light curve and uncalibrated spectra are the only data available, it is difficult to do more in predicting gas and dust flow rates. The remainder of the model parameters are derived, as discussed in the section on derived quantities.

A NOMINAL MODEL OF P/HALLEY'S COMA Following Newburn's (1979a) development of a model for P/Halley, Divine (private communication) programmed the entire theory, removing several assumptions that had been made to simplify the initial hand calculations. The dust tables were modified to include the particles already turned around relative to the sun by radiation pressure and flying back through the coma, as well as the much larger number of particles flying outward. Provision was made for varying the gas and dust flux over the nucleus surface, rather than assuming isotropic flow either from the sunward hemisphere or over the entire nucleus. Work has now been completed (Newburn 1981) to improve the constants in the theory through the use of a larger number of recent comets now available for calibration.

The nominal models currently in use assume a nucleus of 2.5 km radius and 1 g cm^{-3} mean density. The composition of material leaving the surface is 50% volatiles by mass with composition 5/6 H_2O by number and 1/6 other things of mass 44 amu. The surface temperature used is 185 K. The resulting gas production rates in molecules per second are given in Table 1. These numbers are the total production rates of all gases from the entire nucleus.

It is not practical to attempt to reproduce detailed dust tables here. The table for a single trajectory through the comet at a selected time, giving flux and fluence (integrated accumulation on a surface) as a function of particle mass, contains roughly 2000 entires. In order to indicate the general nature of the dust environment, approximate figures for two cases, 1.53 AU preperihelion and 0.90 AU postperihelion, are given in Table 2. The numbers given assume isotropic flow from one hemisphere. The figures for isotropic flow from the entire nucleus would be smaller by somewhat less than a factor of two (except for flux, which is exactly two times smaller), since the velocity also drops somewhat when the gas flux accelerating the particles drops. The density and

Table 1 Gas production predictions for P/Halley in 1985–86

Date	Geocentric distance (AU)	Heliocentric distance (AU)	Nominal gas production (s^{-1})
1985 Oct. 26	1.23	2.0	1.19×10^{28}
Nov. 23	0.63	1.6	2.98×10^{28}
Nov. 28	0.62	1.53	3.55×10^{28}
Dec. 20	0.92	1.2	8.70×10^{28}
1986 Jan. 2	1.18	1.0	1.68×10^{29}
Feb. 4	1.56	0.6	7.44×10^{29}
Feb. 9.7	1.54	0.587	Perihelion
Feb. 15	1.50	0.6	6.12×10^{29}
Mar. 7	1.14	0.8	1.98×10^{29}
Mar. 21	0.79	1.0	1.56×10^{29}
Apr. 29	0.74	1.6	5.56×10^{28}
May 27	1.63	2.0	2.73×10^{28}
July 3	2.80	2.5	1.16×10^{28}
Aug. 12	3.82	3.0	5.59×10^{27}
Sept. 25	4.47	3.5	2.87×10^{27}

Table 2 Nominal near nucleus dust parameters

Particle diameters (cm)	Production rate (s^{-1})	Particle density at 10^3 km (m^{-3})	Particle flux at 10^3 km ($m^{-2}s^{-1}$)	Total fluence on 10^3 km closest approach[a] (m^{-2})	Approximate velocity (ms^{-1})
		1.53 AU preperihelion			
$0.9\text{–}\ 5.0 \times 10^{-4}$	6.4×10^{16}	2.9×10^{1}	1.0×10^{4}	9.1×10^{7}	350
$0.5\text{–}10.0 \times 10^{-3}$	7.7×10^{14}	3.5×10^{-1}	1.2×10^{2}	2.6×10^{6}	150
$0.1\text{–}10.0 \times 10^{-1}$	2.7×10^{10}	1.2×10^{-5}	4.3×10^{-3}	3.4×10^{2}	40
		0.90 AU postperihelion			
$0.9\text{–}\ 5.0 \times 10^{-4}$	4.1×10^{17}	1.6×10^{2}	6.5×10^{4}	4.9×10^{8}	420
$0.5\text{–}10.0 \times 10^{-3}$	3.9×10^{15}	2.2×10^{0}	6.2×10^{2}	7.0×10^{6}	280
$0.1\text{–}10.0 \times 10^{-1}$	1.4×10^{11}	1.9×10^{-4}	2.2×10^{-2}	5.8×10^{2}	120

[a] The fluence is the total accumulation of material on a surface passing through the coma at a velocity that is large relative to the intrinsic velocity of the dust.

flux figures scale to other nucleus distances as R^{-2}, while the fluence scales as R^{-1}. Serious calculations should not be attempted with the crude figures in Table 2.

THE COMING APPARITION OF COMET HALLEY

Recovery Attempts

As of late 1981, Comet Halley has not yet been recovered. The recovery attempts for the coming apparition began on November 13, 1977, when a 30 minute exposure at the Kitt Peak 4 meter telescope failed to indicate the comet's presence at the expected ephemeris position. At the time the comet was at a predicted nuclear magnitude (m_2) of 26 with a heliocentric distance (r) of 19.3 AU and a geocentric distance (Δ) of 18.8 AU. On November 16 and 17 of the same year, a recovery attempt was also made with the 200 inch telescope at Mt. Palomar. Recovery position and magnitude predictions have been provided by Yeomans (1981). Unsuccessful recovery attempts have also been made at Kitt Peak on November 24, 1979, ($r = 16.3$, $\Delta = 15.7$) and December 9, 1980 ($r = 14.6$, $\Delta = 13.8$). For both the 1979 and 1980 Kitt Peak attempts, the limiting magnitude was estimated at 24. A 500 × 500 CCD detector was used on Mt. Palomar's 200 inch telescope for recovery attempts on March 5 and April 9, 10, 1980, while an 800 × 800 CCD detector was used during attempts on January 13, 14, 15, 25, 26, 1981. During the January 1981 Mt. Palomar attempts ($r = 14.4$, $\Delta = 13.5$), eight 300 second exposures were co-added, but poor seeing (2.8″) allowed a limiting magnitude for only 23.6. Other recovery attempts include those made in November 1979 at the Cerro Tololo Inter-American Observatory's 4 meter telescope and the attempt made on December 31, 1980, at the European Southern Observatory's 1.54 meter telescope at La Silla, Chile. Both of these latter attempts had limiting magnitudes of approximately 24. Mention should also be made of recovery attempts at the Canada-France-Hawaii 3.6 meter telescope on Mauna Kea, Hawaii, in December 1980 and during February, March, April, and October 1981. An attempt was also made in early May 1981 at the Anglo-Australian 150 inch telescope at Siding Springs, Australia. As the comet's predicted nuclear magnitude will not brighten below 24 before late 1981 and the comet's apparent position will not exit completely from the Milky Way until early 1984, a successful early recovery will be a difficult undertaking for even the most sophisticated equipment.

Expected Viewing Conditions

Based upon the 1986 orbital elements, and an analysis of the observed past behavior of Comet Halley's brightness, tail lengths, and coma diameters,

Yeomans (1981) has outlined the comet's expected behavior in 1985–86 and has provided a detailed ephemeris through March 23, 1987. This ephemeris begins on Christmas Day 1980, exactly 222 years after the German amateur astronomer Johann Georg Palitzch first successfully recovered Comet Halley based upon a predicted return.

Comet Halley's nuclear magnitude is not likely to be brighter than 21 before early 1984 and should still be a relatively faint 18th magnitude object one year later. During 1985, the comet should brighten rapidly to an apparent total magnitude of 6.0–6.5 during the late November close approach to the Earth (0.62 AU minimum separation) and possibly achieve a brightening to 4^m before passing too near the sun for visual observations in late January 1986. At perihelion (February 9), the comet will be too close to the sun to be visually observable, and by the time the comet exits from solar conjunction in late February or early March, the comet should appear as a 3.5–4.5 magnitude object in the eastern morning sky. By the time the comet makes its closest approach to the Earth on April 20, 1986 (0.42 AU minimum separation), it should be a 5th magnitude evening object in the constellation Hydra. Generally speaking, preperihelion observations of the comet will favor northern hemisphere observatories, while southern observatories will have the advantage postperihelion. Figure 8 indicates the 1985–86 observing conditions for observers located at 35°N and 35°S.

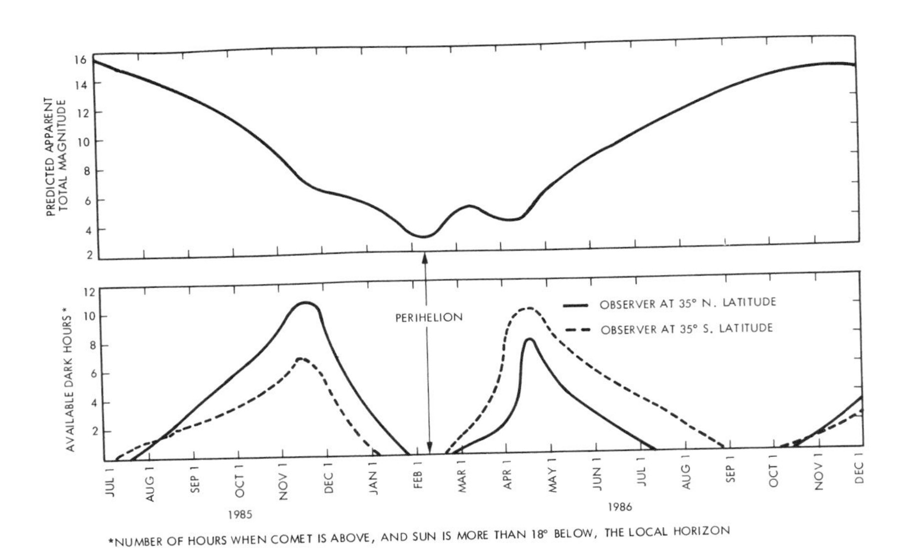

Figure 8 Comet Halley. Ground-based observing conditions during 1985–86.

The International Halley Watch

An effort was made to coordinate and publish observations of P/Halley during the 1909-11 apparition (Comstock et al 1910, 1915). The effort was largely unsuccessful. No archive of the worldwide studies was ever published. Significant pieces appeared 21 and 24 years later (Bobrovnikoff 1931, Perrine 1934). Learning from the mistakes of 1910, the International Halley Watch (IHW) is a contemporary effort of advocacy, coordination, standardization, and archiving of the 1985–86 observations.

The IHW advocates all forms of Halley study: from the ground, from aircraft, balloons, and sounding rockets, from Earth orbit, and from space probes. It will attempt to coordinate ground studies that may aid these flight programs by observation at other scales or wavelengths and by setting the flight results in the overall context of the apparition. It will attempt to standardize in some areas where standardization is needed, such as choice of filters and standard stars. It will ask that all Halley data ultimately be contributed to a Halley archive. It will not attempt to usurp the scientific prerogatives of individual scientists. They can publish in whatever style they wish before they send the data to the archive. They will be encouraged to undertake research in their own way but asked to include at least some observations using standard techniques. The coordination will be achieved in part by simply having many scientists studying the same object, but all will be asked to do as much as possible on specific Halley Watch Days, which may coincide with flight encounters, for example, or which may just be convenient times to try to bring every technology to bear on the comet simultaneously.

The IHW concept was studied by the Jet Propulsion Laboratory (JPL) and by a NASA science working group during 1979–80. In October 1980, a Lead Center was established at JPL to bring the IHW into being. A Steering Group of international advisors, appointed by NASA, held their first meeting during the spring of 1981. Meanwhile, astronomers worldwide were advised that the IHW existed and that seven or more "Discipline Specialists" were being sought to create working nets of astronomers to use various observing techniques. Proposals were to be sent to JPL in late July 1981, with the Discipline Specialists to be selected by the Steering Group from those individuals submitting proposals.

The full apparatus of the IHW will be operational by early 1984, at which time there will be a trial run on P/Encke or another comet of opportunity. The full apparatus will include flight project representatives and a coordinator for amateur observations. A computer will be dedicated to data storage and production of the collected results. The year 1989 should see publication of The Halley Archive, the first collection of data covering the complete apparition of any comet studied by the full panoply of modern astronomical technology.

Literature Cited

Angström, A. J. 1862. Sur deux inégalités d'une grandeur remarquable dans les apparitions de la Comète de Halley. *Actes de la Société Royale des Sciences d'Upsal,* Sér III, Vol. 4

Barnard, E. E. 1914. Visual observations of Halley's Comet in 1910. *Astrophys. J.* 39:373–404

Bessel, F. W. 1835. Schreiben des Herrn Geheimenraths und Ritters Bessel an den Herausgeber. *Astron. Nachr.* 13:3–6

Bessel, F. W. 1836a. Beobachtungen über die Physische Beschaffenheit des Halley'schen Kometen und dadurch veranlafste Bemerkungen. *Astron. Nachr. 13,* 185–232; NASA TT F-16726, Feb. 1976

Bessel, F. W. 1836b. Bemerkungen über Mögliche Unzulänglichkeit der die Anziehungen Allein Berüchsichtigenden Theorie der Kometen. *Astron. Nachr.* 13:345–50

Bobrovnikoff, N. T. 1931. Halley's Comet in its apparition of 1909-1911. *Pub. Lick Obs.* 17:309–482

Bobrovnikoff, N. T. 1942. Physical theory of Comets in the Light of Spectroscopic Data. *Rev. Mod. Phys.* 14:164–78

Bobrovnikoff, N. T. 1951. Comets. In *Astrophysics, A Typical Symposium,* ed. J. A. Hynek, pp. 302–56. New York/Toronto/London: McGraw-Hill. 703 pp.

Brady, J. L. 1967. Note regarding nongravitational forces on Halley's Comet. *Astron. J.* 72:1184–86

Brady, J. L. 1972. The effect of a transplutonian planet on Halley's Comet. *Publ. Astron. Soc. Pac.* 84:314–22

Brady, J. L., Carpenter, E. 1967. The orbit of Halley's Comet. *Astron. J.* 72:365–69

Brady, J. L., Carpenter, E. 1971. The orbit of Halley's Comet and the apparition of 1986. *Astron. J.* 76:728–39

Broughton, R. P. 1979. The visibility of Halley's Comet. *J. R. Astron. S. Can.* 73:24–36

Celoria, G. 1921. Sulle osservazioni di Comete Fatte de Paolo dal Tosconelli. *Pubblicazioni del. . .Osservatorio di Brera.* No. 55

Chang, Y. C. 1978. Halley's Comet: Tendencies in its orbital evolution and its ancient history. *Acta Astron. Sin.* 19:109–18. English transl. *Chin. Astron.* 1979. 3:120–31

Clairaut, A. C. 1758. Memoire sur la Comète de 1682. *J. Scavans.* (Jan. 1759) 41:80–96

Comstock, G. C., Barnard, E. E., Frost, E. B., Perrine, C. D., Pickering, E. C. 1910. Circular respecting observation of Halley's Comet. *Astron. Astrophys. Soc. Am.* Madison, Wis.

Comstock, G. C., Barnard, E. E., Frost, E. B., Pickering, E. C. 1915. Report of Comet Commitee 1909–1913. *Publ. Astron. Astrophys. Soc. Am.* 2:177–218

Cowell, P. H., Crommelin, A. C. D. 1907a. The perturbations of Halley's Comet. *MNRAS* 67:174

Cowell, P. H., Crommelin, A. C. D. 1907b. The perturbations of Halley's Comet. *MNRAS* 67:386–411, 521

Cowell, P. H., Crommelin, A. C. D. 1907c. The perturbations of Halley's Comet. *MNRAS* 67:511–21

Cowell, P. H., Crommelin, A. C. D. 1907d. The perturbations of Halley's Comet in the past. First paper. The period 1301–1531. *MNRAS* 68:111–25

Cowell, P. H., Crommelin, A. C. D. 1908a. The perturbations of Halley's Comet in the past. Second paper. The apparition of 1222. *MNRAS* 68:173–79

Cowell, P. H., Crommelin, A. C. D. 1908b. The perturbations of Halley's Comet in the past. Third paper. The period 1066–1301. *MNRAS* 68:375–78

Cowell, P. H., Crommelin, A. C. D. 1908c. The perturbations of Halley's Comet, 1759–1910. *MNRAS* 68:379–95

Cowell, P. H., Crommelin, A. C. D. 1908d. The perturbations of Halley's Comet in the past. Fourth paper. The period 760–1066. *MNRAS* 68:510–14

Cowell, P. H., Crommelin, A. C. D. 1908e. The perturbations of Halley's Comet in the past. Fifth paper. The period 240 B.C.–760. *MNRAS* 68:665–70

Cowell, P. H., Crommelin, A. C. D. 1910. Essay on the return of Halley's Comet. *Publ. Astron. Gesellschaft,* No. 23. 60 pp.

Damoiseau, M. C. T. 1820. Mémoire sur l'époque du retour au périhélie de la Comète de l'année 1759. *Memorie Della Reale Accademia Delle Scienze di Torino* 24:1–76

Damoiseau, M. C. T. 1829. Sur les perturbations des Comètes. *Conn. des Temps for 1832, Additions,* pp. 25–34

Delsemme, A. H., Combi, M. R. 1976. The production rate and possible origin of O ('D) in Comet Bennett 1970II. *Astrophys. J.* 209:L149–51

de Pontécoulant, G. 1830. Détermination du prochain retour au perihélie de la Comète de 1759. *Conn. des Temps for 1833, Additions,* pp. 104–13

de Pontécoulant, G. 1834. Note sur la détermination du prochain retour de la Comète de 1759. *Conn. des Temps for 1837, Additions,* pp. 102–4

de Pontécoulant, G. 1835. Memoire sur le caleul des perturbations et le prochain retour a son périhelie de la Comète de Halley. *Mém. Présentés Divers Savans Acad. R. Sci.* 6:875–947

de Pontécoulant, G. 1864. Notice sur la Comète de Halley et ses apparitions successives de 1531 à 1910. *Comptes Rendus.* 58: 825–28, 915 de Vaucouleurs, G. 1961. *Astronomical Photography*. London: Faber & Faber. 94 pp. + 21 plates

Donn, B. 1977. A comparison of the composition of new and evolved comets. In *Comets, Asteroids, Meteorites: Interrelations, Evolution and Origins*. ed. A. H. Delsemme, pp. 15–23. Toldeo: Univ. Toledo. 587 pp.

Goldreich, P., Ward, W. R. 1972. The case against Planet X. *Publ. Astron. Soc. Pac.* 84:737–42

Hajduk, A. 1970. Structure of the meteor stream associated with Comet Halley. *Bull. Astron. Inst. Czech.* 21:37–45

Hajduk, A. 1980. The core of the meteor stream associated with Comet Halley. In *Solid Particles in the Solar System,* ed. I. Halliday, B. A. McIntosh, pp. 149–52. Dordrecht: D. Reidel. 441 pp.

Halley, E. 1705. *Astronomiae Cometicae Synopsis,* Oxford. 6 pp.

Halley, E. 1749. *Tabulae Astromicae,* London

Hasegawa, I. 1979. Orbits of ancient and medieval Comets. *Publ. Astron. Soc. Jpn.* 31:257–70

Högnar, W., Richter, N. 1980. *Isophotometric Atlas of Comets, Part I.* Berlin/Heidelberg/New York: Springer. 10 pp + 90 plates

Kamienski, M. 1962. Preliminary determination of the time of the next perihelion passage of Halley's Comet in 1986. *Acta Astron.* 12:227–31

Kepler, J. 1619. *De Cometis Libelli Tres.* Augsburg. 138 pp.

Kiang, T. 1971. The past orbit of Halley's Comet. *Mem. R. Astron. Soc.* 76:27–66

Kiang, T. 1973. The cause of the residuals in the motion of Halley's Comet. *MNRAS* 162:271–87

Klemola, A. R., Harlan, E. A. 1972. Search for Brady's hypothetical trans-plutonian planet. *Publ. Astron. Soc. Pac.* 84:736

Knox-Shaw, H. 1911. Observations of Halley's Comet made at the Khedivial Observatory, Helwan. *Surv. Dept. Pap.* No. 23. 18 pp + 22 plates

Lagrange, J. L. 1783. Theorie des variations periodiques des mouvemens des planetes: Partie 1. *Mem. Acad. Berlin 1783,* pp. 161–224

Lalande, J.-J. L. 1765. Mémoire de la Comète de 1682. *Mém. de l'Acad. Roy. des Sci. de l'Année 1759,* pp.1–40

Larson, S. M., Minton, R. B. 1972. Photographic observations of Comet Bennett, 1970II. In *Comets, Scientific Data and Missions, Proceedings of the Tucson Comet Conference,* ed. G. P. Kuiper, E. Roemer, pp. 183–208. Tucson: Univ. Ariz. 222 pp.

Lehmann, J. W. H. 1835. Versuch die berechnungen zur bestimmung der wiederkehr des Halleyschen Kometen aufs reine zu bringen. *Astron. Nachr.* 12:308–400

Lovell, A. C. B. 1954. The η-Aquarid shower, the Orionid shower. In *Meteor Astronomy,* pp. 263–69, 288–96. Oxford: Clarendon Press 463 pp.

Marsden, B. G. 1968. Comets and nongravitational forces. *Astron. J.* 73:367–79

Marsden, B. G. 1969. Comets and nongravitational forces. II *Astron. J.* 74:720–34

Marsden, B. G., Sekanina, Z., Yeomans, D. K. 1973. Comets and nongravitational forces. V. *Astron. J.* 78:211–25

Meisel, D. D., Morris, C. S. 1976. Comet brightness parameters: Definition, determination, and correlations. In *The Study of Comets,* ed. B. Donn, M. Mumma, W. Jackson, M. A'Hearn, R. Harrington, pp. 410–44. Washington D. C: NASA SP-393. 1083 pp.

Michielsen, H. F. 1968. A rendezvous with Halley's Comet in 1985–1986. *J. Spacercr. Rockets* 5:328–34

Morris, C. S., Green, D. W. E. 1981. A review and recalculation of Bobrovnikoff's photometric power-law solution for P/Comet Halley 1910II. *Int. Comet Q.* 3: 100–3

Newburn, R. L. Jr. 1979a. Physical models of Comet Halley based upon qualitative data from the 1910 apparition. In *The Comet Halley Micrometeoroid Hazard,* ed. N. Longdon, pp. 35–50. Paris: ESA SP-153. 147 pp.

Newburn, R. L. Jr. 1979b. Models of P/Tempel 2. *JPL Publ. 79–60*. Jet Propulsion Lab. Pasadena, Calif.

Newburn, R. L. Jr. 1981. A semi-empirical photometric theory of cometary gas and dust production: Application to P/Halley's gas production rates. In *Comet Halley Dust and Gas Environment Workshop*. Paris: ESA SP-174

Newton, I. 1687. *Philosophiae Naturalis Principia Mathematica*. London: Book 3. 510 pp.

Niedner, M. B. Jr., Brandt, J. C. 1978. Interplanetary gas. XXIII. Plasma tail disconnection events in comets: Evidence for magnetic field line reconnection at interplanetary sector boundaries? *Astrophys. J.* 223: 655–70

Niedner, M. B. Jr., Brandt, J. C. 1979. Interplanetary gas. XXIV. Are cometary plasma tail disconnections caused by sector boundary crossings or by encounters with high speed streams? *Astrophys. J.* 234:723–32

Olivier, C. P. 1925. The Comet Halley's meteors and the Pons-Winnecke's Comet meteors. In *Meteors,* pp. 74–81. Baltimore: Wilkins & Wilkins. 276 pp.

Perrine, C. D. 1934. Observaciones del Cometa Halley durante su aparicion 1910. *Pub. Resultados del Observatorio Nacional Argentino*. 25:108 pp. + 99 plates

Rahe, J., McCracken, C. W., Donn, B. D. 1976. Monochromatic and white-light observations of Comet Bennett 1969i(1970II). *Astron. Astrophys. Suppl.* 23:13–35

Rosenberger, O. A. 1830a. Elemente des Halleyschen Cometen bei Seiner Letzten Sichtbarkeit. *Astron. Nachr.* 8:221–50

Rosenberger, O. A. 1830b. Ueber die Bestimmung des Halleyschen Cometen bei Seiner Vorletzten Erscheinung im Jahre 1682. *Astron. Nachr.* 9:53–68

Rosenberger, O. A. 1834. Ueber die Störungen des Halleyschen Kometen Während Seines Umlaufs um die Sonne vom 15ten September 1682 bis zum 13ten März 1759. *Astron. Nachr.* 11:157–80

Rosenberger, O. A. 1835. Berichtigung und Notiz die Störungen des Halleyschen Kometen Betreffend. *Astron. Nachr.* 12: 187–94

Schwarzschild, K., Kron, E. 1911. On the distribution of brightness in the tail of Halley's Comet. *Ap. J.* 34:342–52

Seidelmann, P. K., Marsden, B. G., Giclas, H. L. 1972. Note on Brady's hypothetical trans-plutonian planet. *Publ. Astron. Soc. Pac.* 84:858–64

Sekanina, Z. 1976. A continuing controversy: Has the cometary nucleus been resolved? See Meisel & Morris 1976, pp. 537–87

Sekanina, Z. 1979. Fan-shaped coma, orientation of rotation axis, and surface structure of a cometary nucleus I. Test of a model on four comets. *Icarus* 37:420–42

Sekanina, Z. 1981. Rotation and precession of cometary nuclei. *Ann. Rev. Earth Planet. Sci.* 9:113–45

Struve, F. G. W. 1839. *Beobachtungen des Halleyschen Cometen bei Seinem Erscheinen im Jahre 1835*. St. Petersburg: Kaiserlichen Akademie der Wissenchaften. 131 pp. + 7 plates

Whipple, F. L. 1950. A comet model. I. The acceleration of Comet Encke. *Astrophys. J.* 111:375–94

Whipple, F. L. 1951. A comet model II. Physical relations for comets and meteors. *Astrophys. J.* 113:464–74

Whipple, F. L. 1978. Rotation period for Comet Donati. *Nature* 273:134–35

Whipple, F. L. 1980. Periodic Comet Halley. *IAU Circ. No. 3459*

Wood, H. E. 1910. Observations of Halley's Comet, 1910. *Transvaal Obs. Circ.* No. 4:23–56

Yeomans, D. K. 1977a. Comet Halley—The orbital motion. *Astron. J.* 82:435–40

Yeomans, D. K. 1977b. Comet Halley and nongrativational forces. See Donn 1977, pp 61–64

Yeomans, D. K. 1981. The Comet Halley handbook: An observer's guide. NASA Doc. JPL 400-91. Jet Propulsion Lab. Pasadena, Calif.

Yeomans, D. K., Kiang, T. 1981. The long term motion of Comet Halley. *MNRAS*. 197: 633–46

Zadunaisky, P. E. 1966. Motion of Halley's Comet during the return of 1910. *Astron. J.* 71:20–27

Ann. Rev. Earth Planet. Sci. 1982. 10:327-53

THE TRANSPORT OF CONTAMINANTS IN THE GREAT LAKES

Wilbert Lick

Department of Mechanical and Environmental Engineering, University of California, Santa Barbara, California 93106

INTRODUCTION

The Great Lakes contain approximately twenty percent of the total fresh water in the world. They serve as an invaluable source of fresh water for municipal, industrial, agricultural, and recreational uses for approximately fifty million people in the United States and Canada. The Lakes also serve as a sink for wastes from human activities surrounding the Lakes, a use of considerable economic value, but one that interferes with other uses of the Lakes. In order to make optimum use of the Lakes, the adverse effects of these wastes must be minimized.

To do this, one must be able to quantitatively predict the transport, fate, and effects of contaminants in the Great Lakes. This in turn depends on being able to answer the following questions.

1. What contaminants are now present in the Lakes and in what amounts, and where and in what amounts are contaminants entering the Lakes?
2. How and where are contaminants transported, and what are the biochemical transformations affecting this transport?
3. How are contaminants transferred through the food chain?
4. What are the effects of contaminants on aquatic organisms and man?

In the present article, the second question concerning the transport of contaminants is considered. Transport is basically a physical process involving convection and diffusion, and that aspect of the problem is emphasized here. Since most contaminants are associated with particulates, special attention is given to the transport of particulates although similar arguments apply to

0084-6597/82/0515-0327$02.00

dissolved substances. Contaminants may be modified by chemical and biological processes as they are transported. To give some indication of how biological and chemical transformations affect the fate of contaminants, a brief discussion of the effects of these transformations on the transport and fate of several important and representative contaminants is given. This review is not meant to be exhaustive or encyclopedic, but hopefully it will give sufficient information and references to illustrate our present understanding of the transport of contaminants.

Several general studies related to the problem of contaminants in the aquatic environment have been made (National Academy of Sciences 1975, 1976, 1977, Hood 1971, Windom & Duce 1976, Marshall 1975) and should be referred to for additional information. All except the last are concerned with the oceanic environment.

Numerous contaminants of significance are present in the Great Lakes. Among them are sediments, radionuclides, phytoplankton (obnoxious in high concentrations), synthetic organics such as PCBs and pesticides, heavy metals (copper, zinc, chromium, cadmium, lead, nickel, vanadium, and mercury, primarily from industrial wastes), asbestos, petroleum, and municipal wastes (especially bacteria and viruses). A thorough discussion of the physical, chemical, and biological factors affecting the transport and fate of all of these contaminants is beyond the scope of this article and so the discussion is limited to a few contaminants.

A review of sediment transport is presented first and in some detail for the following reasons. (*a*) Sediments (especially the fine-grained, clay-sized fraction) readily adsorb many other contaminants such as phosphates, heavy metals, and toxic hydrocarbons. Therefore, if we know the pathways of sediments, we know the pathways of other contaminants. (*b*) Sediments are significant contaminants in themselves, since they increase the turbidity of the water and, when heavy sedimentation occurs, may require that large amounts of dredging be done.

In the following section, the transport and fate of radionuclides, phytoplankton, and toxic chlorinated hydrocarbons, are reviewed. Radioactive materials enter lakes primarily from the air as natural fall-out and as fall-out from nuclear bomb tests, and also as leakage from nuclear power plants on the shore. The amount of radioactive material in and introduced into the Lakes does not seem to be an immediate health hazard but is a potential one. Therefore, the transport of radioactive materials through lakes and accumulation in the aquatic food chain are problems of great interest. For radioactive materials, chemical transformations are relatively simple, involving only radioactive decay. Because of this simplicity and the observational data available, it may be easier to develop and verify a transport model for radioactive material than for other contaminants. Models of this type would serve to verify particulate transport as well as sedimentation rates in the Great Lakes.

Phytoplankton are important because their presence is associated with drinking water taste and odor problems. The analysis of phytoplankton transport is much more complex than either sediments or radionuclides, since complex chemical and biological processes are involved, e.g. growth (which is influenced by the availability of nutrients, light, and temperature) and grazing by zooplankton. Water quality models (which describe the interactions between nutrients, phytoplankton, and zooplankton) are available and are constantly being improved. These models are presently being coupled with hydrodynamic models, at least in a crude sense.

Toxic chlorinated hydrocarbons are the most hazardous contaminants in the Lakes today. They tend to be adsorbed on particulate matter and, hence, the physical processes by which they are transported are generally understood. However, their biochemical transformations are not generally quantitatively known. A description of their ultimate fate depends on this information.

Transport Analysis

Transport analysis is meant to include not only a numerical or analytic description of contaminant transport but more generally a conceptual framework used to systematically organize experimental and field data and to guide the theoretical, experimental, and field work. A schematic diagram illustrating the essential elements of transport analysis is given in Figure 1. Basic to the

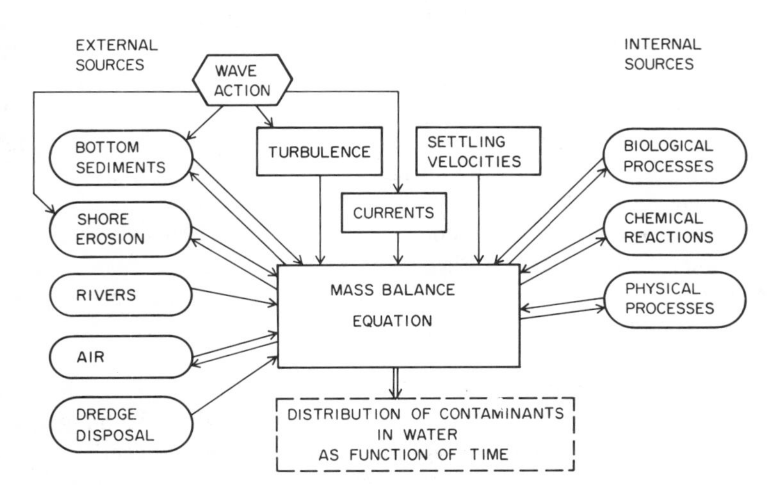

Figure 1 Transport analysis.

analysis is the mass balance, or conservation, equation for the particular contaminant being considered. This equation is as follows:

$$\frac{\partial C}{\partial t} + \frac{\partial (uC)}{\partial x} + \frac{\partial (vC)}{\partial y} + \frac{\partial [(w + w_s)C]}{\partial z} = \frac{\partial}{\partial x}\left(D_H \frac{\partial C}{\partial x}\right) + \frac{\partial}{\partial y}\left(D_H \frac{\partial C}{\partial y}\right) + \frac{\partial}{\partial z}\left(D_v \frac{\partial C}{\partial z}\right) + S,$$

where C is the concentration of the contaminant, t is time, u, v, w are fluid velocities in the x, y, z directions respectively (where z is vertical), w_s is the settling speed of the contaminant, D_H is the horizontal eddy diffusivity, D_v is the vertical eddy diffusivity, and S is a source term due to reactions in the water. The above equation applies to both particulates and dissolved substances. For dissolved substances, the settling velocity is zero.

In order to obtain solutions to this equation and hence to determine the distribution of the contaminant in the water as a function of time, various quantities such as settling velocities, currents, wave action, turbulence, and sources of contaminants (both external and internal) must be known or determined. These quantities and the above equation are discussed in more detail in the following sections.

Time and Length Scales

Characteristic time and length scales for phenomena of importance in the transport of contaminants in the Great Lakes range over many orders of magnitude. For example, significant time scales vary from a characteristic wave period of a few seconds to times of one to hundreds of years required for sediment consolidation and diagenesis. Length scales range from 10^{-4} cm (the characteristic size of a clay particle) to hundreds of kilometers (the characteristic length of the Great Lakes Basins). For comparison and future reference, some of the more significant time and length scales are shown in Figures 2 and 3. A few of these scales are discussed here.

Much of the research on the modeling of contaminant transport needs to be done in the nearshore areas of the Lakes, since (*a*) the nearshore areas are where contaminants are generally introduced and are therefore more contaminated than the offshore areas, and (*b*) the nearshore areas are of particular interest to man for such uses as recreation, fishing, and water supplies.

The extent of this nearshore zone may be defined in several ways. Possible definitions are as follows. (*a*) Regions of upwelling and downwelling (typical widths of 2 to 10 km). Large variations in temperature and concentrations and types of phytoplankton, zooplankton, nutrients, and other contaminants may be present compared with offshore waters. (*b*) Shallow regions where wave action exerts a significant stress on the bottom (approximately 20 m depth).

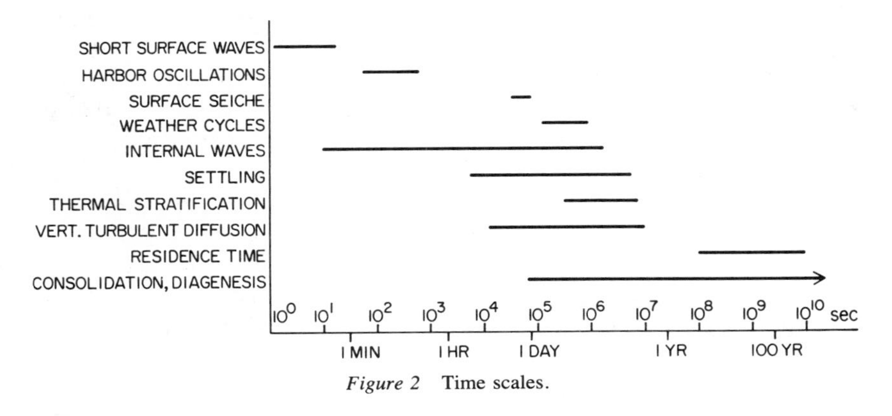

Figure 2 Time scales.

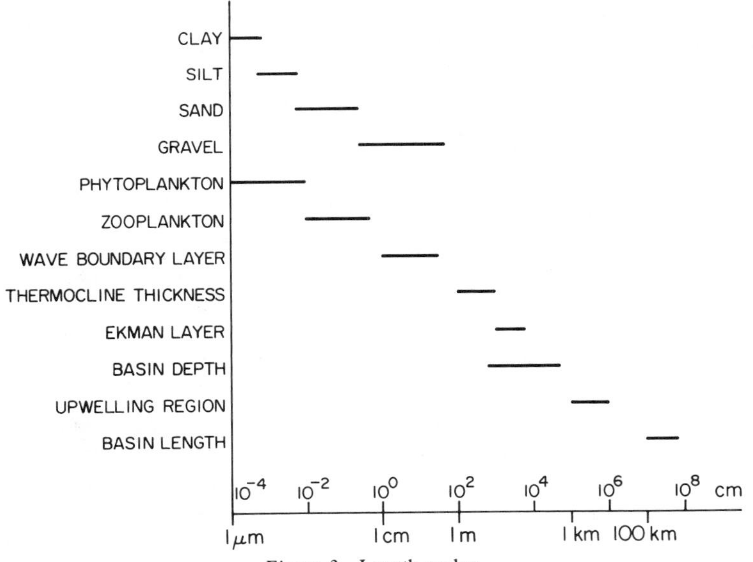

Figure 3 Length scales.

Due to wave action, the sediment concentrations tend to be much larger in this region. (*c*) Shallow regions where turbulent diffusion is more important than settling in transporting particles vertically through the water column. Again, a depth on the order of 20 m is indicated.

The latter definition can be further amplified by a brief discussion of the characteristic times for the vertical transport of particulate matter through the water column. Particulate matter is transported vertically through the water column to the sediment-water interface by a combination of convection, settling, and turbulent diffusion. Vertical convection is generally only significant where strong upwelling and downwelling occur, e.g. in nearshore regions, while settling and turbulent diffusion are ubiquitous phenomena. A characteristic time for settling is $t_s = h/w_s$, while a characteristic time for turbulent diffusion is $t_d = h^2/2D_v$, where h is the depth of the water column. These times are equal when $h = 2D_v/w_s$. For shallow waters where $h \leq 2D_v/w_s$, turbulent diffusion dominates and settling can be neglected to a first approximation. As an example, for particulates of average size in the Western Basin of Lake Erie, $D_v = 25$ cm^2/sec, $w_s = 2.5 \times 10^{-2}$ cm/sec (and therefore $2D_v/w_s = 20$ m) while $h = 7$ m. From this it follows that $t_s = 3 \times 10^4$ sec, $t_d = 10^4$ sec, and settling can be neglected compared to turbulent diffusion. In deeper waters and for larger particles, settling determines the significant time scale.

The above times are characteristic for transport through the water column. The rate at which particulate matter accumulates in the water column is determined by the contaminant flux rates at the air-water and sediment-water interfaces.

SEDIMENT TRANSPORT

Bottom sediments consist primarily of inorganic particles in a matrix with small amounts of organic matter. The inorganic particles vary widely in size and mineralogy, which to some extent are related. Large particles with a diameter greater than 6.25×10^{-2} mm are defined as sands and gravels and consist primarily of quartz and feldspar grains. Smaller particles on the order of a micrometer are defined as clay-size particles and generally consist of clay minerals. The organic matter consists of (*a*) decaying material, such as phytoplankton, zooplankton, and fecal pellets which have settled to the bottom, and (*b*) living benthic organisms. The decay of organic matter drives chemical reactions, which in turn modify the chemical and mechanical properties of the bottom sediments. Benthic organisms are also responsible for major modifications to the sediments due to their excretions and reworking of the sediment. The properties of bottom sediments vary significantly and depend on the distributions of the grain size and mineralogy of the inorganic particles, as well as on the presence of decaying organic matter and benthic organisms.

The primary sources of suspended sediments in lakes are river inflows and shore erosion, while the primary sinks are river outflows and the deposition and ultimate consolidation of sediments into the permanent sedimentary bottom of the lake. As an example, the total average annual load of sediments to Lake Erie is estimated to be approximately 13 million tons with more than 8 million tons from shore erosion and less than 5 million tons from river loading.

The process of the transport of sediments from the primary sources to ultimate sinks occurs by frequent cycles of resuspension, transport, and deposition. Because of this, in shallow areas of lakes, the major immediate source of sediments in the water column is resuspension from the bottom of the lake, the sediment-water interface, rather than river inflows or shore erosion. As an example, in the Western Basin of Lake Erie, a crude calculation indicates that the rate of resuspension or deposition is generally one to three orders of magnitude greater than the rate at which sediments are introduced into the lake from the Maumee and Detroit Rivers.

Resuspension occurs primarily because of wave action and currents, with wave action generally dominant in shallow water. The sediments are then transported both vertically and horizontally by currents, turbulent diffusion, and settling. Deposition at the sediment-water interface occurs by a combination of mechanical and electrochemical actions. This cycle of resuspension, transport, and deposition occurs on the order of a few days, while the time from input to final deposition and consolidation occurs on a scale of months to years.

Transport may occur as suspended load (for finer sediments) or as bed load (for coarser sediments). The emphasis here is on fine-grained sediments, and therefore suspended load, since fine-grained sediments are responsible (because of their large surface area and hence adsorptive capacities per unit mass) for the greater flux of contaminants.

Quantitative predictive models of sediment transport are necessarily predicated on the solution of the mass balance equation, which is repeated here for convenience:

$$\frac{\partial C}{\partial t} + \frac{\partial (uC)}{\partial x} + \frac{\partial (vC)}{\partial y} + \frac{\partial [(w + w_s)C]}{\partial z} = \frac{\partial}{\partial x}\left(D_H \frac{\partial C}{\partial x}\right) + \frac{\partial}{\partial y}\left(D_H \frac{\partial C}{\partial y}\right) + \frac{\partial}{\partial z}\left(D_v \frac{\partial C}{\partial z}\right) + S.$$

Implicit in this equation is the idea that sediments can be described in terms of average quantities, e.g. an average or mean settling velocity w_s. Although this is a valid first approximation, it is becoming clear that a quantitative analysis of sediment transport must consider the fact that sediments consist of a mixture of particles with widely varying grain size and mineralogy. It should be emphasized here that (*a*) the basic building blocks of sediments are the individual grains and these grains differ widely in mineralogy and size; and (*b*) that fine-grained sediments quite often do not exist as individual grains but may join together into aggregates, or flocs, containing many grains more or less loosely bound by electrochemical forces.

A knowledge of the particle and grain-size distribution for each specific sediment is necessary in order to thoroughly understand present-day experimental results and field observations. In future quantitative analyses of sediment transport, it will be necessary to take into account this size distribution (for example, by separating the sediments into components with each component described by its own average quantities). The above equation is then valid for each component. In this case, the source term $S(x, y, z, t)$ must take into account changes in particle sizes due to aggregation or disaggregation.

Considerable work on sediment transport has been done by oceanographers and geologists attempting to predict sediment transport on the continental shelves and much of that work is relevant to our purpose. Recent oceanic work has been reviewed, for example, by Stanley & Swift (1976), McCave (1976), Gorsline & Swift (1977), Smith (1977), and Owen (1977).

Settling Velocities

Although settling velocities can be measured relatively easily, little work has been done to measure the settling velocities of fresh water sediments, and even less work has been done to characterize and, hence, to determine the significant parameters governing these settling velocities.

An example of the variation of settling for a specific sediment (sediment from the Western Basin of Lake Erie) can be seen in Figure 4 (Fukuda & Lick 1980). Shown is the percentage of sediment having settling velocities within various intervals for (*a*) deionized water with dispersant added, and (*b*) tap water, corresponding to lake water. For deionized water with dispersant, it is assumed that the sediments exist as individual grains and therefore the frequency distribution shown in Figure 4(*left*) is due to the variation in individual grain sizes. Ionization increases flocculation, as indicated by Figure 4(*right*).

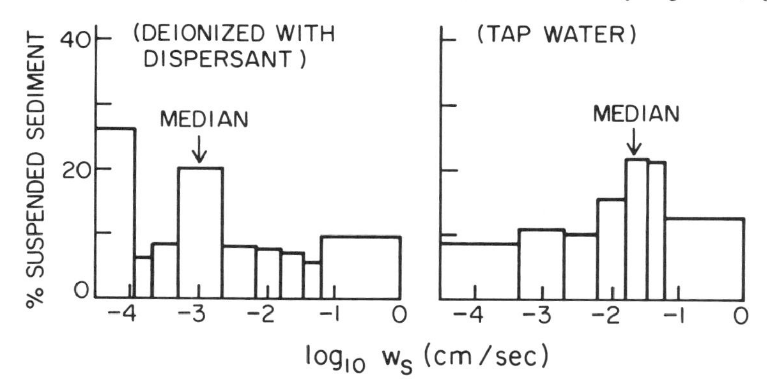

Figure 4 Settling velocity frequency distribution for suspended sediment from the Western Basin.

It is evident that the settling velocities range over four orders of magnitude, a range that must be considered in any quantitative description of sediment transport. Although in shallow water (such as the Western Basin of Lake Erie or Saginaw Bay), settling is not as important as turbulence in distributing sediments through the water column, it is important to note that since settling velocities are distributed over several orders of magnitude, the effective sizes of particles are also distributed over several orders of magnitude. This has important implications for the understanding and prediction of the resuspension and deposition of sediments as well as settling velocities.

For flocculation to occur, particles must collide and, after collision, must cohere. For small particles, collisions are primarily due to Brownian motion, while for larger particles differential settling and fluid shear are the dominant processes. Cohesion of sediments depends primarily on the presence of a significant fraction of clay minerals, particles with sizes generally less than a few micrometers. These clay minerals have a layered structure and form flaky, plate-like crystals that carry negative charges around their edges. The forces between these clay particles depend on the type of clay mineral, the particle sizes, and the quantity and type of cations present in solution. The disaggregation of particles also occurs. The causes are fluid shear and collisions between particles with sufficient relative translational energy.

A special problem of recent interest (e.g. a Conference on Sinking Rates of Particulates at the University of Michigan in February, 1979, chaired by C. L. Schelske) is the fact that organisms in the water column and at the sediment-water interface feed on and process organic and inorganic particles and produce fecal pellets. These fecal pellets are usually much larger than the ingested particles, and therefore sink much faster. The expression "fecal pellet express" has been used to describe this process. In many areas, this process is significant in the transport of particulates and must be considered.

For all of the above reasons, it is not surprising that settling velocities vary widely within a basin and from one basin to another.

Entrainment and Deposition Rates

The net flux of sediment q_s at the sediment-water interface is the difference between the entrainment rate E and the deposition rate D, i.e.

$$q_s = E - D.$$

Here the assumption is that entrainment and deposition are independent processes, i.e. E is the sediment flux when no suspended sediment and therefore no deposition is present, and D is the sediment flux in the absence of entrainment.

Deposition of particles is a result of settling and combined turbulent and Brownian diffusive motion. In describing the deposition process, the simplest plausible hypothesis for the deposition rate is that it is proportional to the local concentration at the sediment-water interface (Monin 1959, Calder 1961, Monin & Yaglom 1973), and therefore $D = \beta C$. The parameter β is a coefficient of proportionality and has units of velocity. As in the case of the mass balance equation, the hypothesis that $D = \beta C$ is strictly valid only for sediments of uniform particle size and is only an approximation for naturally occurring sediments (which have effective particle sizes varying over several orders of magnitude). For small particles, the value of β is primarily determined by diffusion (both Brownian and turbulent), while for large particles, β should be equal to the settling velocity w_s. For large enough particles and shears, inertial effects should influence the value of β.

At the very least, the list of parameters on which the entrainment rate depends includes the following (Lee et al 1981): (*a*) turbulent stress at the sediment-water interface; (*b*) water content of the deposited sediments; (*c*) the composition of the deposited sediments, including mineralogy, particle-size distribution, and organic content; (*d*) vertical distribution of sediment properties, i.e. manner of deposition of sediments; and (*e*) activity of benthic organisms and bacteria.

An example of experimental entrainment data (Fukuda & Lick 1980) is shown in Figure 5, which displays the entrainment rate as a function of applied shear stress for three different types of sediments at different water contents. The three sediments used in this investigation were (*a*) a clay-rich, shale-based sediment, (*b*) a sediment obtained from the Western Basin of Lake Erie, and (*c*) a silty sediment obtained from a harbor area in the Central Basin of Lake Erie. The strong dependence of the entrainment rate on water content and shear stress is evident.

In experiments thus far, only the top few millimeters of sediment have been entrained. Since properties of sediment, such as water content and grain size, change rapidly with depth, it is expected that entrainment rates will also change rapidly with depth due to the consolidation of bed materials as they are deposited and also because of the manner in which the sediments are deposited (Lee et al 1981). The phenomenon of consolidation is a complex matter and understanding it is essential to the prediction of erosion rates. It is known (Krone 1976, Mignoit 1968, Owen 1977) that as sediments are deposited, the consolidation is fairly rapid initially (i.e. the concentration, density, and shear strength increase rapidly as the interstitial waters escape from the bed by percolation through the deposited flocs) but decreases with time. This consolidation is increased by weight of the overlying sediments.

A major influence on sediment properties that has not been quantitatively investigated is the effect of benthic organisms on entrainment and deposition rates. Benthic organisms are plentiful in lakes, especially in the nearshore areas. They influence sediment properties by (*a*) reworking the sediments, i.e.

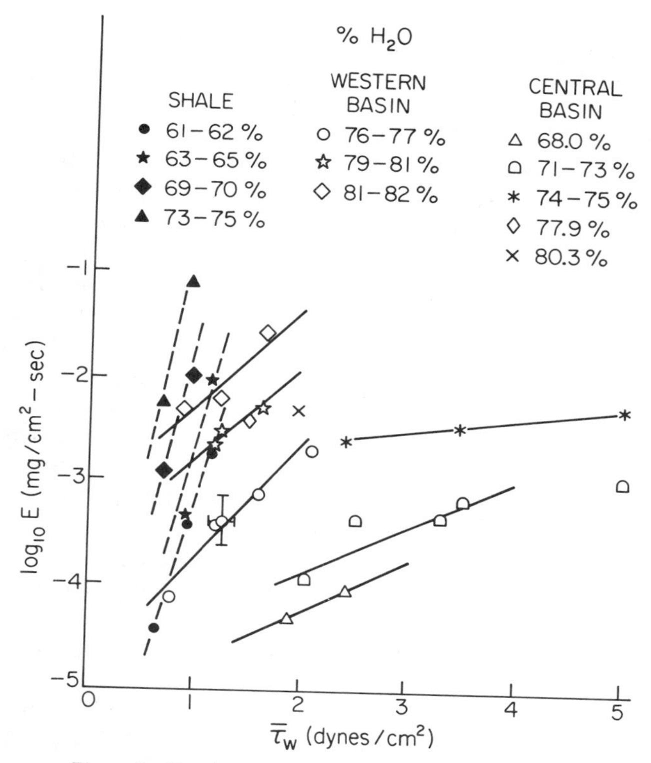

Figure 5 Entrainment rate as a function of shear stress.

by burrowing, passing particulate matter through their guts, and egesting fecal pellets of different shapes, sizes, and contents than the original sedimentary material; and (*b*) excreting mucus on the surface and on burrow walls, which may assist in binding the sediments. Preliminary work (Schink & Guinasso 1977, Robbins et al 1977, Rhoads et al 1977, Yingst & Rhoads 1977, Aller 1977, Fisher et al 1980) has been done on this problem, but adequate information on the effect of benthic organisms on entrainment and deposition rates is not available.

Almost all experimental work on the resuspension and deposition of sediment has been concerned with resuspension and deposition as influenced by a steady flow. Although this is a valid first step in understanding resuspension and deposition, the main cause of bottom shear stress is generally oscillatory wave action. There has been some work on sandy oceanic sediments as influenced by wave action (Rance & Warren 1969, Komar & Miller 1975), but no work on cohesive sediments in fresh water as influenced by wave action has been done. A realistic and more complicated problem is the resuspension and deposition due to the combined action of waves and currents. No experimental work has been done in this area either.

Wave Generation and Bottom Stress

Sediment flux experiments give the entrainment and deposition rates as a function of the applied shear stress. In lakes, this stress is due to wave action and currents, with wave action dominating in shallow water. In order to predict this wave action, a wave generation analysis is needed.

Surface gravity waves are generated by energy transfer from the winds to the water surface. Theoretical analyses of wind-wave generation have been made (Phillips 1957, Miles 1957) but are not entirely successful in quantitatively predicting wave generation. At present, the most widely used procedures for predicting wave parameters are the semiempirical methods, such as the PNJ method developed by Pierson, Neumann, and James (Pierson et al 1955) and the SMB method developed by Sverdrup, Munk, and Bretschneider (Sverdrup & Munk 1947, Bretschneider 1958, CERC 1973). These procedures give the significant wave height and significant wave period as a function of wind speed, fetch, and mean depth. From these relations and by assuming inviscid flow, one can determine the horizontal periodic flow at the sediment-water interface.

Near the sediment-water interface, a turbulent boundary layer exists (on the order of 10 cm thick for typical surface waves) and produces a shear stress at the interface. Kajiura (1968) has analyzed this problem based on the assumption of a time-independent but spatially varying vertical eddy viscosity. His results have been partially verified by Jonsson (1967) and Kamphuis (1975). Recent work has attempted to extend the analysis to the case where waves and currents are present simultaneously (Grant & Madsen 1979). However, no substantial field work has been done to verify these analyses. Instrumentation is now being developed (by the US Geological Survey at the Atlantic-Gulf Branch of Marine Geology, Woods Hole, Massachusetts and at the Pacific-Arctic Branch of Marine Geology at Menlo Park, California, and by NOAA at the Atlantic Oceanographic and Meteorological Laboratories), and measurements of bottom velocities and stresses are now feasible and are being made, at least on the continental shelves.

An example of a calculation based on the SMB procedure and the Kajiura analysis is shown in Figure 6. As can be seen, a difficulty with this type of analysis is that it does not include effects of wave diffraction and refraction, effects which are important in the lee of the islands.

The above and other difficulties with the SMB and similar methods can presumably be overcome by means of modern wave models that are presently being developed (but primarily for oceanic waters). These modern wave models all start from a common base—the energy balance or wave transport

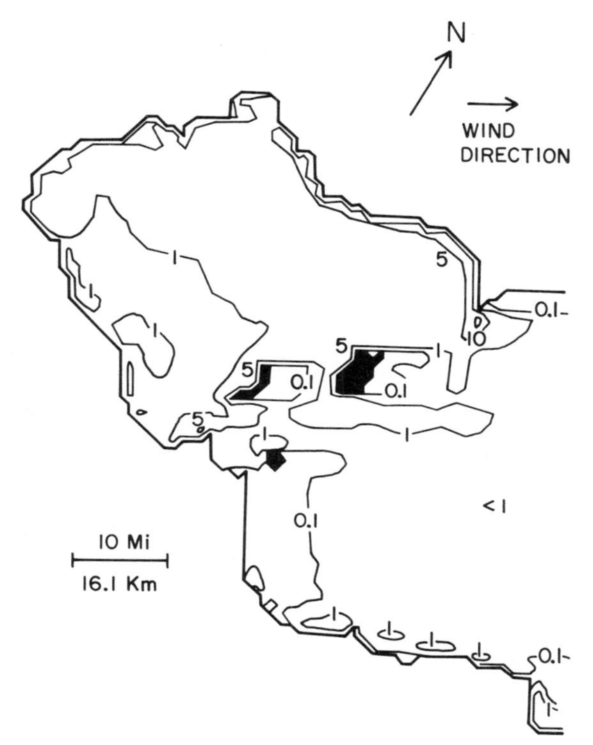

Figure 6 Bottom shear stress in western Lake Erie for wind speed of 11.2 m/sec (25 miles/hr) and southwest wind.

equation (Pierson & Moskowitz 1964, Inoue 1967, Barnett 1968, Hasselman 1978, Gunther et al 1979). The differences in the various models are primarily due to the structure of the source function appearing in this equation, a function which accounts for wind-wave interactions, wave-wave interactions, and wave decay. The models have been partially verified and show good results for many different cases, and they are being actively developed.

As surface gravity waves approach shore, bottom friction effects become increasingly important, and energy dissipation and wave refraction occur. Eventually, in the surf zone, the waves break and transfer their momentum to longshore currents (Longuet-Higgins & Stewart 1962, Noda 1974, Sonu et al 1967, Thornton 1971). These longshore currents are significant transporters of sediment and must be considered in nearshore work.

When thermal stratification is present, internal waves may be generated. These waves behave in a similar manner (including refraction, shoaling, and breaking) to surface waves (Wunsch 1969, Cacchione & Wunsch 1974). This shoaling and breaking in the nearshore may be significant in causing sediment resuspension. The importance of these phenomena in the Great Lakes has not been demonstrated.

Currents

Extensive work is continuing on the numerical modeling of wind-driven currents in lakes. (For recent reviews, see Cheng et al 1976, Lick 1976, and Simons 1979.) The currents and dispersion of contaminants in a nonstratified lake and even the numerical analysis and modeling of these processes are relatively well understood in principle, although the practical application of this knowledge leaves much to be desired. In contrast, the currents and the dispersion of contaminants in a stratified lake are not well understood.

Some of the most important aspects of wind-driven circulation in a large lake can be understood from analytical models, such as those due to Ekman (1923) and Welander (1957), and from more recent modifications and improvements. However, to predict the transport of contaminants in a lake, more general numerical models are needed and have been developed. The most general are three-dimensional, time-dependent models, which come in various shapes and sizes. The simplest is the single-mode, free-surface model (Freeman et al 1972, Katz & Kizlauskas 1974, Haq et al 1975, Sheng & Lick 1976). These models are relatively inefficient in computer time. In order to improve this efficiency, (*a*) rigid-lid, (*b*) two-mode, free-surface, and (*c*) implicit, free-surface models have been developed. Rigid-lid models have been formulated and applied to large lakes by Liggett (1969), Paul & Lick (1974), Vasseur et al (1980), and Bennett (1977, 1978). Rigid-lid models eliminate the motions and time scales associated with surface gravity waves and, hence, allow much larger numerical time steps and reduce computational times.

For situations where free-surface oscillations are important, the two-mode, free-surface model can be and has been used (Simons 1972, 1974, 1975, Sheng et al 1978, Sheng & Lick 1979a, b). In this type of model, the external variables (the free-surface elevation and vertically integrated currents) are treated separately from the internal, three-dimensional flow variables. The free-surface gravity waves no longer limit the internal mode calculations, and much larger time steps may be used for the internal mode calculations, with greatly reduced overall computational times. A recent development—an implicit, free-surface model—is even more efficient and allows time steps comparable to the rigid-lid models (Paul & Lick 1979).

The above models have been extensively applied to lakes when thermal stratification is not significant and, to a lesser extent, when the thermal stratification is prescribed a priori. These models have not been extensively applied to problems in which the interaction between the currents and the temperature field is significant.

It is known of course that thermal stratification significantly affects the transport of contaminants in a lake, but the effects are not quantitatively understood. For example, it is necessary to know how contaminants are transported from the hypolimnion to the epilimnion. After contaminants are released in the hypolimnion, do they mainly diffuse vertically or are they convected horizontally to a nearshore area and then diffused and convected vertically into the hypolimnion? Also, because of thermal stratification, strong internal waves and hypolimnetic currents may be present in sufficient strengths to cause entrainment of bottom sediments.

Considerable work has been done on understanding the basic dynamics of a stratified lake. Three-dimensional models of flow in a stratified lake are presently being constructed. However, these models are inherently complex and are difficult to program and use. For the general understanding of phenomena in a stratified lake and the formation of this stratification, a two-dimensional model (one vertical and one horizontal coordinate) is especially useful (Bennett 1974, Heinrich et al 1981). In this type of model, the vertical dynamics due to turbulent diffusion and convection are present as well as the horizontal dynamics due mainly to convection.

Turbulence

The determination of the turbulent eddy coefficients appearing in the equations of fluid motion and in the mass balance equation (and the effects of turbulence in general) is a major problem associated with the modeling of currents, temperatures, and contaminants. Turbulence in a lake may be produced (*a*) at the air-water interface by pressure and velocity fluctuations of the overlying air and by wave breaking, (*b*) in the interior by shearing motions due to waves and currents, (*c*) at the sediment-water interface, and (*d*) by internal waves due to the presence of thermal stratification. In addition to the production of turbulence, the dissipation, convection, and diffusion of turbulence may be important (e.g. see Launder & Spalding 1972, Reynolds 1976, Amsden & Harlow 1968).

Extensive computations of turbulent flows by means of the governing partial differential equations (pde's) are being made. These models incorporate various levels of sophistication and can be classified as follows (Reynolds 1976): (*a*) zero-equation models—models using only the pde for the mean velocity field and no turbulence pde's; (*b*) one-equation models—models involving an additional pde related to the turbulence velocity scale; (*c*) two equation models—models incorporating an additional pde related to a turbulence length scale; (*d*) stress-equation models—models involving pde's for all components of the turbulent stress tensor; and (*e*) large-eddy simulations—computations of the three-dimensional, time-dependent, large-eddy structure and a low-level model for small-scale turbulence.

In almost all dynamic modeling of currents and temperatures in lakes, it has been assumed that turbulence can be modeled by means of turbulent eddy coefficients (i.e. a zero-equation model). In the most complex situations, these eddy coefficients may be different for the transfer of mass, momentum, and energy and through complex formulas may depend on the local values of temperature, temperature gradient, and velocity gradient, as well as on a scale length, such as the distance from a solid boundary. Nevertheless, the coefficients are determined semiempirically and it is extremely difficult for a particular problem to determine a priori the parameters appearing in the coefficients.

Consider the eddy conductivity in the vertical direction, K_v, which generally is written as the product of the eddy conductivity K_0 in the absence of stratification and a stability function f, which is dependent on the stratification, i.e.

$$K_v = K_0 f(\mathrm{Ri}),$$

where Ri is a Richardson number (ratio of buoyancy to inertia forces) defined by

$$\mathrm{Ri} = \frac{\dfrac{g}{\rho}\dfrac{\partial \rho}{\partial z}}{\left(\dfrac{\partial \bar{u}}{\partial z}\right)^2} = \frac{g\alpha}{\left(\dfrac{\partial \bar{u}}{\partial z}\right)^2}\frac{\partial T}{\partial z}.$$

Here $\bar{u}$ is the horizontal velocity at depth z due to the combined action of waves (including internal waves) and curents, ρ is water density, g is the acceleration due to gravity, and α is the thermal expansion coefficient for water. The coefficient α is strongly dependent on the temperature. The quantity $\partial \bar{u}/\partial z$ is generally parameterized in some fashion by using mean values of $\partial \bar{u}/\partial z$ (Pritchard 1960, Kato & Phillips 1969, Heinrich et al 1981).

Various forms of the stability function $f(\mathrm{Ri})$ have been discussed in the literature (Munk & Anderson 1948, Lumley & Panofsky 1964, Okubo 1962, Kato & Phillips 1969, Sundaram 1969). A typical form is

$$f = (1 + \sigma \mathrm{Ri})^{-3/2},$$

where σ is an empirical constant. K_0, the eddy conductivity in the absence of stratification, unfortunately is not a constant but may be a function of wind stress, depth of the lake, distance from the surface, and wave amplitude and fetch. Formulas for the eddy viscosity and eddy diffusivity are similar to that for the eddy conductivity.

Due to these and other problems with eddy coefficients, recent investigations have attempted to model vertical diffusion of mass, momentum, and energy in lakes by using higher order models of turbulence. For example, Marchuk and co-workers (Marchuk et al 1976, 1977) have used a two-equation model of turbulence to investigate the deepening of the upper well-mixed layer in the ocean. The turbulence model consisted of the turbulent energy equation and an equation for the turbulent energy decay function. These equations were then coupled with the fluid momentum and energy equations. The equations were two dimensional but only vertical variations and mixing were allowed. A reasonable and realistic simulation of the dynamics was made. Similar attempts using higher order models of turbulence are being made in oceanic problems.

Numerical Modeling

The numerical modeling of the transport of various contaminants, including sediments, in the Great Lakes is a fairly recent occurrence. Sydor and coworkers (Sydor et al 1978, Sydor 1979) have recently successfully modeled the transport of particulate matter in Lake Superior. Resuspension and deposition were not taken into account, since the emphasis was on transport.

The resuspension, transport, and deposition of sediments in the Western Basin of Lake Erie has been modeled with some success by Sheng & Lick (1979a). In these calculations, experimental results (Fukuda & Lick 1980) for the resuspension and deposition rates were used. Unfortunately, only parameters for one type of Western Basin sediment were available. It is believed that discrepancies between the observations and calculations were mainly due to the fact that sediment properties varied widely throughout the Basin and this was not taken into account in the modeling. Later analyses of additional samples from the Western Basin confirmed this hypothesis.

A more ambitious modeling effort has been attempted by Lam & Jaquet (1976) who calculated the transport of sediments and the transport and regeneration of total phosphorus in Lake Erie. They considered resuspension, deposition, transport, and various biochemical transformations affecting phosphorus and compared their results with ship data taken approximately 30 days after the initial observation. Because of the short time scales (two to three days) for resuspension and deposition in Lake Erie, it is expected that the sediment and phosphorus concentrations at any time depend significantly only on the events for the few days before the particular observation and certainly not on the initial data thirty days before the observation. Because of this and the wide range of possible values of parameters used in the model, the calculations are not convincing.

TRANSPORT OF OTHER CONTAMINANTS

Sediments are simpler than most contaminants to model since they are relatively unaffected by biochemical transformations. In attempting to predict the transport and ultimate fate of other contaminants, quite complex chemical and biological transformations must be considered, as well as the physical processes discussed in the previous section. These transformations occur not only in the water column but also in the bottom sediments and in aquatic organisms. To give some indication of how biological and chemical transformations affect the fate of contaminants, a brief discussion of the transport and fate of a few important and representative contaminants is given here.

Radionuclides

Radioactive materials enter the Lakes as (*a*) fall-out of naturally occurring material (e.g. precipitation scavenging of ^{210}Pb from the decay of atmospheric ^{222}Rn), (*b*) fall-out from nuclear power bomb tests, (*c*) leakage from nuclear power plants on shore, and (*d*) rainwater runoff (of radioactive fall-out on the surrounding drainage basin) carried by rivers and underground aquifers.

The precipitation of radionuclides from the air to the water surface presumably is uniform over the surface of the lake (although different from the land). Inputs from nuclear power plants and river inflows can be considered as point sources. Once in the aquatic environment, radionuclides may (*a*) remain in solution either in the lake waters or in the interstitial waters of the bottom sediments; (*b*) be adsorbed on particulate matter, which may be either suspended, settling, or part of the bottom sediments; or (*c*) be taken up by plants and animals. Radionuclides of course are being continuously transformed by radioactive decay.

In the lake waters, radionuclides are phycially transported by the processes described in the previous section, i.e. they are affected by currents, wave action, turbulent diffusion, and settling. The processes by which radionuclides are adsorbed on and hence precipitated by particulate matter are not well understood. It is well known that the dominant mechanism for removal of many radionuclides is adsorption on clay particles, with adsorption on the finer particles being favored (Nelson et al 1966). This is highly dependent on the type of radionuclide (Hood 1971). For ^{210}Pb, Leland et al (1973) have concluded that complexing with organic matter is more important than adsorption on clays.

In the sediments, the physical processes of resuspension and deposition are active as well as the physicochemical processes of absorption-desorption and ion exchange between the interstitial waters and the solid sediments. These processes depend on the form of the radionuclides in the interstital waters, the manner of adsorption on the solid sediments, the exchange coefficients, and the water quality. Benthic activity may further modify the distribution of radionuclides in the sediments and the fluxes into the overlying water.

Aquatic organisms accumulate radioactive materials (*a*) directly from the water by ion transport mechanisms or by physical adsorption processes, and (*b*) by ingestion of other organisms or detritus that may contain radioactive material. This uptake of radioactive material by aquatic organisms, although of importance to the organism, probably does not result in a significant transport of radioactive material. An exception (in deep lakes) may be the excretion of radioactive materials in the form of fecal pellets, which may then rapidly sink to the bottom.

The transport and fate of radionuclides in the Great Lakes have been receiving considerable attention recently, mainly to determine the rates of accumulation of recent sediments (Robbins & Edgington 1976). The two radionuclides primarily being used are ^{210}Pb, a naturally occurring radionuclide that is produced by the decay of atmospheric ^{222}Rn and enters the lake by precipitation scavenging, and ^{137}Cs, an anthropogenic radionuclide produced by nuclear detonations over the last 30 years.

^{210}Pb has a half-life of 22.26 years while ^{137}Cs has a half-life of 30.2 years. It is generally assumed that the yearly fall-out of ^{210}Pb is approximately constant. The fall-out of ^{137}Cs is highly variable since its magnitude depends on the number and intensity of nuclear devices exploded. The fall-out was zero before 1950, reached a maximum in 1963, after which it rapidly decreased for a few years and is now slowly decreasing.

Robbins & Edgington and others have used these radionuclides to investigate sedimentation rates in the Great Lakes. From coring and subsequent laboratory measurements, general agreement with the hypothesis of a uniform sedimentation rate has been obtained, and the rate has been determined. Closer examination of the data has revealed variations from this simplistic model due primarily to the activity of benthic organisms and also to variable sedimentation rates and possible erosion. The variable sedimentation and erosion have been tentatively correlated with large storm activity.

The use of radionuclides as tracers is a valuable tool. As more is known of the scavenging of these materials in the water and as more data on their distribution in the sediments is obtained, a realistic model of the transport of radionuclides should be feasible.

Phytoplankton

It is known that drinking water taste and odor problems are closely correlated with high phytoplankton concentrations. In addition, dense growths of phytoplankton cause oxygen depletion (which in turn causes decreased yields of fish and other aquatic life) and esthetic degradation of nearshore areas.

The distribution of phytoplankton in a lake can be quite heterogeneous in both space (horizontally as well as vertically) and time. This distribution is dependent, at least in part, on phytoplankton growth rates, respiration and excretion, natural mortality, grazing by zooplankton, settling, convection, and turbulent diffusion. Growth rates are functions of temperature, light, and nutrients. The most important nutrients are phosphorus, nitrogen, and silicon with phosphorus believed to be the limiting nutrient in most areas in the Great Lakes. To combat the problem of overenrichment by phosphorus, a phosphorus reduction program for the Great Lakes has been initiated.

Numerous water quality models to predict phytoplankton concentrations (and/or the related quantity, phosphorus concentration) have been developed. These models range from simple, empirical models to complex, deterministic ones. Among them are the following (after Bierman 1979).

Vollenweider (1975, 1976, 1977). Vollenweider's model is a steady-state, equilibrium model based on empirical correlations between total phosphorus load and in-lake concentrations of total phosphorus and chlorophyll *a*. For calibration, the initial version of this model used data from 60 temperate-zone lakes representing a range of conditions from oligotrophic to eutrophic. A later version used data only from Lakes Erie and Ontario.

Chapra (1977). Chapra has used a time-variable model suggested by Vollenweider as the basis for a simple dynamic mass balance model with total phosphorus concentration as the primary variable. Total phosphorus is considered to be a nonconservative substance that does not undergo any transformations in the water column, but which is lost from the water column by an apparent settling velocity. This velocity corresponds to the net flux of total phosphorus from the water column into the sediments.

Thomann (Thomann et al 1975, 1976, Hydroscience 1976). Thomann has developed a dynamic mass balance model that includes direct calculations of available and unavailable forms of phosphorus and nitrogen, chlorophyll *a*, and zooplankton. Phytoplankton chlorophyll *a* is a function of temperature, light, and nutrient concentration. Zooplankton concentration is a function of temperature and phytoplankton chlorophyll *a* concentration.

DiToro (DiToro & Matystik 1979, DiToro & Connolly 1979). DiToro has extended the Thomann model to include two different types of phytoplankton and nutrient release from the sediments under anaerobic conditions.

Bierman (Bierman et al 1980). The most complex model is that due to Bierman. In this model, five phytoplankton groups are considered along with more detailed descriptions of phosphorus and nitrogen dynamics.

As the models become more complex, they furnish more information on the biological processes occurring in a lake. They also require a much larger data base. The above models have been discussed by Bierman (1979) and that report should be consulted for details and the results of model comparisons.

Only limited spatial segmentation is included in these models, if at all. It is well known that phytoplankton concentrations vary markedly in the vertical (with large concentrations often appearing near the air-water interface, the thermocline region, or the sediment-water interface) and in the horizontal (probably related to upwelling regions where temperature and nutrient concentrations are high). Satisfactory quantitative explanations of these variations (patchiness) have not been given, although the variations seem to be directly related to hydrodynamics.

None of the above models include hydrodynamics to any significant extent, although present developments are in this direction. To account for hydrodynamics, such quantities as *apparent settling velocity* have been used. This term is used to describe the net loss of phytoplankton, zooplankton, and other quantities to the sediments from the overlying water. Although related to the actual settling velocity of a particle, the apparent settling velocity is more fundamentally related to the hydrodynamics and the resuspension and deposition rates of phytoplankton, zooplankton, and other particulates. The resuspension and deposition rates for phytoplankton and zooplankton at the sediment-water interface are not known and cannot be parameterized or modeled. They need to be investigated, presumably in the same way as the resuspension and deposition of sediments.

A related problem is the interchange of phosphorus and other nutrients between the sediments and the overlying water. Large fluxes of phosphorus from the sediments occur as the overlying water goes anoxic. Although this has been demonstrated by both laboratory experiments and field measurements, the mechanisms that control this pulse are not well understood. This flux is primarily due to molecular diffusion as modified by chemical reactions but may be further enhanced by physical resuspension due to wave action and by the activities of benthic organisms.

Toxic Chlorinated Hydrocarbons

Chlorinated hydrocarbons (CHCs) are widely used in agriculture and industry. Among the best known are DDT and the polychlorinated biphenyls (PCBs). DDT has been widely used as an insecticide, while PCBs are used as transformer oils, heat exchangers, insulators in capacitors, and in many other ways. Many of these chlorinated hydrocarbons are toxic and, being relatively inert chemically, are persistent in the environment. The use of DDT was banned in 1972 and its concentration has since decreased. PCBs were limited to closed uses in 1971 and their production has since been banned entirely. However, they are still persistent in the aquatic environment.

More information is probably available for DDT than for any of the other hydrocarbons. PCBs, which are presently the most serious contaminants in the Great Lakes, are not as well documented but are similar to DDT in properties and behavior and probably follow similar pathways through the environment. DDT is mainly a single compound while PCBs are mixtures of compounds, as many as 50 or more. Both DDT and PCBs have low solubility in water, high solubility in nonpolar materials such as lipids, a low but significant vapor pressure, and a high bioconcentration factor (Murphy & Rzeszutko 1977). DDT degrades slowly in the aquatic environment. Some PCB compounds degrade quickly but others do not.

The transport and fate of CHCs within natural waters and sediments have been studied to some extent, especially with regard to oceanic transport (for general articles and reviews, see, for example, Risebrough et al 1976, Nisbet & Sarofin 1972, Bidleman et al 1976). A thorough review of the transport, fate, and effects of CHCs in the Great Lakes has been given by Swain (1980). However, sufficient information to predict the transport of these substances in lake or oceanic waters is not available. In general, the information that is needed is as follows.

1. Degradation rates of the chlorinated hydrocarbons and their metabolites. Some work has been done on the degradation of DDT and PCBs in the laboratory under ultraviolet light (Kerner et al 1972, Ruzo et al 1972). Wong & Kaiser (1975) have investigated the effects of bacteria in lake water on various commercial mixtures of PCB isomers. No long-term (6 to 12 month) studies of PCB degradation have been done, nor has any work been done on degradation rates of CHCs in sediments under anoxic conditions. These studies need to be undertaken.

2. CHC partition coefficients for particulates. In fresh water, PCBs are extremely insoluble and are therefore generally found associated with suspended particulates (Crump-Wiesner et al 1974, Huang & Liao 1970, Poirrier et al 1972); partition coefficients range from about 10^3 for clay minerals to 10^5 for organic particulates. If one knew partition coefficients, the rate of partitioning, and degradation rates, and also could predict the transport of inert particulates, then the transport and fate of CHCs could be predicted, at least through the water.

3. Transfer rates through the water-air interface. Many CHCs are transported worldwide by the atmosphere; the atmosphere is therefore a significant source of these materials for lake waters. In fact, for Lakes Superior and Michigan (not considering the input from Waukeegan Harbor, where up to 10^6 kilograms of PCBs were dumped by a manufacturer over a 20-year period), the major input is from the atmosphere (Eisenreich et al 1979, Murphy 1978). Transfer from the air to the water can occur by the flux of vapors, by particle deposition, and by rain. The rates at which CHCs are transferred through the water-air interface are not known although estimates have been made (see Bidleman et al 1976).

A related problem is that CHCs are relatively concentrated in a thin film at the water-air interface (Andren et al 1976, Seba & Corcoran 1969). The amount of CHCs in this layer is probably not large but may have a disproportionate effect, since many aquatic organisms are also concentrated at this water-air interface.

4. Transfer rates through the sediment-water interface. CHCs are associated with particulate matter that eventually is deposited as bottom sediment, where they are taken up by benthic fauna and also decay as part of the permanent sediments. Little is known about the flux of CHCs out of the sediments, but it is postulated to occur by dissolution in the interstitial waters, diffusion from the sediments into the overlying water, and subsequent loss to the atmosphere (Neely 1977, Fulk et al 1975, Halter & Johnson 1977). Conceivably an enhanced flux of CHCs out of the sediments could occur during anoxic episodes if their behavior is controlled by metallic oxy-hydroxide particle coating.

ACKNOWLEDGMENT

Much of the research for this article was funded by the US Environmental Protection Agency and the National Oceanic and Atmospheric Administration.

Literature Cited

Aller, R. C. 1977. *The influence of macrobenthos on chemical diagenesis of marine sediments*. PhD Thesis. Yale Univ., New Haven. 600 pp.

Amsden, A. A., Harlow, F. H. 1968. Transport of turbulence in numerical fluid dynamics. *J. Comput. Phys.* 3:94–110

Andren, W. E., Elzerman, A. W., Armstrong, D. E. 1976. Chemical and physical aspects of surface organic microlayers in freshwater lakes. *J. Great Lakes Res.* 2:Suppl. 1, pp. 101–10

Barnett, T. P. 1968. On the generation, dissipation, and prediction of ocean waves. *J. Geophys. Res.* 73:513–30

Bennett, J. R. 1974. On the dynamics of wind-driven lake currents. *J. Phys. Oceanogr.* 4:414–40

Bennett, J. R. 1977. A three-dimensional model of Lake Ontario's summer circulation, I. Comparison with observations. *J. Phys. Oceanogr.* 7:591–601

Bennett, J. R. 1978. A three-dimensional model of Lake Ontario's summer circulation, II. A diagnostic study. *J. Phys. Oceanogr.* 8:1095–1103

Bidleman, T. F., Rice, C. P., Olney, C. E. 1976. High molecular weight hydrocarbons in the air and sea: Rates and mechanisms of air/sea transfer. See Windom & Duce 1976, pp. 323–52

Bierman, V. J. 1979. A comparison of models developed for phosphorus management in the Great Lakes. *Conf. Phosphorus Manage. Strategies Great Lakes, Rochester*. 24 pp.

Bierman, V. J., Dolan, D. M., Stoermer, E. F., Gannon, J. E., Smith, V. E. 1980. The development and calibration of a multiclass, internal pool, phytoplankton model for Saginaw Bay, Lake Huron. *Great Lakes Basin Comm. Great Lakes Environ. Plann. Study No. 33*. 126 pp.

Bretschneider, C. L. 1958. Revisions in wave forecasting: Deep and shallow water. *Proc. 6th Conf. Coastal Eng.*, pp. 30–67

Cacchione, D., Wunsch, C. 1974. Experimental study of internal waves over a slope. *J. Fluid Mech.* 66:223–39

Calder, K. L. 1961. Atmospheric diffusion of particulate matter considered as a boundary value problem. *J. Meteorol.* 18(3):413–16

Chapra, S. E. 1977. Total phosphorus model for the Great Lakes. *J. Environm. Eng. Div. ASCE* 103(EE2):147–61

Cheng, R. T., Powell, J. M., Dillon, J. M. 1976. Numerical models of wind-driven circulation in lakes. *Appl. Math. Modeling* 1:141–59

Coastal Engineering Research Center. 1973. Shore Protection Manual, Vol. 1

Crump-Wiesner, H. J., Feltz, H. R., Yates,

M. L. 1974. A study of the distribution of PCB in the aquatic environment. *Pestic. Monit. J.* 8:157–61

DiToro, D.M., Conolly, J. F. 1979. Mathematical models of water quality in large lakes. II. Lake Erie. *US Environ. Prot. Agency Rep. EPA-600/3-80-065*. 230 pp.

DiToro, D. M., Matystik, W. 1979. Mathematical models of water quality in large lakes. Part I. *US Environ. Prot. Agency Rep. EPA-600/3-80-056*. 165 pp.

Eisenreich, S. J., Hollod, G. J., Johnson, T. C. 1979. Accumulation of PCBs in surficial Lake Superior sediments: Atmospheric deposition. *Environ. Sci. Technol.* 13:569–73

Ekman, V. W. 1923. Ueber horizontalzierkulation bei winderzeugten meeresstromugen, *Arkiv. Mat. Astr. Fys.* 17(26):1–74

Fisher, J. B., Lick, W. J., McCall, P.L., Robbins, J. A. 1980. Vertical mixing of lake sediments by tubificid oligochaetes. *J. Geophys. Res.* 85:3997–4006

Freeman, N. G., Hale, A. M., Danard, M. B. 1972. A modified sigma equations approach to the numerical modeling of Great Lakes hydrodynamics. *J. Geophys. Res.* 77:1050–60

Fukuda, M. K., Lick, W. 1980. The entrainment of cohesive sediments in fresh water. *J. Geophys. Res.* 85:2813–24

Fulk, R., Gruber, D., Willschleger, R. 1975. Laboratory study of the release of pesticide and PCB materials to the water column during dredging and disposal operations. Environ. Effects Lab. Rep. D-75-6., US Army Eng. Waterways Exper. Stn.

Gorsline, D. S., Swift, D. J. P. 1977. Shelf sediment dynamics: A national overview. *Rep. to the Natl. Sci. Foundation (IDOE)*. 134 pp.

Grant, W. D., Madsen, O. S. 1979. Combined wave and current interaction with a rough bottom. *J. Geophys. Res.* 84:1797–808

Gunther, H., Rosenthal, W., Weare, T. J., Worthington, B. A., Hasselman, K., Ewing, J. A. 1979. A hybrid parametrical wave prediction model. *J. Geophys. Res.* 84:5727–38

Halter, M. T., Johnson, H. E. 1977. *A Model System to Study the Desorption and Biological Availability of PCB in Hydrosoils. Aquatic Toxicology and Hazard Evaluations ASTM STP 634*. ed. F. L. Mayer, J. L. Hamelind, Am. Soc. Test. Mater.

Haq, A., Lick, W., Sheng, Y. P. 1975. The time-dependent flow in large lakes with application to Lake Erie. *Case West. Reserve Univ. Rep.*, Cleveland, Ohio

Hasselman, K. 1978. On the spectral energy balance and numerical prediction of ocean waves. In *Turbulent Fluxes Through the Sea Surface, Wave Dynamics, and Prediction*, ed. A. Favre, K. Hasselman, pp. 531–96. New York: Plenum Press

Heinrich, J. C., Lick, W., Paul, J. 1981. The temperatures and currents in a stratified lake—a two-dimensional analysis, *J. Great Lakes Res.* 7:264–75

Hood, D. W. 1971. *Impingement of Man on the Oceans*, New York: Wiley. 738 pp.

Huang, J., Liao, C. 1970. Adsorption of pesticides by clay minerals. *J. Sanit. Eng. Div. ASCE* 96(SA5):1057–78

Hydroscience. 1976. Assessment of the effects of nutrient loadings on Lake Ontario using a mathematical model of the phytoplankton. *Rep. Surveillance Subcomm. Water Qual. Board, IJC*. 116 pp.

Inoue, T. 1967. On the growth of the spectrum of a wind-generated sea according to a modified Nutes-Phillips mechanism and its application to wave forecasting. *Tech. Rep. 67-5*, Geophys. Sci. Lab., New York Univ.

Jonsson, I. G. 1967. Wave boundary layers and friction factors. *Proc. 10th Conf. Coastal Engineering, Tokyo*, pp. 127–48

Kajiura, K. 1968. A model of the bottom boundary layer in water waves. *Bull. Earthq. Res. Int.* 46:75–123

Kamphuis, J. W. 1975. Friction factors under oscillatory waves. *J. Waterways Harbors Div. ASCE* 101(WW3):135–45

Kato, H., Phillips, O. M. 1969. On the penetration of a turbulent layer into a stratified fluid. *J. Fluid Mech.* 37:643–56

Katz, P. L., Kizlauskas, A. G. 1974. A numerical model for summer flows in Lake Michigan. *Arch. Meteorol. Geophys. Bioklimatol.*, Vol. 23

Kerner, I., Klein, W., Korte, F. 1972. Beitrage zur Okologischen Chemie-XXXIII Photochemische Reaktonien von 1.1-dichlor-2 (p, p′-dichlorophenyl) athylen (DDE). *Tetrakedron* 28:1575–78

Komar, P. D., Miller, M. C. 1975. On the comparison between the threshold of sediment motion under waves and unidirectional currents with a discussion of the practical evaluation of the threshold. *J. Sediment. Petrol.* 45(1):362–67

Krone, R. B. 1976. Engineering interest in the benthic boundary layer. In *The Benthic Boundary Layer*, ed. I. N. McCave. New York: Plenum Press

Lam, D. C. L., Jaquet, J. M. 1976. Computations of physical transport and regeneration of phosphorus in Lake Erie in the Fall of 1970. *J. Fish. Res. Board Can.* 33:550–63

Launder, B. E., Spalding, D. B. 1972. *Mathematical Models of Turbulence*, New York: Academic. 169 pp.

Lee, D. Y., Lick, W., Kang, S. W. 1981. The entrainment and deposition of fine-grained sediments in Lake Erie. *J. Great Lakes Res.* 7:224–33

Leland, H. V., Shukla, S. S., Shimp, N. F. 1973. *In Trace Metal and Metail-Organic Interactions in Natural Water,* ed. P. C. Singer. Ann Arbor, Mich: Ann Arbor Sci.

Lick, W. 1976. Numerical modeling of lake currents. *Ann. Rev. Earth Planet. Sci.* 4:49–74

Liggett, J. A. 1969. Unsteady circulation in shallow, homogeneous lakes, *J. Hydraul. Div. ASCE,* 95(HY4):1273–88

Longuet-Higgins, M. S., Stewart, R. W. 1962. Radiation stress and mass transport in gravity waves, *J. Fluid Mech.* 13:481-504

Lumley, J. L., Panofsky, H. A. 1964. *The Structure of Atmospheric Turbulence,* New York: Interscience

Marchuk, G. I., Kachergin, V. P., Klimok, V. I., Sukhorukov, V. A. 1976. Mathematical simulation of surface turbulence in the ocean. *Izv. Atmospher. Oceanic Phys.* 12(8):841–49

Marchuk, G. I., Kachergin, V. P., Klimok, V. L., Sukhorukov, V. A. 1977. On the dynamics of the ocean surface mixed layer. *J. Phys. Oceanography* 7:865–75

Marshall, J. S. 1975. *Proc. 2nd Fed. Conf. Great Lakes, Argonne National Lab.*

McCave, I. N., ed. 1976. *The Benthic Boundary Layer,* New York: Plenum Press 335 pp.

Mignoit, C. 1968. Etude des proprietes physique de differents sediments tres fins et de leur comportement sous des actions hydrodynamiques. *La Houille Blache* 23(7):591–620

Miles, J. W. 1957. On the generation of surface waves by shear flows. *J. Fluid Mech.* 3:185–204

Monin, A. S. 1959. *On the Boundary Condition on the Earth's Surface for Diffusing Pollution, Advances in Geophysics,* Vol. 6, pp. 435–36. New York: Academic

Monin, A. S., Yaglom, A. M. 1973. *Statistical Fluid Mechanics,* Vol. 1. Cambridge, Mass: MIT Press

Munk, W. H., Anderson, E. K. 1948. Notes on the theory of the thermocline. *J. Near. Res.* 7:276–95

Murphy, T. J. 1978. Polychlorinated biphenyls in precipitation in the Lake Michigan Basin. *Environ. Prot. Agency Rep. EPA-600/3-78-071.* 39 pp.

Murphy, T. J., Rzeszutko, C. P. 1977. Precipitation inputs of PCBs to Lake Michigan. *J. Great Lakes Res.* 3:305–12

National Academy of Sciences. 1975. Assessing potential ocean pollutants. *Rep. to the Ocean Aff. Board. Comm Nat. Resour. Nat. Res. Counc.,* 438 pp.

National Academy of Sciences. 1976. Disposal in the Marine Environment: An oceanographic assessment. *Rep. to EPA.* 76 pp.

National Academy of Sciences. 1977. Estuaries, geophysics, and the environment. *Rep. by the Nat. Res. Counc. to NAS.* 127 pp.

Neely, W. B. 1977. A material balance study of polychlorinated biphenyls in Lake Michigan. *Sci. Total Environment* 7:117–29

Nelson, J. L., Perkins, R. W., Nielsen, J. M., Haushild, W. L. 1966. Reactions of radionuclides from the Hanford reactors with Columbia River sediments. In *Disposal of Radioactive Wastes into Seas, Oceans, and Surface Waters,* pp. 139–61, IAEA Proc. Ser., IAEA, Vienna

Nisbet, I. C. T., Sarofin, A. F. 1972. Rates and routes of transport of PCBs in the environment. *Environ. Health Persp* 1:21–38

Noda, E. K. 1974. Wave-induced nearshore circulation. *J. Geophys. Res.* 79:4097–4106

Okubo, A. 1962. A review of theoretical models for turbulent diffusion in the sea. *J. Ocean. Soc. Jpn.* 20th Ann. Vol., pp. 286–318

Owen, M. W. 1977. Problems in the modeling of transport, erosion, and deposition of cohesive sediments. In *The Sea,* ed. E. D. Goldberg, 6:515–38. New York: Wiley

Paul, J. F., Lick, W. 1974. A numerical model of thermal plumes and river discharges, *Proc. 17th Conf. Great Lakes Res., Int. Assoc. Great Lakes Res.,* pp. 445–55

Paul, J. F., Lick, W. 1979. *An implicit, free-surface model for currents in large lakes.* Presented at 22nd Conf. Great Lakes Res.

Phillips, O. M. 1957. On the generation of waves by turbulent wind. *J. Fluid Mech.* 2:417–45

Pierson, W. J. Jr., Moskowitz, L. 1964. A proposed spectral form for fully developed wind seas based on the similarity theory of S. A. Kitaigorodskii. *J. Geophys. Res.* 69:5181–90

Pierson, W. J., Neumann, G., James, R. W. 1955. Observing and forecasting ocean waves by means of wave spectra and statistics. *Publ. No. 603 Hydrogr. Off.* US Dept. Navy, Washington D.C.

Poirrier, M. A., Bordelon, B. R., Laseter, J. L. 1972. Adsorption and concentration of dissolved carbon-14 DDT by coloring colloids in surface waters. *Environ. Sci. Technol.* 6:1033–35

Pritchard, D. W. 1960. The movement and mixing of contaminants in tidal estuaries. *Proc. 1st Int. Conf. Waste Disposed Mar. Environ.,* ed. E. A. Pearson, Pergamon Press

Rance, P. J., Warren, N. F. 1969. The threshold movement of coarse material in oscillatory flow. *Proc. 11th Conf. Coastal Eng. ASCE*

Reynolds, W. C. 1976. Computation of turbulent flows. *Ann. Rev. Fluid Mech.* 8:183–208

Rhoads, D. C., Yingst, J. Y., Ullman, W. J. 1977. Seafloor stability in central Long Island Sound. part I. *4th Bienn. Estuarine Res. Conf. Mt. Pocono, Penn.*

Risebrough, R. W., deLappe, B. W., Walker, W. 1976. Transfer of higher molecular weight chlorinated hydrocarbons to the marine environment. See Windom & Duce 1976, pp. 261–322

Robbins, J. A., Edgington, D. N. 1976. Depositional processes and the determination of recent sedimentation rates in Lake Michigan. *Proc. 2nd Fed. Conf. Great Lakes,* Great Lakes Basin Comm., pp. 287–607

Robbins, J. A., Krezoski, J. R., Mozley, S. C. 1977. Radioactivity in sediments of the Great Lakes: Post-depositional redistribution by deposit feeding organisms. *Earth Planet. Sci. Lett.* 36:325–33

Ruzo, L. O., Zabik, M. J., Schuetz, R. D. 1972. Polychlorinated biphenyls: Photolysis of 3, 4, 3′, 4′-tetrachlorobiphenyl and 4, 4′-dichlorobiphenyl in solution. *Bull. Environ. Contam. Toxicol.* 8:217–18

Schink, D. R., Guinasso, N. L. 1977. Effects of bioturbation on sediment-seawater interaction. *Mar. Geol.* 23:133–54

Seba, D. B., Corcoran, E. F. 1969. Surface slicks as concentrators of pesticides in the marine environment. *Pestic. Mon. J.* 3:190–93

Sheng, Y. P., Lick, W. 1976. Current and contaminant dispersion in the near-shore regions and modification by a jetport. *J. Great Lakes Res.* 2:402–14

Sheng, Y. P., Lick, W. 1979a. The transport and resuspension of sediments in a shallow lake. *J. Geophys. Res.* 84:1809–25

Sheng, Y. P., Lick, W. 1979b. A two-mode, free-surface model of currents in large lakes. *US Environ. Prot. Agency Rep. EPA-600/3-80-047*

Sheng, Y. P., Lick, W., Gedney, R. T., Molls, F. B. 1978. Numerical computation of three-dimensional circulation in Lake Erie: A comparison of a free-surface and a rigid-lid model. *J. Phys. Oceanogr.* 8:713–27

Simons, T. J. 1972. Development of numerical models for Lake Ontario. *Proc. 15th Conf. Great Lakes Res.,* Int. Assoc. Great Lakes Res., pp. 655–72

Simons, T. J. 1974. Verification of numerical models of Lake Ontario, part I, circulation in spring, early summer. *J. Phys. Oceanogr.* 4:507–23

Simons, T. J. 1975. Verification of numerical models of Lake Ontario, part II, stratified circulation and temperature changes. *J. Phys. Oceanogr.* 5:98–110

Simons, T. J. 1979. Hydrodynamic models of lakes and shallow seas. *Can. Cent. Inland Waters, Burlington, Ont.*

Smith, J. D. 1977. Modeling of sediment transport on continental shelves. In *The Sea,* ed. E. D. Goldberg, 6:539–78. New York: Wiley

Sonu, C. J., McCloy, J. M., McArthur, D. S. 1967. Longshore currents and nearshore topographies. *Proc. 10th Conf. Coastal Eng.,* pp. 524–49

Stanley, D. J., Swift, D. J. P. 1976. *Marine Sediment Transport and Environmental Management,* New York: Wiley

Sundaram, T. R. 1969. An investigation of the physical effects of thermal discharges into Cayuga Lake. *Cornell Aeronaut. Lab. Rep. No. VT – 2616-0-2*

Sverdrup, H. U., Munk, W. H. 1947. Wind, sea, and swell: Theory of relations for forecasting. *Publ. No. 601, Hydrogr. Off.,* US Dept. Navy, Washington DC

Swain, W. R. 1980. *An ecosystem approach to the toxicology of residue forming xenobiotic organic substances in the Great Lakes.* Environ. Studies Board, Nat. Res. Counc. Natl. Acad. Sci. 64 pp.

Sydor, M. 1979. Transport of mining waste in Lake Superior. *US-USSR Symp. on "Mathematical Modeling of Aquatic Ecosystems," Environ. Prot. Agency Rep.*

Sydor, M., Stortz, K. R., Swain, W. R. 1978. Identification of contaminants in Lake Superior through Landstat I data. *J. Great Lakes Res.* 4(2):142–48

Thomann, R. V., Winfield, R. P., DiToro, D. M., O'Connor, D. J. 1975. Mathematical modeling of phytoplankton in Lake Ontario, I. *US Environ. Prot. Agency Rep. EPA-660/3-75-005.* 177 pp.

Thomann, R. V., DiToro, D. M., Winfield, R. P., O'Connor, D. J. 1976. Mathematical modeling of phytoplankton in Lake Ontario, II. *US Environ. Prot. Agency Rep. EPA-600/3-76-065.* 87 pp.

Thornton, E. B. 1971. Variations of longshore currents across the surf zone. *Proc. 12th Conf. Coastal Eng.,* pp. 291–308

Vasseur, B., Funkquist, L., Paul, J. F. 1980. Verification of a numerical model for thermal plumes, *Svierges Meteorol. Och Hydrol. Inst., Norrkoping, Swed.* 122 pp.

Vollenweider, R. A. 1975. Input-output models with special reference to the phosphorus loading concept in limnology. *Schweiz. Z. Hydrol.* 37:53–84

Vollenweider, R. A. 1976. Advances in defining critical loading levels for phosphorus in lake entrophication. *Mem. Ist. Ital. Idrobiol.* 33:53–83

Vollenweider, R. A. 1977. Memorandum to members of the Task Group III on phosphorus loadings for the re-negotiation of the US-Canada agreement
Welander, P. 1957. Wind action on a shallow sea. *Tellus* 9:47–52
Windom, H. L., Duce, R. A., eds. 1976. *Marine Pollutant Transfer*. Lexington, Mass: Lexington Books, D.C. Heath. 390 pp.
Wong, P. T. S., Kaiser, K. L. E. 1975. Bacterial degradation of polychlorinated biphenyls, II. Rate studies. *Bull. Environ. Contam. Toxicol.* 13:249–55
Wunsch, C. 1969. Progressive internal waves on slopes. *J. Fluid Mech.* 35:131–44
Yingst, J. Y., Rhoads, D. C. 1977. Seafloor stability in central Long Island Sound, part II. See Rhoads et al 1977, pp. 245–60

Ann. Rev. Earth Planet. Sci. 1982. 10:355-76

REGOLITHS ON SMALL BODIES IN THE SOLAR SYSTEM[1]

Kevin R. Housen and Laurel L. Wilkening

Department of Planetary Sciences, Lunar and Planetary Laboratory,
University of Arizona, Tucson, Arizona 85721

INTRODUCTION

A regolith is defined as a layer or mantle of loose, incoherent, rocky material of whatever origin, that nearly everywhere forms the surface of the land and rests on coherent bedrock (Gary et al 1972). Such a description could well be a concise summary of the appearances of the surfaces of the Moon, Venus, and Mars. Spacecraft observations have shown that the surfaces of Mercury, the Moon, Mars and its satellites, and most of the satellites of Jupiter and Saturn are heavily cratered. The regoliths on these bodies are the result of continual impacts, which transform coherent surfaces into fragmental debris. It seems reasonable to infer that any rocky solar system object has been subjected to an intense bombardment by interplanetary debris and, therefore, should be enveloped by a regolith. The exceptions to this generalization are those planetary bodies with substantial atmospheres or those that were geologically active during, or subsequent to, the epoch of regolith formation. Io, the volcanically active satellite of Jupiter, is a good example of this. With such exceptions, it appears that regoliths must be the most widespread surface unit on solid planetary objects. Consequently, it is important to try to understand their genesis and evolution.

This paper focuses on the special case of regolith formation and evolution on small objects, such as asteroids and meteorite parent bodies. Small objects merit special attention because of their small gravitational fields. One cannot automatically assume that regoliths are formed on objects where the velocity of the crater ejecta may be close to or exceed the escape velocity.

Before delving into this subject, we take a brief detour to look at the lunar regolith, the most extensively studied regolith on a large body. Although the lunar regolith is interesting in its own right and has yielded information

[1] This work has been supported by NASA Grant NSG-7011.

0084-6597/82/0515-0355$02.00

regarding the interplanetary environment, we view it here only as a convenient benchmark for studies of the attributes of regoliths. Following the lunar discussion, we consider the properties of regoliths on small bodies as inferred from meteorites, followed by a summary of theoretical models of asteroidal regoliths. Finally, regoliths on comets and the satellites of Mars are discussed briefly.

THE LUNAR REGOLITH

Because of its heavily cratered surface and proximity to the Earth, the Moon is a natural laboratory for the study of impact-generated regoliths. It is also a standard of comparison. For these reasons, we briefly describe some of the salient features of the lunar regolith and the samples from it. For a much more comprehensive review of the properties of the lunar regolith, see Langevin & Arnold (1977) and Taylor (1975).

The Apollo missions to the Moon showed that the lunar surface is everywhere covered by a regolith. In the younger mare regions it is about 5–10 meters deep (e.g. Quaide & Oberbeck 1968, Shoemaker et al 1970), and it may be even deeper in the older highland regions. In the highlands it is thought to be underlain by an extensively fractured region called the megaregolith. The sizes of fragments in the lunar regolith range from a few micrometers to tens of meters, but most of the material is less than 1 mm in size.

Examination of the samples returned from the lunar surface show that the finer material is composed of mineral grains and glass (up to 50% by volume) in the less than 1 mm size range. While igneous rocks such as basalts are relatively abundant at mare landing sites, breccias are the most abundant rock type in the highlands and thus on the lunar surface. (A breccia is defined as a rock consisting of rounded or angular fragments sometimes embedded in a fine-grained matrix.) The lunar *soils* clearly show that rocky material exposed to space for long periods of time is broken into fragments and further comminuted into individual mineral grains. The existence of *breccias* demonstrates that impacts also recompact comminuted soil and weld it into coherent rocks. These are referred to as microbreccias, or soil breccias. Breccias are also formed by in situ shock transformation of preexisting coherent rock. The bombardment of the lunar surface has occurred over a wide range of size scales. Craters of meter size and larger are primarily responsible for the production of regolith from bedrock and for the formation of breccias. Impacts producing centimeter-size craters result in the fracture and comminution of existing debris fragments. At much smaller scales, micrometeoroids erode exposed rocks, produce glass, and garden the upper layers of regolith (Table 1).

The bombardment of the surface by energetic nuclear particles has also left an unmistakable record (Table 2). Lunar soils and some soil breccias contain

Table 1 Characteristics of gas-rich meteorites and lunar soils and breccias

	Gas-rich meteorites		Lunar samples★	
Impact glass (volume %)	rarely > 1%	d	as much as 50%	g
Agglutinates (volume %)	rare	e	up to 60%	f
Glassy spherules (volume %)	rare[+]	a	up to 10%	g
Micrometeorite craters	rare	a,c	ubiquitous	d
Helium -4(cm^3STP/g)	10^4–10^5	d	$\gtrsim 10^7$	d
Track-rich grains	1–20%	c	20–100%	b

★Lunar soils and unmetamorphosed breccias
[+]Cases employing only achondrites in the comparison
[a]Brownlee & Rajan 1973
[b]Crozaz & Dust 1977
[c]Goswami et al 1976
[d]Data collated from many different sources
[e]Kerridge & Kieffer 1977, Rajan et al 1974
[f]Heiken 1975
[g]Warner 1972

substantial amounts of implanted noble gases having the distinctive isotopic and elemental composition of the solar wind. Energetic particles of both solar and galactic origins also produce detectable amounts of radioactivity and solid-state damage in regolith components. Spallation reactions generate a wide range of nuclear fragments, including noble gases and radioactive species, which can be measured. The concentrations of these radiation effects can be used to determine the evolutionary history of the regolith, as discussed in the next section. The implications of the radiation effects in lunar samples are detailed by Lal (1972) and Langevin & Arnold (1977).

Studies of the core tubes of the lunar regolith show that there are discrete layers in terms of structure, composition, and/or irradiation effects (Crozaz 1977). Low energy irradiation effects are observed at all depths in the cores implying that even the deepest layers (3 m) were at one time exposed on the surface. Burial rates appear to be on the order of a few mm/Myr (Crozaz 1977). On the basis of the early data on the regolith, several models were proposed for the evolution of the lunar regolith. These have been reviewed by Langevin & Arnold (1977).

Table 2 Radiation affecting meteorites and lunar samples

	Energy (MeV/n)	Range (cm)	Ages (y)
Galactic cosmic rays	peaks near 100 extends to > 10^{15}	1-2 × 10^2	~10^6
Solar cosmic rays (heavy nuclei)	1–10 sharply decreasing for higher energy	10^{-2}	10^3–10^4
Solar wind	10^{-3}	10^{-5}	>10^2

REGOLITHS ON THE METEORITE PARENT BODIES

Properties of the Brecciated, Gas-Rich Meteorites

From the earliest observations (Von Reichenbach 1860, Wahl 1952) stony meteorites have been known to be breccias (Figure 1). Although terrestrial breccias may be formed in a variety of processes, meteoritic breccias show the effects of shock and, thus, seem to be more similar to impact breccias than other types. Brecciated meteorites are characterized by a structure in which millimeter- to centimeter-sized clasts are surrounded by fine-grained, usually darker, matrix. These clasts vary in shape from angular to rounded and appear to be fragments of preexisting rocks, either breccias or igneous rocks. In meteoritic breccias, angular clasts are apparently more common than rounded ones (Wahl 1952). The fine-grained matrix between clasts appears to have formed largely by the comminution of the same parent rocks from which the clasts were formed. Shock effects include fracturing and mosaicism of mineral grains, shock darkening and veining, and in some cases transformation of feldspars to glass. In most meteorites, however, glass is rare (less than 1%). A subset of brecciated stony meteorites is known as gas-rich meteorites, because they contain relatively large amounts of noble gases with the same elemental and isotopic signature of the solar wind. The existence of gas-rich

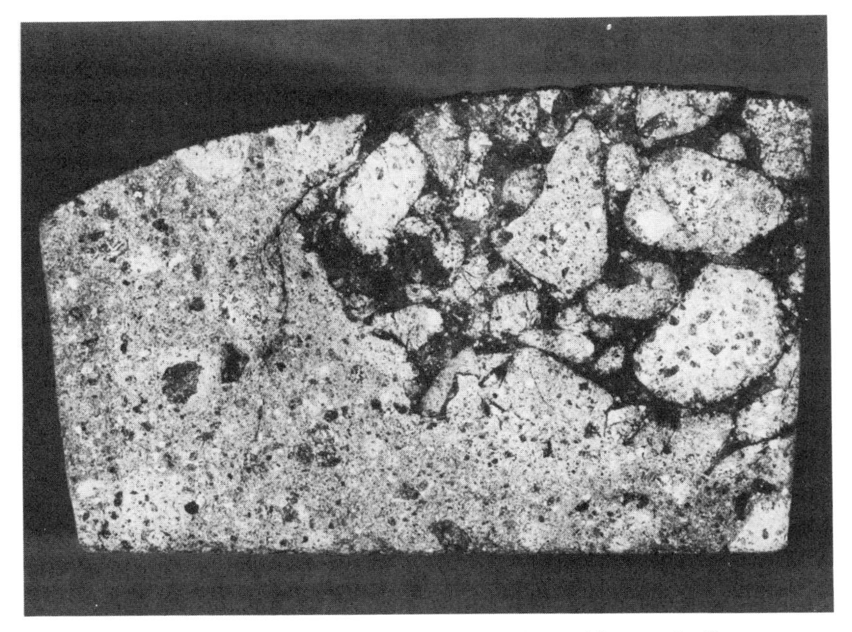

Figure 1 A 4-cm long fragment of the brecciated, gas-rich meteorite Kapoeta.

meteorites has been known since 1956 (Gerling & Levskii 1956). Wänke (1965) suggested that the origin of the noble gases in gas-rich meteorites was the solar wind. His suggestion was fully confirmed by additional studies of gas-rich meteorites and lunar samples. Because of their implanted solar wind gases, other radiation effects, and petrography, gas-rich meteorites are the closest meteoritic analogues to the breccias and soils that comprise the lunar regolith.

The radiation effects in gas-rich meteorites and lunar samples are produced by interactions of energetic particles with solid materials. There are three distinct classes of energetic particles that produce radiation features in meteorites (Table 2). (*a*) The highest energy particles are galactic cosmic rays (GCR) with energies ranging upward from 1.0 MeV/nucleon or more and peaking near 100 MeV/nucleon. These cosmic rays produce irradiation effects (spallation nuclides and nuclear particle tracks) to characteristic depths in silicate materials of 2 to 3 meters. (*b*) Less energetic solar cosmic rays (SCR) have energies on the order 1–10 MeV/nucleon and form particle tracks to depths of approximately 1 mm. (*c*) Solar wind (SW) particles (a few keV/nucleon) are so weak that they are simply deposited on silicate surfaces.

The density of radiation effects provides a record of the integrated exposure of the sample to each of the three classes of radiation. This record can be converted into an "exposure age" for each class of radiation, given a known or estimated production rate. Typical exposure ages for gas-rich meteorites are shown in Table 1.

Usually, the effects of irradiation by penetrating GCR can be seen throughout the entire volume of a meteorite. The effects are most often uniform or vary smoothly between contigous samples. This is not the case for the lower energy radiations. Both SW and SCR effects are localized within the meteorites. In gas-rich meteorites, which are by definition the meteorites containing implanted gases, SW gases and SCR tracks are confined to the fine-grained material interstitial to the larger fragments making up the breccia. Even within the interstitial material, solar flare tracks, which can be observed on a grain-by-grain basis, are found to be present in 10% or fewer of the grains.

Comparison with Lunar Breccias

Lunar soil breccias are similar to gas-rich meteorites in the sense that they both exhibit the textural characteristics and radiation features described above. For example, both lunar and meteoritic breccias exhibit particle tracks and spallation-produced noble gas isotopes and radioactive species as a result of GCR irradiation. Both contain grains with SCR tracks and SW-implanted noble gases. Grains are found with steep track density gradients (which indicate nearly direct exposure to space) and asymmetric track densities (which imply preferential irradiation on one side of a grain). The SW and SCR effects are localized in meteorites, just as in lunar breccias. Additionally, both lunar and meteoritic breccias contain impact-produced glass, microcraters, and agglutinates.

It was this overall similarity that prompted the suggestion of a regolith origin for meteorites. There is, however, a fundamental difference between lunar and meteoritic breccias. All of the diagnostic indicators of exposure to space irradiation and reworking of regolith material by cratering are lower in the meteorites than lunar materials, i.e. the gas-rich meteorites are relatively less *mature* regolith samples. For example, in comparison to lunar breccias, the GCR exposure ages of meteorites are generally two orders of magnitude smaller (Anders 1975). The SCR and SW exposure ages are generally 3 and 6 orders of magnitude smaller respectively (Anders 1975). Although microcraters, glasses, and agglutinates are found in meteorites, they are much less common than in the lunar regolith samples (Price et al 1975).

Another index of maturity is the size distribution of grains in a breccia. Size distribution measurements have been summarized by Bhattacharya et al (1975). For lunar breccias the number of grains rapidly increases at small sizes. On the other hand, gas-rich meteorites tend to have rather flat size distributions, i.e. meteoritic breccias tend to be rather coarse by lunar standards.

Because the physical properties of a breccia are determined by the manner in which the parent regolith evolves, the characteristics of meteorites and their differences from lunar samples are best understood by constructing theoretical models of regolith evolution. We now briefly review existing models of small body regoliths and the insights they have provided into the origins of meteorites.

ASTEROIDAL REGOLITHS

Asteroids have probably experienced two distinct epochs of regolith formation. During accretion, material that impacted protoasteroid surfaces was fractured and comminuted, although not extensively because the impacts had to be slow enough to result in net accumulation. Asteroids probably grew by building up layers of fragmental debris, i.e. layers of regolith. Part of such early regoliths in many bodies may have been destroyed by being converted into cohesive material by heating or gravitational compaction. Still, many asteroids, perhaps the small ones or those that escaped thermal metamorphism, should have survived, composed largely of regolith. Such massive collections are sometimes referred to as "accretionary megaregoliths."

The second epoch of regolith evolution began when the relative velocities of debris in the asteroid belt were raised to the presently observed value of approximately 5 km/s. The resulting hypervelocity impacts produce craters that comminute and eject surface material. The impact velocities are high enough to launch part of the crater ejecta to escape velocity. In fact, most asteroids are presently experiencing net erosion rather than accretion. Even so, if an asteroid is large enough to retain a nonnegligible fraction of its ejected debris, then the continual bombardment of its surface results in the formation of a regolith layer. Of course, for those bodies that accreted and retained a primordial regolithlike surface by escaping thermal metamorphism, the bombardment merely serves to further comminute the extant regolith. On bodies with consolidated surfaces, regolith is created when large craters penetrate the existing debris layer and excavate "pristine" material. The regolith will continue to grow until an energetic impact catastrophically fragments the body. For small bodies, regolith evolution stops at this point. However, for a large asteroid, impacts can occur which cause major internal fracturing but which are not energetic enough to disperse the fragments against their mutual gravitational field. These large bodies are expected to undergo several generations of regolith evolution in between fragmentation events and should, therefore, develop extensive "megaregoliths" prior to being dispersed by an energetic impact.

Because the nature of the early solar system environment is very poorly known, none of the existing regolith models have addressed the first epoch of regolith formation. Therefore, our review is confined to the second, i.e. modern-day, epoch. As such we need to concern oourselves with three factors: (*a*) the rate at which any given size crater forms on the surface; (*b*) the distribution of ejection velocities associated with a cratering event; and (*c*) the lifetime of an asteroid against collisional fragmentation. Before discussing the regolith models, we briefly review the sources of information that bear on these three quantities.

Cratering and Collisional Environment of Asteroids

CRATER SIZE-FREQUENCY DISTRIBUTION IN THE ASTEROID BELT Unlike the lunar case, there are no observations or measurements of the size distribution of craters on asteroids. Therefore, the crater distribution must be derived indirectly. One method, discussed in Housen et al (1979a), is based on estimates of the mass frequency distribution of impactors in the asteroid belt. This is combined with relationships between impact kinetic energy and resulting crater diameter to find the frequency with which craters of various sizes are formed, i.e. the crater size frequency distribution. Unfortunately the mass flux of projectiles in the asteroid belt is not well known. Observations abound for 1 AU (for example, see reviews by Dohnanyi 1972 or McDonnell 1978), but it is not known how the flux varies with heliocentric distance. For now, theoretical models are the best source of information regarding the debris population in the asteroid belt (Kessler 1970, Dohnanyi 1976). These models are constrained at very large masses by telescopic observations of asteroids and at very small masses by spacecraft measurements of interplanetary dust. Observations of centimeter-size particles between 1 and 3.5 AU were made by the Asteroid/Meteoroid Detector on the Pioneer 10 and 11 spacecrafts (Soberman et al 1974), but the results have been plagued with calibration difficulties (Auer 1974). Thus, over much of the mass range of interest, our estimates of the mass flux are unconstrained by observations; errors as large as an order of magnitude cannot be ruled out.

In order to derive the crater size distribution, we require crater-scaling laws, i.e. relationships between the kinetic energy of a projectile and the size of the resulting crater. The functional form of the cratering laws changes depending primarily on the size of the crater, the strength of the target material, and the magnitude of the local gravity field (Chabai 1977, Gault & Wedekind 1977, Holsapple & Schmidt 1979). Exact expressions for the cratering laws, for all possible values of the dependent variables, are not known. However, two limiting relationships exist. If the effects of material strength dominate gravitational forces (i.e. if craters are small, material strength is high or gravity is small), then crater diameter is proportional to $E^{1/3}$, where E is the impact energy and material strength is constant. This is referred to as the "strength-scaling" regime. When gravitational forces are dominant, crater diameter is proportional to $E^{0.29}$ at fixed impact velocity. Additionally, in this "gravity-scaling" regime, diameter is also proportional to g^{-a},where g is the magnitude of the local gravity field and a is a constant. Various estimates for a, in the range of 1/4 to 1/8, have been developed (e.g. Chabai 1977).

The proportionality constants involved in the cratering laws can be evaluated from actual cratering experiments. Impacts into cohesive targets have been performed by Gault et al (1963), Gault (1972), Bloch et al (1971), Vedder (1971), and Moore (1976). Impacts into less cohesive targets have been performed by Culp & Hooper (1961), Braslau (1970), Vedder (1972), Stoffler et al (1975), and Moore (1976). Many explosion cratering studies have also been carried out (see, for example, Roddy et al 1977) and can be related to impact cratering (Oberbeck 1971, Holsapple 1980).

By specifying the impact velocity of debris (5 km/s; Dohnanyi 1969), the cratering laws can be combined with the mass flux estimates to yield the desired crater size frequency distribution. The resulting expressions are given in Housen et al (1979a).

An alternate method for finding the crater size distribution was used by Langevin & Maurette (1980). By using cratering laws they "inverted" the observed mare lunar crater distribution to obtain the mass distribution of projectiles at 1 AU. They assumed the mass distribution at 3 AU to have the same shape as that at 1 AU, although the rate of impacts was taken to be 30 times higher at 3 AU. They then used crater-scaling laws to find the crater distribution in the asteroid belt, taking into account differences in impact velocity and target strength between the Moon and the asteroids. While this method does not rely on a specific estimate of the projectile mass distribution at 3 AU, there may be significant uncertainties introduced by the assumption of similar impacting projectile mass distributions for the Moon and the asteroids. The distribution of asteroidal debris is the result of mutual collisional evolution over a period of time. Conversely, much of the debris delivered to the Moon may have originated in discrete catastrophic events (Wetherill 1976). The mass distributions resulting from discrete collisional events and from multiple events (i.e. fragmentation of fragments) are not the same.

CRATER EJECTA VELOCITIES Due to the difficulty in accurately measuring velocities of ejected debris, only a few measurements of crater ejecta velocities have been made. Gault et al (1963) determined the velocity distribution of ejecta for small craters in basalt. Most of the material is ejected at speeds less than $\lesssim$ 100 m/s. Note, the escape velocity for a $\sim$ 100 km diameter asteroid is of the order of 70 m/s, so a significant fraction of crater ejecta is retained by these and larger bodies.

The velocity of ejecta in less cohesive targets is considerably lower than that for basalt, primarily because some of the impact energy is used on compaction of porous target materials. Stoffler et al (1975) measured the fraction of mass ejected beyond a given range for small craters in unbonded sand targets. Typical ejection velocities are of the order of meters per second. Thus, it is apparent that the more regolith a body accumulates, the more ejecta it can retain.

Additional information related to crater ejecta velocities for various types of target materials and crater sizes can be found in Oberbeck & Morrison (1976), Ivanov (1976), McDonnell et al (1976), and O'Keefe & Ahrens (1976).

ASTEROID COLLISIONAL LIFETIMES An asteroid is catastrophically fragmented, that is, fractured into a multitude of smaller objects, when an impact occurs with energy exceeding a critical value. The critical projectile energy per unit target mass has been determined experimentally for various target materials. For basalt targets and glass targets, the energy required for fragmentation is of the order 10^7–10^8 erg/g (Moore & Gault 1965, Gault & Wedekind 1969, Fujiwara et al 1977, Hartmann 1978). Hartmann (1978) also performed experiments using weaker, cabonaceous-chondrite-like, targets. Fragmentation occurred when the energy exceeded roughly 10^4–5×10^4 erg/g.

Notice that this is the energy required to extensively fracture a target. For large asteroids the kinetic energy of the collisional fragments may not exceed the gravitational binding energy. Hence, a body may be highly fragmented and then reaccumulate into a gravitationally bound ball of debris (Housen et al 1979a, Davis et al 1979, Fujiwara & Tsukamoto 1980). Of course, regolith evolution suffers a great discontinuity during such events, and so regolith models generally consider the evolution only until fragmentation occurs.

It should also be noted that considerable errors may arise in extrapolating the results of small-scale experiments to the fragmentation of asteroids. The scaling problem for such experiments has not yet been solved. Thus, the accuracy of our estimates of asteroid fragmentation lifetimes remains somewhat uncertain.

Models of Asteroidal Regolith Evolution

Early regolith models were relatively simple attempts to understand problems related to asteroids or meteorites. Most of these models were not focused on the same problem and cannot be directly compared with one another. Because of recent advances in our understanding of cratering physics, detailed models have emerged as a result of two parallel efforts, one in France and the other in Arizona. Principal points of divergence between these efforts are input parameters and modeling techniques. Each of the regolith models is now briefly reviewed in approximately chronological order.

CHAPMAN'S MODEL The earliest model of asteroidal regoliths was developed by Chapman (1971) in order to understand the texture of the uppermost microns of asteroidal surfaces as inferred from astronomical observations. Chapman (1976) also appealed to this model in speculations on the origin of brecciated meteorites. Chapman's model emphasized the erosive effects of numerous small impacts on the wide-spread ejecta deposits of large craters. He concluded that asteroidal regoliths are very thin, except for those on the largest bodies and that even large bodies must have regoliths only "skin-deep" (< 100m). This conclusion, in conjunction with (*a*) the fact that a significant fraction (tens of percent) of all meteorites are brecciated, and (*b*) the assumption that most meteorites are derived from large cratering events that sample parent bodies to kilometer depths, led Chapman to believe that the formation and irradiation of meteorites must have occurred during very early epochs of solar system evolution. Only the megaregoliths developed during asteroidal accretion were believed to be thick enough to produce the observed ratio of brecciated to nonbrecciated meteorites. More detailed models have shown that asteroidal regoliths are thicker than indicated by Chapman's work, hence, later formation of regolith is not excluded.

ANDER'S MODEL In order to deduce the formation location of gas-rich meteorites, Anders (1975, 1978) constructed a simple model using the observation that these meteorites have shorter cosmic-ray exposure ages and lower gas contents than do lunar soils. He argued that the amount of implanted solar wind gases should be inversely proportional to the square of the distance from the Sun and directly proportional to the mean residence time of a grain at the surface. Anders ascribed the differences between the gas contents and exposure ages of meteorites and lunar soils to differences in cratering rates. In fact, he argued that mean residence times are inversely proportional to mean cratering rates. The data implied to Anders that the meteorites have come from an environment in which the cratering rate is 1 to 3 orders of magnitude greater than in the vicinity of the Moon and at a location a few times farther from the Sun, i.e. the meteorites have come from the asteroid belt. Anders' model isolated the critical parameters that differentiate the lunar and asteroidal regolith environments; however, the model ignored the detailed differences among the asteroids.

THE MODEL OF BORG AND CO-WORKERS Borg et al (1975) modified a Monte Carlo program, designed to simulate the effects of the charged particle irradiation of the lunar regolith, and applied it to asteroids. This work was the first statistical consideration of the irradiation of regoliths on asteroids, and the first in a series of studies of small body regoliths by the French group. Simulations of the irradiation of grains contained in the Kapoeta meteorite suggested an origin on a small body (diameter 50 km) with a regolith stirring rate roughly 15 times greater than that on the Moon.

HOUSEN'S EARLY MODEL In a preliminary model, Housen (1976) determined regolith depth at a given time by computing the distance below an asteroid's surface where only one excavation had occurred. Rocky bodies 200 km in diameter were found to accumulate debris layers roughly 100 m thick over a period of 1 Gyr. Although these calculations gave results a factor of ten below those required by Anders (1975), they represented the first quantitative model estimates of regolith depths and demonstrated that regoliths on bodies much smaller than the Moon are considerably more than mere coatings of dust, as others had assumed. Refined modeling techniques by Housen et al (1979 a,b) and improved input parameters have revised depth estimates upward, as discussed later.

THE WORK OF MATSON AND CO-WORKERS Matson et al (1977) took a unique approach to the consideration of asteroidal regoliths. They addressed the question of whether lunar-regolith-like processes occur on asteroids by examining asteroid spectral data for the signature of optical "maturation," involving an inverse correlation between redness and albedo. Finding no such evidence, Matson et al considered several possible explanations for the differences between asteroids and the Moon. They concluded that asteroidal regoliths are thinner and coarser than the lunar regolith, and that they are created by impacts at velocities too low to produce much glass. Neither the evidence cited by Matson et al nor the other remote sensing data about asteroidal surfaces is really capable of addressing the question of how deep asteroidal regoliths may be.

THE HOUSEN ET AL MODEL Following Housen's (1976) early model, Housen et al (1979a) developed the first reasonably detailed model of regolith evolution on small bodies. This was the first attempt to account for the dependence of cratering laws on asteroidal size and compositional strength.

Housen et al recognized that regolith depth varies from point to point on an asteroid's surface. An analytic expression for the surficial distribution of depths is very difficult to determine and Monte Carlo calculations can become quite expensive, so they computed an average regolith depth. If the entire surface were considered, then the average could become heavily weighted by the effects of a few large craters which are not representative of most of the surface. So, the averaging was not done over the entire surface, but only over those areas saturated by the effects of numerous small impacts. On this portion of the surface it was thought that the regolith should be relatively uniform in depth and so could adequately be described by an average value. The modeled portion of the surface was referred to as the "typical region."

The model of Housen et al (1979a) applies only to bodies sufficiently small such that ejecta from craters are globally distributed (i.e. rocky bodies of diameter $<$ 100–300 km and weaker asteroids, where ejecta velocities are lower, of diameter $<$ 10 km). For these bodies small craters garden and deplete the regolith, while ejecta from large craters contribute to regolith buildup in the typical region. The crater bowls themselves were excluded from the typical region until a time when they became sufficiently numerous to meet a mathematical criterion for saturation.

The depth of regolith as a function of time and the extent to which surficial material is gardened by meteoroid impact was computed. Regolith depths on moderate-size, differentiated bodies are of the order of a few kilometers. Small rocky asteroids (diameter $<$ a few tens of km) develop negligible regoliths because the velocity of ejecta from impact craters exceeds the escape velocity. Small weak bodies develop centimeter- to meter-scale debris layers, because the low ejection velocities allow retention of most ejecta. In all cases studied, surface debris are buried quickly by widespread ejecta from impact events. Both moderate-size (diameter 100–300 km), differentiated objects and small undifferentiated objects are found to provide suitable environments for the production of gas-rich meteorites, i.e. the computed times of exposure at or near the surface to charged particle irradiation are consistent with those observed in meteorites.

The model for small bodies was extended and applied to larger bodies, where ejecta are no longer globally distributed (Housen et al 1979b). In a manner similar to that in which craters were treated, the debris from larger craters were excluded from the typical region until a time when the ejecta deposits became sufficiently numerous to saturate the surface.

For the largest asteroids (diameter 500–100 km) the regolith depth in the typical region is smaller than that on moderate-size bodies because the high gravity fields of large asteroids produce less-widespread ejecta blankets. Thus, much of the ejecta that is widespread (and so builds up the regolith in the typical region) on moderate-size bodies is excluded from the typical region on large bodies. Furthermore, as asteroid size increases, more craters tend to become gravity scaled, as opposed to the predominantly strength-scaled craters on smaller rocky bodies. Compared to a strength-scaled population of craters, gravity-scaled craters have relatively less volume concentrated in large diameters and more in small ones. Thus, gravity-scaled craters are less efficient in generating new regolith and more efficient in reworking existing debris. This transition in scaling laws tends to make the regolith in the typical region on large bodies thinner and more extensively gardened compared to smaller asteroids.

As a test case, Housen et al (1979b) applied their large body model to regolith development on the lunar mare. A regolith depth of several meters was computed, in agreement with actual observations of regolith depth on the Moon.

THE WORK OF CINTALA AND CO-WORKERS Through a qualitative discussion of the effects on impact cratering on small bodies, Cintala et al (1978, 1979) suggested some processes that should influence regolith evolution. They pointed out that the small radii of curvature and weak gravity fields will result in widely spread ejecta (Cintala et al 1978) and because the coarsest debris ejected from a crater also have the lowest velocity, regoliths on small asteroids, where escape velocities are low, should be quite blocky whereas larger bodies will retain the high velocity fine-grained material. Cintala et al (1979) suggested that impact-generated seismic effects should be important. Shock waves from moderate-size cratering events may loft surface debris over a large part of an asteroid. On small bodies this mechanism may contribute to regolith erosion. On large bodies seismic shaking may enhance regolith gardening. Higher energy events are expected to cause spallation of asteroids.

THE DURAUD AND CO-WORKERS MODEL Duraud et al (1979) briefly described a model for the equilibrium thickness of regolith on small bodies. The erosive and depositional effects of cratering on an existing regolith layer were considered. For a 20 km diameter asteroid, an equilibrium thickness of 2 m was computed. For a 200 km body, the thickness was found to be 200 m.

In order to assess the characteristic time required to reach equilibrium, Duraud et al assumed the flux of debris in the asteroid belt is 10 times higher than at 1 AU. Using this flux they found that the 20 km body reaches equilibrium in less than 100 Myr and that the regolith subsequently recedes into the interior of the asteroid at a rate of 10 m/Gyr. The rate for a 200 km asteroid is 2 m/Gyr. Emplacement of crater ejecta is envisioned to occur as a "steady rain" on small bodies, rather than in discrete layers as observed on the Moon. Hence, it was concluded that small-body regoliths should be devoid of layers.

The factor of ten used in this model for mass flux increase between 1 AU and 3 AU is too low. As discussed in a preceding section, the impacting projectiles that are most pertinent to regolith formation are the large ones. Various observations can be used to estimate the flux difference (Kessler 1970, Dohnanyi 1972, Chapman 1976). A reasonable assumption for the increase in flux of large bodies is 10^2 or perhaps 10^3, rather than the factor of 10 assumed by Duraud et al. It is worthwhile to note that the rate of small-asteroid surface erosion calculated (10m/Gyr) is roughly 50 times smaller than that computed by Housen et al (1979a) for a 10 km diameter asteroid. A more reasonable impact rate in the Duraud et al model would produce agreement between the two models.

THE DRAN AND CO-WORKERS MODEL Dran et al (1979) applied the calculations of Duraud et al to the irradiation of regolith material. The rate at which the regolith recedes into an asteroid's interior dictates the time of exposure of regolith grains to charged particles. Dran et al predicted, for the 20 km body, that galactic cosmic-ray exposure effects for regolith material should be lower by a factor of > 10 relative to lunar soils. The densities of solar flare particle tracks should be roughly 300 times less than those observed for the Moon. It was suggested that these predictions fit observations of irradiated grains in the Kapoeta meteorite. That is, a recent origin of Kapoeta on a small body was proposed, and origins early in the history of the solar system were discarded. In particular, irradiation while the grains floated freely in space prior to parent body accretion was rejected because the exposure time to both galactic and solar cosmic-ray particles would be similar, contrary to observations. Furthermore, irradiation during accretion (i.e. a megaregolith origin) apparently would have resulted in exposure times smaller than those observed, due to the presumed high flux of impacting debris during accretion.

The erosion rate calculated by Dran et al for a 20 km asteroid results in an exposure time to galactic cosmic rays of 10^8 yr for regolith material. This is two orders of magnitude greater than the observed exposure ages in meteorites. Unless another mechanism is called on to limit the exposure times, e.g. catastrophic rupture, the claim that model results are in accord with observations is clearly unfounded. However, as discussed above, if a more reasonable value for the impact flux in the asteroid belt is assumed, the erosion rate increases (thus the exposure times decrease) by a factor of 10 to 100 relative to those given by Dran et al. Clearly this would improve the calculated exposure times.

THE MODELS OF LANGEVIN AND MAURETTE Langevin & Maurette (1976) developed a regolith model in order to isolate the input parameters that are most critical in determining regolith thickness. Their estimate of the asteroidal cratering distribution was based on the lunar crater distribution, as discussed earlier.

The other important input parameter addressed is the velocity distribution of crater ejecta. They assumed that the fraction of ejecta with velocity greater than v is equal to $(v_r/v)^2$ where v_r is the velocity of ejecta at the crater rim. For strength-scaled craters, the value of v_r was taken to be a function of target strength only, while for gravity scaling, v_r was assumed proportional to gD, where g is the gravitational acceleration and D is the crater diameter.

The evolution of regolith depth at a point on the surface was modeled by evaluating the depletion due to local cratering and the buildup due to deposition of crater ejecta, although ejecta from the largest craters were excluded. Thus, by excluding from their model the parts of the surface occupied by large-crater ejecta (i.e. nonsaturated ejecta deposits), Langevin & Maurette modeled a "typical region" similar to Housen et al (1979b).

Although both the projectile mass distribution and the crater ejecta velocity distribution are poorly known, Langevin & Maurette concluded that the velocity distribution is the most critical parameter in regolith evolution. This distribution governs the extent of localization of ejecta, which dictates when ejecta are included in the regolith depth computations. For example, large ejecta velocities imply more extensive ejecta deposits, which saturate quickly. In this case, ejecta are quickly included so that relatively thick regoliths result.

Regolith depths at the time of asteroid fragmentation were computed for various sizes and strengths of bodies. Small (17.5 km diameter) weak bodies accumulated 70 m of regolith during their 700 Myr collisional lifetime. Larger weak bodies built up thinner debris layers due to the higher gravity fields, which resulted in more-localized ejecta deposits. Small and moderate-size, strong objects (diameter < 150 km) retained negligible regolith due to escape of most ejecta. Larger bodies of diameter 300 km developed roughly 800 m of regolith over a collisional lifetime greater than 4 Gyr. Regolith thickness on the Moon was estimated to be a few to several meters, depending on the material strength assumed.

Note that these regolith depths are a factor of a few smaller than those computed by Housen et al (1979a,b). This is primarily due to differences in how ejecta blankets were modeled, and to the fact that Housen et al may have slightly overestimated ejecta velocities. (See Housen 1981a for a discussion.)

Langevin & Maurette (1981) modeled the grain size and maturity of the lunar and asteroidal regoliths. They considered the competing processes of agglutination and comminution. On the Moon, grains are quickly comminuted to sizes less than a few hundred microns whereupon a change in the meteoritic mass distribution reduces the role of fragmentation. For these small grains an equilibrium is reached between agglutination and comminution. On asteroids, the high flux of large craters results in rapid burial of surface grains, thus increasing the lifetime against fragmentation. On the other hand, the large impacts enhance shock comminution and make it the dominant destructive process for asteroidal regolith grains. Agglutination is not very efficient due to the lower velocity of debris and the rapid rate of burial. The net result is that regoliths on basaltic asteroids should be coarser than the lunar regolith. Weaker asteroids should be more fine-grained, because comminution increases in porous target materials.

Langevin & Maurette also considered the vertical and lateral mixing of regolith material and the preservation of deposited strata. Because of the low gravity fields of asteroids, only rather thick strata are preserved against lateral dispersion. That is, only thick strata behave as "closed systems." While this applies to weak asteroids, basaltic asteroids are often shaken by impact-generated seismic events, which homogenize the regolith.

THE MODEL OF HORZ AND SCHAAL Horz & Schaal (in preparation) considered the formation of agglutinates in asteroidal regoliths. They noted that 5 km/s impacts into porous, fine-grained targets result in the formation of agglutinates, which are ubiquitous in lunar soils but are rare in brecciated meteorites. They then addressed the question of mechanisms that might prevent asteroidal regoliths from becoming fine-grained.

Based on cratering theory and experiments, Horz & Schaal proposed that energetic impacts on asteroids should generate seismic waves of sufficient intensity to cause spallation at free surfaces. The spallation products are expected to be very blocky and should be ejected with low velocities of the order of m/sec. Moreover, it is suggested that the volume of spalled ejecta may be an order of magnitude larger than the crater volume. This mechanism is expected to make asteroidal regoliths more coarse-grained than the lunar regolith, thus reducing the agglutinate content of meteoritic breccias. This may also increase the burial rate of surface debris beyond that computed in existing regolith models.

HOUSEN'S STOCHASTIC MODEL Housen (1981b) considered the stochastic evolution of asteroidal regoliths. He noted that current regolith models characterize the depth of an asteroid's regolith by a single, average value. However, regolith depth is a function of the number of craters of given size on a surface, the relative positions of craters, and their order of occurrence. Because these are all random quantities (for example, we can predict the mean number of craters on an asteroid, but the actual number will differ from the mean), our estimates of regolith depth will have an associated stochastic variability. Moreover, the depth of regolith varies from point to point on an asteroid's surface. Thus, the depth at a surface point will differ from the computed mean value for two reasons: (*a*) the variability arising from stochastic fluctuations in the number of craters on a surface, their relative positions, and their times of formation; and (*b*) the surficial variation in depth. The total variability is large; it is of the same order as the mean value itself. The relative magnitude of the two components of variation were estimated. For small bodies whose crater ejecta are widely spread over a surface, the two components are roughly equal. For larger asteroids, where surfaces are made rather "lumpy" by the more localized ejecta deposits, the second component is roughly 1.5 to 2 times larger than the first.

One of the major reasons for constructing regolith models is to try to constrain the origins of meteorites. The statistical uncertainties associated with computed regolith depths, or functions of the depth, serve to limit the utility of regolith models in predicting the sizes of meteorite parent bodies.

For the most part, the models discussed above do not address the same topics. There are, however, some areas of overlap. When the charged particle irradiation of regoliths is considered (Housen et al 1979a,b, Dran et al 1979), even though the models are still rather crude, there seems to be general agreement that the gas-rich meteorites could have formed in modern-day regoliths. Recent estimates of regolith depth (Housen et al 1979a,b, Langevin & Maurette 1980) differ by a factor of a few primarily because of differences in modeling techniques and assumed values of input parameters (Housen 1981b). Collectively, these models have altered our picture of modern-day asteroidal regoliths from thin coatings of dust to rather substantial accumulations of debris, which are capable of producing many brecciated and gas-rich meteorites.

A Comparison of Asteroidal Regoliths with the Lunar Regolith

The depth of the lunar regolith is of the order of a few meters. On the other hand, regolith depths on asteroids, which are smaller than the Moon and so retain less crater ejecta, can be as large as a few kilometers. This somewhat paradoxical situation arises for two reasons, illustrated in Figure 2 and discussed below.

1. The crater flux for asteroids is higher than at 1 AU. For purposes of illustration, consider a Vesta-sized object at 3 AU (Figure 2). From the Housen et al (1979b) calculations we expect roughly 1.5 km of regolith to develop over a period of 3.5 Gyr. If this body were moved to 1 AU, it would accumulate only 30 m of regolith in 3.5 Gyr due solely to the reduced flux at 1 AU. Obviously, for equal evolution times, if the cratering flux is reduced, then the amount of regolith is also reduced. The smaller mass flux and higher impact velocity at 1 AU result in a cratering rate that is a factor of 100 below that at 3 AU. The reason that the regolith depth only decreases by a factor of 50, rather than by a factor of 100, is because regolith growth is not linear in time.

2. Size of the body. Comparing the Vesta-sized asteroid at 1 AU with the Moon, we see that the Moon develops the lesser amount of regolith. This occurs for the same reasons that the largest asteroids have deeper regoliths than slightly smaller bodies; higher gravity fields imply smaller craters and less widespread ejecta.

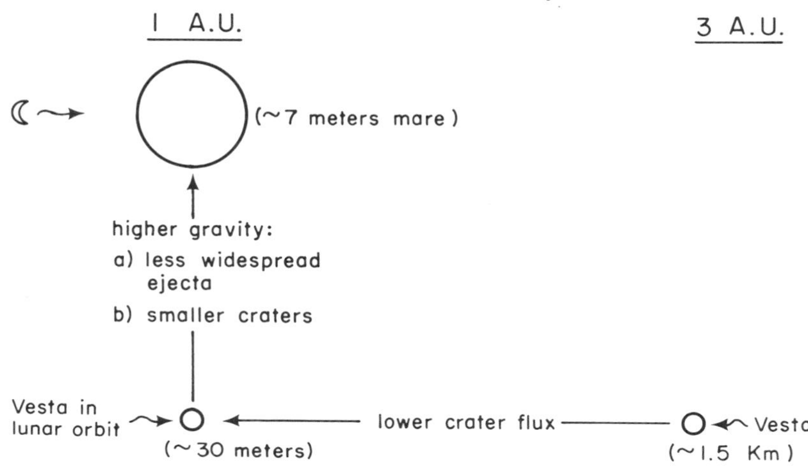

Figure 2 An illustration from Housen et al (1979b) summarizing the processes that make asteroidal regoliths differ from the lunar regolith. An asteroid at 3 AU develops more regolith in the same period of time than does a similar-sized body at 1 AU because of the higher flux of large craters at 3 AU. For two bodies of different size, both at 1 AU (or 3 AU), the larger body develops less regolith because the higher gravity makes less-widespread ejecta blankets and smaller craters.

As discussed earlier, the lunar regolith is quite mature compared to meteoritic breccias. That is, lunar breccias exhibit, on the average, greater exposure times to solar wind and solar flare irradiation and higher contents of glasses, agglutinates, and microcraters. The short exposure times have previously been attributed to higher regolith stirring rates for asteroids (Price et al 1975, Goswami et al 1976) or to short residence times in a regolith due to ejection to space. After detailed regolith models had been constructed, it became apparent that short exposure ages are due chiefly to rapid burial (Housen et al 1979a,b). The high cratering rates and more-widespread ejecta deposits tend to bury surface materials on asteroids faster than on the Moon. The rapid burial rates occur for the same reasons that asteroidal regoliths are deeper than the lunar regolith.

REGOLITHS ON OTHER SMALL BODIES

The only small bodies whose surfaces have been observed at high resolution are the satellites of Mars—Phobos and Deimos. Their small sizes—Phobos is $27 \times 21 \times 19$ km, and Deimos is $15 \times 12 \times 11$ km—make them of special interest. Both are heavily cratered and completely covered with lunar-like regolith (see, for example, Figure 3). However, there are a number of mor-

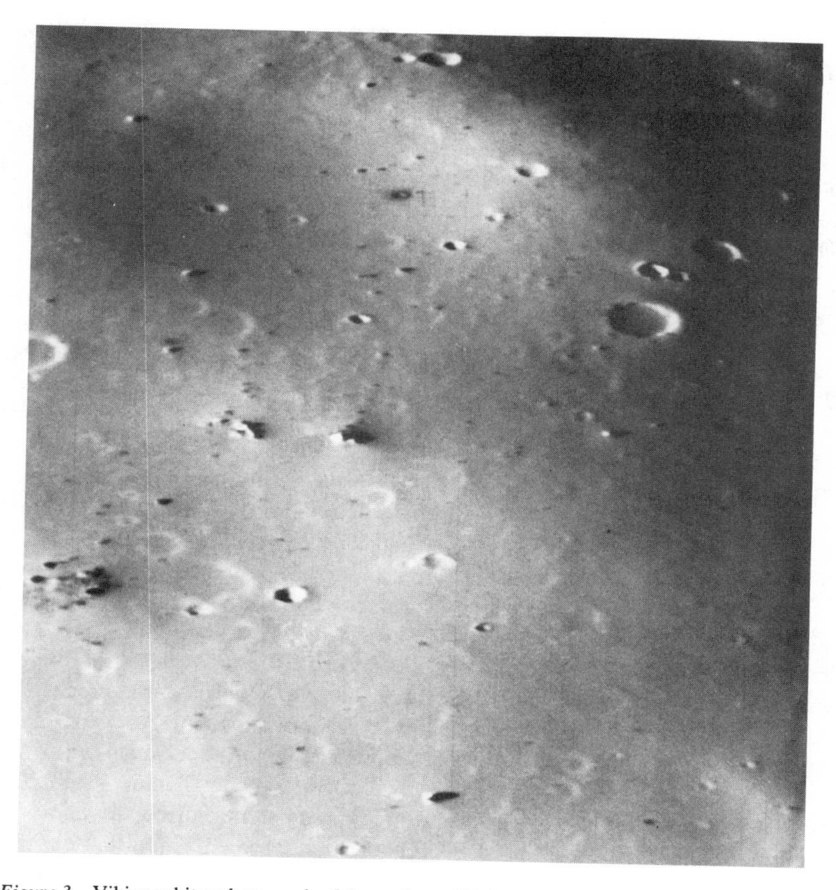

Figure 3 Viking orbiter photograph of the surface of Deimos. The smallest features seen in this image are roughly one meter in width.

phological differences between the two (Thomas 1979). Veverka & Thomas (1979) have described Phobos and Deimos with reference to their similarities to small asteroids. An important difference between the martian satellites and asteroids is that the satellites are in the gravitational field of Mars. Soter (1971) has described a mechanism in which ejecta are recaptured by the satellites. Hence, regoliths on Phobos and Deimos probably have an evolutionary history and a character different from those on asteroids.

As discussed by Anders (1975, 1978), one would not expect breccias similar to the gas-rich meteorites to develop on the surface of active comets. However, Cintala (1981) has suggested that short-period comets might accrete meteoroids as a consequence of collisions with asteroidal debris. As the comet is devolatilized an accumulation regolith would be left behind. Such a regolith would be expected to have different properties (e.g. grain size, radiation effects, composition) from the regoliths described for asteroids.

CONCLUSIONS

Studies of lunar samples and meteorites have yielded data that have permitted construction of first order models of regolith evolution on asteroidal surfaces. The picture that has emerged is one in which regolith formation proceeds by deposition of discrete layers of the widely spread ejecta primarily from the larger impacts. Moderate-size (100–300 km diameter) asteroids are covered by modest regoliths of the order of one km in depth. Small rocky asteroids of diameter tens of km develop negligible regoliths. Small weak asteroids develop centimeter-meter-scale debris layers. The larger bodies are expected to have experienced many cycles of regolith development and fragmentation before finally being dispersed by an energetic impact. These cycles of fracturing mean that the larger asteroids are composed of impact-produced megaregolith under their surface layers of regolith. As a result, the larger asteroids are envisioned as being highly fragmented balls of megaregolith.

However, modeling to reproduce our detailed knowledge of the radiation histories of meteorites is hampered by inadequate knowledge of some of the necessary input parameters and certain aspects of the cratering process. The most critical gaps in our knowledge are the mass frequency distribution of matter in the asteroid belt, past and present, and the physics of the process in low gravity environments. Both deficiencies are amenable to some improvement by possible, albeit difficult, observations or experiments.

In short, regolith models have reached a level of detail that is roughly similar to the precision of the required input parameters. Further advances in our understanding of regoliths on small bodies must come from further experimentation.

Literature Cited

Anders, E. 1975. Do stony meteorites come from comets? *Icarus* 24:363–71

Anders, E. 1978. Most stony meteorites come from the asteroid belt. In *Asteroids: An Exploration Assessment,* ed. D. Morrison, W. C. Wells, pp. 57–76. NASA Conf. Pub. 2053

Auer, S. 1974. The asteroid belt: Doubts about the concentration measured with the Asteroid/Meteoroid detector on Pioneer 10. *Science* 186:650–52

Bhattacharya, S. K., Goswami, J. N., Lal, D., Patel, P., Rao, M. N. 1975. Lunar regolith and gas-rich meteorites: Characterization based on particle tracks and grain-size distributions. *Proc. Lunar Sci. Conf., 6th,* pp. 3509–26

Bloch, M. R., Fechtig, H., Gentner, W., Neukum, G., Schneider, E. 1971. Meteorite impact craters, crater simulations, and the meteoroid flux in the early solar system. *Proc. Lunar Sci. Conf., 2nd.* 3:2639–52

Borg, J., Durand, J. P., Langevin, Y., Maurette, M. 1975. A Monte Carlo model for the accumulation of solar flare tracks and spallation products in extraterrestrial regoliths. *Meteoritics* 10:365–68

Braslau, D. 1970. Partitioning of energy in hypervelocity impact against loose sand target. *J. Geophys. Res.* 70:5075–98

Brownlee, D. E., Rajan, R. S. 1973. Micrometeorite craters discovered on Chondrule-like objects from Kapoeta meteorite. *Science* 182:1341–44

Chabai, A. J. 1977. Influence of gravitational fields and atmospheric pressures on scaling of explosion craters. In *Impact and Explosion Cratering*, ed. D. J. Roddy, R. O. Pepin, R. B. Merrill

Chapman, C. R. 1971. *Surface properties of asteroids*. PhD thesis. Mass. Inst. Tech., Cambridge

Chapman, C. R. 1976. Asteroids as meteorite parent bodies: The astronomical perspective. *Geochim. Cosmochim. Acta* 40:701–19

Cintala, M. J. 1981. Meteoroid impact into short-period comet nuclei. *Nature* 291: 134–36

Cintala, M. J., Head, J. W., Veverka, J. 1978. Characteristics of the cratering process on small satellites and asteroids. *Proc. Lunar Planet. Sci. Conf., 9th*, pp. 3803–30

Cintala, M. J., Head, J. W., Wilson, L. 1979. The nature and effects of impact cratering on small bodies. In *Asteroids*, ed. T. Gehrels, pp. 579–600. Univ. Ariz. Press.

Crozaz, G. 1977. The irradiation history of the lunar soil. *Phys. Chem. Earth* 10:197–214

Crozaz, G., Dust, S. 1977. Irradiation history of lunar cores and the development of the regolith. *Proc. Lunar Sci. Conf., 8th*, pp. 3001–16

Culp, F. L., Hooper, H. L. 1961. Study of impact cratering in sand. *J. Appl. Phys.* 11:2480–85

Davis, D. R., Chapman, C. R., Greenberg, R., Weidenschilling, S. J., Harris, A. W. 1979. Collisional evolution of asteroids: Populations, rotations, and velocities. In *Asteroids*, ed. T. Gehrels, pp. 528–57. Univ. Ariz. Press

Dohnanyi, J. S. 1969. Collisional model of asteroids and their debris. *J. Geophys. Res.* 74:2531–54

Dohnanyi, J. S. 1972. Interplanetary objects in review: Statistics of their masses and dynamics. *Icarus* 17:1–48

Dohnanyi, J. S. 1976. Sources of interplanetary dust: Asteroids. In *Interplanetary Dust and Zodiacal Light, Proc. IAU Colloq. 31*, ed. H. Elsasser, H. Fechtig, pp. 187–205. Springer-Verlag

Dran, J. C., Duraud, J. P., Langevin, Y., Maurette, M. 1979. The predicted irradiation record of asteroidal regoliths and the origin of gas-rich meteorites. *Lunar Planet. Sci. X*, pp. 309–11

Duraud, J. P., Langevin, Y., Maurette, M. 1979. An analytical model for the regolith evolution of small bodies in the solar system. *Lunar Planet. Sci. X*, pp. 323–25

Fujiwara, A., Tsukamoto, A. 1980. Experimental study on the velocity of fragments in collisional break-up. *Icarus* 44:142–53

Fujiwara, A., Kamimoto, G., Tsukamoto, A. 1977. Destruction of basaltic bodies by high-velocity impact. *Icarus* 31:277–88

Gary, M., McAfee, R. Jr., Wolf, C. L., eds. 1972. *Glossary of Geology*, p. 598. Washington, D.C: Am. Geol. Inst.

Gault, D. E. 1972. Displaced mass, depth, diameter, and effects of oblique trajectories for impact craters formed in dense crystalline rocks. *The Moon* 6:32–44

Gault, D. E., Wedekind, J. A. 1969. The destruction of tektites by micrometeoroid impact. *J. Geophys. Res.* 74:6780–94

Gault, D. E., Wedekind, J. A. 1977. Experimental hypervelocity impact into quartz sand: II, effects of gravitational acceleration. In *Impact and Explosion Cratering*, ed. D. J. Roddy, R. O. Pepin, R. B. Merrill, pp. 1231–44, New York: Pergamon

Gault, D. E., Shoemaker, E. M., Moore, H. J. 1963. Spray ejected from the lunar surface by meteoroid impact. *NASA TN D-1767*

Gerling, E. K., Levskii, L. K. 1956. On the origin of the rare gases in stony meteorites. *Dokl. Akad. Nauk SSSR* 110:750–53

Goswami, J. N., Hutcheon, I. D., MacDougall, J. D. 1976. Microcraters and solar flare tracks in crystals from carbonaceous chondrites and lunar breccias. *Proc. Lunar Sci. Conf., 7th*, pp. 543–62

Hartmann, W. K. 1978. Planet formation: Mechanism of early growth. *Icarus* 33: 50–61

Heiken, G. 1975. Petrology of lunar soils. *Rev. Geophys. Space Phys.* 13:567–87

Holsapple, K. A. 1980. The equivalent depth of burst for impact cratering. *Proc. Lunar Planet. Sci. Conf., 11th*, pp. 2379–401

Holsapple, K. A., Schmidt, R. M. 1979. A material-strength model for apparent crater volume. *Proc. Lunar Planet. Sci. Conf., 10th*, pp. 2757–77

Housen, K. R. 1976. A model of regolith formation on asteroids. *Meteoritics* 11:300–1

Housen, K. R. 1981a. A comparison of current asteroidal-regolith models. *Lunar Planet. Sci. XII*, pp. 471–73

Housen, K. R. 1981b. The stochastic variability of asteroidal regolith depths. *Proc. Lunar Planet. Sci. Conf., 12th*. In press

Housen, K. R., Wilkening, L. L., Chapman, C. R., Greenberg, R. 1979a. Asteroidal regoliths. *Icarus* 39:317–51

Housen, K. R., Wilkening, L. L., Chapman, C. R., Greenberg, R. 1979b. Regolith development and evolution on asteroids and the moon. In *Asteroids*, ed. T. Gehrels, pp. 601–27. Univ. Ariz. Press

Ivanov, B. A. 1976. The effect of gravity on crater formation: Thickness of ejecta and concentric basins. *Proc. Lunar Sci. Conf., 7th*, pp. 2947–65

Kerridge, J. F., Kieffer, S. W. 1977. A constraint on impact theories of chondrule formation. *Earth Planet. Sci. Lett.* 35:35–42

Kessler, D. J. 1970. Meteoroid environment model-1970 (Interplanetary and planetary). *NASA SP-8038*

Lal, D. 1972. Hard rock cosmic ray archaeology. *Space Sci. Rev.* 14:3–102

Langevin, Y., Arnold, J. R. 1977. The evolution of the lunar regolith. *Ann. Rev. Earth. Planet. Sci.* 5:449–89

Langevin, Y., Maurette, M. 1976. A Monte Carlo simulation of galactic cosmic ray effects in the lunar regolith. *Proc. Lunar Sci. Conf., 7th,* pp. 75–91

Langevin, Y., Maurette, M. 1980. A model for small body regolith evolution: The critical parameters. *Lunar Planet. Sci. XI,* pp. 602–4

Langevin, Y., Maurette, M. 1981. Grain size and maturity in lunar and asteroidal regoliths. *Lunar Planet. Sci. XII,* pp. 595–97

Matson, D. L., Johnson, T. V., Veeder, G. J. 1977. Soil maturity and planetary regoliths: the Moon, Mercury, and the asteroids. *Proc. Lunar Sci. Conf., 8th,* pp. 1001–11

McDonnell, J. A. M., Flavill, R. P., Carey, W. C. 1976. The micrometeoroid impact crater comminution distribution and accretionary populations on lunar rocks: Experimental measurements. *Proc. Lunar Sci. Conf., 7th,* pp. 1055–72

McDonnell, J. A. M. 1978. Microparticle studies by space instrumentation. In *Cosmic Dust,* ed. J. A. M. McDonnell, pp. 337–426. New York: Wiley

Moore, H. J. 1976. Missile impact craters (White Sands Missile Range New Mexico) and applications to lunar research. *USGS Prof. Paper 812-B*

Moore, H. J., Gault, D. E. 1965. The fragmentation of spheres by micrometeoroid impact. *USGS Ann. Rep.,* pp. 127–50

Oberbeck, V. R. 1971. Laboratory simulation of impact cratering with high explosives. *J. Geophys. Res.* 76:5732–49

Oberbeck, V. R., Morrison, R. H. 1976. Candidate areas for in situ ancient lunar materials. *Proc. Lunar Sci. Conf., 7th,* pp. 2983–3005

O'Keefe, J. D., Ahrens, T. J. 1976. Impact ejecta on the moon. *Proc. Lunar Sci. Conf., 7th,* pp. 3007–25

Price, P. B., Braddy, D., Hutcheon, I. D. 1975. Track studies bearing on solar system regoliths. *Proc. Lunar Sci. Conf., 6th,* pp. 3449–69

Quaide, W. L., Oberbeck, V. R. 1968. Thickness determinations of the lunar surface layer from lunar impact craters. *J. Geophys. Res.* 73:5247–70

Rajan, R. S., Brownlee, D. E., Heiken, G. H., McKay, D. S. 1974. Glassy agglutinate-like objects in the Bununu howardite. *Meteoritics* 9:394–97

Roddy, D. J., Pepin, R. O., Merrill, R. B. 1977. *Impact and Explosion Cratering.* New York: Pergamon

Shoemaker, E. M., Hait, M. H., Swann, G. A., Schleicher, D. L., Schaber, G. G., Sutton, R. L., Dahlem, D. H., Goddard, E. N., Water, A. C. 1970. Origin of the lunar regolith at Tranquility Base. *Proc. Apollo 11 Lunar Sci. Conf.* 3:2399–2412

Soberman, R. K., Neste, S. L., Lichtenfeld, K. 1974. Optical measurement of interplanetary particulates from Pioneer 10. *J. Geophys. Res.* 79:3685–94

Soter, S. 1971. The dust belts of Mars. *Cent. Radiophys. Space Res. Rep. 462,* Cornell Univ., Ithaca, NY

Stoffler, D., Gault, D. E., Wedekind, J., Polkowski, G. 1975. Experimental hypervelocity impact into quartz sand: Distribution and shock metamorphism of ejecta. *J. Geophys. Res.* 80:4062–77

Taylor, S. R. 1975. *Lunar Science: A Post-Apollo View,* New York: Pergamon. 372 pp

Thomas, P. 1979. Surface features of Phobos and Deimos. *Icarus* 40:223–43

Vedder, J. F. 1971. Microcraters in glass and minerals. *Earth Planet. Sci. Lett.* 11: 291–96

Vedder, J. F. 1972. Craters formed in mineral dust by hypervelocity microparticles. *J. Geophy. Res.* 77:4304–9

Veverka, J., Thomas, P. 1979. Phobos and Deimos: A preview of what asteroids are like. In *Asteroids,* ed. T. Gehrels, pp. 628–54. Univ. Ariz. Press

von Reichenbach, F. 1860. I. Meteoriten in meteoriten. *Ann. Phys. Chem.* 111:353–86

Wahl, W. 1952. The brecciated stony meteorite and meteorites containing foreign fragments. *Geochem. Cosmochim. Acta* 2: 91–117

Wänke, H. 1965. Der Sonnenwind als Quelle der Uredelgase in Steinmeteoriten, *Z. Naturforsch. Teil A* 20:946–94

Warner, J. L. 1972. Metamorphism of Apollo 14 breccias. *Geochim. Cosmochim. Acta* 1:623–43

Wetherill, G. W. 1976. Where do the meteorites come from? A reevaluation of the Earth-crossing Apollo objects as sources of chondritic meteorites. *Geochim. Cosmochim. Acta* 40:1297–1317

Ann. Rev. Earth Planet. Sci. 1982. 10:377-95

HEAT AND MASS CIRCULATION IN GEOTHERMAL SYSTEMS

Ian G. Donaldson

Physics and Engineering Laboratory, Department of Scientific and Industrial Research, Lower Hutt, New Zealand

INTRODUCTION

It is likely that hot water flowing out of the ground has been an attraction to man ever since he first stumbled across it. In Europe and Japan such water has been used for bathing for many centuries. In other parts of the world, it has been used for cooking and as a stimulus for tourism.

With the advent of mechanized drilling, we are no longer restrained to use only the fluid that escapes at the surface. We now have an indication of the extent of the resource and ready access to it. Information from the many wells drilled has also led to our greater understanding of the subsurface heat and mass movement. As the exploitation of these resources has intensified, demands on this knowledge have increased. Current research is directed to many aspects of the overall problem.

To engineers developing a geothermal reservoir, potential users of the energy, and financiers or entrepreneurs carrying the risks of development, the primary requirement is a good estimate of the energy *reserve* of that reservoir, i.e. the identified geothermal energy that can be extracted legally today at a cost competitive with other energy sources (Nathenson & Muffler 1975, Muffler & Cataldi 1978). These people also want to know the rate at which it would be best to extract this energy, the time span over which they might expect to extract it at that rate, and the changes that may occur in the reservoir due to the exploitation.

Given even relatively limited information about the reservoir, such as temperature and area, it is usually possible to estimate the in situ stored heat above some appropriate depth. The problem is estimating the fraction of this heat that is recoverable. For their recent assessments of the geothermal resources of the United States, White & Williams (1975) and Muffler (1978) used a model of heat extraction based on intergranular flow, or the sweep process, put forward

0084-6597/82/0515-0377$02.00

by Bodvarsson (1974) and Nathenson (1975) to estimate the fraction of the stored heat that might be mined. Donaldson & Grant (1978), in contrast, used the similar nature of New Zealand fields and their knowledge of the Wairakei, Broadlands, and Kawerau reservoirs in their estimate of the electric power production potential of the New Zealand system.

The fraction of the energy that can be extracted must depend, however, on many factors: the nature of the reservoir, i.e. its size, structure, degree of fracturing, and temperature variation; the nature of the fluid, i.e. water, water and steam, large or small quantities of noncondensable gas; and the way in which the field is operated, i.e. the well distribution, reinjection strategy, and rate of withdrawal. This review looks at a selection of the work that has expanded our knowledge of the nature of geothermal systems and reservoirs, the effects of the different fluid states, and the basic consequences of exploitation.

Discussion is restricted to one type of geothermal system, the hydrothermal system, in which heat is transported primarily by the circulation of water and/or steam. There will be no discussion of naturally conductive "hot-dry-rock" systems, or of magma systems. Nor will there be discussion of geopressured systems, even though these are water charged.

GEOTHERMAL SYSTEMS

Before we can discuss the effects of fluid or heat withdrawal from a geothermal reservoir, we must have a conceptual picture of heat and mass circulation in the system that sustains that reservoir. Unfortunately, in general, only indirect information about the system at depth is available. It is thus necessary to speculate to some extent on both the flow paths for the fluid and the source of the heat.

Perhaps the most significant information available is that, in general, some 90–95% of the water in geothermal systems is of meteoric origin. This was first suggested early this century by V. Knebel (1906) and Thorkelsson (1910) (references from Einarsson 1942) but was not confirmed until oxygen (O^{18}/O^{16}) and hydrogen (D/H) isotope ratios of geothermal waters were measured (White 1957a,b, 1961). This meteoric water is believed to circulate to depths of 2–6 km.

Without evidence indicating contact with magma, it is difficult to prove magmatic material as the primary source of heat in these systems, even in active volcanic areas. Certainly there are many geothermal systems in the world where the water is hot and there is no obvious volcanism. One well-known example of such a system is the Carpathian basin in Europe (Boldizsar 1975, Boldizsar & Korim 1975). In this and similar systems, normal heat flow from the Earth's core is sufficient to maintain temperature. These systems would thus presumably have stabilized to a steady state.

The more intensive geothermal areas are commonly associated with volcanism, often recent and active. Magmatic intrusions are suggested as one potential source of heat (Elder 1965, 1966). The cooling of such intrusions would supply additional local heat. Geothermal systems associated with such intrusions will, however, be transient.

For many fields, such as Wairakei, New Zealand, for which there is evidence suggesting a continuous existence over a period of 100,000 years or more (Grindley 1965), such intrusions would need to be extremely large or intermittently recharged. This time scale has inspired many researchers to consider such systems as steady, rather than transient.

Models of geothermal systems are of two types, transient and steady. To those interested in exploitation there is probably little difference. The time scale of any exploitation is so short in comparison with any natural development that the natural state of the system may always be taken as pseudo-steady.

Transient Models

Magmatic intrusion as a source of heat is by no means a new idea. Ingersoll & Zobel (1913), for example, considered the conductive problem. Convective flows stimulated by intrusion have, however, received detailed study only relatively recently. All of these studies, in effect, assume that the hot intrusion is suddenly injected into a deep, cold, water-saturated zone.

Norton (1977, 1978) and Norton & Knight (1977) recognize that both regional tectonic activity and the entry of the intrusion would lead to fracturing in the area, and thereby provide significant paths for convective fluid flow above and around the intrusion. The detailed analyses of Norton & Knight (1977) show that convective heat flux above the pluton could maximize at eight times the heat flux attained by conduction alone. Norton (1978) shows that fluid flow through the pluton itself accelerates cooling. He associates this flow with thermally induced stress cracking that would occur as the pluton cools.

In an independent, complementary study, Cathles (1977) computed the heat and mass flow developed in a similar system. Due to differences in scale and parameters, the peak (conductive + convective) surface heat flux above the pluton is only 3.6 times the peak flux that would be attained without convection. Cathles (1977) allowed the fluid to change phase as it circulated. He did not permit water and steam to coexist.

These transient models of Norton (1978) and Cathles (1977), reviewed in fuller detail by Garg & Kassoy (1981), illustrate some of the problems that arise in considering the source of heat as an integral part of our system. Nonetheless, these analyses have been used by Smith & Shaw (1978) in their assessment of the geothermal energy available in the United States from igneous-related geothermal sources.

Fluid behavior in the immediate vicinity of an intrusive is also receiving attention. Cheng (1976) discussed single-phase boundary layer flows along a dike and the cooling that these flows might induce. This work has recently been extended (Cheng & Verma 1980) to allow boiling in the boundary layer. The analysis depends critically on the assumptions that two-phase fluid does not exist in the boundary layer, and that the vapor-liquid interface is smooth.

The cooling of a lava sheet subject to direct rainfall has been studied recently by Shaw et al (1977) and Peck et al (1977). Here there is almost instantaneous contact of hot rock and water, both at the surface and internally, via a complex of contraction joints and cracks. While such sheets may be fully cooled in many cases before they are buried, the flow channels may be important in future geothermal systems. For example, flow channels at the surface of rhyolite domes are important features in the Whakarewarewa-Rotorua system in New Zealand (Donaldson & Grant 1981b).

Steady Models

Steady-state models of geothermal systems have developed along two lines: pipe models, in which it is assumed that the fluid flow is restrained to a network of channels, and porous medium models, in which the overall structural system is approximated as a homogeneous (although not necessarily isotropic) permeable zone.

PIPE MODELS Pipe systems have been proposed and described for several geothermal systems. The first detailed was that by Einarsson (1942) for the system feeding the hot springs in west Iceland. Einarsson (1942) suggested a deep circulation of meteoric water through cracks and fractures in otherwise virtually impermeable tertiary plateau basalts. Einarsson's work was extended and elaborated on by Bodvarsson (1961), in particular for the system associated with the more intensive activity found in central Iceland.

Pipe systems have also been proposed and discussed for US systems (White 1957a, 1961). White's conceptualization of a system is illustrated in Figure 1. In this model the water circulates to depths of 2 to 6 km where it receives heat from the hot rock, which is, in turn, heated by magma at greater depth. The heated fluid, being of lower density than the cold fluid, is then driven upwards through the available cracks and fractures by the difference in cold water/hot water head.

This model, being inherently simple, has not stimulated a great deal of general heat and mass transfer research. Both Elder (1966) and Donaldson (1970) used it to represent deep circulation, but were primarily interested in porous medium flows in and around the hot upflow column. Donaldson (1968) also used it for the deep circulation in his two-phase model of Wairakei.

Probably the most interesting recent use of a pipe model is by Goyal &

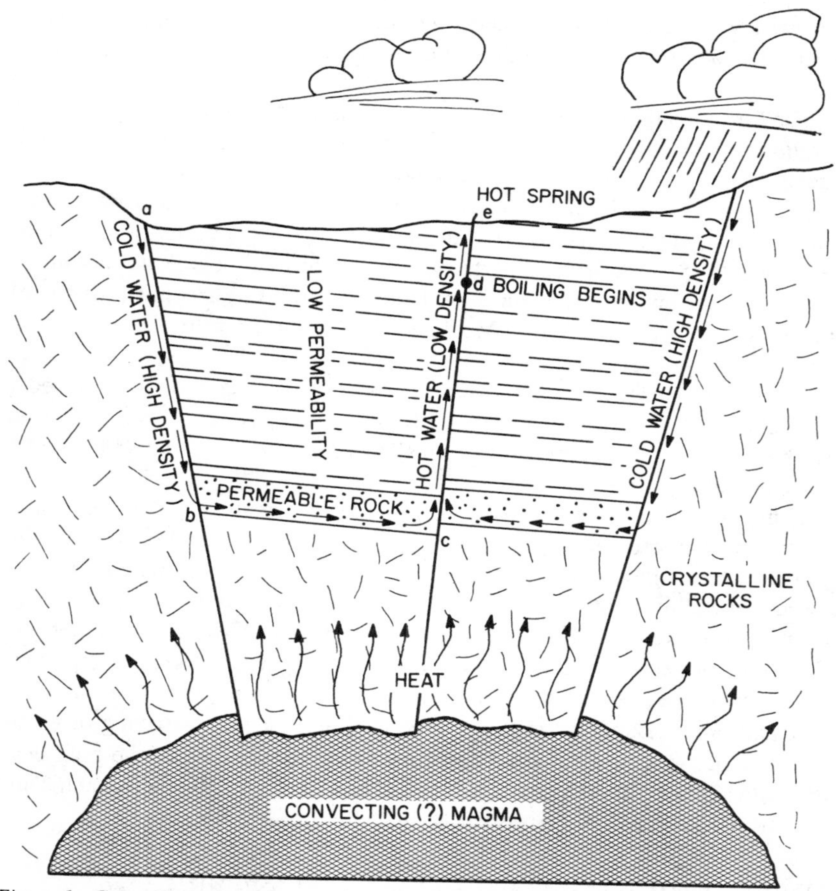

Figure 1 Generalized pipe model of a geothermal system showing the deep circulation of meteoric water. (White 1968)

Kassoy (1977, 1980) and Goyal (1978) in their conceptualization of the East Mesa system in the Imperial Valley, California. Although they are discussing the reservoir rather than the system, they suggest that the hot fluid flows up a single fault from an extensive basement fracture system in which the heating takes place. In the reservoir, this fluid is forced to move out horizontally by an overlying capping layer, vertical mixing in the reservoir being restrained by impermeable strata intermixed with the permeable beds.

POROUS MEDIUM MODELS It is now acknowledged that most geothermal systems and reservoirs are well fractured. To simulate these systems many researchers have used models featuring homogeneous permeable structures.

For steady and background system studies, such simulations appear to have been adequate. In reservoir studies, transient effects and two-phase flows may be different in the fractured and porous materials.

The form of a porous medium model depends on the basic assumptions and requirements of the modeler. In the early period of research, the models were idealized and the studies aimed at the determination of the conditions of the onset of convection (following Horton & Rogers 1945, Lapwood 1948). Later the modelers commenced to look at the form of the convective circulation. Wooding (1957, 1958) used perturbation methods to include the nonlinear terms; Donaldson (1962), on the other hand, used relaxation (finite difference) methods. Wooding (1963) and McNabb (1965) worked with the hot column alone, treating it as a jet flow.

Since that time an extensive literature on steady convection in porous media has developed, both for idealized and simulated real systems. This literature has been fully reviewed by Combarnous & Bories (1975), Cheng (1978), and Garg & Kassoy (1981).

If a pipe system is assumed it is possible to visualize the surface manifestation of a geothermal system at almost any location. In contrast, the convective circulation in a porous medium model defines a horizontal spacing for any upwelling (hot) flows. Thus, it might be assumed that the pipe model is the more likely in many situations. Wooding (1978), allowing for the difference in vertical and horizontal structuring by using anisotropic permeability, was able to show, however, that using a permeable bed depth of 3 km, he could produce upflows in his porous medium model at a spacing of about 11 km. This spacing is in good agreement with the spacing of the high heat anomalies in the Taupo Volcanic Zone in New Zealand. Whether systems are pipe or porous medium controlled is thus still an open question.

UNDISTURBED GEOTHERMAL RESERVOIRS

For this discussion we call the hot section of the geothermal system that is tapped and affected by the wells once exploitation is underway the *geothermal reservoir*. In general this is the hot zone at the top of the upflow column, although in capped systems it may be at some depth. It is usually assumed to extend horizontally to the boundaries of the anomaly at approximately the level of exploitation. The depth of the reservoir may be defined by the structures or by some analysis of the extent of the effects of exploitation.

Although each reservoir is unique, there are enough similarities between them to be able to group them. Donaldson & Grant (1981a) put forward definitions that depend on the state of the reservoir fluid tapped by the wells once exploitation is underway and the vertical pressure gradient in the reservoir. If the pressure gradient is close to hydrostatic, Donaldson & Grant

(1981a) use the term *liquid-dominated,* as the liquid water must be the connective phase even though water and steam may coexist in some sections of the reservoir. In contrast, if the pressure gradient is close to vapo-static, they use the term *vapor-dominated*, following White et al (1971). To date there appear to be no reservoirs with intermediate gradients.

Within the liquid-dominated class, Donaldson & Grant (1981a) define 3 subclasses: *warm water,* reservoirs in which no boiling will occur; *hot water,* in which boiling does or may occur, but within which the majority of wells are likely to tap liquid water, rather than water and steam; and *two-phase,* in which boiling also occurs, but at sufficient depth that the majority of wells will be tapping this boiling region. Typical examples of the three types might be Heber, Imperial Valley, California (warm water), Wairakei, New Zealand (hot water), and Broadlands, New Zealand (two-phase).

Liquid-Dominated Reservoirs

Many aspects of the behavior of a liquid-dominated geothermal reservoir can be studied with a relatively simple model (Donaldson 1978, Donaldson & Grant 1981a). This model, illustrated in Figure 2, basically consists of a column of hot fluid flowing up through the formations, surrounded by, and in

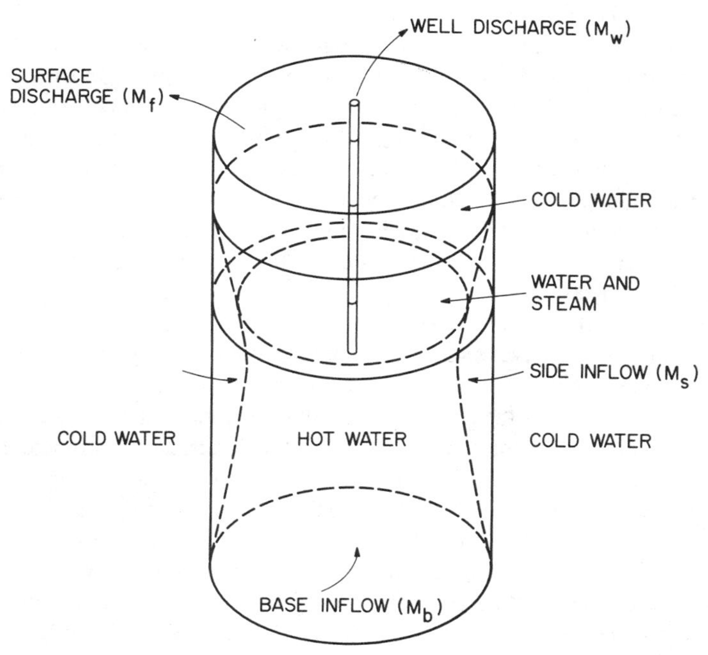

Figure 2 A simple model of a geothermal reservoir. (Donaldson 1978)

good hydrological contact with, cooler fluid. By adjustment of the temperature of the hot column at depth, the vertical permeability of the formations, the rate of upward flow, and (if necessary) the noncondensable gas content, the fluid may be made to flow up as water all the way to the surface or boil to various depths on the way up. It may thus be used to simulate warm water, hot water, and two-phase reservoirs. Structural stratification may be incorporated, although complete capping is only possible if there is no net upward mass flow.

Although this model has proved useful for some general studies—it has been used, for example, for studies of two-phase flow (Donaldson 1968) and to illustrate the effects of extraction of heat and mass from geothermal reservoirs (Donaldson & Grant 1981a)—it is of limited value for the study of particular reservoirs. These commonly have specific features that play an important role in the circulation of mass and heat within them.

We have already discussed the effect of the feed fracture, capping structure, and aquifer structural stratification on the fluid flow in the East Mesa reservoir, Imperial Valley, California (Goyal & Kassoy 1977, 1980, Goyal 1978). In that model the structure also affects the heat flow. As the heat can only escape by conduction through the capping layer, the cooling only extends to the deeper parts of the aquifer as we move out from the feeder fault. The temperature profiles thus are dome shaped.

In their study of the Heber reservoir in Imperial Valley, Tansev & Wasserman (1977) use a model similar to that used for East Mesa, in that it has a capping structure and some aquifer structural stratification. In their model, however, there is no central feed fracture and the overall vertical permeability of the aquifer is sufficient to allow circulation of the fluid. The water in the aquifer thus rises over the heated area in the center of the aquifer base, moves out beneath the capping structure, and sinks as it cools to return in along the base of the aquifer. The isotherms in this case are mushroom shaped. Thus, relatively small changes in structure can make significant differences in the natural flows in reservoirs.

A hydrological model of Cerro Prieto, Mexico, has been developed by Mercado (1975). This was established before production began and was based on temperature, pressure, enthalpy and flow measurements in wells, and the geothermochemistry of the discharged fluids. Mercado's (1975) model shows a horizontal and ascending movement of hot fluid from the eastern and central zones toward the west beneath a thick clay cap rock. It also suggests some recharge to the eastern section of the field, where the permeable reservoir structure extends to greater depth.

East Mesa and Cerro Prieto studies suggest both horizontal flow in the reservoir and some fracture control. Both of these are features of many reservoirs. Healy & Hochstein (1973) suggested that the El Tatio geothermal reservoir in Chile is a horizontal flow aquifer. Horizontal flow is also postulated in the Rotorua section of the Whakarewarewa-Rotorua geothermal reservoir in New Zealand. A recent detailed analysis of all the available data suggests that some of the fluid coming up from depth in the Whakarewarewa area is being driven out to the north through channels and fractures in the outer layers of a shallow rhyolite dome. Other fractures and faults may carry more fluid out to the northeast (Donaldson & Grant 1981b).

Other factors that can play a role in reservoir form are the extent of the two-phase zone and the existence of noncondensable gases in the reservoir fluid. The coexistence of water and steam in a reservoir in its natural state is difficult to confirm, as any fluid withdrawal can affect the state of the fluid in the reservoir around a well. The early Wairakei data have, however, recently been analyzed by Grant & Horne (1980). This confirms a preexploitation boiling profile and indicates the variation of the upper and lower boundaries of this two-phase zone along a profile across the field.

The noncondensable gases, such as CO_2, found in significant quantities in many geothermal reservoirs, are now also being incorporated in the reservoir models (see, for example, Grant 1977). Sutton and McNabb (1977) showed that pressure-temperature data for the Broadlands geothermal reservoir, New Zealand, can be fitted very closely by the boiling curve of a CO_2-water mixture (4% CO_2 by weight). Boiling commences at a depth of about 1500 m at a temperature of 304°C and a pressure of 166 bars. Straus & Schubert (1979) found that the buoyancy of geothermal fluids depends critically on this CO_2, because of the large fluid volume changes that occur as this gas enters or leaves solution. They also showed that the thermal expansivity, compressibility, specific heat, and adiabatic temperature gradient of steam-water-CO_2 mixtures are significantly greater than those of liquid water—for some properties by as much as 5 orders of magnitude (Schubert & Straus 1981).

Vapor-Dominated Reservoirs

Although there were several earlier models of vapor-dominated geothermal reservoirs, there appears to have been no new general model proposed since that of White et al (1971). White et al (1971) suggest a reservoir containing coexisting steam and water, the water saturation being sufficiently low that the liquid phase is almost immobile and the steam maintains the vertical pressure gradient. This steam is assumed to move up through the reservoir to an overlying condensation layer. The small amount of mobile water flows back down. The existence of this system requires very low permeability in all surrounding structures. White et al (1971) therefore suggested that the reservoir developed from a more free-flowing liquid-dominated form through a process of *self-sealing* of the bounding flow channels, i.e. by chemical deposition in these channels. This process of development has recently been followed through in a numerical study by Pruess & Truesdell (1980).

Although the upflow of steam and water through porous beds has received only limited attention (Donaldson 1968, Sheu et al 1979), counter-current flow, as postulated for vapor-dominated reservoirs, has received considerable attention. Soldergeld & Turcotte (1977) studied this upflowing steam/downflowing water condition in a laboratory sandbox, while Herkelrath (1977), Schubert & Straus (1977, 1979, 1980), Straus & Schubert (1981), and Schubert et al (1980) have addressed various aspects of the problem theoretically.

Schubert & Straus (1977) considered the convective nature of the flow and showed that convection occurs more readily in a porous medium containing saturated liquid by the phase-change instability than it would in a porous layer filled with liquid water by the Rayleigh-Bénard buoyancy-driven instability. They also indicate that phase-driven convection is concentrated toward the bottom of the porous layer, and that the cells are narrow in comparison to their depth.

Concern over the ability of a thick layer of liquid condensate to rest stably on top of the vapor-dominated reservoir stimulated the studies by Schubert & Straus (1980) and Schubert et al (1980). These studies show that the water layer will remain stable provided the permeability of the rock at the steam-water/liquid water interface does not exceed about 40 nm^2 (0.04 millidarcy).

In their most recent paper, Straus & Schubert (1981) model vapor-dominated reservoirs similar to the Geysers in California and Kawah Kamojang, West Java, as one-dimensional flow systems in a porous medium saturated with water and steam. Temperature and pressure data for the Kamojang reservoir are best fitted by models with a net mass flow rate/thermal conductivity ratio near 2.5×10^{-7} K s^2 m^{-3} and a vertical permeability/thermal conductivity ratio between 10^{-15} and 10^{-14} m s^3 K kg^{-1}. By analyzing the gas contents of discharging wells, Grant (1979) has deduced a water saturation of 35% for this reservoir.

EXPLOITED GEOTHERMAL RESERVOIRS

When water is extracted from wells tapping a warm water geothermal reservoir, the pressure transient propagates out from the well (or wells) in the same way as in any other liquid-saturated system. The theory is well documented in both the groundwater and petroleum literature for a wide range of system types and constraints (see, for example, Bear 1972, Earlougher 1977).

The heat extracted from such reservoirs is that contained in the water unless cooler water is brought into contact with the hot rock. Such a cool flow may be induced in two ways: by the pressure drop in the hot reservoir propagating out into the colder surrounding region, or by the direct injection of cool water into the reservoir.

In the former case, the reservoir boundaries will move in with time as the cool water extracts the heat from the boundary rock (Donaldson & Grant 1981a). Under ideal conditions, i.e. the reservoir being uniform in every respect, Donaldson & Grant (1981a) estimate that about 50% of the heat would be extracted from a reservoir 3 km deep and 4 km in diameter through wells tapping a zone about 1 km deep and 1 km in diameter before the cold front reached the outer wells. The rate of movement of a front has been computed and discussed by Bodvarsson (1974).

Reinjection of the cold fluid will establish a cooling front around each injection well (or group of injection wells). As this front expands it will "sweep" a proportion of the heat through to the extraction wells. For conceptual ideal reservoirs good results have been predicted (see, for example, Martin 1978), but as Horne (1981) points out in his analysis of geothermal reinjection in Japan, in many cases, reinjected water moves through fractures or fissures of extremely high permeability in the reservoir. In many reservoirs around the world, fluid has been found to move hundreds of meters in periods of only a few hours. Estimates of recoverability of energy from reservoirs in which short-circuiting possibly takes place thus may be markedly different from the ideal. Any boiling in a reservoir also introduces some differences in the response of that reservoir to exploitation.

Fractured Reservoirs

The first models of fractured reservoirs involved single fractures. In one approach (Bodvarsson 1974), a planar fracture was assumed to be continually recharged at one end with cool water. Classical heat-conduction theory then gives the heat theoretically extractable per unit fracture area under a minimum outflow temperature assumption. This single fracture system was extended to a multiple system by Nathenson (1975).

The Nathenson (1975) model was one of the models used by Muffler & Cataldi (1978) in their discussion of heat recovery factors for geothermal reservoirs. For an original rock temperature of 250°C, a recharge temperature of 40°C, a minimum outflow temperature of 162°C, a fracture spacing of 338 m, and a timescale of 25 yr, Muffler & Cataldi (1978) computed a *theoretical* heat recovery factor of just under 20%. They point out that in a real situation it could be much lower.

Pressure transient studies in systems with fractures are another method of learning more about local and total reservoir behavior under exploitation. Type curves for pressure transients in wells tapping single horizontal, vertical, and sloping planar fractures have been developed by Gringarten et al (1974), Gringarten & Ramey (1975), and Cinco-L. (1974), respectively.

On account of its initial performance and relationship to nearby wells in the

Travale-Radicondoli geothermal reservoir in Italy, Travale Well 22 has been extensively tested. These tests have been analyzed by Barelli et al (1975, 1978) and Atkinson et al (1978a). Although the short time data fit curves for a well intersecting a fully penetrating vertical fracture in a finite system, at a longer time (about 400 days) the system seems to reach steady flow. A new model, in which the well is intersected by a partially penetrating vertical fracture in a parallelepiped whose bottom side is a constant pressure boundary, was therefore proposed. The data appear to match the curve for a dimensionless formation thickness (reservoir thickness/half fracture length) of about 2.5 (Barelli et al 1978).

Multiple and randomly fractured beds of rock saturated with water may simulate real geothermal reservoirs more closely than the above idealized models. Such beds have recently been under study by Hunsbedt et al (1978). In a series of experiments a volume of such saturated rock has been heated to 260°C and pressurized to 55 bars and then swept of heat by passing through cold water. The results show that up to 175 kilo-Joule of heat per kilogram of rock mass could be extracted by this process (Hunsbedt et al 1978). The rock elements were not permeable.

Permeable, fractured systems have not been neglected. The pioneering isothermal studies for groundwater and petroleum reservoirs were carried out by Barenblatt & Zheltov (1960) and Warren & Root (1963). These analytic studies consider flow from primary porosity blocks to secondary porosity fissures. They do not, however, describe the flow within the blocks. The finite difference study by Kazemi (1969) and the analytic work of Boulton & Streltsova (1977) take this flow into account. In recent extensions of this work, Da Prat (1981 and Da Prat et al 1980) have obtained the longer time-pressure transients. It is thought that their results may be applicable to geothermal reservoirs. A fuller survey of the background literature is given by Evans (1981).

Nonisothermal flow in such fractured, permeable structures has been studied by Moench (1978), who developed a radial flow, finite difference model. This was later used to simulate pressure buildup data for a steam well in Larderello, Italy (Moench & Neri 1979). In that model the blocks were assumed to be impermeable, but capable of conducting heat to the fissures as they cooled because of vaporization of water to steam. In a recent study, Moench & Denlinger (1980) have revised the model to allow for steam transport and vaporization in the blocks.

In an effort to better understand the process of heat transfer within and around a single block, Pinder et al (1979) carried out a simple numerical experiment. They assumed a steam-saturated block to be suddenly surrounded with cool reinjection water. The simulations indicated that the liquid water propagated into the block and was heated to the original reservoir temperature.

A fractured, permeable model of the Wairakei geothermal reservoir was proposed by A. McNabb (unpublished report) in 1975. A main role for the fractures in this model was for the drainage of mobile water in the two-phase zone down to the liquid water/two-phase interface. This model has recently been shown to be the physical counterpart of the lumped parameter model of Fradkin (1981, Fradkin et al 1981).

Reservoirs in Which Boiling Occurs

Once boiling occurs within a geothermal reservoir, some changes in the behavior of the reservoir under withdrawal and injection are to be expected. In the hot water reservoir these changes are limited, because the pressure transients will still propagate out to the side boundaries through the liquid water, as was the case in the warm water reservoir.

These pressure transients will, however, also propagate in the vertical direction and hence, in time, reach the liquid water/two-phase interface in the hot water reservoir. At this interface the pressure and temperature are interrelated (at saturation conditions). Any drop in pressure there thus stimulates a drop in temperature and, hence, additional boiling as heat transfers from the rock to the fluid. The interface, therefore, will only drop slowly and tend to act as a pressure-stabilizing boundary (Donaldson & Grant 1981a). Any drop in the interface level will have two effects: the pressure will drop in the two-phase layer, and the vertical pressure gradient through that layer will be reduced. The drop in pressure will mean more boiling and the transfer of heat from the rock to the fluid. The drop in pressure gradient will reduce the upward water flow. With a sufficient drop in gradient the water flow will in fact reverse, i.e. it will commence to drain down toward the interface (Donaldson & Grant 1981a). These pressure gradient changes have been found in Wairakei, New Zealand (Grant & Horne 1980).

When production takes place from within the two-phase zone of the reservoir, withdrawn fluid is replaced by steam supplied by vaporizing some of the liquid water. The pressure drops only when cooling takes place due to boiling and the associated transfer of heat from the rock matrix to the fluid. If the pressure changes are small, or if one phase is immobile, the pressure variation with time in the two-phase fluid may be solved by using the linear diffusion equation (Grant 1978, Garg 1978, Moench & Atkinson 1978, Grant & Sorey 1979). The *compressibility* in this equation is a two-phase one, i.e. it takes into account the boiling process, and may be 100–10,000 times that of liquid water, or 10–100 times that of superheated steam.

For larger pressure changes nonlinear effects are to be anticipated, and these have been studied by Sorey et al (1980) using numerical and quasi-analytical solutions of the two-phase flow equations for a well discharging at constant mass rate. The flowing enthalpy is shown to increase as the liquid saturation decreases during drawdown. It does, however, reach a stable value near the well face at sufficiently short times that well-test analyses can still be carried out. Since this work was done, several two-phase transient analyses have, in fact, been carried out with credible results. One such study is reported by Grant (1980). The studies are now being extended to cases in which phase boundaries occur, i.e. where the boiling only takes place in the immediate vicinity of the well (Horne & Satman 1980).

For reservoir analysis, the major effect of the two-phase zone is the slowing down of the propagation of pressure drawdown across the field. The unified drawdown of a two-phase reservoir, thus, may not occur for some time. In the case of low permeability reservoirs, it may never occur. Specific fields, such as Broadlands and Ngawha in New Zealand, are discussed in this regard by Donaldson & Grant (1981a).

Although the water may be virtually immobile and the pressure gradient approaching vapo-static, the behavior of vapor-dominated geothermal reservoirs will be similar to that of two-phase liquid-dominated ones. Vapor-dominated reservoirs have, however, been the specific topic of several studies. Many more field data have become available since the effects of exploitation were discussed qualitatively by Truesdell & White (1973). Data analyses can thus be carried out and theories tested much more readily (see, for example, Atkinson et al 1978a,c, Lipman et al 1978).

Theoretical and experimental studies relating to fluid withdrawal from vapor-dominated geothermal reservoirs have been carried out by Moench & Atkinson (1978) and Herkelrath & Moench (1978, 1980). Moench & Atkinson (1978) used a finite difference model for the radial horizontal flow of steam through a porous medium containing immobile but vaporizing water to evaluate pressure transient effects. The enhanced compressibility due to vaporation has already been discussed above. Herkelrath & Moench (1978, 1980) extended that study and cross-checked their numerical results with laboratory experiments.

Although reinjection is being carried out in several geothermal fields, it has not been as successful as hoped, nor does the heat and fluid movement stimulated by the reinjection match the idealized theoretical conception (Horne 1981). When cold fluid is reinjected into a liquid-saturated section of the reservoir, it is probably only the heterogeneous nature of the reservoir structures that creates problems. In a recent study, however, Grant (1981) showed that reinjection of cold fluid into a two-phase zone can cause a decrease in pressure over and above that due to the extraction of the hot fluid, rather than the increase in pressure that would be anticipated if we injected into liquid. The cold fluid must condense some of the steam in order to come into thermal balance with the fluid and rock in place. Only if the temperature of the reinjected fluid is close to that of the reservoir will the volume of fluid injected make up for the steam condensed and, hence, maintain or increase the pressure. In most real situations the pressure will drop. Grant (1981) further points out that the removal of heat alone, as, for example, through the use of a downhole heat exchanger, gains nothing in this situation. The heat must be supplied from the fluid and rock around the well, and under saturation conditions that must mean a drop in pressure.

Real Reservoirs

In studies of real reservoirs, hard field data must be matched. It is thus surprising that in spite of the extreme complexity of the reservoirs, many of the simplest models have been moderately successful in matching the real field behavior. Zais (1979, 1980) has shown decline curve methods, using the exponential equation, to work well on geothermal production data; other workers are matching the behavior of various reservoirs with lumped-parameter or simple material balance models. The recent analysis of Wairakei data by Fradkin (1981) produced a lumped-parameter model with only three identified parameters. Vapor-dominated systems are being matched using the linear nature of the p/Z v cumulative production behavior suggested by Brigham & Morrow (1977). This approach has been applied recently to the Serrazano (Atkinson et al 1978c) and Gabbro (Brigham & Neri 1980) zones of Larderello, and to Travale-Radicondoli (Atkinson et al 1978a). (All of these fields are in Italy.) Atkinson et al (1978b) have also applied the procedure to the reservoir at Bagnore, Italy. This reservoir has a very high content of noncondensable gas.

To understand the movement of heat and fluid within a geothermal reservoir in detail it is obviously necessary to include reservoir structure in the model. In this event, numerical modeling may be the only approach. Its use, however, is dependent on obtaining extensive and detailed information concerning the reservoir. To date, various models of several geothermal reservoirs have been attempted, with varying degrees of success (see, for example, the Heber model of Tansev & Wasserman 1977; the East Mesa models of Riney et al 1979 and Morris & Campbell 1981; and the Wairakei models of Mercer & Faust 1979 and Pritchett et al 1980).

Considerable effort is now going into the improvement and application of such modeling. A recent intercomparison test of most models available that are capable of analyzing mixed single- and two-phase systems showed little spread in results (Stanford Geothermal Program 1980).

CONCLUSION

On paper, at least, an understanding in general terms of how heat and fluid move in geothermal systems and reservoirs has now been reached. We have assessments of flows in ideal, fractured, boiling, or gas-charged reservoirs; in liquid- or vapor-dominated states; and under natural or exploited conditions. We appear to have the tools, in lumped-parameter or numerical models, to forecast the flows, the energy recovery, and other behavior changes of a reservoir if it is exploited or if there is a change in exploitation. However, there remains this paradox—until a variety of geothermal reservoirs have been developed, we cannot prove our models, but until be prove our models, we cannot be sure that geothermal reservoirs will be developed.

ACKNOWLEDGMENTS

This review was written while the author was at the Department of Petroleum Engineering, Stanford University. He would like to thank his colleagues there for their support. He would particularly like to thank Dr. R. N. Horne for his comments and suggestions.

This work was supported by a Fulbright-Hayes Travel Award, a New Zealand Department of Scientific & Industrial Research Study Award, and US Department of Energy Contract No. DE-AT03-80SF11459.

Literature Cited

Atkinson, P. G., Barelli, A., Brigham, W., Celati, R., Manetti, G., Miller, F. G., Neri, G., Ramey, H. J. Jr. 1978a. Well-testing in Travale-Radicondoli field. *Geothermics* 7(2-4):145–84

Atkinson, P. G., Celati, R., Corsi, R., Kucuk, F., Ramey, H. J. Jr. 1978b. Thermodynamic behavior of the Bagnore geothermal field. *Geothermics* 7(2-4):185–208

Atkinson, P. G., Miller, F. G., Marconcini, R., Neri, G., Celati, R. 1978c. Analysis of reservoir pressure and decline curves in Serrazzano zone, Larderello geothermal field. *Geothermics* 7(2-4):133–42

Barelli, A., Celati, R., Manetti, G., Neri, G. 1975. Horner's method applied to buildup test on Travale 22 well. *Proc. Workshop Geotherm. Reservoir Eng., 1st*, pp. 101–12

Barelli, A., Brigham, W. E., Cinco, H., Economides, M., Miller, F. G., Ramey, H. J., Schultz, A. 1978. Pressure drawdown analysis for the Travale 22 well. *Proc. Workshop Geotherm. Reservoir Eng., 4th*, pp. 165–75

Barenblatt, G. I., Zheltov, U. P. 1960. On the basic flow equations of homogeneous liquids in fissured rocks. *Dok. Akad. Nauk SSSR* 132(N3):545–48 (In Russian)

Bear, J. 1972. *Dynamics of Fluids in Porous Media*. New York: Am. Elsevier. 764 pp.

Bodvarsson, G. 1961. Physical characteristics of natural heat resources in Iceland. *Proc. U.N. Conf. New Sources Energy, Rome, Italy*, 2:82–89

Bodvarsson, G. 1974. Geothermal resource energetics. *Geothermics* 3:83–92

Boldizsar, T. 1975. Research and development of geothermal energy production in Hungary. *Geothermics* 4:44–56

Boldizsar, T., Korim, K. 1975. Hydrogeology of the Pannonian Geothermal Basin. *Proc. U.N. Symp. Devel. Use Geoth. Resour., 2nd, San Francisco*, pp. 297–303

Boulton, N. S., Streltsova, T. D. 1977. Unsteady flow to a pumped well in a fissured water-bearing formation. *J. Hydrol.* 35: 257–70

Brigham, W. E., Morrow, W. B. 1977. p/z behavior for geothermal steam reservoirs. *Soc. Pet. Eng. J.* 17(6):407–12

Brigham, W. E., Neri, G. 1980. *A depletion model for the Gabbro Zone (Northern part of Larderello field)*. Presented at DOE-ENEL Workshop Coop. Res. Geotherm. Energy, 2nd, Berkeley

Cathles, L. M. 1977. An analysis of the cooling of intrusives by ground-water convection which includes boiling. *Econ. Geol* 72:804–26

Cheng, P. 1976. Buoyancy induced boundary layer flows in geothermal reservoirs. *Proc. Workshop Geotherm. Reservoir Eng., 2nd*, pp. 236–46

Cheng, P. 1978. Heat transfer in geothermal systems. *Adv. Heat Transfer* 14:1–105

Cheng, P., Verma, A. K. 1980. Boiling heat transfer from a dike. *Proc. Workshop Geotherm. Reservoir Eng., 6th*, pp. 243–46

Cinco-L., H. 1974. *Unsteady-state pressure distributions created by a slanted well or a well with a slanted fracture*. PhD thesis. Stanford Univ., Stanford. 173 pp.
Combarnous, M. A., Bories, S. A. 1975. Hydrothermal convection in saturated porous media. *Adv. Hydrosci.* 10:231–307
Da Prat, G. 1981. *Well test analysis for naturally fractured reservoirs*. PhD thesis. Stanford Univ., Stanford. 202 pp.
Da Prat, G., Cinco-L., H., Ramey, H. J. Jr. 1980. *Decline curve analysis using type-curves for two-porosity systems*. SPE 9292 presented at the Ann. Fall Tech. Conf. Exh. Soc. Pet. Eng. AIME, 55th, Dallas
Donaldson, I. G. 1962. Temperature gradients in the upper layer of the Earth's crust due to convective water flows. *J. Geophys. Res.* 67:3449–59
Donaldson, I. G. 1968. The flow of steam water mixtures through permeable beds: a simple simulation of an undisturbed hydrothermal region. *N. Z. J. Sci.* 11:3–23
Donaldson, I. G. 1970. The simulation of geothermal systems with a simple convective model. *Geothermics* Special Issue 2:649–54
Donaldson, I. G. 1978. Geothermal reservoir engineering research in New Zealand: a simplistic model and the Wairakei geothermal reservoir. See Barelli et al, pp. 36–41
Donaldson, I. G., Grant, M. A. 1978. An estimate of the resource potential of New Zealand geothermal fields for power generation. *Geothermics* 7(2–4):243–52.
Donaldson, I. G., Grant, M. A. 1981a. Heat extraction from geothermal reservoirs. In *Geothermal Systems: Principles and Case Histories,* ed. L. Rybach, L. J. P. Muffler, pp. 145–79. London: Wiley. 328 pp.
Donaldson, I. G., Grant, M. A. 1981b. *The development of a conceptual model of the Rotorua-Whakarewarewa geothermal reservoir*. SPE 9923 presented at Ann. SPE Calif. Reg. Meet., 51st, Bakersfield
Earlougher, R. C. Jr. 1977. *Advances in well test analysis*. Mono. Vol. 5, Dallas: Soc. Pet. Eng. AIME
Einarsson, T. 1942. On the nature of the Iceland's hot springs. *Rit. Visind. Isl.* 26:1–92 (In German)
Elder, J. W. 1965. Physical processes in geothermal areas. In *Terrestrial Heat Flow, Geophys. Mono. No. 8,* ed. W. H. K. Lee, pp. 211–39. Washington D.C: Am. Geophys. Union
Elder, J. W. 1966. Heat and mass transfer in the Earth: hydrothermal systems. *N. Z. Dept. Sci. Ind. Res. Bull. No. 169*
Evans, R. D. 1981. *A proposed model for multiphase flow through naturally fractured reservoirs*. SPE 9940 presented at Ann. SPE Calif. Reg. Meet., 51st, Bakersfield
Fradkin, L. J. 1981. Identification of the Wairakei geothermal system. *Water Resour. Res.* 17(4):921–27
Fradkin, L. J., Sorey, M. L., McNabb, A. 1981. On identification and validation of some geothermal models. *Water Resour. Res.* 17(4):929–36
Garg, S. K. 1978. *Pressure transient analysis for two-phase (liquid water/steam) geothermal reservoirs*. Presented at Ann. Fall Conf. Soc. Pet. Eng. AIME, 53rd, Houston
Garg, S. K., Kassoy, D. R. 1981. Convective heat and mass transfer in hydrothermal systems. In *Geothermal Systems: Principles and Case Histories,* ed. L. Rybach, L. J. P. Muffler, pp. 37–76. London: Wiley. 328 pp.
Goyal, K. P. 1978. *Heat and mass transfer in a saturated porous medium with application to geothermal reservoirs*. PhD thesis. Univ. Colo., Boulder
Goyal, K. P., Kassoy, D. R. 1977. A fault-zone controlled model of the Mesa anomaly, *Proc. Workshop Geotherm. Reservoir Eng., 3rd,* pp. 209–13
Goyal, K. P., Kassoy, D. R. 1980. Fault-zone controlled charging of a liquid dominated geothermal reservoir. *J. Geophys. Res.* 85:1867–75
Grant, M. A. 1977. Broadlands—a gas-dominated geothermal field. *Geothermics* 6:9–29
Grant, M. A. 1978. Two-phase linear geothermal pressure transients—a comparison with single-phase transients. *N. Z. J. Sci.* 21: 355–64
Grant, M. A. 1979. Water content at the Kawah Kamojang geothermal reservoirs. *Geothermics* 8:21–30
Grant, M. A. 1980. The testing of KA28—pressure analysis in a two-phase reservoir. See Cheng & Verma 1980, pp. 170–77
Grant, M. A. 1981. The effect of cold-water entry into a liquid-dominated two-phase geothermal reservoir. *Water Resour. Res.* 17(4):1033–43
Grant, M. A., Horne, R. N. 1980. The initial state and response to exploitation of Wairakei geothermal field. *Geotherm. Resour. Counc., Trans.* 4:333–36
Grant, M. A., Sorey, M. L. 1979. The compressibility and hydraulic diffusivity of a water-steam flow. *Water Resour. Res.* 15(3):684–86
Grindley, G. W. 1965. The geology, structure and exploitation of the Wairakei geothermal field, Taupo, New Zealand, *N. Z. Geol. Surv. Bull. No. 75*. 131 pp.
Gringarten, A. C., Ramey, H. J. Jr. 1975. Unsteady-state pressure distributions created by a well with a single horizontal fracture, partial penetration, or restricted entry. *Soc. Pet. Eng. J.* 14:413–26; *Trans. AIME,* p. 257

Gringarten, A. C., Ramey, H. J. Jr., Raghaven, R. 1974. Unsteady-state pressure distributions created by a well with a single infinite-conductivity vertical fracture. *Soc. Pet. Eng. J.* 14:347–60; *Trans. AIME,* p. 257
Healy, J., Hochstein, M. P. 1973. Horizontal flow in hydrothermal systems. *J. Hydrol. (N. Z.)* 12(2):71–82
Herkelrath, W. N. 1977. The 'heat-pipe' effect in vapor-dominated geothermal systems. See Goyal & Kassoy 1977, pp. 43–48
Herkelrath, W. N., Moench, A. F. 1978. Laboratory investigations of steam pressure-transient behaviour in porous materials. See Barelli et al 1978, pp. 54–59
Herkelrath, W. N., Moench, A. F. 1980. Transient steam flow in porous media–theory and experiment. See Cheng & Verma 1980, pp. 322–27
Horne, R. N. 1981. *Geothermal reinjection experience in Japan.* SPE 9925 presented at Ann. SPE Calif. Reg. Meet., 51st, Bakersfield
Horne, R. N., Satman, A. 1980. A study of drawdown and buildup tests in wells with phase boundaries. *Geotherm. Resour. Counc., Trans.* 4:345–48
Horton, C. W., Rogers, F. T. 1945. Convection currents in a porous media, *J. Appl. Phys.* 16:367–70
Hunsbedt, A., Kruger, P., London, A. L. 1978. Energy extraction from a laboratory model fractured geothermal reservoir. *J. Pet Tech. (May)* 30:712–18
Ingersoll, L. R., Zobel, O. J. 1913. *Mathematical Theory of Heat Conduction.* Boston: Ginn
Kazemi, H. 1969. Pressure transient analysis of naturally fractured reservoirs. *Trans. AIME* 256:451–61
Lapwood, E. R. 1948. Convection of a fluid in a porous medium. *Proc. Camb. Philos. Soc.* 44:508–21
Lipman, S. C., Strobel, C. J., Gulati, M. S. 1978. Reservoir performance of the Geysers field. *Geothermics* 7(2-4):209–20
Martin, J. C. 1978. The replacement of geothermal reservoir brine as a means of reducing solids precipitation and scale formation. See Barelli et al 1978, pp. 42–49
McNabb, A. 1965. On convection in a porous medium. *Proc. Australas. Conf. Hydraul. Fluid Mech.* 2:C161–71
Mercado, G. S. 1975. Movement of geothermal fluids and temperature distribution in the Cerro Prierto geothermal field, Baja, California, Mexico. See Boldizsar & Korin 1975, pp. 492–94
Mercer, J. W., Faust, C. R. 1979. Geothermal reservoir simulation: 3. Application of liquid- and vapor-dominated hydrothermal modeling techniques to Wairakei, New Zealand. *Water Resour. Res.* 15(3):653–71
Moench, A. F. 1978. The effect of thermal conduction upon pressure drawdown and buildup in fissured vapor-dominated geothermal reservoirs. See Barelli et al 1978, pp. 112–17
Moench, A. F., Atkinson, P. G. 1978. Transient-pressure analysis in geothermal steam reservoirs with an immobile vaporizing liquid phase. *Geothermics* 7(2-4): 253–64
Moench, A. F., Denlinger, R. 1980. Fissure-block model for transient pressure analysis in geothermal steam reservoirs. See Cheng & Verma, pp. 178–87
Moench, A. F., Neri, G. 1979. Analysis of Gabbro I-steam pressure buildup test. *Proc. Workshop Geotherm. Reservoir Eng., 5th,* pp. 99–104
Morris, C. W., Campbell, D. A. 1981. Geothermal reservoir energy recovery—a three-dimensional simulation study of the East Mesa field. *J. Pet. Tech.* 33:735–42
Muffler, L. J. P., ed. 1978. *Assessment of Geothermal Resources of the United States—1978.* Washington: US Geol. Surv. Circ. 790. 163 pp.
Muffler, L. J. P., Cataldi, R. 1978. Methods for regional assessment of geothermal resources. *Geothermics* 7(2-4):53–90
Nathenson, M. 1975. Physical factors determining the fraction of stored energy recoverable from hydrothermal convection systems and conduction-dominated areas. *US Geol. Surv. Open-File Rep. 75-525.* 35 pp.
Nathenson, M., Muffler, L. J. P. 1975. Geothermal resources in hydrothermal convection systems and conduction-dominated areas. In *Assessment of Geothermal Resources of the United States—1975,* ed. D. E. White, D. L. Williams, pp. 104–21. Washington: U.S. Geol. Surv. Circ. 726
Norton, D. 1977. Fluid circulation in the Earth's crust. In *The Earth's Crust,* ed. J. G. Heacock, pp. 693–704, Geophys. Mono. No. 20. Washington: Am. Geophys. Union
Norton, D. 1978. Sourcelines, sourceregions and pathlines for fluids in hydrothermal systems related to cooling plutons. *Econ. Geol.* 73:21–28
Norton, D., Knight, J. 1977. Transport phenomena in hydrothermal systems: cooling plutons. *Am. J. Sci.* 277:937–81
Peck, D. L., Hamilton, M. S., Shaw, H. R. 1977. Numerical analysis of lava lake cooling models; Part II, Application to Alae lava lake, Hawaii. *Am. J. Sci.* 277:415–37
Pinder, G. F., Ramey, H. J. Jr., Shapiro, A., Abriola, L. 1979. Block response to reinjection in a fractured geothermal reservoir. See Moench & Neri 1979, pp. 189–96
Pritchett, J. W., Rice, L. F., Garg, S. K. 1980. Reservoir simulation studies: Wai-

rakei geothermal field, New Zealand. *Rep. SSS-R-80-4313,* Systems, Science & Software, La Jolla, Calif. 147 pp.

Pruess, K., Truesdell, A. H. 1980. A numerical simulation of the natural evolution of vapor-dominated hydrothermal systems. See Cheng & Verma 1980, pp. 194–203

Riney, T. D., Pritchett, J. W., Rice, L. F., Garg, S. K. 1979. A preliminary model of the East Mesa hydrothermal system. See Moench & Neri 1979, pp. 211–14

Schubert, G., Straus, J. M. 1977. Two-phase convection in a porous medium. *J. Geophys. Res.* 82(23):3411–21

Schubert, G., Straus, J. M. 1979. Steam-water counterflow in porous media. *J. Geophys. Res.* 84(B4):1621-28

Schubert, G., Straus, J. M. 1980. Gravitational stability of water over steam in vapor-dominated geothermal systems. *J. Geophys. Res.* 85(B11):6505–12

Schubert, G., Straus, J. M. 1981. Thermodynamic properties for the convection of steam-water-CO_2 mixtures. *Am. J. Sci.* 281:318–34

Schubert, G., Straus, J. M., Grant, M. A. 1980. A problem posed by vapour-dominated geothermal systems. *Nature* 287(5781):423–25

Shaw, H. R., Hamilton, M. S., Peck, D. L. 1977. Numerical analysis of lava lake cooling models; Part I, Description of the method. *Am. J. Sci.* 277:384–414

Sheu, J. P., Torrance, K. E., Turcotte, D. L. 1979. On the structure of two-phase hydrothermal flows in permeable media. *J. Geophys. Res.* 84:7524–32

Smith, R. L., Shaw, H. R. 1978. Igneous-related geothermal systems. In *Assessment of Geothermal Resources of the United States—1978,* pp. 12–17. Washington: US Geol. Surv. Circ. 790

Soldergeld, C. H., Turcotte, D. L. 1977. An experimental study of two-phase convection in a porous medium with applications to geological problems. *J. Geophys. Res.* 82:2045

Sorey, M. L., Grant, M. A., Bradford, E. 1980. Nonlinear effects in two-phase flow to wells in geothermal reservoirs. *Water Resour. Res.* 16(4):767–77

Stanford Geothermal Program. 1980. *Proc. Spec. Panel Geotherm. Model Intercomparison Study*. Stanford: Stanford Geothermal Program, SGP-TR-42. 120 pp

Straus, J. M., Schubert, G. 1979. Effects of CO_2 on the buoyancy of geothermal fluids. *Geophys. Res. Lett.* 6(1):5–8

Straus, J. M., Schubert, G. 1981. One-dimensional model of vapor-dominated geothermal systems. *Aerosp. Rep. No. ATR-81(7684)-1.* 19 pp.

Sutton, F. M., McNabb, A. 1977. Boiling curves at Broadlands geothermal field, New Zealand. *N. Z. J. Sci.* 20:333–37

Tansev, E., Wasserman, M. L. 1977. Modeling the Heber geothermal reservoir. See Goyal & Kassoy 1977, pp. 107–15

Thorkelsson, Th. 1910. The hot springs of Iceland. *Kgl. Danske Videnskabernes Selskabs Skrifter*

Truesdell, A. H., White, D. E. 1973. Production of superheated steam from vapor-dominated geothermal reservoirs. *Geothermics* 2(3-4): 154

V. Knebel, W. 1906. Studien in den Thermengebieten Islands. *Naturwissenschaftliche Rundschau* (In German)

Warren, J. E., Root, P. J. 1963. The behavior of naturally fractured reservoirs. *SPE J.* (Sept.), pp. 245–55

White, D. E. 1957a. Thermal waters of volcanic origin. *Geol. Soc. Am. Bull.* 68(12):1637–58

White, D. E. 1957b. Magmatic, connate, and metamorphic waters. *Geol. Soc. Am. Bull.* 68(12):1659–82

White, D. E., 1961. Preliminary evaluation of geothermal areas by geochemistry, geology, and shallow drilling. *Proc. U.N. Conf. New Sources Energy, Rome* 2:402–9

White, D. E. 1968. Hydrology, activity, and heat flow of the Steamboat Springs thermal system, Washoe County, Nevada. *Geol. Surv. Prof. Pap. 458-C.* 109 pp.

White, D. E., Muffler, L. J. P., Truesdell, A. H. 1971. Vapor-dominated hydrothermal systems compared with hot-water systems. *Econ. Geol.* 66:75–97

White, D. E., Williams, D. L., eds. 1975. *Assessment of Geothermal Resources of the United States—1975.* Washington: U.S. Geol. Surv. Circ. 726. 155 pp.

Wooding, R. A. 1957. Steady state free thermal convection of liquid in a saturated permeable medium. *J. Fluid Mech.* 2:273–85

Wooding, R. A. 1958. An experiment on free thermal convection of water in saturated permeable material. *J. Fluid Mech.* 3:582–600

Wooding, R. A. 1963. Convection in a saturated porous medium at large Rayleigh number or Péclet number. *J. Fluid Mech.* 15(4):527–44

Wooding, R. A. 1978. Large-scale geothermal field parameters and convection theory. *N. Z. J. Sci.* 21:219–28

Zais, E. J. 1979. A technical analysis of geothermal production data by decline curve methods. See Moench & Neri 1979, pp. 205–10

Zais, E. J. 1980. Production decline analysis using influence functions. See Cheng & Verma 1980, pp. 121–25

Ann. Rev. Earth Planet. Sci. 1982. 10:397-408

MAGMA MIGRATION

D. L. Turcotte

Department of Geological Sciences, Cornell University, Ithaca, New York 14853

INTRODUCTION

Although plate tectonics provides a general framework for understanding the distribution of volcanism over the Earth's surface, many important aspects are poorly understood. Probably the best understood volcanism occurs at mid-ocean ridges. As the surface plates diverge or spread, hot mantle rock ascends to fill the gap. Pressure-release melting occurs, which produces a basaltic magma (Verhoogen 1954, Green & Ringwood 1967, Oxburgh & Turcotte 1968a). This magma migrates to the surface because of the buoyancy forces associated with the magma's lower density. The basaltic magma solidifies to form the oceanic crust. Since the general framework for volcanism at ocean ridges is reasonably well understood, the processes of magma migration can probably be best studied in this environment.

Extensive volcanism is also associated with subduction zones. Linear chains of volcanoes lie parallel to many ocean trenches. The generation of magmas at ocean trenches is still a subject of considerable controversy. The volcanic lines appear to be closely associated with the descending lithosphere. The volcanoes generally lie about 150 km above the Benioff zone defined by earthquakes believed to occur within the descending lithosphere. Offsets in the volcanic line lie above breaks in the descending lithosphere.

Alternative models have been proposed for the volcanism associated with subduction. In one hypothesis, frictional heating on the slip zone between the descending lithosphere and overlying plate results in partial melting (McKenzie & Sclater 1968, Oxburgh & Turcotte 1968b). However, as the rock solidus is approached the viscosity drops to such low levels that very little frictional heating occurs (Yuen et al 1978). Thus it is difficult to envision how steady-state frictional heating can lead to partial melting. An alternative hypothesis argues that the descending lithosphere induces a secondary flow in the overlying mantle and that this secondary flow induces partial melting (Toksoz & Hsui 1978, Hsui & Toksoz 1981). However, since the secondary flow is likely to be descending it is doubtful that pressure-release melting is significant in

0084-6597/82/0515-0397$02.00

this region. Also, the very direct geometrical association of the volcanic line with the descending lithosphere must be explained.

A more complex hypothesis suggests that frictional heating and/or the increase in pressure with depth leads to the release of water from the descending oceanic crust. This water reduces the melting temperature of the overlying mantle, resulting in partial melting (Anderson et al 1976). However, much of the volcanism associated with subduction is basaltic and does not appear to be significantly different than that produced at ocean ridges. Some geochemical studies have associated island arc volcanism directly with subducted sediments, but the evidence is still considered to be somewhat ambiguous. Thus, it must be concluded that a comprehensive understanding of subduction-related volcanism does not exist at this time.

It is generally accepted, however, that magmas must migrate upwards some 150 km from their point of origin to form the surface volcanoes. The mechanism for this migration is poorly understood. Alternative models include diapiric upwelling and magma fracturing. Little direct evidence for the rate of upward migration is available.

Volcanism also occurs within plate interiors. An example is the extensive volcanism associated with the Hawaiian Islands. One hypothesis for this volcanism is rising mantle plumes beneath the plate (Morgan 1972). Unfortunately there is no evidence for the existence of such plumes. If intraplate volcanism is associated with plumes then pressure-release melting is likely to occur. The volcanism at Hawaii penetrates the full thickness of the oceanic lithosphere. Since there is no regional heat flow anomaly adjacent to the Hawaiian Islands, the magma must follow a narrow, heated path to the surface. Presumably considerable magma solidifies along the mantle path in order to heat the intially cool mantle rocks. No fully satisfactory explanation for magma migration through the lithosphere exists. Many aspects of the magma migration problem have been recently reviewed by Spera (1980).

MAGMA MIGRATION AT OCEAN RIDGES

At a mid-ocean ridge, the lithosphere essentially has zero thickness and the asthenosphere extends to the ridge axis, where volcanism is continuously occurring to create the basaltic ocean crust. Thus, it is only necessary to consider how magma migrates through the asthenosphere. It appears appropriate to consider normal mid-ocean ridges as a passive phenomenon. Ridges migrate with respect to each other and migrate over the mantle beneath. The position of a ridge is determined by the surface geometry of plate tectonics. Near-symmetrical spreading is due to the surface cooling that determines the thickening of the oceanic lithosphere. As the ridge migrates over the mantle, it induces an ascending flow of mantle rock. This ascending flow is adiabatic so that the change in temperature is quite small. However, the mantle solidus temperature is a relatively strong function of depth. Melting relationships for deriving basalt from a model mantle composition have been given by Ringwood (1975). We approximate this melting relationship by

$$f = A\{\exp[B(T - C_z)] - 1\}, \tag{1}$$

where f is the degree of partial melt as a function of temperature T and depth z (depth and pressure are equivalent through the relationship $p = \rho g z$). Taking $A = 0.4$, $B = 3.65 \times 10^{-3}$ °C^{-1}, $C_z = 3.0 \times 10^{-5}$ °C/cm, and $D = 1{,}100$°C, the dependence of f on temperature and depth is given in Figure 1.

As a specific example we consider mantle rock that ascends isothermally (a reasonable approximation for adiabatic ascent over a narrow depth range) with a temperature of 1297°C. It intercepts our assumed solidus (f=0) at a depth of 62 km as shown in Figure 1. As the mantle rock ascends, further additional melting will occur at the expense of the internal energy of the rock. The temperature of the rock will follow a "wet" adiabat. The decrease in temperature ΔT is related to the degree of partial melting, the latent heat of fusion L, and the specific heat at constant pressure c_p by

$$\Delta T = fL/c_p. \tag{2}$$

We assume that L = 80 cal/gm and c_p = 0.25 cal/gm °C.

A reasonable value for the degree of partial melting associated with the basaltic ocean crust is f=0.25. For this case, we see from Figure 1 that melting extends continuously from a depth of 60 km to the base of the oceanic crust.

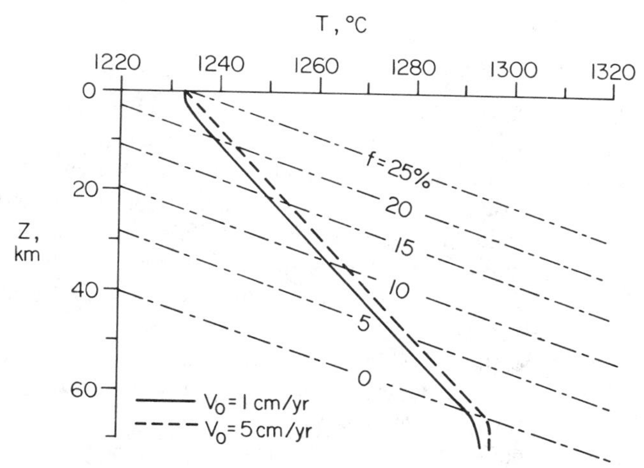

Figure 1 Dependence of the temperature on depth through the melt zone.

The magma produced by partial melting must migrate through the asthenosphere in order to form the oceanic crust. Magma is produced along grain boundary intersections (Waff & Bulau 1979). This magma fills an equivalent porosity χ. When sufficient magma is produced, connected magma porosity will result in a magma permeability. Since the magma is lighter than the residual crystalline matrix, the buoyancy body force will drive it upwards. Magma migration results.

This mechanism for magma migration can be treated quantitatively assuming a porous flow model (Frank 1968, Sleep 1974, Turcotte & Ahern 1978, Walker et al 1978). This model has been applied to magma migration below ocean ridges by Ahern & Turcotte (1979). In order to relate the porosity χ to the permeability k, it is necessary to assume a model for the connected porosity. Based on the observation that magma is produced on grain boundary intersections, it is appropriate to assume a cubic matrix of circular tubes. The circular tubes have a diameter δ and the cubic matrix has a scale b; b is associated with the grain size. The diameter of the channels can be related to the connected porosity $\chi - \chi_0$ where χ_0 is the volume fraction of isolated pockets of liquid by

$$\chi = \chi_0 + 3\,\pi\,\delta^2/b^2 4. \tag{3}$$

The associated permeability (Bear 1972) is given by

$$k = b^2\,(\chi - \chi_0)^2/72\pi. \tag{4}$$

Alternative geometrical models for the permeability result in small variations in the numerical coefficient in (4).

The migration velocity of the magma through the crystalline matrix is obtained from Darcy's law:

$$v_l - v_s = 3kg(\rho_s - \rho_l)/\eta(\chi - \chi_0), \tag{5}$$

where v_l is the absolute vertical velocity of the magma in the magma channels, v_s is the vertical velocity of the matrix, and η is the viscosity of the magma. In writing (5), it is assumed that the differential buoyancy between the magma and the crystalline matrix is balanced by the laminar viscous pressure drop due to the flow of the magma through the channels. Implicit in this assumption is the additional assumption that the crystalline matrix can freely deform as magma is withdrawn, i.e. the magma pressure is equal to the lithostatic pressure. At the velocities associated with plate tectonics and mantle convection and at temperatures above the solidus, the solid-state viscosity (or equivalent viscosity for a non-Newtonian rheology) of the crystalline matrix is sufficiently small that the matrix is free to deform.

The details of the porous flow model for an ocean ridge have been given by Ahern & Turcotte (1979). Assuming $\rho_s - \rho_l = 0.7$ gm/cm^3, $b = 0.2$ cm, and $\chi_0 = 2\%$, the liquid fraction (porosity) χ is given as a function of depth in Figure 2 for vertical mantle rock ascent velocities of 1 and 5 cm/yr and magma viscosities of 10 and 100 poise. These values for the viscosity of a basaltic magma would appear to cover the range of possible values, based on the experimental studies of Kushiro et al (1976) and Kushiro (1980). It should be noted, however, that on the small scales of individual grains, surface effects may be important. Magma velocities are given in Figure 3. It is seen that the magma velocities are one to two orders of magnitude greater than the mantle ascent velocities. The magma drains upward to the surface almost as rapidly as it is produced. Waff (1980) has argued that surface tension will prevent the upward migration of magma. However, geometrical considerations indicate that surface tension can only play a role on the scale of the individual grains. Thus, if magma can migrate along a grain boundary it would be expected to migrate through the asthenosphere.

Pressure-release melting requires that low degrees of partial melting occur at depths of 60 km or greater if the total partial melt fraction is of the order of 25%. The higher degrees of partial melting occur at shallower depths. The porous flow model shows that magma will rapidly migrate to the surface. Thus, near-surface magma flows are the result of the mixing of magmas of different degrees of partial melting that have been produced over a depth range

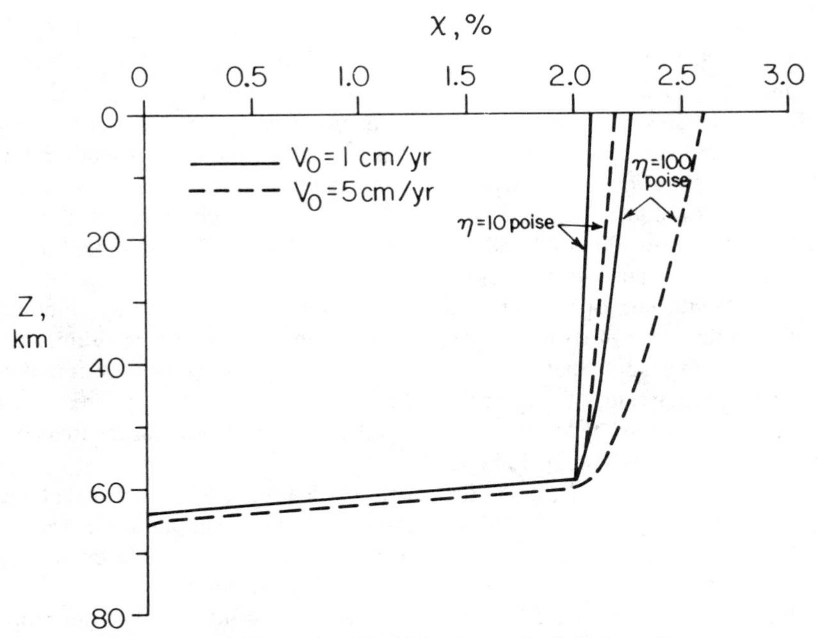

Figure 2 Dependence of the liquid fraction on depth in the melt zone.

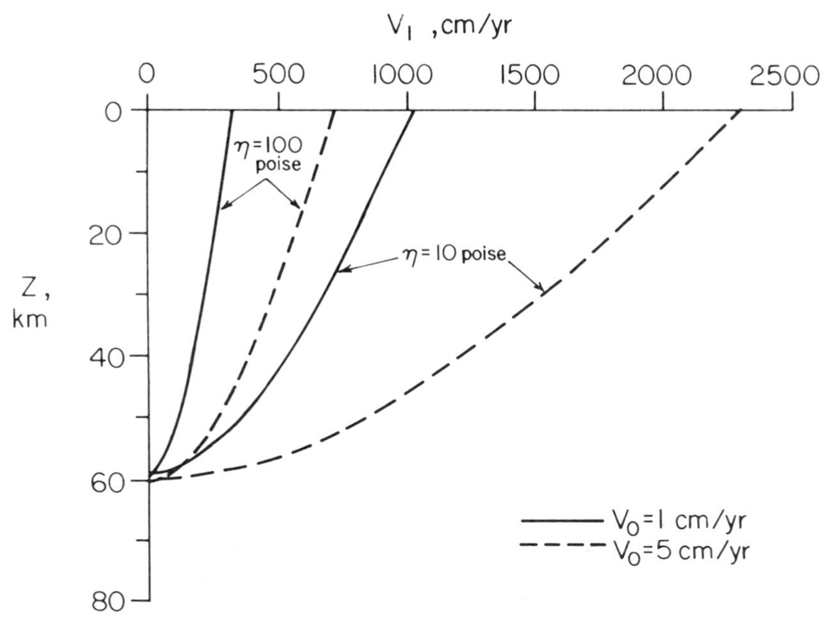

Figure 3 Dependence of the magma ascent velocity on depth in the melt zone.

of some 50–60 km. Since this mixing is unlikely to be perfect, it is not surprising that considerable variations in the composition of the basaltic rocks of the oceanic crust are observed over small horizontal distances. These differences need not reflect variations in mantle source composition.

The ascent of magma to the surface beneath an oceanic ridge resembles the descent of rain through an ascending thermal in the atmosphere. In both cases, the liquid is produced along a wet adiabat and it is the difference in density and the gravitational body force that causes the relative velocity of the liquid. In the case of rain, small droplets of moisture initially condense and are entrained in the atmospheric circulation. Subsequently these droplets combine to form rain drops of sufficient size to fall to the Earth's surface. Similarly, the rivulets of magma that are produced along grain boundaries may combine to form larger streams of magma that ascend through the asthenosphere. If this is the case, magma velocities may be orders of magnitude larger than the porous flow values obtained above.

Since the gravitational body force acts vertically, it is expected that the magma will rise vertically. With this assumption and a simple model for the ascent velocity of the mantle rock, the thickness of the oceanic crust as a function of distance from the ocean ridge can be predicted.

We assume that the base of the oceanic crust is a solidification front propagating into the partially molten asthenosphere. The thickness of the lithosphere (Oldenburg 1975) is given by

$$y_l = 2\lambda_1 (\kappa t)^{\frac{1}{2}}, \tag{6}$$

where κ is the thermal diffusivity and t is the age of the lithosphere. The parameter λ_1 is a function of $c_p(T_m - T_0)/\chi L \pi^{\frac{1}{2}}$ where T_m is the mantle solidus and T_0 the surface temperature. Value of λ_1 are given by Carslaw & Jaeger (1959, Figure 38). Assuming the mantle flow that adds mass to the thickening lithosphere is vertical, the mantle velocity is given by

$$U_s = dy_l/dt. \tag{7}$$

This is illustrated in Figure 4. The flux of magma reaching the base of the lithosphere per unit area is given by

$$q_m = f u_s, \tag{8}$$

where the melt fraction as a function of depth is given by

$$f = 0.25 (1 - y_l/y_m), \tag{9}$$

and where y_m is the depth at which melting begins. Combining equations (6) through (9), we obtain

$$q_m = 0.25 \lambda_1 (\kappa/t)^{\frac{1}{2}} [1 - 2\lambda_1 (\kappa t)^{\frac{1}{2}}/y_m]. \tag{10}$$

Integration of this equation with respect to time gives the thickness of the oceanic crust as a function of age:

$$y_c = 0.50 \lambda_1 [(\kappa t)^{\frac{1}{2}} - \lambda_1 \kappa t/y_m]. \tag{11}$$

The oceanic crust continues to thicken until $y_l = y_m$; this occurs when $t = y_m^2/4\lambda_1^2 \kappa$. The corresponding maximum thickness of the oceanic crust is

$$y_{oc} = 0.125 y_m. \tag{12}$$

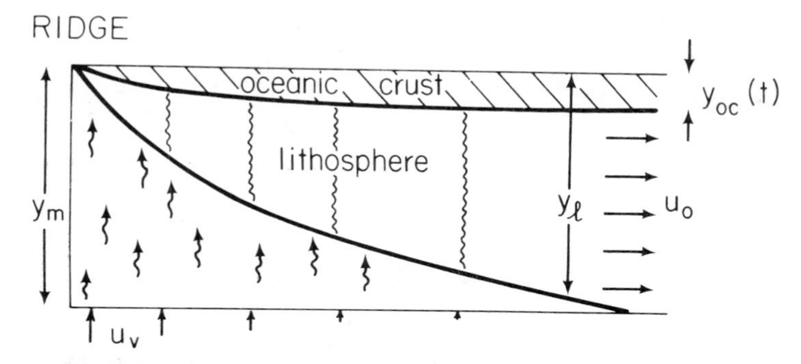

Figure 4 Illustration of magma migration through the asthenosphere to the base of the lithosphere and its subsequent migration through the lithosphere to form the oceanic crust.

Taking $y_m = 60$ km, the total predicted thickness of the oceanic crust is 7.5 km independent of the spreading rate. Assuming $c_p = 0.25$ cal/gm °C, $T_m - T_o = 1200$ °C, $L = 80$ cal/gm, and $\chi = 0.02$ we find from Carslaw & Jaeger (1959, Figure 38) that $\lambda_1 = 2$. With $\kappa = 10^{-2}$ cm^2/sec, the predicted thickness of the oceanic crust as a function of age from Equation (11) is given in Figure 5. The dependence on the distance from the ridge crest is also given for spreading rates of 1 and 5 cm/yr.

The analysis predicts that the crust reaches 80% of its total thickness at an age of 2 million years. There is some evidence, based on seismic refraction and reflection studies, that the crust reaches a large fraction of its final thickness in the immediate vicinity of the oceanic ridge. Some authors (Kidd 1977, Sleep 1978) attribute this initial thickening to a magma chamber at the ridge axis. The structure of the oceanic crust studied in ophiolites is consistent with a magma chamber of at least moderate size. The porous flow model suggests that significant amounts of magma penetrate the thickening oceanic lithosphere and thicken the oceanic crust away from the immediate vicinity of the ridge crest. If this is not the case, a mechanism must be proposed to draw the magma horizontally to the ridge crest.

MAGMA MIGRATION THROUGH THE LITHOSPHERE

Viable mechanisms are available for the migration of magma through the asthenosphere. This does not appear to be the case for magma migration through the lithosphere, although several alternative mechanisms have been proposed.

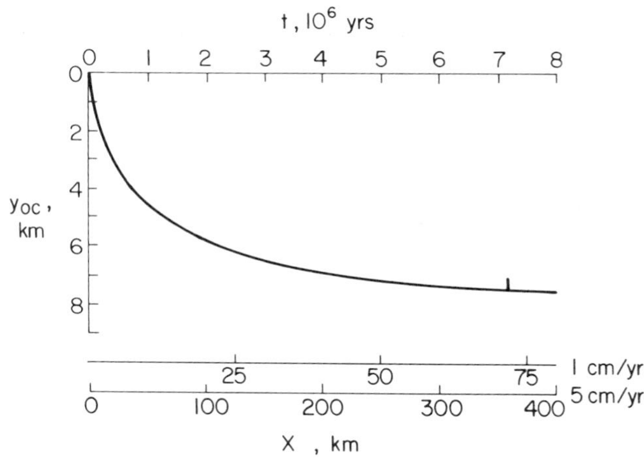

Figure 5 Dependence of the thickness of the oceanic crust on age and distance from the ridge crest.

One possible mechanism for the ascent of magma through the lithosphere is to establish a conduit. Such a conduit could take the form of a pipe or channel. A number of strong arguments can be made against this mechanism. The first is that observed surface flows are episodic rather than continuous. In order for a conduit to be effective for the transport of magma, it must remain open. Once the flow stops, the lithostatic pressure will close the conduit and reestablishing the flow requires the displacement of solid mantle rock. This is the inherent problem in providing a viable migration mechanism in the lithosphere. Another problem with the conduit model is that the flow rates through a conduit of a reasonable size would be extremely high.

It is evident that a heated path must exist for the passage of magma through the lithosphere. Without a heated path, magma would solidify at depth through contact with the cold mantle rock. However, this solidification will heat the adjacent mantle rock, providing a heated path for subsequent magma. Before a heated path is provided through the lithosphere, a substantial amount of magma must have solidified within the lithosphere. This problem has been considered quantitatively by Turcotte (1981).

Heating of the lithosphere could take place as magma attempts to ascend diapirically through the mantle. This type of magma migration has been studied by Marsh & Carmichael (1974), Marsh (1976, 1978, 1981), and Marsh & Kantha (1978). One approach to the diapiric migration of magma is to treat the lithosphere as a Newtonian viscous fluid. For this approximation to be valid the lithosphere would have to be preheated to a substantial fraction of its melt temperature.

If it is further assumed that the magma body can be approximated as a sphere, its ascent velocity can be related to the viscosity of the fluid. The ascent velocity U of a fluid, spherical body of radius a and density ρ_m through a very viscous fluid with viscosity μ and density ρ (Lamb 1945, pp. 596–604) is given by

$$U = a^2 g (\rho - \rho_m)/3\mu. \tag{13}$$

If the velocity and size are specified, the required viscosity can be estimated.

The rate at which magmas ascend can be estimated from the size of xenoliths entrained in surface flows. Carmichael et al (1977) have estimated a velocity of 50 cm/sec for typical xenoliths found in Hawaii. The volume of a mantle magma diapir could correspond to the volume of a single eruption. Volumes of eruption at Kilauea have been estimated by Swanson (1972). A typical volume for a single eruption is 1 km^3, which for a spherical body yields $a = 0.25$ km. Also taking $g = 10^3$ cm/sec^2 and $\rho - \rho_m = 0.5$ gm/cm^3, the required lithospheric viscosity from (13) is $\mu = 2 \times 10^9$ poise. This is a very low viscosity. It is doubtful that mantle rock will have this low a viscosity even with a substantial melt fraction present.

Several factors could substantially increase the required viscosity. If the body was elliptical with a large vertical dimension, the differential buoyancy would be larger. Also a non-Newtonian rheology would be helpful. But as long as large velocities ($\sim$100 cm/sec) are required, the diapiric model would appear to require too small a mantle viscosity.

The essential difficulty with diapiric models is that solid mantle rock must be displaced by viscous solid-state creep. This is inherently a slow process. An alternative mechanism for the displacement of a solid is to utilize elastic displacements. This occurs during crack propagation. Alternative models for magma migration through the lithosphere have been proposed using various mechanisms of magma fracturing.

Magma often erupts at the surface along fractures. In some cases, these fractures may have existed prior to the eruption and simply provide an accessible path to the surface. In other cases, however, there is good evidence that the high pressure magma fractures competent rock. The role of magma in fracturing near surface rock has been considered by a large number of authors including Anderson (1936, 1938), Roberts (1970), Weertman (1971, 1973), Pollard (1973, 1976), Pollard & Muller (1976), Nakamura (1977), and Nakamura et al (1977). A recent review of this subject has been given by Shaw (1980).

Magma fracturing may also play an important role in the migration of magma at depth. One approach to the propagation of a magma fracture is to apply the theory used to study hydro-fractures in the crust. This approach is discussed by Shaw (1980). An alternative mechanism for crack propagation involving the Peach-Koehler force on dislocations has been discussed by Weertman (1971). A third propagation mechanism is stress corrosion, which has been applied to the problem of magma migration by Anderson & Grew (1977).

Magma fracturing is an attractive hypothesis for the migration of magma through the lithosphere. The migration velocity is expected to be relatively rapid in agreement with the inferred values. However, analysis to date has not included some important thermal considerations. For instance, how does magma solidification influence the propagation of a magma filled crack?

Concluding Remarks

Many aspects of magma migration are poorly understood. One of the major problems is the lack of relevant data. Our knowledge of the rate of magma migration is based on indirect observation subject to large possible errors. One source of information on alternative mechanisms comes from the study of various surface exposures of mantle rocks. Detailed studies of ophiolites should yield relevant data; similar studies can be carried out on mantle rocks found in kimberlites.

One important conclusion of theoretical studies is that considerable quantities of magma must solidify in the mantle in order to provide a heated path to the surface. Thus, mantle inhomogeneities within the lithosphere may be atttributed to basaltic intrusions. In some cases, there may be insufficient magma to provide a heated path to the crust. Thus not every melting anomaly in the mantle would be expected to lead to extrusive or intrusive crustal volcanism.

An inescapable conclusion is that much remains to be learned about magma migration. Although plate tectonics provides a general framework for understanding volcanism, many aspects of volcanism are poorly understood and receive relatively little study. One of these aspects is magma migration.

ACKNOWLEDGMENTS

This research has been supported by the Earth Sciences Section of the National Science Foundation under Grant EAR-7919421.

Literature Cited

Ahern, J. L., Turcotte, D. L. 1979. Magma migration beneath an ocean ridge. *Earth Planet. Sci. Lett.* 45:115–22

Anderson, E. M. 1936. The dynamics of the formation of cone-sheets, ring-dykes, and caldron-subsidences. *Proc. R. Soc. Edinburgh* 56:128–63

Anderson, E. M. 1938. The dynamics of sheet intrusion. *Proc. R. Soc. Edinburgh* 58: 242-51

Anderson, O. L., Grew, P. C. 1977. Stress corrosion theory of crack propagation with applications to geophysics. *Rev. Geophys. Space Phys.* 15:77–104

Anderson, R. N., Uyeda, S., Miyashiro, A. 1976. Geophysical and geochemical constraints at converging plate boundaries. Part I: Dehydration in the downgoing slab. *Geophys. J. R. Astron. Soc.* 44:333–57

Bear, J. 1972. *Dynamics of Fluids in Porous Media*, p. 163. New York: Elsevier

Carmichael, I. S. E., Nicholls, J., Spera, F. J., Wood, B. J., Nelson, S. A. 1977. High-temperature properties of silicate liquids: applications to the equilibration and ascent of basic magma. *Philos. Trans. R. Soc. London Ser. A* 286:373–431

Carslaw, H. S., Jaeger, J. C. 1959. *Conduction of Heat in Solids*. Oxford: Oxford Univ. Press. 2nd ed.

Frank, F. C. 1968. Two-component flow model for convection in the Earth's upper mantle. *Nature* 220:350–52

Green, D. H., Ringwood, A. E. 1967. The genesis of basaltic magmas. *Contrib. Mineral. Petrol.* 15:103–90

Hsui, A. T., Toksoz, M. N. 1981. Back-arc spreading: Trench migration, continental pull or induced convection? *Tectonophysics* 74:89–98

Kidd, R. G. W. 1977. A model for the process of formation of the upper oceanic crust. *Geophys. J. R. Astron. Soc.* 50:149–83

Kushiro, I. 1980. Viscosity, density, and structure of silicate melts at high pressures, and their petrological applications. In *Physics of Magmatic Processes*, ed. R. B. Hargraves, pp. 93–120. Princeton: Princeton Univ. Press

Kushiro, I., Yoder, H. S., Mysen, B. O. 1976. Viscosities of basalt and andesitic melts at high pressures. *J. Geophys. Res.* 81: 6351–56

Lamb, H. 1945. *Hydrodynamics*. New York: Dover. 738 pp.

Marsh, B. D. 1976. Mechanics of Benioff zone magmatism. In *The Geophysics of the Pacific Ocean Basin and Its Margin*, ed. G. H. Sutton, M. H. Manghnani, R. Moberly, Am. Geophys. Union Monogr. 19:337–50. Washington D.C: Am. Geophys. Union

Marsh, B. D. 1978. On the cooling of ascending andesitic magma. *Philos. Trans. Roy. Soc. London Ser. A* 288:611–25

Marsh, B. D. 1981. On the mechanics of igneous diapirism, stoping, and zone melting, *Am. J. Sci.* In press

Marsh, B. D., Carmichael, I. S. E. 1974. Benioff zone magmatism. *J. Geophys. Res.* 79:1196–1206

Marsh, B. D., Kantha, L. H. 1978. On the heat and mass transfer from an ascending magma. *Earth Planet. Sci. Lett.* 39:435–43
McKenzie, D. P., Sclater, J. G. 1968. Heat flow inside the island arcs of the northwestern Pacific. *J. Geophys. Res.* 73: 3173–79
Morgan, W. J. 1972. Deep mantle convection plumes and plate motions. *Am. Assoc. Petrol. Geol. Bull.* 56:203–13
Nakamura, K. 1977. Volcanoes as possible indicators of tectonic stress orientation: principle and proposal. *J. Volcanol. Geotherm. Res.* 2:1–16
Nakamura, K., Jacob, K. H., Davie, J. N. 1977. Volcanoes as possible indicators of tectonic stress orientation: Aleutians and Alaska. *Pure Appl. Geophys.* 115:87–112
Oldenburg, D. W. 1975. A physical model for the creation of the lithosphere. *Geophys. J. R. Astron. Soc.* 43:425–51
Oxburgh, E. R., Turcotte, D. L. 1968a. Mid-ocean ridges and geotherm distribution during mantle convection. *J. Geophys. Res.* 73:2643–61
Oxburgh, E. R., Turcotte, D. L. 1968b. Problems of high heat flow and volcanism associated with zones of descending mantle convective flow. *Nature* 216:1041–43
Pollard, D. D. 1973. Derivation and evaluation of a mechanical model for sheet intrusions. *Tectonophysics* 19:233–69
Pollard, D. D. 1976. On the form and stability of open hydraulic fractures in the earth's crust. *Geophys. Res. Lett.* 3:513–16
Pollard, D. D., Muller, O. H. 1976. The effect of gradients in regional stress and magma pressure on the form of sheet intrusions in cross section. *J. Geophys. Res.* 81:975–84
Ringwood, A. E. 1975. *Composition and Petrology of the Earth's Mantle*. New York: McGraw Hill
Roberts, J. L. 1970. The intrusion of magma into brittle rocks. In *Mechanism of Igneous Intrusion*, ed. G. Newhall, N. Rast, pp. 287–338. Liverpool: Galery Press
Shaw, H. R. 1980. The fracture mechanisms of magma transport from the mantle to the surface. See Kushiro 1980, pp. 201–64
Sleep, N. H. 1974. Segregation of magma from a mostly crystalline mush. *Geol. Soc. Am. Bull.* 85:1225–32
Sleep, N. H. 1978. Thermal structure and kinematics of mid-oceanic ridge axis, some implications to basaltic volcanism. *Geophys. Res. Lett.* 5:426–28
Spera, F. J. 1980. Aspects of magma transport. See Kushiro 1980, pp. 263–323
Swanson, D. A. 1972. Magma supply rate at Kilauea Volcano, 1952–1971. *Science* 175: 169–70
Toksoz, M. N., Hsui, A. T. 1978. Numerical studies of back-arc convection and the formation of marginal basins. *Tectonophysics* 50:177–96
Turcotte, D. L. 1981. Some thermal problems associated with magma migration, *J. Vulcanol. Geotherm. Res.* 10:267–78
Turcotte, D. L., Ahern, J. L. 1978. A porous flow model for magma migration in the asthenosphere. *J. Geophys. Res.* 83:767–72
Verhoogen, J. 1954. Petrological evidence on temperature distribution in the mantle of the earth. *Trans. Am. Geophy. Union* 35:85–92
Waff, H. S. 1980. Effects of the gravitational field on liquid distribution in partial melts within the upper mantle. *J. Geophys. Res.* 85:1815–25
Waff, H. S., Bulau, J. R. 1979. Equilibrium fluid distribution in an ultramafic partial melt under hydrostatic stress conditions. *J. Geophys. Res.* 84:6109–14
Walker, D., Stolper, E. M., Hays, J. F. 1978. A numerical treatment of melt/solid segregation: Size of the Eucrite parent body and stability of the terrestrial low-velocity zone. *J. Geophys. Res.* 83:6005–13
Weertman, J. 1971. Theory of water-filled crevasses in glaciers applied to vertical magma transport beneath oceanic ridges. *J. Geophys. Res.* 76:1171–83
Weertman, J. 1973. Oceanic ridges, magma filled cracks and mantle plumes. *Geofis. Int.* 13:317–36
Yuen, D. A., Fleitout, L., Schubert, G., Froidevaux, C. 1978. Shear deformation zones along major transform faults and subducting slabs. *Geophys. J. R. Astron. Soc.* 54:93–119

Ann. Rev. Earth Planet. Sci. 1982. 10:409-40

THE BASIN AND RANGE PROVINCE: Origin and Tectonic Significance

Gordon P. Eaton

Texas A&M University, College Station, Texas 77843

INTRODUCTION

The Basin and Range province is a vast arid tract of regionally corrugated, angular topography of high relief in the western Cordillera. It is characterized by evenly spaced parallel mountain ranges and intervening desert basins (Figure 1*a*). The range flanks are marked by poorly sorted gravel aprons that slope smoothly basinward, interrupted here and there by low fault scarps that parallel the range front faults and by alluvial fans at the mouths of canyons draining the ranges. Thermal springs located at, or near, range-bounding faults attest to vigorous hydrothermal circulation within zones of fracture porosity created and maintained by faulting. In the southern part of the province, especially in southeastern California and southwestern Arizona, range fronts have been worn back by erosion, leaving a thin veneer of gravel on an erosion-cut, bedrock surface that slopes gently outward. The range-bounding faults of these mountain blocks are buried at the outer edge of such pediments, often at considerble distances from the erosional remnants of the ranges themselves.

The American physiographer N. M. Fenneman (1928, 1931) named the Basin and Range province and defined its general boundaries. As thus circumscribed, the province includes some 800,000 km^2 of area in eight western states. Later students (Pardee 1950, Lawrence 1976, Reynolds 1979, Eaton 1979b) have observed that many of the fundamental geological and geophysical characteristics of the province are found well beyond the boundaries drawn by Fenneman, which were based on physiography alone. As a *tectonophysical* entity, its areal extent is greater than 1 million km^2, more than 10% of the area of the United States (Figure 1).

Fenneman (1931) subdivided the province into five physiographic sections, the largest of which is the Great Basin (see Figure 1*b*). It is not, as its name implies, a single regional depression with a common topographic center, but is characterized instead by isolated networks of interior drainage, divisible into

0084-6597/82/0515–0409$02.00

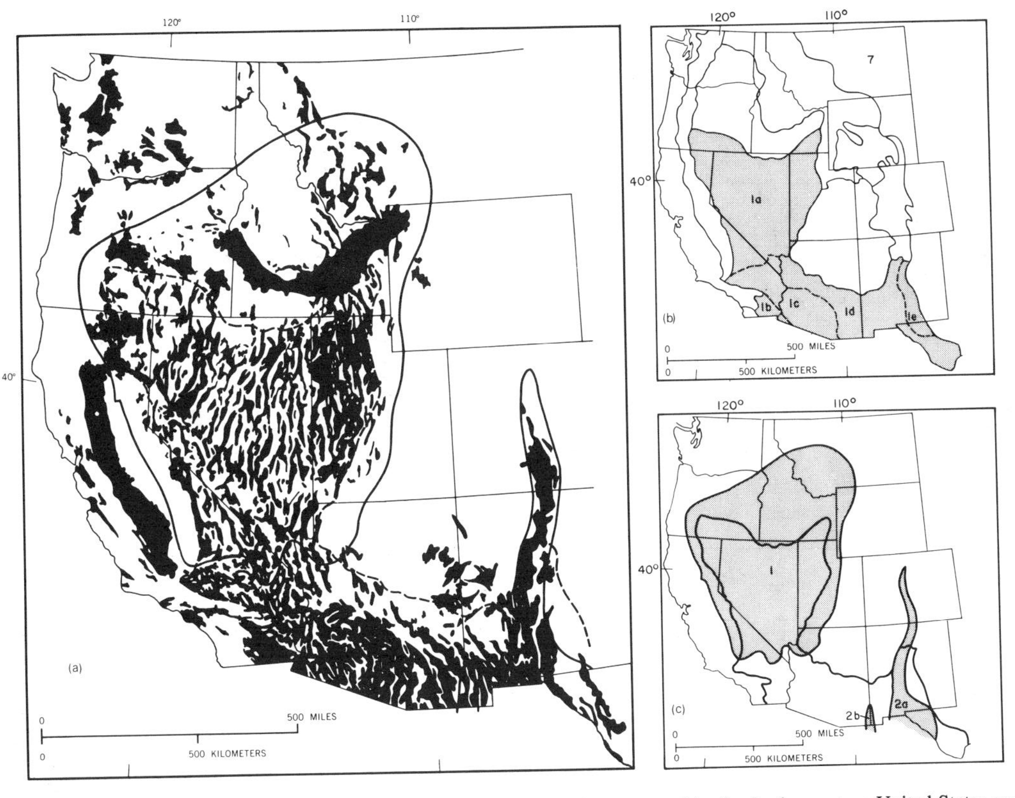

Figure 1 Maps of the Basin and Range province: (*a*) Distribution of grabens and other structural basins in the western United States containing Miocene, Pliocene, and Quaternary sedimentary rocks, as well as Quaternary volcanic rocks; (*b*) Map of physiographic subdivisions of the western United States, with sections of the Basin and Range province as follows—1a, Great Basin; 1b, Salton Trough; 1c, Sonoran Desert; 1d, Mexican Highland; 1e, Sacramento; (*c*) Map of regions tectonophysically active in Quaternary time, exclusive of coastal California. Sources: Fenneman 1928, 1931, King & Beikman 1974, Eaton 1979b.

200 or more separate surface hydrographic areas, many of them individually closed basins. The Great Basin, in fact, is not a basin at all, for along its north and south edges it stands nearly a kilometer above the adjacent terrain (see Figure 2*d*). It is the highest of the subdivisions in elevation, averaging between 1,500 and 1,700 meters. It is also the most active tectonically, as evidenced by (*a*) an abundance of faults and fault scarps with young displacements, (*b*) numerous active thermal springs, many with reservoir temperatures exceeding 100°C, and (*c*) high seismicity, especially near its margins. Its ranges show a strong similarity of trend, with northerly and north-northeasterly strikes.

While basin-range topography is the most obvious characteristic of the physiographic province, it is also notable for the broadly distributed nature of its normal faulting to which that topography is genetically linked. With the possible exception of the northern part of the East African rift system, it is unusual among the regions of any continent for high heat flow, thin lithosphere, the occurrence of low seismic velocities in the underlying upper mantle, a history of long-lived episodic magmatism, and a pronounced layer of low seismic velocity and high electrical conductivity in midcrust (Thompson & Burke 1974, Eaton 1980). Finally, it has well-developed geophysical bilateral symmetry (Eaton et al 1978; see also Figure 2*d* in this paper). Today, we recognize many of these characteristics as fundamental attributes of actively spreading ocean ridges. The implication is basically the same for the Basin and Range province. It is a full-scale operating model of the predrift rifting of continental lithosphere, but one in which rifting is broadly distributed, more like that of a marginal back-arc basin than a spreading ocean ridge.

The purpose of this review is to describe the nature of the Basin and Range province and present a hypothesis of origin for its unique structure. The development of that structure is interpreted as the combined product of the behavior of a rheologically layered crust that stems from an unusual thermal history and evolving interactions between the North American plate and neighboring plates at the western margin of the continent.

FUNDAMENTAL CHARACTERISTICS OF THE PROVINCE

Variations in Structural Style and the Composition of Related Magmas

The prominence of today's basin-range topography and structure has obscured, until recently, the fact that its development succeeded an earlier regime of extensional deformation in which vertical structural relief was much less pronounced and deformation was more localized, though geographically distributed throughout the province (Figure 7 of Zoback et al 1981). One characteristic feature of the earlier regime—normal faults with low dips—was first described by Longwell (1933, 1945). An equally significant feature is the spatial association of coeval volcanic rocks of calc-alkaline composition. In places, the two features went hand-in-hand, listric faulting occurring in a regional extensional stress field in the shallow crust above passively emplaced plutons or in association with major caldera collapse. In other localities, maximum episodes of fault movement occurred during apparent peaks in igneous activity.

Classic Basin and Range structure dates from approximately 17 m.y. ago and later (middle Miocene time), but the earlier extensional deformation began at least as long ago as 29 to 30 m.y. and, locally, as long ago as 36 to 37 m.y. (earliest Oligocene time; see Gans 1981). Locally, it continued up to, and in a few places into, the time of general block faulting.

Differences in style between these contrasting types of brittle extension are related, in part, to the shapes of the faults in cross section. Block faulting is perceived to occur on steep faults that penetrate deeply into the crust. Thin-skinned extension occurs on curved, concave-upward, listric faults that "bottom out" or "sole" at shallow crustal depths. The latter style has been recognized from surface mapping (Hamblin 1965, Anderson 1971), from subsurface geologic exploration (Proffett 1977), and from seismic reflection investigations (McDonald 1976, Pls. I–IV; Effimoff & Pinezich 1981, Figures 8 and 9).

Block faults may cut through the full thickness of the crust as essentially planar features, or they may actually reflect only the steep upper part of very large-scale listric faults of great vertical extent, faults whose radii of curvature in cross-section are much larger than those of more obvious thin-skin faults. If faults such as these bottom out at a detachment surface at depth, or intersect such a surface at a steep angle, they do so well within the crystalline basement.

I do not subscribe to the "tilted buoyant block" model of Stewart (1978, 1980a), in which the faults cut through a rigid surface layer to an unspecified substratum on which the surface layer floats. My reasons are based partly on the grounds of an absence of isostatic compensation for the ranges (Eaton et al 1978), but also on analog modeling and on arguments (presented below) that suggest a lower crust that deforms by steady-state creep. If my view of normal faults is correct, a basic question is posed: What determines the level of "soling" or detachment? It may be a function of the position of a brittle-ductile transition in the crust, or some more abrupt contrast in mechanical properties. It is argued below that the location of such a brittle-ductile (or semibrittle) transition may in part be a function of the thermal state of the crust, but it is equally obvious, at least in some places in the province, that it may also be determined by a shallow condition of nonthermally activated ductility, such as the presence of an evaporite section or weakly consolidated, fine-grained rocks within the sedimentary section. Seismic reflection data suggest, in some places, that such detachments originate at the interface between layered Paleozoic and massive Precambrian basement rocks; in others, at a Tertiary-Paleozoic interface; and in still others, within the Tertiary section itself. Geological and geophysical observations suggest that it may also occur wholly within the basement, as do those thrust faults that incorporate parts of the crystalline basement within their upper plate.

Early students (e.g. King 1878, Dutton 1880) noted the presence of Mesozoic compressional structures in the region, and Nolan (1943) later made the observation that Mesozoic and early Tertiary folding and thrusting, which ended in Eocene time, had been followed rather closely by extensional faulting. He also commented on the obvious near-coincidence of the easternmost geographic limits of folding and block faulting. The two phenomena, compression and extension, seemed linked somehow, both in time and space.

From detailed information on the timing and style of extensional deformation, we now recognize that crustal spreading was initiated in a calc-alkaline igneous setting inferred to be that of a continental volcanic arc, that it evolved in a back-arc setting, and that it came to be influenced only later (in the manner suggested by Atwater 1970), by the growth of the transform boundary at the western margin of the continent. The direction of spreading changed significantly at this later time. For the evidence and arguments supporting these views, see Scholz et al (1971), Eaton et al (1978), Stewart (1978), Zoback & Thompson (1978), Eaton (1979a), and Zoback et al (1981). Changes in the state of stress in the continental lithosphere, and changes in the strain rate once extension had begun, resulted in the development of fundamentally different kinds of structures, and produced related changes in the composition of contemporary magmas (Rehrig et al 1980, Zoback et al 1981).

It was initially thought that the change from calc-alkaline intermediate-to-basaltic or bimodal basalt-rhyolite magmatism marked a fundamental change from compressional to extensional states of stress (Lipman et al 1972, Christiansen & Lipman 1972). More recent observations suggest, instead, the following relations: (*a*) magmas emplaced during convergence-related compression are of calc-alkaline andesitic, rhyolitic, and quartz-latitic composition; (*b*) magmas emplaced during the succeeding period of intra-arc and back-arc spreading at rapid strain rates are of high-silica, (locally, peralkaline) rhyolitic composition, accompanied by basaltic andesites, alkali basalts, and locally, tholeiites; and (*c*) magmas emplaced during the final period of extensional block faulting, at reduced extensional strain rates, are of tholeiitic and alkalic basalt composition (Elston & Bornhorst 1979).

Active Block Faulting

Faults of known late Cenozoic age, for which movement in Quaternary time is known or suspected, are shown in Figure 2*a*. They are characterized by steep dips and relatively high structural relief; stratal rotations have been relatively mild. The map is dominated by two rather sharply defined domains of young faulting. (Those elements involving large lateral displacement near the coast of California are excluded.) Both are enclosed by heavy lines for the purpose of geographic reference. One, the Rio Grande rift system, runs northward, through central New Mexico and Colorado. It represents an integral part of the same extensional tectonic regime as that of the Basin and Range province.

The other domain, a large, broad region roughly ovoid in plan, extends across eastern California, the whole of Nevada, and western Utah (thus coinciding with the Great Basin), northward into eastern Oregon and southern Idaho, and northeastward into western Montana and Wyoming. Its width varies from 450 to more than 950 km, its length being slightly less than 1,350 km.

If these two regions, both of which also display evidence of earlier extension on low-dipping faults, are included as parts of a single province of extensional faulting, interrupted by the Colorado Plateau, and including those parts of the Basin and Range province in southwestern Arizona and Mexico, the combined region has dimensions of 1,550 by nearly 3,200 km (see Stewart 1978, Figure 1-1).

Because a consensus has developed that early crustal spreading was of intra-arc and back-arc origin, it is perhaps instructive to compare the dimensions of this province, and its individual components, with those of a variety of Pacific marginal and oceanic back-arc basins of different sizes and shapes. It can be seen from the data in Table 1 that the regions of late Cenozoic extension in western North America fit a dimensional continuum of back-arc-spreading features better than they fit the dimensions of ocean ridges ($L/W >> 10$).

Variation in Relative Total Extension

Spacings of mapped faults in the Great Basin range from 12 to 26 km, averaging 15 ± 2.5 km. The widest part, at 42° N, has the largest number of faults in a single traverse; the narrowest part, at 36° N, the smallest. If the dip of these faults and the dip-slip displacements were both more or less uniform, the sum of the horizontal components of displacement (a measure of the total extension across the region) would be proportionately greatest in the widest part, and least in the narrowest part.

We know that such strain is variable along cross-province transverses

(Thompson & Burke 1974, Proffett 1977, Zoback et al 1981), but in general, the variation in width of the region of young faulting suggests a dramatic increase in total extension from its narrowest to its widest part. Such increases are incrementally abrupt and discontinuous across major strike-slip faults and related broad, oblique zones within the extended region. The regional variation is in keeping with the concept of rotational spreading of a spherical shell along small circle paths about poles of rotation close to the deforming region. Unless an opening of this kind is accommodated within the plate by matched shortening, the outboard part must necessarily be rotated away as a rigid or quasi-rigid subplate. Such rotation is suggested by the paleomagnetic data of Magill et al (1981) for the coastal region of Oregon and Washington. These data suggest clockwise rotation of the Oregon Coast ranges of as much as 30° in Miocene and later times (20 to 0 m.y. ago) outboard of the western Great Basin.

Evidence for a Ductile or Elasticoplastic Lower Crust

A comparison of active continental rift systems of the world reveals that the Great Basin and the Afar region of East Africa have dimensions different from the others, with the maximum width of the Great Basin exceeding that of Afar by a factor of three. The distributed nature of this deformation places in question the degree to which brittle failure is the principal deformational mode at depth. A surface layer (Eaton 1980) apparently only 15 km or so thick (T) and up to 950 km wide (W; $T/W = 0.016$) has been stretched and fragmented in brittle fashion, but there is little or no evidence to suggest that brittle failure is, or has been, occurring at depth. Rather, several observations support the possibility of pervasive flow, as first suggested by Thompson (1959) and Hamilton & Myers (1966).

The concept of uniform flow at depth by cataclasis, intragranular gliding and/or recrystallization, appears supported by several lines of evidence. One is seismogenesis. A regional compilation of some 2,500 earthquake foci in the region (see histogram, left side of Figure 2*b*) shows that 98.1% of the local earthquakes occur at depths of less than 15 km, and 80.3% at depths less than 10 km (Eaton 1980). The crust is 20 to 30 km thick; hence, instantaneous faulting and abrupt stress drops related to it seem limited to the upper half of the continental crust and the upper quarter, or less, of the approximately 65 km-thick lithosphere. This observation, plus that of Hamilton & Myers (1966) on the limiting nature of the fault spacing, suggests that most of the faults do not cut the full thickness of the continental crust, let alone that of the lithosphere (for an opposing view, see Wernicke 1981). This view is further supported by isostatic observations: (*a*) there is a notable absence of isostatic compensation for all but a few of the largest of the more than one hundred ranges of the Basin and Range province (Eaton et al 1978), and (*b*) compen-

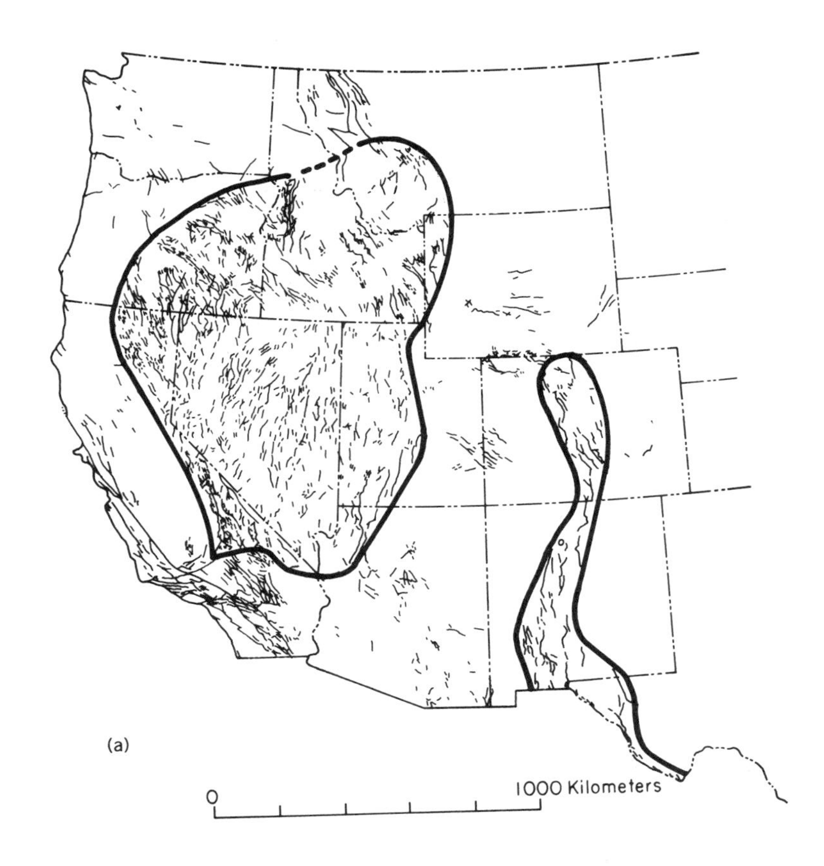
(a)
0
1000 Kilometers

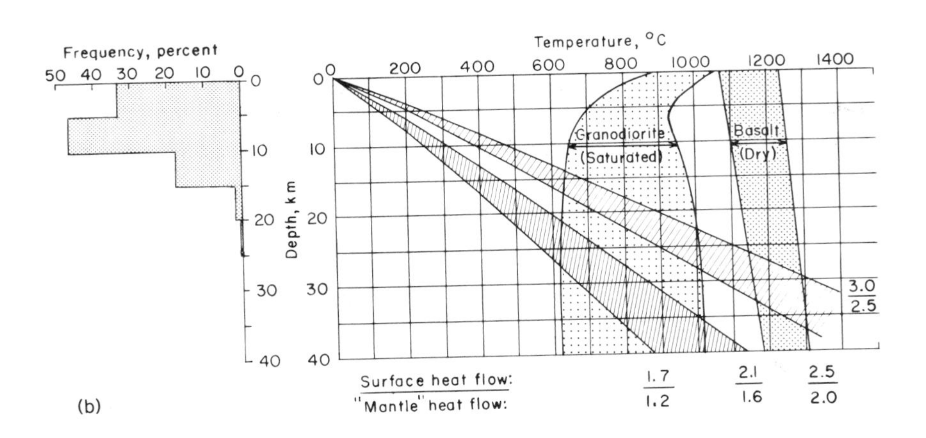
Frequency, percent
50 40 30 20 10 0
0
10
20
30
40
Temperature, °C
0 200 400 600 800 1000 1200 1400
Depth, km
Granodiorite
(Saturated)
Basalt
(Dry)
3.0
2.5
Surface heat flow:
"Mantle" heat flow:
1.7
1.2
2.1
1.6
2.5
2.0
(b)

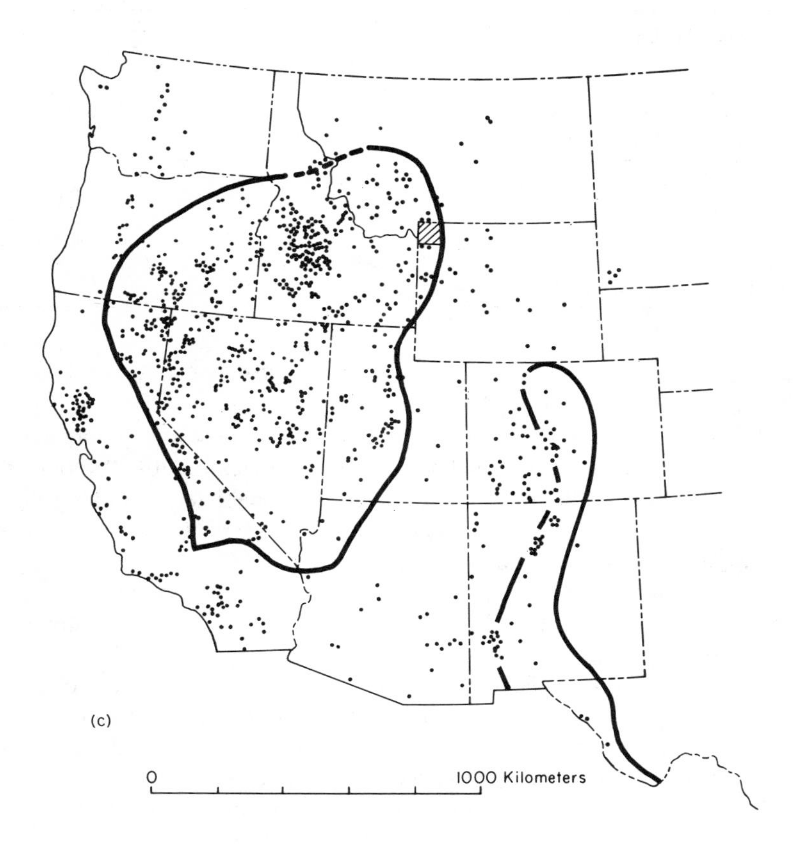

Figure 2 Fundamental characteristics of the Basin and Range province: (*a*) Faults active in past 10 to 15 m.y.; Quaternary movement suspected. Source: Howard et al 1978. (*b*) Conductive temperature profiles for the Basin and Range crust (ranges of temperature shown by cross-ruling, with wide-spaced cross-ruling identifying Battle Mountain heat flow high and closer cross-ruling denoting the rest of province). On the left is shown the statistical depth distribution of 2,475 earthquakes in the region and on the right, the melting fields of granodiorite (coarse stippling) and basalt (fine stippling). Sources: Lachenbruch & Sass 1977, Eaton 1980. (*c*) Thermal springs with surface water temperatures more than 8°C above local mean annual air temperature. Source: Waring 1965.

Table 1 Dimensions of Basin and Range Province and oceanic back-arc basins

Spreading region	Length by width (km)	Aspect ratio (L/W)
Rio Grande Rift (including that part in Mexico; Seager & Morgan 1979)	1,400 × 150	9.3
New Caledonian Basin	1,600 × 250	6.4
Shikoku and Parece Vela Basin	2,000 × 500	4.0
South China Basin	1,500 × 550	2.7
Basin and Range Province and Rio Grande Rift Together	3,250 × 1,550	2.1
Japan Basin	900 × 450	2.0
West Phillipine Basin	2,000 × 1,000	2.0
South Fiji Basin	1,250 × 800	1.6
Aleutian Basin	900 × 600	1.5
Great Basin and Northern Environs	1,350 × 950	1.4

sation for features as large as the western Snake River Plain appears to take place in the upper 20 km of the crust (Mabey 1976).

Other evidence supporting the concept of uniform flow at depth includes a smooth variation in crustal thickness, from averages of 20–30 km in the extended regions to 40–50 km in the regions immediately adjoining them. This variation, based on seismic refraction measurements, when registered with variations in regional topography (see Figure 2*d*) yields a cross section with the appearance of a ductilely "necked" plate. Although few of the relevant refraction lines are reversed, abrupt changes in thickness should be readily detectable on unreversed lines and are not seen.

The effects of actual penetrative, cataclastic, or ductile flow are observed at the base of normal faults in some parts of the province. Relatively thin horizontal zones of mylonitic and metamorphic rocks are exposed beneath faulted and severely rotated, unmetamorphosed continental sediments and volcanic rocks (some as young as Miocene in age) in western Utah, eastern Nevada, southeastern California, and southwestern Arizona (Compton et al 1977, Coney 1979, and Davis 1980). Controversy surrounds the age of latest cataclasis and metamorphism, however, and some investigators question its genetic relation to crustal extension or to the detachment faults associated with it. In some areas, the development of cataclasites clearly predates extensional deformation by a few tens of millions of years. In at least one of these areas, however, K-Ar dates of middle Miocene age were found in peraluminous sheetlike intrusions just below the base of the faulted section (Martin et al 1980). In some places, such radiometric ages increase downward in the uppermost part of the lower plate from Miocene to Paleocene or Cretaceous. Such

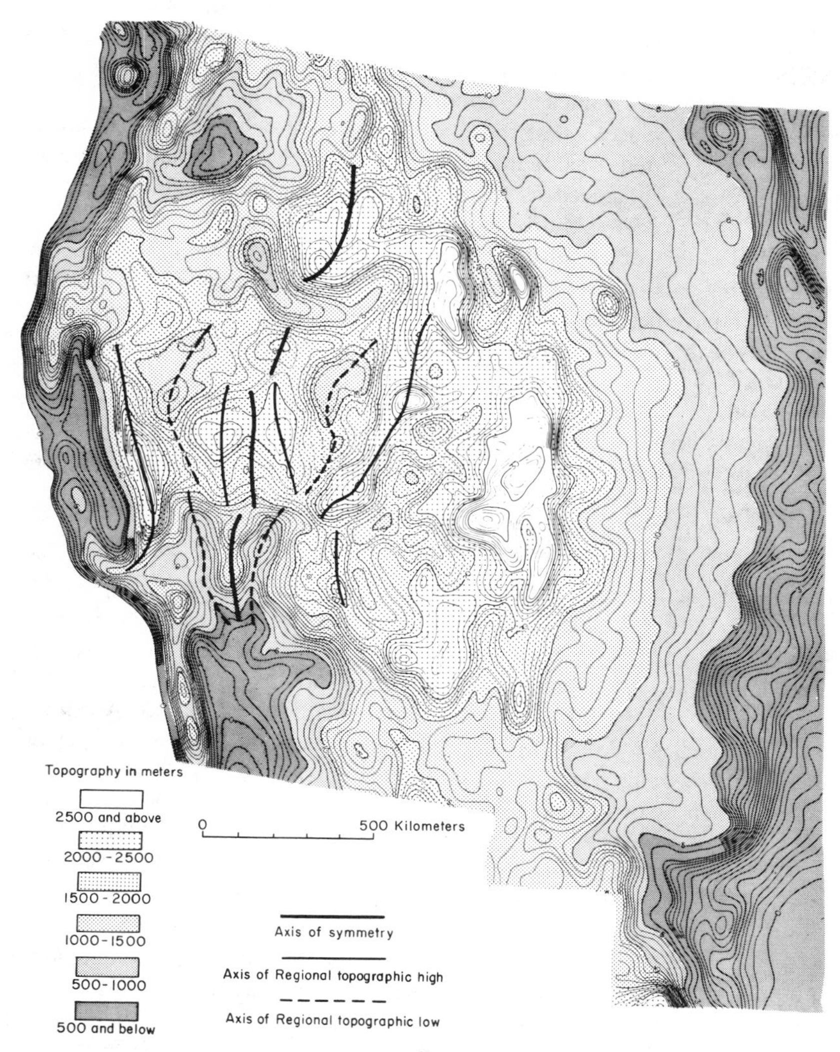

Figure 2 (*d*) Smoothed topography of the western United States, contour interval, 100 m; heavy line identifies axis of bilateral topographic symmetry. Sources: Diment & Urban 1981, Eaton et al 1978.

evidence suggests Miocene resetting of radiometric clocks first set during the compressional regime of Mesozoic and early Tertiary time. In other localities, plutonic rocks as young as Miocene in age are, themselves, penetratively deformed and lineated, with well-developed, subhorizontal fabrics (Coney

1979), while in at least one other (Compton et al 1977), temperatures exceeding 400°C apparently prevailed from the time of convergence-related, compressional thrusting until 10 m.y. ago, long after the initial phase of thin-skinned extension had ended and continuing up to, and into, the time of block faulting. In those places where the age of initial cataclasis and metamorphism clearly predates extensional faulting, the younger detachment faults are nevertheless strongly influenced as to their spatial location and attitude by the existence of the older subhorizontal structures and fabrics.

Finally, on the subject of ductility, strain rates of both the initial phase of extension and the succeeding block faulting were low enough, at what are believed to have been significantly elevated temperatures, to suggest that the fundamental deformation mode at depth was slow creep. We examine this topic below.

While there seems to be widespread agreement that the *lithosphere* is rheologically layered (Turcotte et al 1978, Beaumont 1979), what is suggested here for the Basin and Range province is a rheologically layered, continental crust.

Thermal Regime and Seismicity

Tectonically active parts of the Basin and Range crust have temperatures higher than those of stable continental crust (Blackwell 1978, Lachenbruch & Sass 1977, 1978). The evidence is manifested in high values of observed and reduced heat flow, in an abundance of thermal springs, and in the widespread distribution of young volcanic rocks (Figures 2*b, c,* 3, 4, and 5). According to Lachenbruch & Sass (1978), reduced heat flow values in the province (those for which radiogenic heat production in the crust has been accounted for) are greater than those of stable regions by as much as 50 to 100%, and in the hotter subprovinces, such as the Battle Mountain High, by as much as 300%. Much of the anomalous heat is believed to be transferred into the lithosphere by penetrative convection from below. Lachenbruch & Sass (1978) suggested the viability of the alternative mechanisms of basaltic dike intrusion, solid-state stretching (uniform flow of the lithosphere), and underplating. Combinations of such mechanisms are physically plausible and all may be operative in some proportion. Each is sufficient to account for the observed high heat loss without recourse to an anomalously high conductive heat flow from the base of the lithosphere.

Figure 2*b* shows generalized temperature profiles for typical Basin and Range crust and for the Battle Mountain High region within it (Lachenbruch & Sass 1977). Also shown are fields of melting for water-saturated granodiorite and dry basalt. At the left is a histogram of earthquake focal depths.

The mean temperature profile for the Battle Mountain heat flow high intersects the solidus curve for granodiorite at a depth of roughly 15 km (the level above which 98% of the earthquakes in the province are observed). The upper temperature profile for characteristic Basin and Range crust intersects this solidus at about 20 km, and an average one, just above 25 km. Less than 0.5% of all earthquakes observed in the province occur at depths greater than 20 km, and none have been observed below 25 km (Eaton 1980). Whether or not the assumptions on which the downward extrapolation of the crustal temperatures represented by these conductive temperature curves are correct (Lachenbruch & Sass 1978, pp. 217–18), they should at least be meaningful to those depths where convective transport becomes significant.

Laboratory studies by Bauer et al (1981) indicate substantial loss in ultimate strength for rocks a few hundred degrees below the solidus temperature, even at simulated depths as shallow as one to two km. At greater depths and lithostatic pressures, the loss of strength with temperature is higher, as it would be at the much slower strain rates believed to have governed extension in the province (see below).

I believe that the base of the seismogenic zone marks the base of the region of brittle behavior. If, as Lachenbruch & Sass (1978) have suggested, the province heat flow increases systematically with extensional strain rate, isotherms will rise in the lithosphere with increased deformation rate, and the boundary separating a region of uniform creep from one of brittle failure, above, will also rise. Under such circumstances, the seismogenic zone should grow thinner.

Distribution of Thermal Springs

Thermal springs are shown in Figure 2*c*. Borders surrounding them were taken from Figure 2*a*, where they were drawn around families of faults active in late Cenozoic time. The spatial coincidence is striking. It suggests convection within a fracture porosity created and maintained by fault movement. Both features are sparse in southeastern California and the southwestern half of Arizona, despite basin-range topography there (cf Figure 1*a*). The explanation may lie in tectonic inactivity, perhaps with a sealing of old fractures by the deposition of silica, calcium carbonate, or other fracture fillings of the sort seen in outcrops.

Young-faulting and hydrothermal circulation are characteristic of ocean ridges. In the Basin and Range province the areal distribution of hot springs and faults is much broader, and the availability of recharge water a great deal less than at ocean ridges, but the parallel is meaningful. It extends through the coincidence of other phenomena: an extensional state of stress, appreciable metallogenesis, and elevated regional topography (Eaton 1979a,b, Eaton et al 1978).

Regional Topography

The western two fifths of the United States is dominated by terrain more than 1,400 m above sea level (Figure 2*d*). The average elevation of the Great Basin, which exceeds 1,400 m, is similar to that of the interior of the Colorado Plateau. The inactive part of the Basin and Range province (southeastern California and southwestern Arizona) is less than 600 m in average elevation.

The most plausible explanation for the high elevation of this region is that of thermal expansion, as at a spreading ocean ridge. McKenzie (1978) suggested that subsidence should be associated with continental crustal thinning and that after such thinning ceases, subsidence should continue, owing to thermal contraction. This model does not fit the Great Basin section, however, nor even, strictly speaking, the tectonically inactive Sonoran Desert section, both of which are underlain by thinned crust (Smith 1978, Prodehl 1979). While the latter stands lower in elevation and has been cooling for perhaps the last 10 m.y. (Eaton 1980), its loss of elevation has, in part, been the result of erosion that has exposed the rocks of deeper levels of the shallow crust. An alternative hypothesis, a possible doubling of the thickness of the lithosphere because of the presence of a relatively light and buoyant Farallon plate immediately beneath the North American plate, is supported neither by the geophysical data, which indicate an abnormally thin lithosphere (Thompson & Burke 1974), nor by geologic reasoning that suggests the possibility of a gigantic hole in the Farallon plate beneath the region (Stewart 1978).

It seems probable, therefore, that most, if not all, of the high stand of the Great Basin follows from vertical expansion of the lithosphere due to heating from below. Hot material moved upward from depth by mass transport to replace that which moved laterally away by crustal stretching and/or diking. This is required to maintain the observed, regional isostatic balance (Eaton et al 1978, Lachenbruch & Sass 1978). Upward expansion is somewhat offset buoyantly by a thinning of the relatively low density crust, but augmented by a thinning of the denser lithospheric mantle, below which an asthenosphere of slightly lower density (than the mantle) has risen.

At the east and west margins of the Great Basin, the Sierra Nevada and Wasatch Mountains tower above it along great fault scarps, as do the ramparts of a slowly spreading ocean ridge. The same is true for the Rio Grande rift. Such major border faults may penetrate deeply into the lithosphere (if not entirely through it), but there is little convincing evidence at present that they do.

State of Stress

A state of deviatoric tensile stress has existed in the Basin and Range lithosphere for much of the past 35 m.y. Direct and indirect measurements of the state of stress and their compilation and analysis have been the object of intensive study over the past few years (Smith & Sbar 1974, Rehrig & Heidrick 1976, Zoback & Thompson 1978, Eaton 1979a, Zoback & Zoback 1980, Zoback et al 1981). Some of the results of the last study are shown in Figure 2*f* and *g* (where they are supplemented by new data, as described in the figure caption), and in Figure 2*e*, an entirely new compilation.

Northeast-directed compression, stemming from relative convergence of the Farallon and North American plates, was aligned in a direction approximately normal to the oceanic trench that existed through late Mesozoic and early Tertiary time at the western margin of North America. Its effects, plus those of earlier episodes of Paleozoic compression, are shown in Figure 2*e*. The Mesozoic and early Tertiary events produced, far inland, folding, thrusting, uplift, and the emplacement of plutons and dikes of calc-alkaline magma, the plutons and dikes in the more brittle portions of the crust, elongated in the direction of maximum compressive stress (σ_1). A compressional state of stress in the overriding North American plate reflects a *Chilean* mode of subduction, according to the scheme of Uyeda & Kanamori (1979). The dip of the downgoing oceanic lithosphere evolved over time from moderate to gentle (Coney & Reynolds 1977) and, according to the interpretation of Dickinson & Snyder (1978), may have come into what was essentially full contact with the overriding plate over a downdip distance of more than 1,200 km inland from the trench, "scraping" along beneath the underside of that plate and providing unusually strong coupling, as well as creating an amagmatic condition between the trench on the west, and the continental volcanic arc, far inland.

Magmatism as an Indicator of Stress History

Figure 3 shows data illustrating a transgression and regression of subduction-related calc-alkaline magmatism along a 650 km-wide corridor extending roughly east-west through southern California, southern Arizona, and southern New Mexico (Coney & Reynolds 1977). It includes a tectonic interpretation, new here, in which changes in state of stress are identified by timing. Coney & Reynolds interpreted these igneous data in terms of a variably dipping, subducted slab near the upper surface of which magma was generated at an essentially constant depth (or over a limited depth range). Based on attendant, measurable variations in rock composition, Keith (1978) suggested that constant-dip and variable source-depth, as well as variable-dip, variable source-depth modes, may have also been operative. In Coney & Reynolds' (1977) interpretation, negative slopes on the upper bounding curve represent inland advance of the zone of magma generation and, consequently, a reduction in dip of the subducting Farallon plate. Changes in slope may reflect changes in rate of advance of the zone of magma generation and rate of reduction in dip. Coney & Reynolds (1977) and Keith (1978) agreed that

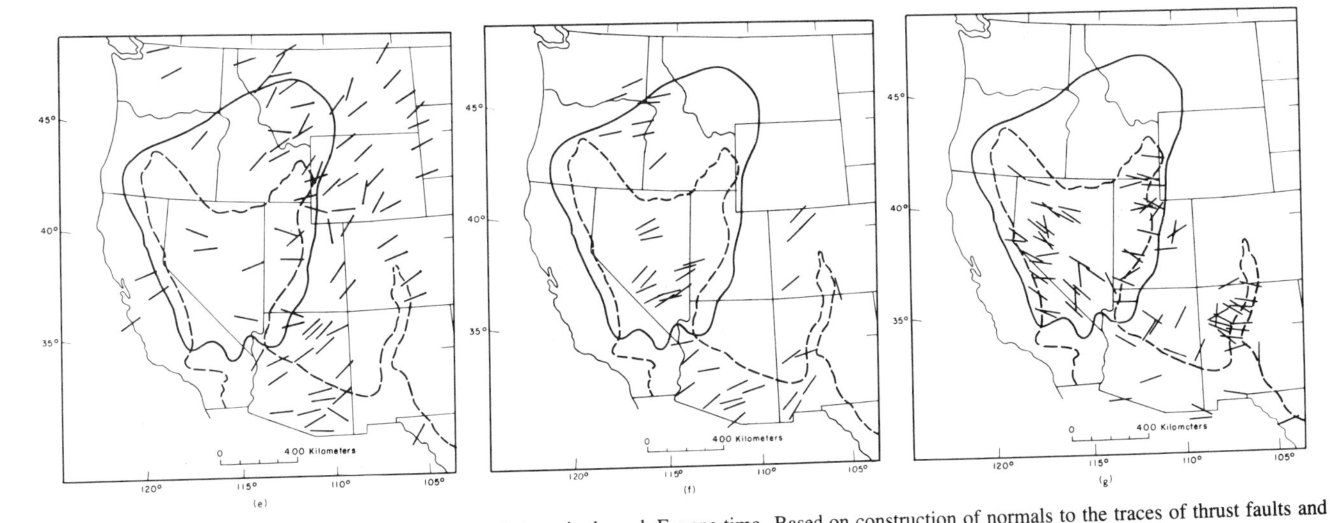

Figure 2 (*e*) Directions of maximum principal stress, Paleozoic through Eocene time. Based on construction of normals to the traces of thrust faults and folds more than 25 km in length, as well as modal directions of elongation of Laramide plutons. Stress trajectories in Nevada mark E.-M. Mesozoic thrusting. Sources: Cohee 1961, Rehrig & Heidrick 1976, Davis 1978. (*f*) Directions of minimum principal stress in Oligocene and Miocene time, based on construction of normals to dike swarms, cinder cone alignments, normal faults, and grabens, as well as directions of stratal tilting. Sources: Robinson 1970, Swanson et al 1979, and principally, Zoback et al 1981. (*g*) Directions of minimum principal stress today. Source: Zoback et al 1981.

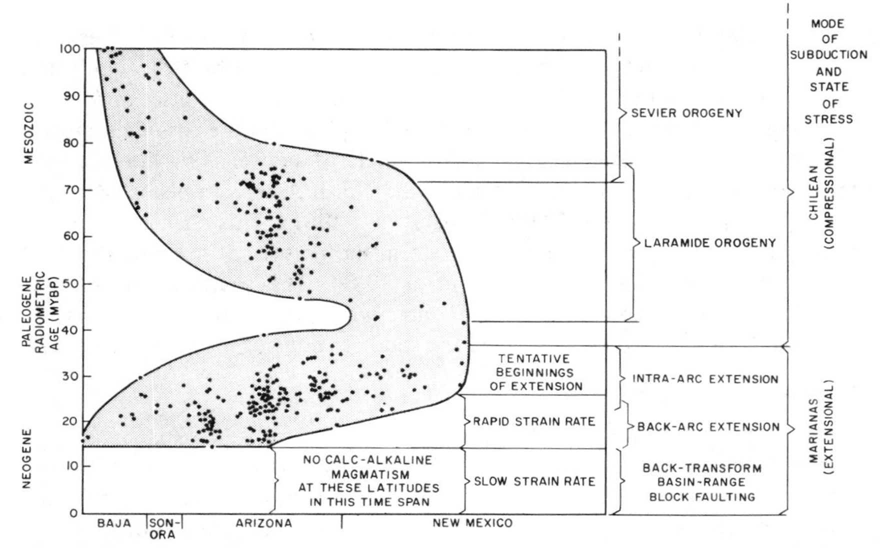

Figure 3 Transgression and regression of subduction-related, calc-alkaline magmatism in the southwestern United States. Sevier and Laramide orogenies represent compressional states of stress in the continental lithosphere. The associated subduction mode was Chilean. Episodes of crustal extension took place during a Marianas mode of subduction. Extension continued after subduction ceased, but in a different direction and largely in a back-transform environment. Source of geochronometric compilation: Coney & Reynolds 1977.

flattening of the dip took place between 80 and 50 m.y. ago and steepening of the dip, between 40 and 20 m.y. ago. Keith's data base (the more limited of the two) has a gap in the period 55 to 37 m.y. ago; hence, our understanding of the "fine structure" for this period of time is limited to the earlier data.

The outer bounding curve in Figure 3 shows a very high positive slope after roughly 37 m.y. ago, although control is sparse. I believe that it represents the time of onset of a *Marianas* mode of subduction, one in which the state of stress in the North American plate was deviatoric tension. Coupling between the plates had weakened and crustal extension had begun. The rate of extension was slow at first, but increased in the period between roughly 25 and 17 m.y. ago. Because plate convergence was continuing and the vector of relative motion between the plates had not changed direction substantially (Coney 1978, compare Figures 2-5 and 2-6), the azimuth of the minimum principal stress (σ_3) became that of the former maximum principal stress (σ_1). A comparison of Figures 2*e* and *f* suggests this was the case. The direction of convergence of the plates was unchanged, but the state of stress underwent a very fundamental change from compressional to extensional owing to a slowing in the rate of convergence and a reduction in plate-plate coupling.

Figure 2*g* identifies the present direction of minimum principal stress. It followed a change in trajectory from southwest to west-northwest, roughly 10 m.y. ago (Zoback et al 1981), that is believed to reflect the onset of *lateral* coupling with the northward-migrating Pacific plate and the resultant superposition of a dextral shear stress (the Atwater 1970 model) along the growing transform boundary between the Pacific and North American plates (Zoback & Thompson 1978, Eaton 1979a, Zoback et al 1981). This change seems to have occurred at a time of increased rate in the northward migration of the Mendocino triple junction (Zoback et al 1981). The southern end of the genetically linked continental volcanic arc (which lay to the east) migrated northward with it, as presumably did the southern edge of the back-arc extension region.

Magmatic History

Figure 3, which was interpreted tectonically above, shows that calc-alkaline magma was emplaced almost continuously throughout two periods of time in central and eastern Arizona: from 80 to 55 m.y. ago, and again from 38 to 14 m.y. ago. Once these magmatic regimes ended, there were further episodic eruptions of basaltic lava continuing locally into Quaternary time (not shown in Figure 3). The record's implication is clear: mass transport of heat to the shallow crust by penetrative convection of magma has been a long-lived phenomena. It may have kept crustal temperatures elevated over this entire time span.

Wholesale magmatic invasion of the crust appears to have established or blocked out the entire tectonophysical province, probably through thermal weakening. Figures 4*a* and *b,* which identify fields of igneous activity for the past 54 m.y. (Eocene through Holocene time), seem to imply that magma sequentially invaded nearly every part of the province.

The magmatic record of Nevada, a state that occupies fully half the Great Basin, is particularly instructive (Figure 5). Magma genesis appears to have reached a maximum there in the period 34 to 6 m.y. ago (Figures 5*e* and *f*), a time embracing that of rapid early extension and the earliest part of the period of later block faulting. Magmatic flux has been greatly reduced in the past 6 m.y. despite continuing extension, suggesting possible reduction in the extensional strain rate.

Figure 5*h* integrates Nevada magmatism for the whole of Mesozoic and Cenozoic time. Even taking into account the fact that much of what is shown on these maps represents flat-lying lavas and tuffs constituting volumetric proportions much lower than their areal proportions, it is still impressive that so much magma was pumped through the shallow crust over so long a period of geologic time. Because it has been estimated that transient cooling of the lithosphere takes approximately 50 m.y. or so, it would seem that the Great Basin lithosphere has had little chance to begin to cool.

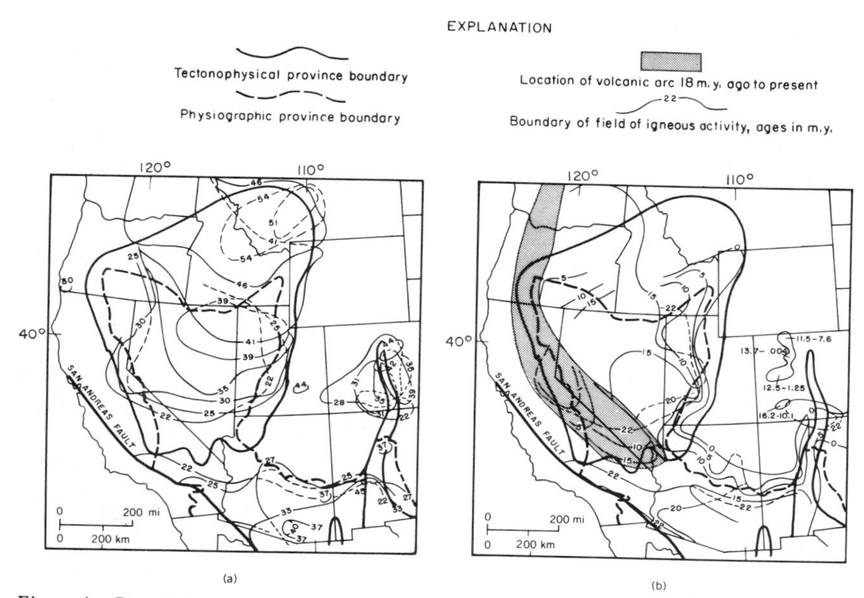

Figure 4 Boundaries of fields of igneous activity in the western United States, 54 m.y. ago to present. By 22 m.y. ago, the tectonophysical province embracing the Basin and Range physiographic province and the region to its north had been thermally defined, the few remaining gaps being filled after 22 m.y. ago. (*a*) Calc-alkaline magmatism, 54 to 22 m.y. ago. Source: Cross & Pilger 1978. (*b*) Calc-alkaline magmatism (shaded) and bimodal basalt-rhyolite magmatism (unshaded). Source: Eaton 1979b.

The sharply defined magmatic gap in southern Nevada, between 36° and 37° N, corresponds to a scalloped, regional topographic slope that separates the Great Basin and Sonoran Desert sections, as well as to a regional gravity gradient with an amplitude of nearly 100 mgals (Eaton et al 1978). Its northern edge coincides with the southern edge of the repeatedly heated Great Basin lithosphere. The gap also coincides with a region separating contrasting directions of latest extension (northwest, on the north; southwest, on the south). Recognition of this feature followed from the compilation of Figure 5*h*. Its origin is as yet unexplained. It appears to be a significant tectonic feature, perhaps even a fundamental one, in the history of the region.

ORIGIN OF BASIN AND RANGE STRUCTURE

Mechanical History

The initiation of what is known as Basin and Range structure does not represent the initiation of extension. From the standpoint of a fundamental tectonic phenomenon, the beginning of extension is the more significant event. It took

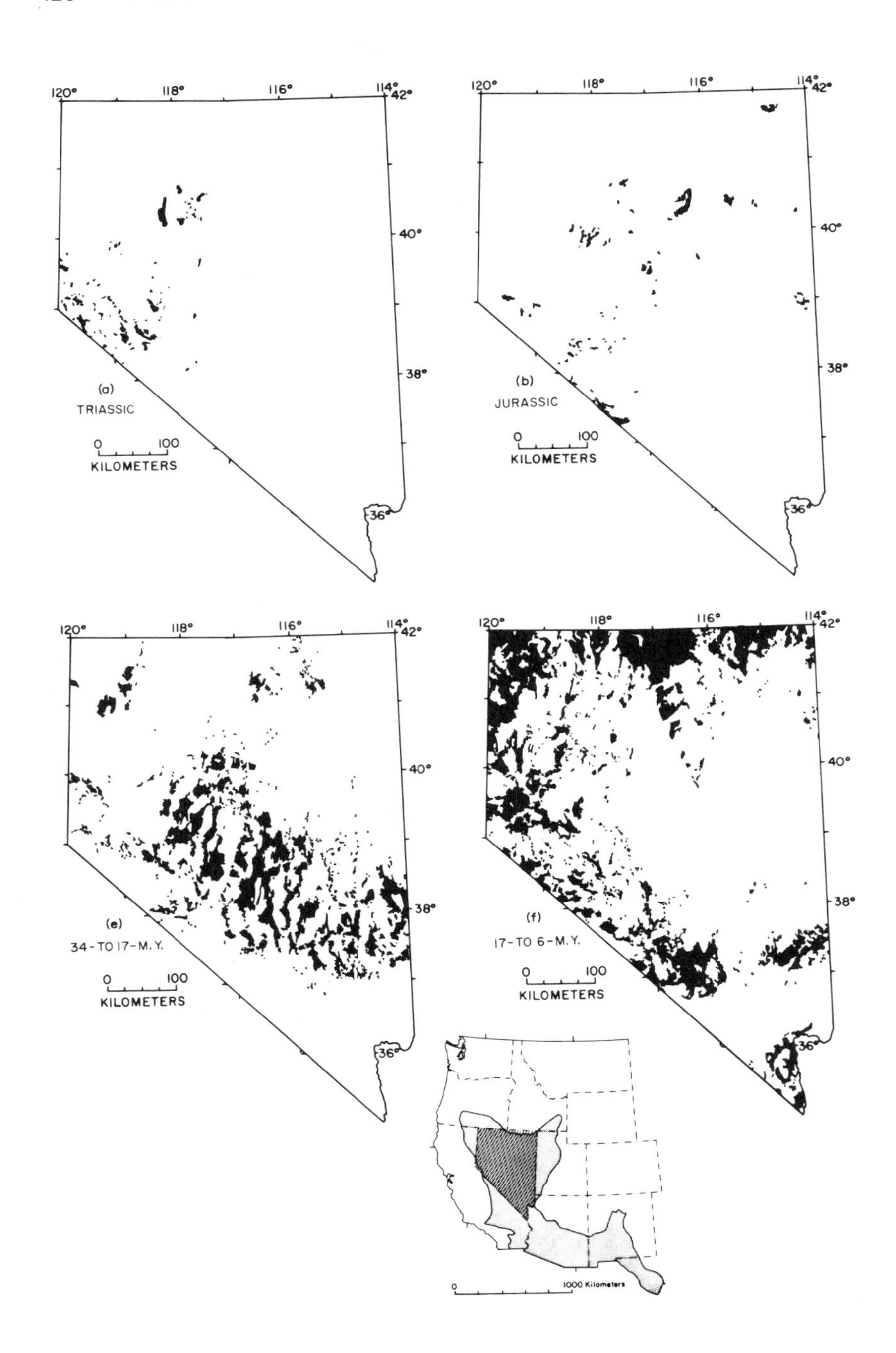
120°
118°
116°
114°
42°
40°
38°
36°
(a)
TRIASSIC
0 100
KILOMETERS
(b)
JURASSIC
0 100
KILOMETERS
(e)
34-TO 17-M.Y.
0 100
KILOMETERS
(f)
17-TO 6-M.Y.
0 100
KILOMETERS
0
1000 Kilometers

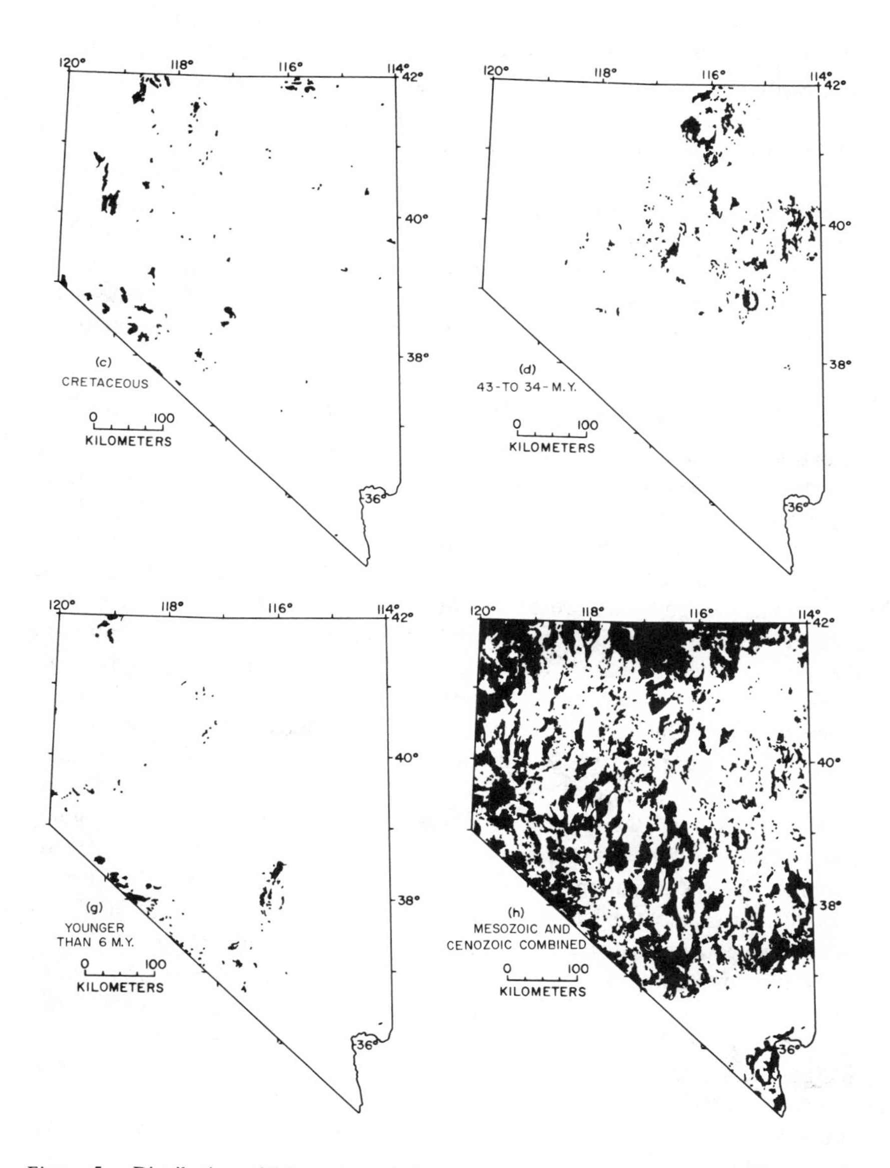

Figure 5 Distribution of Mesozoic and Cenozoic rocks of igneous derivation in Nevada, including plutonic rocks, lavas and pyroclastics, and volcaniclastic sediments of local origin. Index map shows extent of the Great Basin occupied by Nevada. The magmatic history of this state has been long, episodic, and profound. Source: Stewart 1980b.

place at a relatively high strain rate and locally produced strong stratal rotations and closely spaced normal faults, the faults themselves being rotated to relatively low dips. In those areas where extreme regional erosion, coupled with continuous isostatic rise, has been at play for 5 to 10 m.y. (as in the Sonoran Desert section), these structures (as noted above) are found to terminate downward at large-scale, subhorizontal detachment surfaces or zones of extreme cataclasis and/or ductile shear, some of which developed prior to the onset of extension (Compton et al 1977, Coney 1979, Davis &Coney 1979, Davis et al 1979, Rehrig et al 1980). While the ductile flow of these rocks in some places clearly predated the initiation of extension, temperatures during the extensional episode were sufficiently high to reset radiometric clocks and, in other places, apparently remained high from the time of compression to the time of extension.

Role and Origin of Large-Scale Detachment Surfaces

Initiation and maintenance of horizontal shear at the level of such detachments probably stemmed from increased shear stress, owing to reduction in lateral support in the shallow crust—the result of thermal expansion, uplift (and the related increase in surface area that such uplift brings because of a local, incremental increase in earth radius), and lithospheric extension at depth. It was further served by a lowered shear strength, stemming from (*a*) the presence of zones of strong anisotrophy, inhomogeneity, and stress concentration that were created by earlier episodes of compressional thrusting and decollement, as well as by mechanical layering, particularly the presence of ductile layers within, at the base of, and below the sedimentary pile that thins against the massive buttress of the North American craton to the east; and (*b*) high pore pressure at the base of the brittle faulted column, its presence reflected in a compressional wave velocity inversion and elevated electrical conductivity (Eaton 1980). At deeper levels, beneath the reheated mylonites or metamorphic rocks that underlie the normal faults (and across which a strong, shear stress gradient existed), extension is believed to have taken place by inhomogeneously distributed, uniform flow, the result of thermal preweakening of the lithosphere by repeated magmatic invasion. Known zones of inherited compressional decollement originated in pre-Tertiary time and early Tertiary time, but crustal temperatures high enough for extensional flow at natural strain rates, even at shallow lithospheric levels, apparently were maintained from the time of compression until at least mid-Cenozoic time when brittle extension, basaltic volcanism, regional uplift, and, locally, erosion and rapid cooling began.

Rheological Considerations

The intracrustal boundary between a surface zone of elastic-brittle behavior and one of possible remobilized uniform flow by steady-state creep at depth, is believed to be fundamental to basin-range structure. Where the boundary zone is transitional in nature and has finite thickness, it may be locally necked. It also has an undulating configuration in cross section, with a wavelength of tens of kilometers.

The depth of brittle-ductile transition is controlled, in part, by intrinsic rock properties, and in part, by the mechanical effect of lithostatic pressure (which dominates in the shallow crust). It is dominated, however, by temperature. At moderate temperatures, the additional presence of pore fluids helps weaken rocks mechanically, enhancing their ductility. If such fluids are also moderately saline, they may still further enhance such ductile behavior. The Basin and Range crust has had a long history of hydrothermal "brine" flux (Eaton 1979b, p. 26–30, 1980).

The effects of temperature on the mechanical behavior of rocks outweigh the effects of pressure, except at shallow levels (Carter 1976). Mechanical behavior is strongly dependent on the ratio of ambient temperature to melting temperature (T/T_{m}, in degrees Kelvin). At laboratory (i.e. relatively high) strain rates, steady-state creep appears to be possible only when T/T_m exceeds 0.5. Figure 2*b* suggests that values of 0.5 are exceeded both for the solidus and liquidus temperatures of water-saturated granodiorite at depths of 10 and 20 km. At a depth of 10 km, a T/T_{m} value of 0.5 is exceeded even for the solidus temperature of dry basalt in the Battle Mountain heat flow high. The value of T/T_{m} required for steady-state flow at geological strain rates is believed to be appreciably lower than 0.5 (Carter 1976); hence, ductility seems almost assured in the lower basin-range crust.

Transposition of the published values of Zoback et al (1981) for calculated extensional strain rates in the Basin and Range province yields magnitudes of 10^{-14}/s to 10^{-16}/s, 10 to 12 orders of magnitude slower than those of most laboratory tests. Reducing the strain rate (or increasing the duration of deforming stress) decreases rock strength (Carter & Kirby 1978). Elevating the temperature drives the system in the same direction. Elevating temperatures at constant stress difference enhances the rates of both primary transient creep and secondary steady-state creep, favoring the steady state over the transient. Elevating temperature and decreasing the strain rate both tend to lower ultimate strength by reducing the tendency to strain-harden. Carter & Kirby (1978) suggested that under crustal conditions at depths greater than 10 to 20 km, creep strains are probably dominated by steady-state deformation.

The effect of temperature on mechanical behavior becomes particularly pronounced as solidus temperatures are approached, even at high strain rates. Laboratory tests on granodiorite exhibit declines in ultimate strength with increasing temperature up to 1000°C (Bauer et al 1981). Similar tests on basalt, from temperatures of 600° to 1000°C, show similar results.

Studies of basalt at temperatures up to 1127°C and at confining pressures up to 7 kbars (the depth equivalent of 22 km), reveal that the brittle deformation state evolves, with increasing confining pressure, from extension fracturing through shear fracturing to cataclasis, at very high strain rates (10^3–10^{-4}/s; Lindholm et al 1974). These states represent fracture, but are instructive nonetheless. Under conditions postulated for the base of the brittle, faulted rock column, one might anticipate a transition zone between the brittle and ductile regions, a zone mechanically indistinguishable from that formed in thrusting.

Because of its fundamental dependence on temperature, the depth of a thermally activated brittle-ductile transition zone should vary with the level of critical isotherms in the crust. The model of Lachenbruch & Sass (1978), which postulates that heat flux (and, therefore, geothermal gradient, given constant rock thermal properties) varies directly with extensional strain rate, suggests that isotherms should move up or down in the crust with increasing or decreasing strain rate. A rapid strain rate (as the region experienced early) should result in higher mass transport of heat into the lithosphere and in more elevated isotherms. This, in turn, should result in shallower crustal ductility, a thinner brittle zone, more closely spaced listric normal faults, and more highly tilted Cenozoic strata. A slower strain rate would result in a deeper brittle-ductile transition, faults with steeper near-surface dips and greater depth of penetration, and greater structural relief (i.e. block faults).

Schematic models illustrating the effects of such differences are presented in Figure 6. Figures 6*a* through *c* show the results of incremental step increases in the strain rate. Note that as continued extension rotates the strata, it also rotates earlier-formed faults, as postulated by Morton & Black (1975).

These idealized models show the ductile region cut by dikes of basalt, which would seem to imply brittle failure. Obviously, magma has made its way to the surface through conduits of some sort. Its rise through what is identified here as the ductile region may be likened to that of basalt at an ocean ridge, rising buoyantly as a discrete packet of magma in a crack that pinches shut behind it by creep, rather than as a nearly instantaneously emplaced dike or hydrofracture that propagates rapidly across the full thickness of its ideally elastic host layer (see Weertman 1971). The model has its origin by analogy with water-filled crevasses in glacial ice, an elasticoplastic substance, the overall mass movement of that ice reflecting bulk plastic behavior, but the propagation of crevasses signifying elastic behavior below the yield stress. While dike injection provides a means for elongating the crust, it provides no means for thinning it (Wernicke 1981). Such thinning requires plastic stretching or low-dipping faults that traverse the full thickness of the crust.

The concept of a swarm of dikes (or other plutons) beneath the faulted layer was first proposed by Thompson (1959), who regarded basin-range normal faults as converging downward toward their upper ends. It is an attractive concept, especially when linked with that of a horizontal detachment surface, because it provides a rationale for the apparent local absence of extensional strain in basement rocks beneath isolated exposures of the sheared transition zone. Thus, discontinuous stretching or elongation of the basement may be spatially separated in an area of obvious extension from limited surface exposures of the detachment surface (as in the Whipple Mountains of southeastern California). The Whipples are associated with an elongate, north-trending zone of high gravity values interpretable as an expression of a zone of shallow densification of the crust caused by the injection of broad, sheeted swarms of basaltic dikes (see Eaton et al 1978, Pl. 3–1).

Figure 6*d* simulates the effect of a slow strain rate imposed on a crust that had earlier been deformed more rapidly. This is the basic two-fold sequence of extension recognized in the Basin and Range province. The model is little more than suggestive, for it is based on an instantaneous change in strain rate and the rapid thermal-seeking of a new level for brittle-ductile transition. Given a pronounced thermal lag, one would anticipate a gradual deepening of the transition zone and attendant effects.

As the boundary separating brittle and ductile behavior moves up or down in the crust, with varying strain rate and temperature, it may encounter abrupt, subhorizontal boundaries or zones of inherited mechanical contrast. Stress concentrations that develop at flaws (such as zones of former compressional thrusting, stratigraphic layering between rocks of unlike mechanical properties, or major nonconformities such as the top of a massive crystalline basement) may give rise to the development of surfaces of detachment. This may explain the geographic coincidence between regions of sequential compressional and extensional structures, e.g. the Basin and Range province and the Newark province of Late Triassic-Early Jurassic rifting in eastern North America (Figure 7).

COMPARATIVE EXTENSIONAL TECTONICS: THEIR SIGNIFICANCE

The Basin and Range province and Newark rift province are both products of extensional rifitng that followed intense folding, thrusting, and mountain building. Similarities between these two regions include the following: (*a*) the width of these extended regions (when one includes the Mesozoic rift basins of the northwest margin of Africa with those of North America); (*b*) their location within the compressional orogens; (*c*) the faithful reflection of the salients and recesses of the orogen by chains of younger extensional structures; (*d*) the distribution and size of the basins produced; (*e*) their coarse, locally fanglomeratic, cross-bedded sandstones and fine-grained lacustrine facies; (*f*) the local presence of evaporites; (*g*) the related flows, dikes, and sills of mafic

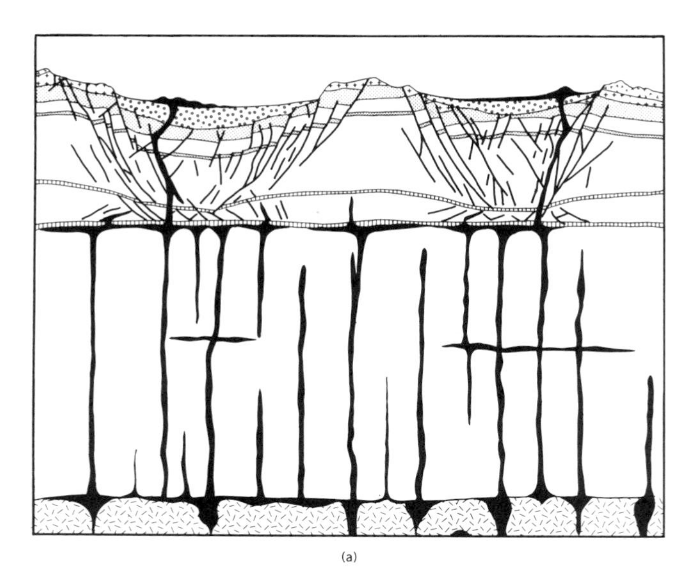

(a)

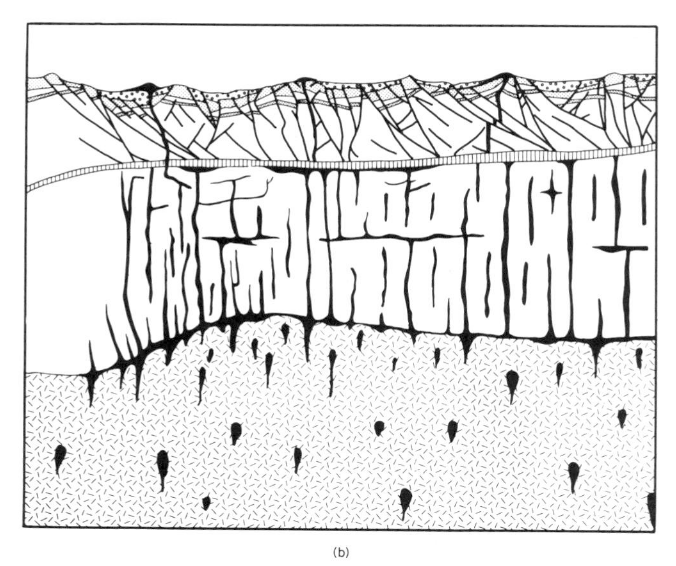

(b)

Figure 6 Schematic diagrams illustrating contrasting styles of extensional faulting in the Basin and Range Province. Hachuring represents lithospheric mantle: (*a*) small total strain developed at relatively slow strain rate (vertically ruled layers in lower part of faulted section represent old thrust soles or zones of earlier decollement); (*b*) intermediate strain developed at somewhat higher

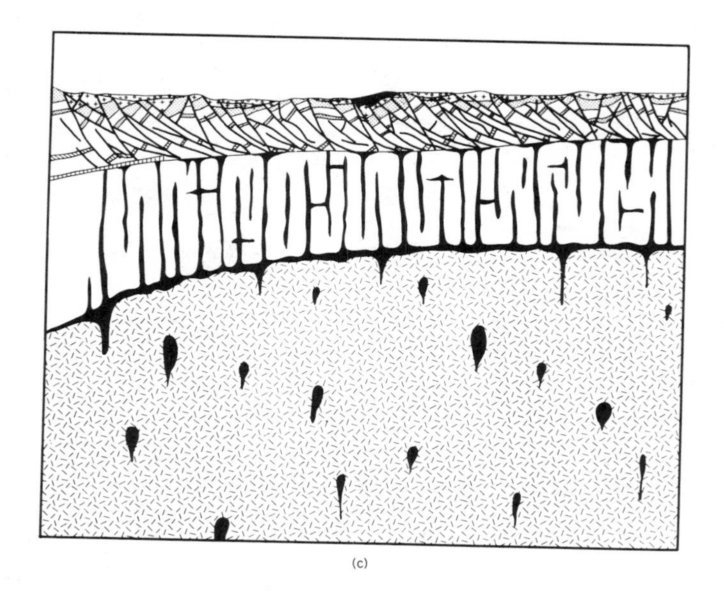

(c)

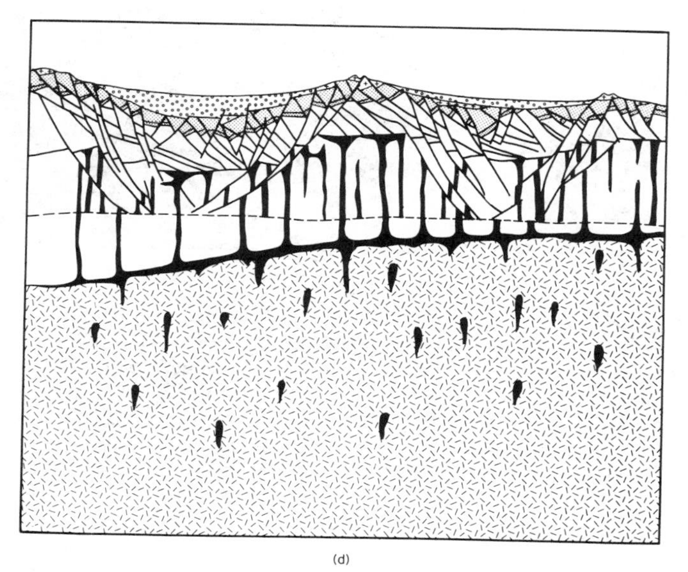

(d)

strain rate; (*c*) large extensional strain developed at relatively high strain rate; (*d*) block faulting developed at slow strain rate [as in (*a*)] superimposed on a crust previously deformed at higher strain rate, a simulation of the extensional strain history of the province.

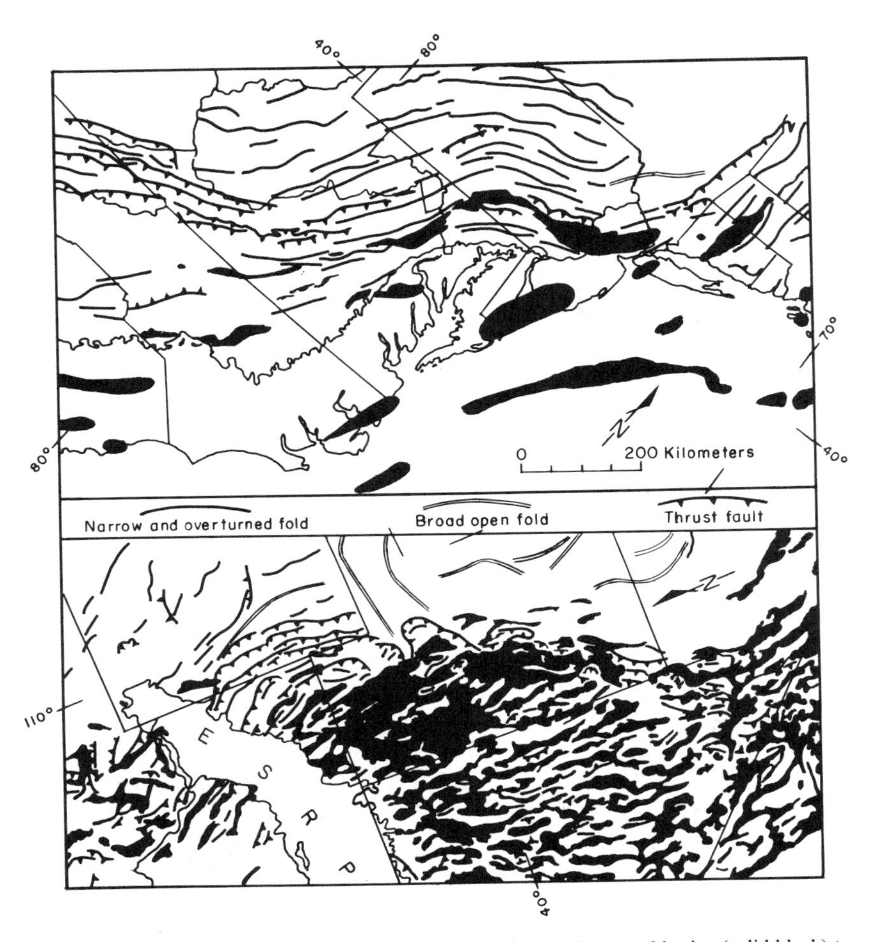

Figure 7 Maps showing spatial relationships of extensional grabens and basins (solid black) to older compressional structures: (*top*) eastern United States; (*bottom*) western United States. Note north arrows at right of both maps. Note also how chains of extensional basins follow salients and recesses in the compressional orogens concentrically. The inland edge of these basin chains lies immediately behind the leading edge of the zone of compressional thrusting, i.e. they are generally developed in the upper plate(s) of thrusts. Letters ESRP identify the Eastern Snake River Plain. Sources: Cohee 1961, King & Beikman 1974.

igneous rocks; (*h*) the normal growth faults with dips decreasing downward; (*i*) the half-grabens, some tilted one way, some the other; (*j*) the accompanying rotation of strata; and (*k*) the regional geophysical bilateral symmetry. Steep, seemingly planar faults (like the Ramapo fault of New Jersey and New

York) and obvious curviplanar listric faults with reverse drag flexure (like the eastern border fault of the Connecticut Valley and Culpeper, Virginia, Triassic-Jurassic basins) are both observed.

The Appalachian lithosphere, unlike that of the Great Basin, continued to rift and neck until it parted, opening the Atlantic Ocean. Once begun, such spreading need not lead inevitably to continental separation. It may slow and cease, depending on plate dynamics, leaving a broad swarm of rift basins such as we see today in the Basin and Range province. The significant observation here is that the separation of a continent is not required to begin with a loss of continuity at a single line of fracture, but instead may develop across a 500 to 1000 km wide zone before spreading is finally concentrated at a narrow zone, parting takes place, and continental drift begins. The process has a nonprecise and homely analogy in a highly necked rod of soft pyrex glass finally parting, under continuous applied tension, above a laboratory burner.

SUMMARY AND CONCLUSIONS

The Basin and Range province, a region of distributed continental extension with a thin brittle carapace, has attributes both of marginal ocean basins and spreading ocean ridges. The thermal history of the province played a dominant role in creating and maintaining a rheologically layered crust. That layering is fundamental to the development of basin-range structure. Such structure typifies one of two contrasting styles of extensional deformation in the province. It developed at a relatively low strain rate in the past 10 to 17 m.y. and was strongly influenced by lateral traction from the northward-migrating Pacific plate. Earlier extension, of intra-arc and back-arc origin, took place in isolated regions at higher strain rates and in a different direction. It was subduction-related in origin and was associated with shallow igneous activity. It followed a regime of antiparallel, back-arc, compressional folding and thrusting.

Further study of the geodynamic history of this province, its physical and compositional states, past and present, the movement of energy and mass into and through its lithosphere, and the seeking of a better understanding of its structure at depth should increase our understanding of the general processes of rifting and continental separation.

ACKNOWLEDGEMENT

I am indebted to M. L. Zoback and L. C. Rowan for helpful discussions and constructive reviews of this manuscript. They improved it in significant ways.

Literature Cited

Anderson, R. E. 1971. Thin skin distension in Tertiary rocks of southeastern Nevada. *Geol. Soc. Am. Bull.* 82:43–58

Atwater, T. 1970. Implications of plate tectonics for the Cenozoic tectonic evolution of western North America. *Geol. Soc. Am. Bull.* 81:3513–36

Bauer, S. J., Friedman, M., Handin, J. 1981. Effects of water-saturation on strength and ductility of three igneous rocks at effective pressures to 50 Mpa and temperatures to partial melting. *Proc. 22nd US Symp. Rock Mech., Cambridge, Mass.*, pp. 73–78

Beaumont, C. 1979. On rheological zonation of the lithosphere during flexure. *Tectonophysics* 59:347–65

Blackwell, D. D. 1978. Heat flow and energy loss in the western United States. In *Cenozoic Tectonics and Regional Geophysics of the Western Cordillera,* ed. R. B. Smith, G. P. Eaton, pp. 175–208. *Geol. Soc. Am. Mem. 152*

Carter, N. L. 1976. Steady state flow of rocks. *Rev. Geophys. Space Phys.* 14:301–60

Carter, N. L., Kirby, S. H. 1978. Transient creep and semibrittle behavior of crystalline rocks. *Pageoph* 116:807–39

Christiansen, R. L., Lipman, P. W. 1972. Cenozoic volcanism and plate-tectonic evolution of the western United States, II, Late Cenozoic. *Philos. Trans. R. Soc. London Ser. A* 271:249–84

Cohee, G. V. 1961. Tectonic map of the United States, exclusive of Alaska and Hawaii. *US Geol. Surv. & Am. Assoc. Pet. Geol. map,* scale 1:2,500,00

Compton, R. R., Todd, V. R., Zartman, R. E., Naeser, C. W. 1977. Oliogocene and Miocene metamorphism, folding, and low-angle faulting in northeastern Utah. *Geol. Soc. Am. Bull.* 88:1237–50

Coney, P. J. 1978. Mesozoic-Cenozoic Cordilleran plate tectonics. In *Cenozoic Tectonics and Regional Geophysics of the Western Cordillera,* ed. R. B. Smith, G. P. Eaton, pp. 33–50. *Geol. Soc. Am. Mem. 152*

Coney, P. J. 1979. Tertiary evolution of Cordilleran metamorphic core complexes. *3rd Symp. SEPM Pac. Coast Paleogeogr.*, pp. 14–28

Coney, P. J., Reynolds, S. J. 1977. Cordilleran Benioff zones. *Nature* 270:403–6

Cross, T. A., Pilger, R. H. 1978. Constraints on absolute motion and plate interaction inferred from Cenozoic igneous activity in the western United States. *Am. J. Sci.* 278: 865–902

Davis, G. A. 1980. Problems of intraplate extensional tectonics, western United States. In *Continental Tectonics,* chm. B. C. Burchfiel, J. E. Oliver, L. T. Silver, pp. 84–95. Washington DC: Natl. Res. Counc.

Davis, G. A., Anderson, J. L., Frost, E. G., Shackelford, T. J. 1979. Regional Miocene detachment faulting and early Tertiary (?) mylonitization, Whipple-Buckskin-Rawhide Mountains, southeastern California and western Arizona. In *Geological Excursions in the Southern California Area: Original Papers and Field Trip Road Logs Prepared for the Geol. Soc. Am Ann. Meet., 1979*, ed. P. L. Abbott, pp. 75–108

Davis, G. H. 1978. Monocline fold patterns of the Colorado Plateau. In *Laramide Folding Associated with Basement Block Faulting in the Western United States,* ed. V. Matthews III, pp. 215–33. *Geol. Soc. Am. Mem. 151*

Davis, G. H., Coney, P. J. 1979. Geologic development of the Cordilleran metamorphic core complexes. *Geology* 7:120–24

Dickinson, W. R., Snyder, W. S. 1978. Plate tectonics of the Laramide orogeny. In *Laramide Folding Associated with Basement Block Faulting in the Western United States,* ed. V. Matthews III, pp. 355–66. *Geol. Soc. Am. Mem. 151*

Diment, W. H., Urban, T. C. 1981. Average elevation map of the conterminous United States (Gilluly Averaging Method). *US Geol. Surv. Geophys. Inv. Map GP-933,* scale 1:2,500,000

Dutton, C. E. 1880. Geology of the High Plateaus of Utah. *US Geol. Geol. Surv. Rocky Mtn. Region.* 307 pp.

Eaton, G. P., Wahl, R. R., Prostka, H. J., Mabey, D. R., Kleinkopf, M. D. 1978. Regional gravity and tectonic patterns: their relation to late Cenozoic epeirogeny and lateral spreading in the western Cordillera. In *Cenozoic Tectonics and Regional Geophysics of the Western Cordillera,* ed. R. B. Smith, G. P. Eaton, pp. 51–92. *Geol. Soc. Am. Mem. 152*

Eaton, G. P., 1979a. A plate-tectonic model for late Cenozoic crustal spreading in the western United States. In *Rio Grande Rift: Tectonics and Magmatism,* ed. R. E. Riecker, pp. 7–32. Washington DC: Am. Geophys. Union

Eaton, G. P. 1979b. Regional geophysics, Cenozoic tectonics, and geologic resources of the Basin and Range Province and adjoining regions. In *1979 Basin and Range Symposium,* ed. G. W. Newman, H. D. Goode, pp. 11–39. Denver, Colo: Rocky Mtn. Assoc. Geol. and Utah Geol. Assoc.

Eaton, G. P. 1980. Geophysical and geological characteristics of the crust of the Basin and Range province. In. *Continental Tec-*

tonics, chm. B. C. Burchfiel, J. E. Oliver, L. T. Silver, pp. 96–110. Washington, DC: Natl. Res. Counc.

Effimoff, I., Pinezich, A. R. 1981. Tertiary structural development of selected valleys based on seismic data: Basin and Range province, northeastern Nevada. *Philos. Trans. R. Soc. London Ser. A* 300:435–42

Elston, W. E. Bornhorst, T. J. 1979. The Rio Grande rift in context of regional post-40 m.y. volcanic and tectonic events. In *Rio Grande Rift: Tectonics and Magmatism,* ed. R. E. Riecker, pp. 416–38. Washington DC: Am. Geophys. Union

Fenneman, N. M. 1928. Physiographic divisions of the United States. *Ann. Assoc. Am. Geog., 3rd ed.* 18:261–353

Fenneman, N. M. 1931. *Physiography of Western United States.* New York: McGraw-Hill. 534 pp.

Gans, P. B. 1981. Geometry of pre-basin and range extension east-central Nevada. *EOS* 62:399 (Abstr.)

Hamblin, W. K., 1965. Origin of "reverse drag" on the downthrown side of normal faults. *Geol. Soc. Am. Bull.* 76:1145–64

Hamilton, W., Myers, W. B. 1966. Cenozoic tectonics of the western United States. *Rev. Geophys.* 4:509–49

Howard, K. A., Aaron, J. M., Brabb, E. E., Brock, M. R., Gower, H. D., Hunt, S. J., Milton, D. J., Muehlberger, W. R., Nakata, J. K., Plafker, G., Prowell, D. C., Wallace, R. E., Witkind, I. J. 1978. Preliminary map of young faults in the United States as a guide to possible fault activity. *US Geol. Surv. Misc. Field Studies Map MF-916, Scale 1:5,000,000*

Johnson, D. W. 1903. Block mountains in New Mexico. *Am. Geol.* 31:135–39

Keith, S. B. 1978. Paleosubduction geometries inferred from Cretaceous and Tertiary magmatic patterns in southwestern North America. *Geology* 6:516–21

King, C. 1878. *US Geol. Expl. 40th Par. Rep.,* Vol. 1. 803 pp.

King, P. B., Beikman, H. M. 1974. Geologic map of the United States. *US Geol. Surv. map*, scale 1:2,500,000

Lachenbruch, A. H., Sass, J. H. 1977. Heat flow in the United States and the thermal regime of the crust. In *The Earth's Crust,* ed. J. G. Heacock, pp. 626–75. *Am. Geophys. Union Mono. 20*

Lachenbruch, A. H., Sass, J. H. 1978. Models of an extending lithosphere and heat flow in the Basin and Range province. In *Cenozoic Tectonics and Regional Geophysics of the Western Cordillera,* ed. R. B. Smith, G. P. Eaton, pp. 209–50. *Geol. Soc. Am. Mem. 152*

Lawrence, R. D. 1976. Strike-slip faulting terminates the Basin and Range province in Oregon. *Geol. Soc. Am. Bull.* 87:846–50

Lindholm, U. S., Yeakley, L. M., Nagy, A. 1974. The dynamic strength and fracture properties of Dresser basalt. *Int. J. Rock Mech. Min. Sci.* 11:181–91

Lipman, P. W. 1980. Cenozoic volcanism in the western United States: implications for continental tectonics. In *Continental Tectonics,* pp. 161–74. Washington DC: Natl. Acad. Sci. 197 pp.

Lipman, P. W., Prostka, H. J., Christiansen, R. L. 1972. Cenozoic volcanism and plate-tectonic evolution of the western United States, Pt. I, Early and middle Cenozoic. *Philos. Trans. R. Soc. London Ser. A* 271:217, 248

Longwell, C. R. 1933. Rotated faults in the Desert Range, southern Nevada. *Geol. Soc. Am. Bull.* 44–93 (Abstr.)

Longwell, C. R. 1945. Low-angle normal faults in the Basin and Range province. *Trans. Am. Geophys. Union* 26:107–18

Mabey, D. R. 1976. Interpretation of a gravity profile across the western Snake River Plain, Idaho. *Geology* 4:53–55

Magill, J., Cox, A., Duncan, R. 1981. Tillamook volcanic series: further evidence for tectonic rotation of the Oregon Coast Range. *J. Geophys. Res.* 86:2953–70

Martin, D. L., Barry, W. L., Krummenacher, D. 1980. K-Ar dating of mylonitization and detachment faulting in the Whipple Mountains, San Bernardino County, California and the Buckskin Mountains, Yuma County, Arizona. *Geol. Soc. Am. Abstr. with Programs* 12(3):118

McDonald, R. E. 1976. Tertiary tectonics and sedimentary rocks along the transition: Basin and Range province to plateau and thrust belt province, Utah. In *RMAG Symp. Geol. Cordilleran Hingeline,* ed. J. G. Hill, pp. 281–317 *Rocky Mtn. Assoc. Geol.*

McKenzie, D. P. 1978. Some remarks on the development of sedimentary basins. *Earth Planet. Sci. Lett.* 40:25–32

Morton, W. H., Black, R. 1975. Crustal attenuation in Afar. In *Afar Depression of Ethiopia,* ed. A. Pilger, A. Rossler, pp. 55–65. Stuttgart: Deutsche Forschungsgemeinschaft

Nolan, T. B. 1943. The Basin and Range province in Utah, Nevada, and California. *US Geol. Surv. Prof. Pap. 197-D*, pp. 141–96

Pardee, J. T. 1950. Late Cenozoic block faulting in western Montana. *Geol. Soc. Am. Bull.* 61:359–406

Prodehl, C. 1979. Crustal structure of the western United States. *US Geol. Surv. Prof. Pap. 1034.* 74 pp.

Proffett, J. M. Jr. 1977. Cenozoic geology of the Yerington district, Nevada, and implications for the nature and origin of Basin and Range faulting. *Geol. Soc. Am. Bull.* 88:247–66

Rehrig, W. A., Heidrick, T. L. 1976. Regional tectonic stress during the Laramide and late Tertiary intrusive periods, Basin and Range province, Arizona. *Ariz. Geol. Soc. Dig.* 10:205–28

Rehrig, W. A., Shafiqullah, M., Damon, P. E. 1980. Geochronology, geology, and listric normal faulting of the Vulture Mountains, Maricopa County, Arizona. *Ariz. Geol. Soc. Dig.* 12:89–110

Reynolds, M. W. 1979. Character and extent of basin-range faulting, western Montana and east-central Idaho. In *1979 Basin and Range Symp.*, ed. G. W. Newman, H. D. Goode, pp. 185–93. *Rocky Mtn. Assoc. Geol. and Utah Geol. Assoc.*

Robinson, E. S. 1970. Relations between geologic structure and aeromagnetic anomalies in central Nevada. *Geol. Soc. Am. Bull.* 81:2045–60

Scholz, C. H., Barazangi, M., Sbar, M. L. 1971. Late Cenozoic evolution of the Great Basin, Western United States, as an ensialic interarc basin. *Geol. Soc. Am. Bull.* 82: 2979–90

Seager, W. R., Morgan, P. 1979. Rio Grande rift in southern New Mexico, west Texas, and northern Chihuahua. In *Rio Grande Rift: Tectonics and Magmatism,* ed. R. E. Riecker, pp. 87–106. Washington DC: Am. Geophys. Union

Smith, R. B. 1978. Seismicity, crustal structure, and intraplate tectonics of the interior of the western Cordillera. In *Cenozoic Tectonics and Regional Geophysics of the Western Cordillera,* ed. R. B. Smith, G. P. Eaton, pp. 111–44. *Geol. Soc. Am. Mem. 152*

Smith, R. B., Sbar, M. L. 1974. Contemporary tectonics and seismicity of the western United States with emphasis on the Intermountain Seismic Belt. *Geol. Soc. Am. Bull.* 85:1205–18

Snyder, W. S., Dickinson, W. R., Silberman, M. L. 1976. Tectonic implications of space-time patterns of Cenozoic magmatism in the western United States. *Earth Planet. Sci. Lett.* 32:91–106

Stewart, J. H., 1978. Basin-range structure in western North America, a review. In *Cenozoic Tectonics and Regional Geophysics of the Western Cordillera,* ed. R. B. Smith, G. P. Eaton, pp. 1–13. *Geol. Soc. Am. Mem. 152*

Stewart, J. H. 1980a. Regional tilt patterns of late Cenozoic basin-range fault blocks, western United States. *Geol. Soc. Am. Bull.* 91:460–64

Stewart, J. H. 1980b. Geology of Nevada. *Nev. Bur. Mines Geol. Spec. Publ. 4.* 136 pp.

Swanson, D. A., Wright, T. L., Hooper, P. R., Bentley, R. D. 1979. Revisions in stratigraphic nomenclature of the Columbia River basalt group, Contributions to Stratigraphy. *US Geol. Surv. Bull. 1457-G.* 59 pp.

Thompson, G. A. 1959. Gravity measurements between Hazen and Austin, Nevada—a study of Basin-Range structure. *J. Geophys. Res.* 64:217–29

Thompson, G. A., Burke, D. B. 1974. Regional geophysics of the Basin and Range province. *Ann. Rev. Earth Planet. Sci.* 2:213–38

Turcotte, D. L., McAdoo, D. C., Caldwell, J. G. 1978. An elastic-perfectly plastic analysis of the bending of the lithosphere at a trench. *Tectonophysics* 47:193–205

Uyeda, S., Kanamori, H. 1979. Back-arc opening and the mode of subduction. *J. Geophys. Res.* 84:1049–61

Waring, G. A. 1965. Thermal springs of the United States and other countries of the world—a summary. *US Geol. Surv. Prof. Pap. 492.* 383 pp.

Weertman, J. 1971. Theory of water-filled crevasses in glaciers applied to vertical magma transport beneath oceanic ridges. *J. Geophys. Res.* 76:1171–83

Wernicke, B. 1981. Low-angle normal faults in the Basin and Range province: nappe tectonics in an extending orogen. *Nature* 291: 645–48

Zoback, M. L., Anderson, R. E., Thompson, G. A. 1981. Cainozoic evolution of the state of stress and style of tectonism of the Basin and Range province of the western United States. *Philos. Trans. R. Soc. London Ser. A* 300:407–34

Zoback, M. L., Thompson, G. A. 1978. Basin and Range rifting in northern Nevada: clues from a mid-Miocene rift and its subsequent offsets. *Geology* 6:111–16

Zoback, M. L., Zoback, M. D. 1980. State of stress in the conterminous United States. *J. Geophys. Res.* 85:6113–56

Ann. Rev. Earth Planet. Sci. 1982. 10:441-57

PHANEROZOIC OOLITIC IRONSTONES—Geologic Record and Facies Model

Franklyn B. Van Houten

Department of Geological and Geophysical Sciences, Princeton University, Princeton, New Jersey 08544

Deba P. Bhattacharyya

Department of Earth and Planetary Sciences, Washington University, St. Louis, Missouri 63130

INTRODUCTION

Oolitic ironstones[1] composed predominantly of ooids[1] of ferric oxide and chamosite accumulated throughout much of Phanerozoic time (Figure 1), and some of them have been important ore deposits. They are built of two very common products of weathering, iron oxide and clay, but they constitute a distinctive and subordinate sedimentary facies for which there is no simple modern analogue. As a result considerable disagreement has attended more than 125 years of discussion about their origin.

Early analyses of these rocks (for example, the minette ore of France) focused mainly on their chemical and mineral composition and on processes of diagenesis. More recent work has described their sedimentary textures and structures, as well as their general facies and depositional environments (Adeleye 1973, Brookfield 1973, Corbin 1980, Hallam 1975, Karpov et al 1967,

[1]*Ooid*—a multi-coated particle less than 2 mm in diameter; pisoids are larger. *Proto-ooids*—pellets with only a few concentric sheaths. *Oolite*—a sedimentary rock containing more than 50% ooids. *Ironstone*—an iron-rich (more than 15%) sedimentary rock. *Iron formation*—a mappable stratigraphic unit composed mostly of ironstones (Kimberley 1978).

0084-6597/82/0515-0441$02.00

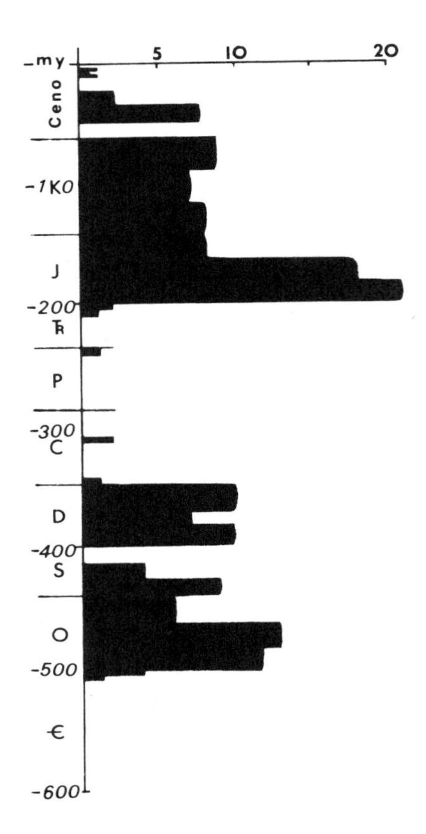

Figure 1 Histogram of stratigraphic distribution of Phanerozoic oolitic ironstones. Tallies of localities for early, middle, and late subdivisions of each period. Data mainly from Braun (1964), Kimberley (1978), and Zitzmann (1977, 1978).

Kimberley 1978, Schellmann 1969). In contrast, little attention has been directed toward either the general tectonic framework in which oolitic ironstones formed or to their distribution in space and time (Cooper 1980, Petranek 1964, Strakhov 1969).

Our review summarizes the stratigraphic record of oolitic ironstones (Figure 1, Appendix A), identifies the characterisitc basins in which they accumulated (Figure 2), and reconstructs the relation between changing patterns of land and sea and the Phanerozoic development and distribution of ferriferous oolites (Figure 3). We also propose a facies model (Figure 4) that creates constraints for further discussion about the origin of ferric oxide and chamosite ooids. Such a synthesis is timely because of the recent revival (Dimroth 1979, Kimberley 1979) of an inconclusive hypothesis of replacement of calcareous ooids as the mode of origin of both Phanerozoic and Proterozoic oolitic ironstones.

GEOLOGIC RECORD

Basin Framework

Oolitic ironstones accumulated in three kinds of cratonic basins flooded by shallow seas. 1. Some developed in foredeeps along the interior side of mobile belts (Figure 2,f) at times of diminished deformation and curtailed detrital influx. 2. Many others accumulated in intracratonic basins (Figure 2,c) generally dominated by prolonged stability. The widespread middle and late Mesozoic ironstones of northwestern Europe were deposited in a complex intracratonic setting in the northwestward transgression of Tethys across faulted Caledonian and Variscan terranes (Sellwood & Jenkyns 1975). 3. Ironstones also accumulated readily along cratonic margins (Figure 2,m) at times of divergence or initial convergence of lithospheric plates. Deposits of this sort are difficult to reconstruct because many of them were later deformed by orogeny. Strakhov (1969, Figure 87, p. 222) assigned these ironstones to a geosynclinal facies.

Major Patterns

DISTRIBUTION IN SPACE According to the continental drift reconstructions we have followed (Figure 3), early and middle Paleozoic ferriferous oolites were deposited between about 45°N and 65°S when many of the drifting fragments of Laurasia and Gondwana were in the southern hemisphere (Figures 2 and 3). During this episode most of the ironstones accumulated along cratonic margins of blocks scattered around a vaguely defined east-trending precursor of Paleotethys and the Proto-Atlantic Ocean.

After Middle Triassic time all but one of the oolites developed between about 10°S and 70°N on land masses of Laurasia and Gondwana that had drifted northward (Figures 2 and 3). During this episode most of the ironstones accumulated in intracratonic basins on blocks around east-trending Tethys, which had spread across Europe, western Russia, the West Siberian plate, and northeastern Gondwana.

DISTRIBUTION IN TIME The Phanerozoic scenario started with dispersal of Laurasian cratonic fragments of a single supercontinent that had prevailed in late Precambrian time (Morel & Irving 1978, Figure 6). Oolitic ironstones began to accumulate locally in late Cambrian time (Figures 2 and 3, Appendix A) and then rapidly became widespread, producing a major development from earliest Ordovician to latest Devonian time (170 m.y.). Subsequent consolidation of Pangaea in late Paleozoic and early Mesozoic time (150 m.y.) was followed by renewed block dispersal, a gradual rise in sea level, and the advent of a second remarkable ironstone episode that began locally in late

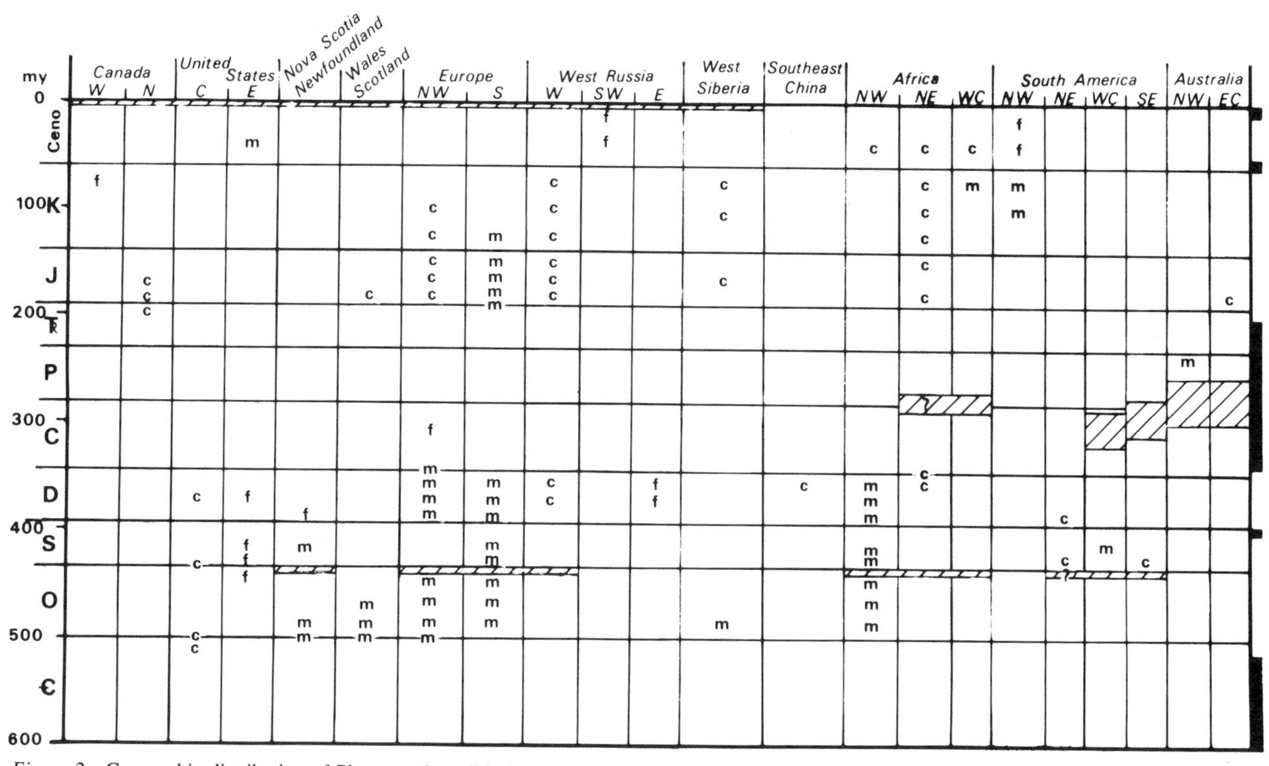

Figure 2 Geographic distribution of Phanerozoic oolitic ironstones on cratonic landmasses; c—intracratonic basin, f—foredeep, and m—cratonic margin. Unfavorable episodes and intervals—thick line along right side of chart. Diagonal pattern—continental glaciation.

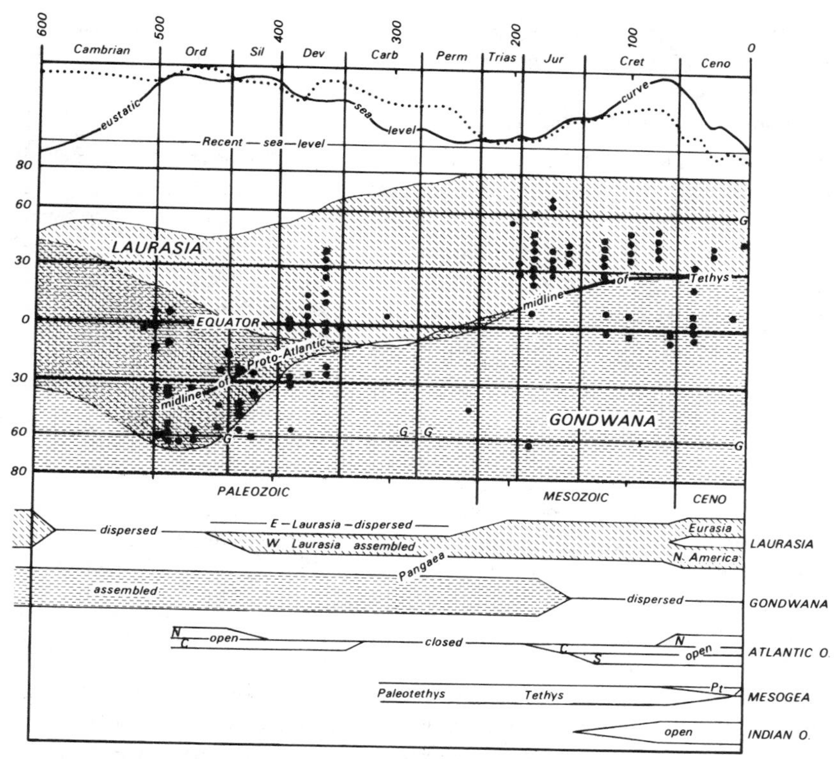

Figure 3 Time-latitude chart of distribution of Phanerozoic oolitic ironstones on cratonic blocks of Laurasia (diagonal pattern) and Gondwana (horizontal pattern) scattered around east-trending Proto-Atlantic and Tethyan seaways. At the top of the chart is a generalized eustatic sea level curve relative to Recent sea level (solid line), after Vail et al (1977), and relative amount of continental flooding (dotted line), after Ronov et al (1980). Lower part of chart diagrams trends in assemblage and dispersal of blocks of Laurasia and Gondwana, and in opening and closing of ocean basins. Based on paleocontinental reconstructions by Scotese et al (1979), and Smith & Briden (1977). G—continental glaciation, N—northern, C—central, and S—southern Atlantic Ocean, Pt—Paratethys.

Triassic time (Appendix A) and persisted from earliest Jurassic to middle Cenozoic time (170 m.y.). The two congenial periods (Figure 1) were essentially Fischer's (1981) "greenhouse" stages of Phanerozoic history, marked by mild climate and the generation of prolific organic matter (Pigott 1981). They were also times of a high relative rate of marine detrital sedimentation on the continents (Ronov et al 1980, Figure 4).

Our review of the geologic record (Figures 1, 2, and 3) reveals that oolitic ironstones flourished when open oceanic circulation around dispersed cratonic blocks was accompanied by a relatively high stand of sea level, extensive marine transgression, a mild maritime climate, and relatively subdued tectonic activity. In addition, these regional factors combined to produce deep weathering, which released the iron and clay concentrated in the ferriferous ooids.

Favorable but not Necessary Factors

The favorable factors of craton and climate identified here (Figures 1, 2, and 3) worked in differing combinations and intensities to foster the local environmental conditions portrayed in our facies model (Figure 4). Although development of an ironstone did not require all of the favorable factors simultaneously (Appendix B), at least some of them were needed to effect development. Among these, a mild maritime climate, subdued tectonic activity, and deep weathering probably were the most crucial.

FACIES MODEL

Introduction

Phanerozoic iron-bearing beds comprise three rather distinct facies: (*a*) nodular, commonly pyritic, sideritic mudstone in nonmarine to paralic "coal measures," and locally in muddy offshore deposits; (*b*) sandy and shelly shallow marine sediment with abundant pellets of glauconite; and (*c*) ferric oxide-chamosite (mostly 7Å iron-rich clay mineral) oolite. At least locally ferriferous oolite may replace the others vertically or interfinger with them laterally. Examples include a few minor oolitic deposits in the paralic facies of late Carboniferous cyclothems in northern England (Chowns 1966), latest Triassic (Rhaetic) "coal measures" in Hungary (Zitzmann 1977, p. 195, 1978, p. 102), and an early Jurassic cyclothem in southern Sweden (Arkell 1956,

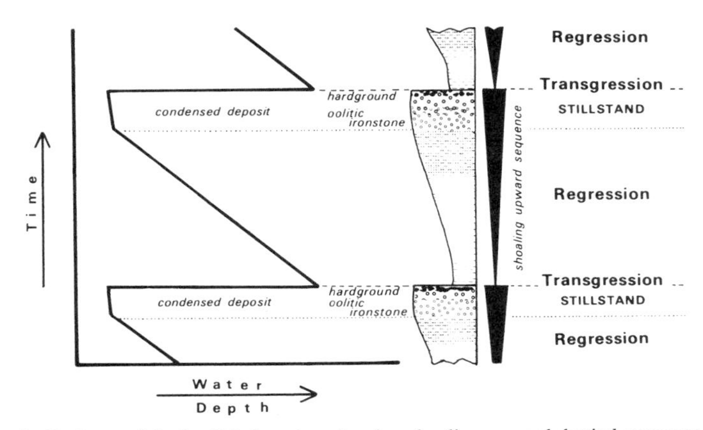

Figure 4 Facies model of oolitic ironstone-bearing shoaling-upward detrital sequence, emphasizing relation to prolonged regression and relatively rapid transgression.

p. 475, Troedsson 1951), as well as an extensive ferric oxide-chamosite oolite in a shallow marine tongue in early Jurassic coal-bearing deposits in east-central Australia (Mollan et al 1972, pp. 45–50). More commonly, oolitic ironstones are associated with glauconite-rich beds, as in the early Silurian Clinton Group in eastern United States (Hunter 1970), Middle Devonian iron formations in southwestern Russia (Karpov et al 1967), Middle Jurassic deposits in Switzerland (Gygi 1981), and some early Cenozoic sandstones in southern United States (Jones 1969).

Most of the oolitic ironstones occur in detrital (siliciclastic) deltaic and nearshore marine deposits. Yet, some sequences include offshore calcareous mudstone with an interbedded bioclastic or oolitic facies (Hunter 1970, Talbot 1974), or a bioclastic shoreline facies (Deverin 1945, Geyer & Hinkelbein 1971, Lusser 1982, Nicolini 1967, Talbot 1973), or consist mostly of calcareous mudstone (marl-clay) and argillaceous limestone (marl) (Gygi 1981).

Oolitic ironstones are condensed deposits that accumulated during a transitional stage, which developed either at the end of a regional regression[2] (Hallam & Bradshaw 1979, Sellwood & Jenkyns 1975) or the beginning of renewed transgression[2] (Gygi 1981, Kimberley 1979), while thicker correlative marine sediments were deposited elsewhere. An iron formation may consist of only a few or of tens of shoaling-upward sequences produced by small-scale regressions, and one or several of these may have led to the accumulation of an ironstone.

Specific aspects of ferriferous ooid accumulation after the waning of an asymmetrical coarsening-upward detrital sequence have been documented by Bubenicek (1961, 1971), Chowns & McKinney (1980), James & Van Houten (1979), Kaiser (1972), Kimberley (1980), Van Houten & Karasek (1981), and Wright (1977). Bhattacharyya (1980) has elaborated the basic role of prograding[2] deltaic and shoreline sequences in a genetic facies model for the origin of oolitic ironstones. Kimberley (1979) recognized this fundamental association, but his very general proposal included the unlikely accumulation of symmetrical calcareous ooids in the initial transgression that spread over prograded deltaic deposits. Data and concepts in these studies are largely the basis for our environmental reconstruction.

Oolitic Ironstones

Oolitic iron formations accumulated in relatively low-energy paralic to shallow marine environments (Figure 5), commonly along broadly embayed coastlines. Although these sites experienced some agitation by waves and tides,

[2]*Regression*—retreat of water from a land area with basinward shifting of the shoreline. *Transgression*—landward advance of water, shifting the shoreline inland and spreading offshore sediments over coastal deposits. *Progradation*—advance of shoreline sedimentation seaward, producing a coarsening-upward sequence of coastal deposits overlying offshore sediments.

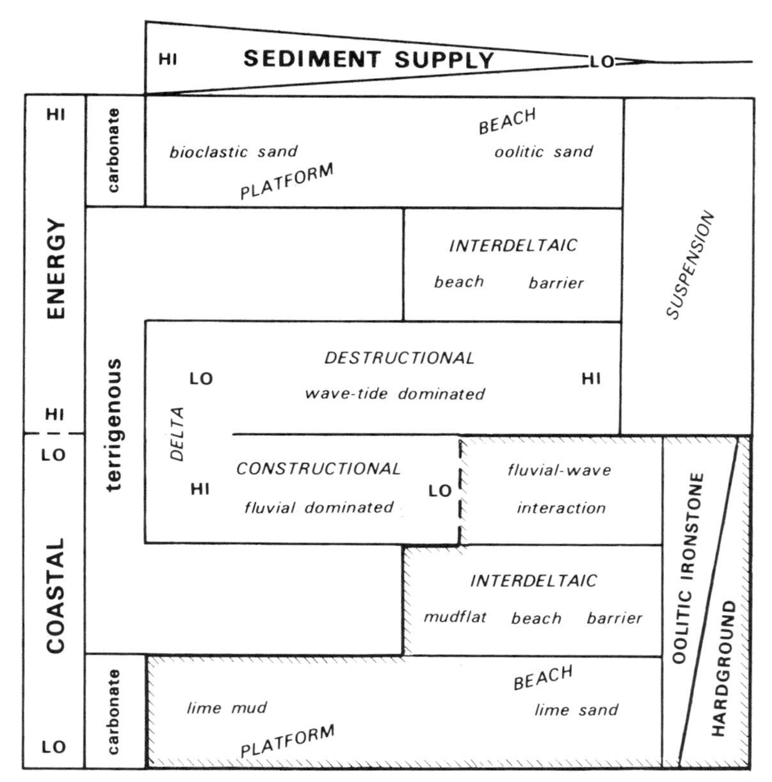

Figure 5 Major shore-zone facies relative to sediment supply and coastal (wave and tide) energy, showing favorable setting for development of oolitic ironstones and mineralized hard-grounds.

there are no high-energy tidal deposits or large well-winnowed upper shoreface sandbodies. Processes and products along the detrital coast may have been like Recent ones at the front of the low-energy wave-dominated Rhone Delta (Oomkens 1970), or on the broad shelf of southwestern Louisiana (Beall 1968) with its low tidal range and supply of fine-grained sediment from a distant delta.

Ferric oxide and chamosite ooids developed in detritus-starved habitats that supported abundant microflora, microfauna, and burrowers. Some ooid beds apparently accumulated in the littoral environment of shallow open seas with abundant benthic fauna and normal salinity (Hallam 1975, Hunter 1970). Others, with meager (Talbot 1974, Van Houten & Karasek 1981) or dwarfed (Simpson & Gray 1968) fauna, probably developed on microtidal mudflats in more brackish lagoons behind protective breaker bars (Sheldon 1965). In a similar Recent setting, chamosite proto-ooids[1] are forming on muddy interdistributary banks of the Mahakam Delta in Kalimantan (Allen et al 1979), ferric oxide proto-ooids and chamosite pellets in shallow marine sediments of the Niger, Ogooue, and Orinoco deltas (Giresse 1969, Porrenga 1965), and ferruginous proto-ooids in delta-front mud in shallow and brackish Lake Chad (Lemoalle & Dupont 1973).

Association of ooid development with reduced influx of detritus (Figures 4 and 5) reasonably accounts for the rarity of detrital grains in many of the thick ironstones and as nuclei of the ooids. Absence of markedly asymmetric ooids characteristic of very low energy environments, except rarely in early stages of ooid accretion (Knox 1970), points to repeated rolling of the grains by currents and stirring by burrowers. This required agitation that was sufficient to induce mechanical accretion of laminae yet mild enough to preserve the delicate gelatinous particles. Most of the plastic ooids were carried from their place of origin by coastal currents and concentrated in accreting, cross-bedded bars. During transportation a few were broken, and some of the fragments served as nuclei for other ooids. After burial, chamosite-rich ooids commonly were distorted by compaction whereas ferric oxide-rich ones were not. Repeated interruptions in accumulation, probably due to shifting currents, permitted increased burrowing and precipitation of ferric oxide cement in thin hardgrounds[3] (Figures 4 and 5). Locally, deposition of marine mud accompanied lapses in bar-building.

Although most of the oolitic ironstones developed after accumulation of a shoaling shoreline sequence, some were formed in a late stage of regression as, for example, during temporary waning of sediment influx along a prograding shoreline, or before the end of regression in areas remote from deltaic influence. Moreover, some thin ironstones, as in the early Silurian Clinton Group of central Pennsylvania, are associated with offshore deposits. These are distinctive in containing abundant intraclasts and bioclastic debris, subordinate ooids, and both ferric oxide and calcite cement. The contrast between these thin deposits and the more common oolitic ironstones suggests that the former were spread seaward by storms that swept across coastal ooid banks.

Some ooid bars were covered progressively by either marine mud or thin, fine-grained basal sand of an advancing transgression developed on an intersequence lithofacies discordance. Sandy deposits of this sort have accumulated along the low energy coast of the modern Rhone Delta (Oomkens 1970) and on the late Devonian Catskill muddy shoreline in central Pennsylvania (Walker 1971, Walker & Harms 1971). More commonly, however, no such sandy transgressive sediment accumulated. Instead, many of the oolites in both detrital and calcareous sequences were interrupted or succeeded by, and

[3]*Hardground*—extensive thin crusts of cemented, bored, and mineralized sediments developed on the sea floor during minor interruptions in accumulation.

were laterally correlative with, a thin lenticular and nodular ferruginized hardground that developed when influx of clay and calcareous mud ceased altogether and the barren sea floor was subjected to submarine weathering, burrowing, and mineralization by ferric oxide and phosphate (e.g. Gygi 1981). In addition, a few oolitic ironstones were covered by a thin ferruginous, phosphatic sandy intraclast layer, or bonebed, containing scattered ooids and phosphatic and kaolinite-chamosite pellets, as well as fish teeth and fragments of bones and shells. The intraclasts were eroded from a preceding ironstone hardground. Similar intraclast lenses may also overlie a thin nodular ferruginous hardground that is laterally equivalent to a thick oolitic ironstone. Lag deposits of this kind developed locally where relatively high-energy winnowing and transport by waves and currents of renewed transgression (or paths of stormy seas—see Parrish 1978) spread across detritus-starved mudflats and crests of ooid bars.

Prograding Sequences

Asymmetrical shoaling-upward sequences containing oolitic ironstones (Figure 4) commenced with muddy open shelf sediments locally associated with bioclastic debris, culminated with accumulation at the front of a small prograding delta or a shoreline complex of bars and lagoons, and ended with waning of detrital influx and the development of abundant ferriferous ooids. The succession of local facies was essentially that of a prograding sandy shoreline (Harms 1975). More variable shoaling-upward carbonate sequences commonly began with offshore fossiliferous calcareous mud with patches of shell debris and carbonate ooids, succeeded by shallow nearshore limy mud. Some sequences ended with coastal oolitic and bioclastic deposits.

Within the framework of prograding detrital sequences (Figure 4), renewed accumulation in the shallow marine transgression normally consisted of mud that had settled from turbulent and colloidal suspension, as well as of thin beds of sand and silt, commonly with hummocky cross-bedding. During deposition, vertical burrows penetrated the muddy facies and temporary cessation led to bioturbation and sea-floor ferruginization. The sandy layers probably were spread by storm-surge currents (see La Fon 1981) and then bioturbated during fair weather sedimentation. Gradually the muddy marine facies was replaced by a prograding coastal zone inhabited by burrowers such as *Skolithus, Monocraterion, Diplocraterion, Thalassinoides,* and *Chondrites*. In some places the coast consisted of deltaic distributary channel-mouth sands reworked by waves and littoral currents to form shoreface and delta-front sandbodies. In other places, sand and silt from a distant delta formed thin littoral and sublittoral sheeted sandbodies comparable to some of the late Cretaceous marine sandstones in the Western Interior Seaway (Rice 1980, Tillman & Martinsen 1980). Eventually a chenier-type coast developed, and its shoreface sandbodies formed protective shoals on which wave energy was dissipated. Both sandy bottoms and microtidal mudflats were teeming with burrowers. Along coasts remote from sandy input, the upper part of a shoaling sequence was dominated by a marginal mudflat, on which local patches of scattered ooids and phosphatic kaolinite pellets developed, or by barriers constructed of bioclastic (shelly) debris. In each of these situations, beds of iron-rich ooids formed when the supply of sediment waned.

Most of the "punctuated aggradational cycles" (Anderson & Goodwin 1980) are bounded above by a lithofacies discordance, with no record of well-developed transgressive shoreline sedimentation (Figure 4). In fact, the discordance is commonly overlain abruptly by basinal or open marine mudstone, with no upward transition from the oolitic ironstone to fine-grained offshore sediments. Some formations yield faunal evidence of a hiatus between sequences, but only a few are marked by significant erosion (Hemingway 1974).

There is no consensus regarding the origin of prograding sequences of this sort, or of the associated rapid change in baselevel (Mörner 1976). In fact, the control probably differed from one basin to another. Some sequences may reflect diversion of a major river to a more distant part of the coastal plain while the abandoned muddy shelf continued to subside and was inundated by transgression (Walker 1971). With slowly renewed detrital input, the shallow sea gave way to mudflats along an embayed coast. In contrast, many of the sequences, such as the Jurassic ones in southern England (Talbot 1973) and Cretaceous ones in Utah (Ryer 1977), suggest a more regional control. This may have been tectonic control of intermittent subsidence (Hemingway 1951, 1974, Sellwood & Jenkyns 1975), or repeated eustatic rise in sea level (Lusser 1980).

As with any facies model, ours portrays only the general relations within an iron formation. Most of the Phanerozoic deposits do fit this pattern. Nevertheless, different combinations and variations of facies, especially in the uppermost prograding stage, characterize specific successions and lateral patterns. For example, some shallow marine sequences with limited sediment influx contain repeated beds of ooids and associated hardgrounds. Calcareous sequences commonly record more repetitions of ooid development and more interruptions producing hardgrounds because there was a subtler balance between influx of clay and nondeposition.

CONCLUSIONS

Major development of Phanerozoic oolitic ironstones was fostered by episodes of mild climate, widespread transgression of the continents, and tectonic stability or waning orogeny accompanied by decreased detrital influx into shallow seas flooding cratonic margins, intracratonic basins, and foredeeps.

The geologic record of these deposits reflects three motifs.

1. A bimodal distribution through Phanerozoic time (Figure 1). Almost all of the ferric oxide-chamosite oolites accumulated during early Ordovician to late Devonian and early Jurassic to middle Cenozoic time. These long, well-documented episodes of mild climate and extensive transgression constitute fundamental features of Phanerozoic history.

2. A change in basin framework through time (Figure 2). In early and middle Paleozoic time, most of the ironstones accumulated along submerged margins of dispersed Laurasian blocks, and only locally along the margin of assembled Gondwana. After Triassic time, ironstones developed mostly in intracratonic basins on Laurasia that had been assembled during successive Paleozoic orogenies. They also developed locally on large drifting blocks of Gondwana.

3. A maritime distribution on flooded landmasses adjacent to a crudely outlined east-trending seaway (Figure 3). In early and middle Paleozoic time, the Proto-Atlantic Ocean dominated this pattern in the southern hemisphere; in early Jurassic to middle Cenozoic time, Tethys prevailed in the northern hemisphere. Enhanced circulation through these open gateways (Berggren 1982) and around dispersed cratonic blocks contributed to the development of ironstones along a broad belt 30–40° north and south of the midline of the seaways. If the dispersal and assemblage of wandering continents had been different, the distribution of Phanerozoic oolitic ironstones presumably would have differed accordingly.

Within the conducive regional framework, formation of oolitic ironstones was favored by a combination of specific physico-chemical conditions associated most commonly with low energy deltas and strandlines with an embayed or lagoonal coast. Our model (Figure 4) emphasizes the role of repeated shoaling-upward sequences, of abrupt waning of sediment supply, and of rapid renewed rise of sea level. Each ironstone and its associated ferruginized hardground and lag deposit developed most readily at the lithofacies discordance between successive sequences.

ACKNOWLEDGMENTS

T. Chowns, P. T. Hayes, R. E. Hunter, R. Karasek, D. Ottensman, P. E. Schenk, J. Schreiber, and S. Thompson helped us gather the data, and A. G. Fischer, R. Hargraves, and S. Judson criticized the manuscript. Much of the research was supported by National Science Foundation grant EAR77-06007 and Princeton University. Field study in Libya was sponsored by the Libyan National Oil Company, and in Egypt by NSF grant 01P75-07943 administered by the University of South Carolina Earth Sciences and Resources Institute.

APPENDIX A

The geologic age of ferriferous oolites noted here does not fit precisely the stratigraphic range of the most abundant ironstones, plotted in Figures 1, 2, and 3.

Cambrian Deposits

In view of the remarkable development of ferriferous oolites during the Ordovician Period, the presence of a few in Cambrian sequences is significant.

Report of a Middle Cambrian ironstone in Nova Scota (Gross 1967, p. 17) apparently is an error. Hayes (1919, p. 113) had described this deposit and assigned it a probable late Cambrian or early Ordovician age.

The glauconitic late Cambrian Reagan Sandstone of Oklahoma (Hayes 1933) and Riley Formation of Texas (Barnes & Bell 1977), and latest Cambrian to earliest Ordovician Bliss Sandstone in southern New Mexico (Kelley 1951, Hayes 1975) contain ferric oxide and chamosite oolites. Mixed deposits of glauconite pellets and ferriferous ooids are laterally equivalent to a few of the well-developed ferric oxide-chamosite oolites. Latest Cambrian or earliest Ordovician (Tremadocean) chamosite oolite is also present in Wales and northern Norway.

Late Carboniferous Ironstone

Although ferric oxide-chamosite oolite is not associated with sideritic mudstone in nonmarine facies of coal measures, a few minor deposits do occur locally with sideritic mudstone in paralic facies of coal-bearing cyclothems in northern England (Chowns 1966).

Late Permian Ironstone

The only late Permian oolitic ironstone is a well-developed deposit that accumulated in northwestern Australia (Edwards 1958) when it was at about 45°S latitude.

Triassic Ironstones

Because of the extensive development of oolitic ironstones in early Jurassic time, reports of a few Triassic ones are noteworthy.

A minor early Triassic deposit of hematite in the West Carpathians, Czechoslovakia, cited erroneously as an oolitic ironstone by Ilavsky (in Zitzmann 1977, pp. 121–22), is actually a sedimentary-exhalative type related to basic volcanism (Mahel et al 1968, pp. 279–80, 285).

The one reported late Triassic (Karnian) oolitic ironstone accumulated in the Sverdrup Basin of Arctic Canada (A. Embry, personal communication) when it was at about 55°N latitude.

The only latest Triassic (Rhaetic) ferric oxide-chamosite oolites are a minor one in paralic coal measures in Hungary (Zitzmann 1977, p. 195, 1978, p. 102) and thin beds in a predominantly carbonate sequence in the West Carpathians, Czechoslovakia (Mahel et al 1968, p. 195, 211, Zitzmann 1977, p. 122).

Late Cenozoic Ironstones

The only ironstones that accumulated after the Mesozoic-middle Cenozoic congenial episode are numerous thin beds in a Late Miocene deltaic formation in northeastern Colombia, and the gigantic Middle Pliocene Kerch oolitic iron ore in southwestern Russia. Both deposits accumulated in a flooded foredeep during relatively reduced influx of sediment in a very late stage of orogeny.

APPENDIX B

The geologic record noted here confirms that the development of an ironstone did not depend on the simultaneous effect of all of the favorable regional factors. One or more of them may not have prevailed.

Dispersal of Cratonic Blocks and High Stand of Sea Level

Some oolitic ironstones accumulated when cratonic blocks were consolidated and sea level was relatively low, as in late Permian, late Triassic, earliest Jurassic, and late Cenozoic time.

Mild Climate

Late Ordovician and early Silurian ironstones in high southern latitudes (Figure 3) may have been at least remotely affected by the latest Ordovician "Saharan" glaciation (Bigarella 1973, pp. 456–60, Chauvel & Massa 1981), but the detailed environmental setting of these deposits has not been reconstructed. This glacial episode is also an anomaly in the geologic record of the biosphere (Fischer 1981, pp. 121–22).

The late Permian ironstone in northwestern Australia (Edwards 1958) accumulated soon after late Paleozoic glaciation in southern Gondwana, possibly during a time of "sudden global warming" (Herman 1981).

The Middle Pliocene Kerch oolitic iron ore in southwestern Russia (Zitzmann 1978, p. 236–38) accumulated during late Cenozoic cooling of the climate, and it too may have coincided with a brief interval of amelioration (Savin et al 1975, Figures 4 and 6).

Nearshore Marine Environment

The only reported nonmarine oolitic ironstone is a ferric oxide oolite with minor chamosite in late Oligocene fluvial deposits in southwestern Russia (Bronevoi et al 1967, Strakhov 1969, p. 147–53).

Deep Weathering and Abundant Vegetation

The fact that growth and decay of terrestrial vegetation play a significant role in the present deep-weathering process does not make vegetated uplands a necessary factor. Oolitic ironstones developed abundantly in Ordovician time before vascular plants flourished in source areas.

Literature Cited

Adeleye, D. R. 1973. Origin of ironstones, an example from the middle Niger Valley, Nigeria. *J. Sediment. Petrol.* 43:709–27

Allen, G. P., Laurier, D., Thouvenin, J. 1979. Etude sedimentologique du delta de la Mahakam. *Comp. Franc. Petroles, Notes et Mem.* Vol. 15. 156 pp

Anderson, E. J., Goodwin, P. W. 1980. Helderberg PACs. *Eastern Sect. Soc. Econ. Paleontol. Mineral. Field Conf. Guidebook.* 32 pp.

Arkell, W. J. 1956. *Jurassic Geology of the World.* Edinburgh: Oliver & Boyd. 757 pp.

Barnes, V. E., Bell, W. C. 1977. The Moore Hollow Group of central Texas. *Univ. Tex. Bur. Econ. Geol. Rep. Invest.* Vol. 88. 169 pp.

Beall, A. O. 1968. Sedimentary processes operative along the western Louisiana shoreline. *J. Sediment. Petrol.* 38:869–77

Berggren, W. A. 1982. Role of ocean gateways in climate changes. In *Studies in Geophysics, Pre-Pleistocene Climates,* Natl. Res. Counc. In press

Bhattacharyya, D. 1980. *Sedimentology of the Late Cretaceous Nubia Formation at Aswan, southeast Egypt, and the origin of the associated ironstones:* PhD thesis. Princeton Univ., Princeton, N.J. 122 pp.

Bigarella, J. J. 1973. Paleocurrents and continental drift. *Geol. Rundsch.* 62:447–77

Braun, H. 1964. *Zur Entstehung der Marin-Sedimentaren Eisenerze.* Berlin: Gebruder Borntraeger. 133 pp.

Bronevoi, V. A., Garetskii, R. G., Kiryukhin, L. G. 1967. New area of middle Oligocene iron ore deposits in the north Aral region and in the northeastern Ustyurt. *Lithol. Mineral Res.* 4:436–45

Brookfield, M. E. 1973. The palaeoenvironment of the Abbotsbury Ironstone (Upper Jurassic) of Dorset. *Palaeontology* 16:261–74

Bubenicek, L. 1961. Recherches sur la construction et la repartition du minerai de fer dans l'aalenien de Lorraine. *Sci. de la Terre* 8:5–204

Bubenicek, L. 1971. Geologie du gisement de fer de Lorraine: *Centre Rech. Pau. Soc. Nat. Petrol. Aquitaine Bull.* 5:223–320

Chauvel, J.-J., Massa, D. 1981. Paleozoique de Libye occidentale constantes geologiques et petrographiques. Signification des niveaux ferrugineux oolithiques. *Comp. Franc. Petroles, Notes et Mem.* Vol. 16, pp. 25–66

Chowns, T. M. 1966. Depositional environment of the Cleveland Ironstone Series. *Nature* 211:1286–87

Chowns, T. M., McKinney, F. K. 1980. Depositional facies in Middle-Upper Ordovician and Silurian rocks of Alabama and Georgia. *Geol. Soc. Am. Guidebook,* Field Trip 16:323–48

Cooper, J. C. 1980. A model for Phanerozoic sedimentary iron deposition. *Geol. Soc. Am. Abstr. with Programs* 12(7):405–6

Corbin, S. G. 1980. *A facies analysis of the Lower-Middle Jurassic boundary beds of north-west Europe.* PhD thesis. Univ. Birmingham, Birmingham, Engl.

Deverin, E. L. 1945. Etude petrographique des minerais de fer oolithiques du Dogger des Alpes suisses. *Beitr. Geol. Schweiz, Geotechnische Serie* 13(2), 115 pp.

Dimroth, E. 1979. Facies models 15. Models of Physical sedimentation of iron formations. In *Facies Models,* ed. R. G. Walker, pp. 175–82. Geosci. Can. Repr. Ser. 1. Toronto: Geol. Assoc. Can. Publ.

Edwards, A. B. 1958. Oolitic iron formations in northern Australia. *Geol. Rundsch.* 47:668–82

Fischer, A. G. 1981. Climatic oscillations in the biosphere. In *Biotic Crises in Ecological and Evolutionary Time.* ed. M. Nitecki, pp. 103–31. New York: Academic

Geyer, O. F., Hinkelbein, K. 1971. Eisenoolithische Kondesations-Horizonte im Lias der Sierra Espuña (Provinz Murcia, Spanien). *Neues. Jahrb. Geol. Palaeont. Monatsh.,* pp. 398–414

Giresse, P. 1969. Etude des differents grains ferrugineux authigenes des sediments sousmarins au large delta de Ogooue (Gabon). *Sci. de la Terre.* 14:27–62

Gross, G. A. 1967. Iron deposits in the Appalachian and Grenville regions of Canada. In *Geology of Iron Deposits in Canada,* Vol. 22. Geol. Surv. Can. Econ. Geol. Rep. 111 pp.

Gygi, R. A. 1981. Oolitic iron formation: marine or not marine?: *Eclogae Geol. Helv.* 74:233–54

Hallam, A. 1975. *Jurassic Environments*. Cambridge, Engl: Cambridge Univ. Press. 269 pp

Hallam, A., Bradshaw, M. J. 1979. Bituminous shales and oolitic ironstones as indicators of transgressions and regressions. *J. Geol. Soc. London* 136:157–64

Harms, J. C. 1975. Stratification and sequence in prograding shoreline deposits. In *Depositional Environments as Interpreted from Primary Sedimentary Structures and Stratification Sequences*, pp. 81–102. Soc. Econ. Paleontol. Mineral. Short Course N. 2.

Hayes, A. O. 1919. Nova Scotia oolitic iron deposits of sedimentary origin. *Can. Min. Inst. Trans.* 22:112–22

Hayes, A. O. 1933. Cambrian oolitic hematite in the Reagan sandstone of Oklahoma. *Geol. Soc. Am. Bull.* 44:86–7 (Abstr.)

Hayes, P. T. 1975. Cambrian and Ordovician rocks of southern Arizona and New Mexico and westernmost Texas. *US Geol. Surv. Prof. Pap. 873*. 94 pp.

Hemingway, J. E. 1951. Cyclic sedimentation and the deposition of ironstone in the Yorkshire Lias. *Yorkshire Geol. Soc. Proc.* 28:67–74

Hemingway, J. E. 1974. Jurassic. In *The Geology and Mineral Resources of Yorkshire*, ed. D. H. Rayner, J. E. Hemingway, pp. 161–223. Leeds: York. Geol. Soc.

Herman, Y. 1981. Causes of massive biotic extinctions and explosive evolutionary diversification throughout Phanerozoic time. *Geology* 9:104–8

Hunter, R. E. 1970. Facies of iron sedimentation in Clinton Group. In *Studies of Appalachian Geology, Central and Southern*, ed. G. W. Fisher, F. J. Pettijohn, J. C. Reed, Jr., K. N. Weaver, pp. 101–21. New York: Wiley-Interscience.

James, H. E., Van Houten, F. B. 1979. Miocene goethitic and chamositic oolites northeastern Colombia. *Sedimentology* 26: 125–33

Jones, H. L. 1969. *Petrology, mineralogy, and geochemistry of the Chamositic Iron Ores of north-central Louisiana*. PhD thesis. Univ. Okalhoma, Norman, Okla. 196 pp.

Kaiser, W. R. 1972. *Delta cycles in the middle Devonian of central Pennsylvania*. PhD thesis. Johns Hopkins Univ., Baltimore, Md. 240 pp.

Karpov, P. A., Losev, A. L., Shilin, A. V. 1967. Mineralogy and conditions of Devonian oolitic iron ore formation on the eastern slope of the Voronezh anticlise. *Litol. Mineral Res.* 3:321–30

Kelley, V. C. 1951. Oolitic iron deposits of New Mexico. *Am. Assoc. Petrol. Geol. Bull.* 35:2199–2228

Kimberley, M. M. 1978. Paleoenvironmental classification of iron formations. *Econ. Geol.* 73:215–29

Kimberley, M. M. 1979. Origin of oolitic iron formation. *J. Sediment. Petrol.* 49:111–32

Kimberley, M. M. 1980. The Paz de Rio oolitic inland-sea formation. *Econ. Geol.* 75:97–106

Knox, R. W. 1970. Chamosite ooliths from the Winter Gill Ironstone (Jurassic) of Yorkshire, England. *J. Sediment. Petrol.* 40: 1216–25

La Fon, N. A. 1981. Offshore bar deposits of Semilla Sandstone Member of Mancos Shale (Upper Cretaceous), San Juan Basin, New Mexico. *Am. Assoc. Petrol. Geol.* 65:706–21

Lemoalle, J., Dupont, B. 1973. Iron-bearing oolite and the present conditions of iron sedimentation in Lake Chad (Africa). In *Ores in Sediments*, ed. G. C. Amstutz, A. J. Bernard, pp. 167–78. Berlin: Springer-Verlag

Lusser, C. 1980. *Sedimentologie und palaeogeographie des unteren Doggers in zentralen und noerdlichen Jura*. PhD thesis. Univ. Basel, Basel, Schweiz. 134 pp.

Lusser, C. 1982. Upper Aalenian and Lower-Middle Bajocian oolitic ironstones, northwestern Jura Mountain, Switzerland. In preparation

Mahel, M., Tibor, B., and others. 1968. *The West Carpathians, Regional Geology of Czechoslovakia, Part II*. Stuttgart: E. Schweizerbartsche Verglagsbuchhandlung. 732 pp.

Mollan, R. G., Forbes, V. R., Jensen, A. R. Exon, N. F., Gregory, C. M. 1972. Geology of the Eddystone, Taroom, and western part of the Mundubbera sheet areas, Queensland. *Bur. Mineral Res. Geol. Geophys. Rep. 142*. 137 pp.

Morel, P., Irving, E. 1978. Tentative paleocontinental maps for the early Paleozoic and Proterozoic. *J. Geol.* 86:536–61

Mörner, N. -A. 1976. Eustacy and geoid changes. *J. Geol.* 84:123–52

Nicolini, P. 1967. Remarques comparatives sur quelques elements sedimentologiques et paleogeographiques lies aux gisements de fer oolithiques du Djebel Ank (Tunisie) et de Lorraine (France). *Mineral Depos.* 2: 95–101

Oomkens, E. 1970. Depositional sequences and sand distribution in the post-glacial Rhone Delta complex. *Soc. Econ. Paleontol. Mineral. Spec. Publ. No. 15*, pp. 198–212

Parrish, W. C. 1978. Paleoenvironmental analysis of a Lower Permian bonebed and adjacent sediments, Wichita County, Texas.

Palaeogeogr. Palaeoclimatol. Palaeoecol. 24:209–37

Petranek, J. 1964. Ordovician—a major epoch in iron deposition. *Int. Geol. Congr. 22nd,* 15:51–57

Pigott, J. D. 1981. Global tectonic control of secular variations in Phanerozoic sedimentary rock/ocean/atmospheric chemistry. *Am. Assoc. Petrol. Geol. Bull.* 65:971–72 (Abstr.)

Porrenga, D. H. 1965. Chamosite in Recent sediments of Niger and Orinoco deltas. *Geol. Mijnbouw* 44:400–3

Rice, D. D. 1980. Upper Cretaceous Mosby Sandstone, central Montana—example of thin, widespread storm-generated sandstone cycles. *Am. Assoc. Petrol. Geol. Bull.* 65:772–73 (Abstr.)

Ronov, A. B., Khain, V. E., Balukhovsky, A. N., Seslavinsky, K. B. 1980. Quantitative analysis of Phanerozoic sedimentation. *Sediment. Geol.* 25:311–25

Ryer, T. A. 1977. Patterns of Cretaceous shallow-marine sedimentation, Coalville and Rockport areas, Utah. *Geol. Soc. Am. Bull.* 88:177–88

Savin, S. M., Douglas, R. G., Stehli, F. G. 1975. Tertiary marine paleotemperatures. *Geol. Soc. Am. Bull.* 86:1499–1510

Schellmann, W. 1969. Die Bildungsbedingungen sedimentärer Chamosit-und-Hämatit Eisenerze am Beispiel der Lagerstätte Echte: *Neues Jahrb. Mineral. Abhandlungen* 111: 1–31

Scotese, C. R. Bambach, R. K., Barton, C., Van der Voo, R., Ziegler, A. H. 1979. Paleozoic base maps. *J. Geol.* 87:217–68

Sellwood, B. W., Jenkyns, H. C. 1975. Basins and swells and the evolution of an epeiric sea (Pliensbachian-Bajocian of Great Britain): *J. Geol. Soc. London* 131:373–88

Sheldon, R. P. 1965. Barrier island and lagoonal iron sedimentation in the Silurian of Alabama. *Geol. Soc. Am. Spec. Pap.* 82:182 (Abstr.)

Simpson, T. A., Gray, T. R. 1968. The Birmingham red ore district, Alabama. In *Ore Deposits of the United States, 1933-1967,* ed. John D. Ridge, 1:187–206. New York: Inst. Min. Metall. Petrol. Eng.

Smith, A. G. Briden, J. C. 1977. *Mesozoic and Cenozoic Paleocontinental Maps.* Cambridge, Engl: Cambridge Univ. Press. 63 pp.

Strakhov, N. M. 1969. *Principles of Lithogenesis,* Vol. 2. Edinburgh: Oliver & Boyd. 609 pp.

Talbot, M. R. 1973. Major sedimentary cycles in the Corallian Beds. *Palaeogeog., Palaeoclimatol. Palaeoecol.* 14:293–317

Talbot, M. R. 1974. Ironstones in the Upper Oxfordian of southern England. *Sedimentology* 21:433–50

Tillman, R. W., Martinsen, R. S. 1980. Shannon Sandstone (Upper Cretaceous) offshore bar facies distribution, Salt Creek area, Wyoming. *Am. Assoc. Petrol. Geol. Bull.* 65:793 (Abstr.)

Troedsson, G. 1951. On rhythmic sedimentation in the Rhaetic-Liassic beds of Sweden: *Int. Geol. Congr. 18th,* 4:64–72

Vail, P. R., Mitchum, R. M. Jr., Thompson, S. III. 1977. Seismic stratigraphy and global changes of sea level, Part 4, Global cycles of relative changes of sea level. In *Seismic Stratigraphy—Applications to Hydrocarbon Exploration,* ed. C. E. Payton, *Am. Assoc. Petrol. Geol. Mem.* 26:83–97

Van Houten, F. B., Karasek, R. 1981. Sedimentologic framework of the Late Devonian oolitic iron formation, Shatti Valley, west-central Libya. *J. Sediment Petrol.* 51: 415-27

Walker, R. G. 1971. Nondeltaic depositional environments in the Catskill clastic wedge (Upper Devonian) of central Pennsylvania. *Geol. Soc. Am. Bull.* 82:1305–26

Walker, R. G., Harms, J. C. 1971. The "Catskill Delta:" A prograding muddy shoreline in central Pennsylvania. *J. Geol.* 79:381–99

Wright, J. K. 1977. The Callovian succession (excluding Cornbrash) in the western and northern parts of the Yorkshire Basin. *Proc. Geol. Assoc.* 89:239–61

Zitzmann, A., ed. 1977. *The Iron Ore Deposits of Europe and Adjacent Areas,* Vol. 1. Hannover: Fed. Inst. Geosci. Nat. Resour. 418 pp.

Zitzmann, A., ed. 1978. *The Iron Ore Deposits of Europe and Adjacent Areas,* Vol. 2. Hannover: Fed. Inst. Geosci. Nat. Resour. 386 pp.

Ann. Rev. Earth Planet. Sci. 1982. 10:459-81

THE HEAT FLOW FROM THE CONTINENTS

Henry N. Pollack

Department of Geological Sciences, University of Michigan, Ann Arbor, Michigan 48109

INTRODUCTION

The terrestrial heat flow is defined as the quantity of heat escaping per unit time from the Earth's interior across each unit area of the Earth's solid surface. The quantity varies from place to place over the surface of the Earth, as well as with time throughout Earth history. The total heat being lost from the Earth at a given time is the integral of the heat flow taken over the entire surface of earth. The heat flow from the continents is therefore but a part of the larger picture of global heat loss, indeed the lesser part when compared to the heat loss through the floor of the ocean basins. (Pollack 1980, Sclater et al 1980, Davies 1980). This is so not only because of the lesser continental area, but also because of the generally smaller heat flow found on the continents than in the ocean basins. Thus, a full discussion of the thermal regime of the Earth and the mechanisms by which it exhausts heat from the interior must center on the heat loss through the oceans, a topic which lies beyond the scope of this review. Nonetheless, because of the geological antiquity of at least some of their constituent terranes, the continents provide the only direct evidence about the thermal, tectonic, and petrologic processes of the Earth at times before the birth of any of the modern ocean basins some two hundred million years ago. Because inferences about earlier times are drawn wholly from materials now preserved in continents, one must be cautious not to overgeneralize about global tectonothermal processes from observations confined to continents.

MEASUREMENT OF CONTINENTAL HEAT FLOW

The heat flow through the continental crust in all but a few regions is largely by conduction, and can be represented by Fourier's law $\mathbf{q} = -K \text{ grad } \mathbf{T}$,

0084-6597/82/0515-0459$02.00

where **q** is the heat flux vector, K is the thermal conductivity of the material through which the heat is being conducted, and grad **T** is the local temperature gradient. In practice, the determination of the heat flow comprises separate measurements of the temperature gradient and thermal conductivity. A useful general review and discussion of field and laboratory equipment and methods is given by Beck (1965).

Temperature gradients for heat flow determinations derive principally from measurements in boreholes, most of which have been drilled for other purposes, such as exploration for economic minerals, petroleum, and water, or engineering site evaluation for construction projects; a few boreholes have been drilled specifically for heat flow measurements. Boreholes drilled for economic minerals typically range from 50 to 300 meters, with occasional deeper holes. However, few satisfactory temperature measurements emerge from the upper 50 meters of most boreholes, principally because of temperature disturbances associated with circulating groundwater. Occasionally, as in karst terranes, such disturbances can extend to a kilometer or more in depth, and render futile the attempt to measure a local temperature gradient. Conversely, in massive sparsely jointed crystalline bodies, in which circulation is inhibited, or in certain arid terranes where there is little water to circulate, satisfactory gradients can be determined within a few tens of meters of the surface. Temperature measurements in mineral exploration boreholes are usually taken as continuous logs or at depth intervals of a few meters.

Boreholes drilled for municipal or domestic water supplies are seldom deeper than 200 meters, are usually sited in aquifers, and frequently are of little use for geothermal investigations. Unsuccessful or abandoned water boreholes sometimes provide satisfactory temperature observations, particularly when several are clustered together so that a measure of redundancy is obtained.

Temperatures in shallow boreholes are perturbed to varying degree by the irregularities of the local topography and of the surface temperature distribution. Vegetative patterns, soil moisture, slope orientation, sun angle, and many other parameters influence the surface temperature distribution significantly (Blackwell et al 1980). Boreholes to depths less than or on the order of magnitude of the local relief require corrections to the observed temperature, in order to estimate the true geothermal gradient that would exist in the absence of topography and surficial temperature variations.

Boreholes drilled for petroleum are generally much deeper than mineral exploration or water bores, with depths of a few to several kilometers not uncommon. Temperature measurements in such boreholes are usually carried out by commercial service companies in conjunction with the taking of the common borehole logs. Only occasionally are temperatures logged continuously; more commonly spot temperatures are obtained at the bottom of the hole from time to time as drilling progresses. The rock at the bottom of the hole is in that segment of the borehole most recently excavated by the drill bit, and therefore least disturbed by the drilling process. However, "bottom hole temperatures" are not measured immediately after the drill reaches a given depth, but typically are taken after a period of circulating and flushing of the drilling fluid and extraction of the drill rods from the hole, procedures that may take a day or more and that may lead to bottom hole temperatures significantly different from the virgin rock temperature. These few bottom hole temperatures at different depths, when corrected for the drilling disturbance, enable an estimate of the mean geothermal gradient over the total depth of the hole, but ordinarily do not provide enough detail to resolve variation in the temperature gradient that may derive from lithologic variation with depth.

A temperature gradient can also be established from measurements at various levels in an underground mine. Commonly the observations are made in horizontal boreholes outward from the walls of drifts. A temperature disturbance propagates into the wall rock following the opening of the drift and the commencement of cooling ventilation. The distance into the wall rock that the perturbation propagates is dependent on how long the drift has been opened; even after several decades virgin rock temperatures can be found only a few tens of meters away from the wall. The temperatures so obtained at different levels unfortunately are seldom vertically beneath one another, and commonly temperatures obtained from different drifts at the same level show significant differences, particularly when the mine is not deep and topographic effects perturb the subsurface temperature field. Thus to infer a "true" vertical gradient, considerable massaging of the observations is necessary (Blackwell et al 1980, Henry 1981), and a greater uncertainty in the resulting value must be recognized.

Heat flow measurements have also been undertaken in lakes, utilizing marine techniques (Von Herzen & Vacquier 1967, Sclater et al 1970, Degens et al 1971). Five to ten meter probes, with temperature sensors arrayed over the length, are allowed to plunge into the soft sediment on the lake bottom. Because saturated uncompacted sediment is a relatively poor conductor, easily measureable temperature differences exist over the probe length, and thus a temperature gradient is determined. However, because of the very shallow penetration compared to typical boreholes, the method is particularly susceptible to errors arising from lake bottom perturbations such as annual overturn and sedimentation.

Indirect geochemical methods also exist for estimating subsurface temperatures, based on the solubility of various chemical species in water as a function of temperature. In particular, the silica geothermometer has been used to develop an empirical heat flow estimator (Swanberg & Morgan 1978).

Thermal conductivity measurements are made in a laboratory setting on rock samples taken from the site of the field temperature measurements. The labortory measurement contrasts with in situ techniques that are useful in the soft sediments characteristic of marine (and lake) sites. The most suitable conductivity samples are drawn from the solid cylindrical rock core extracted from the borehole in which temperature measurements were obtained. The number of samples taken is dependent on the variability of the core lithology and on the depth interval at which temperatures were obtained; ideally, at least one sample will be available to represent the depth interval between temperature measurements.

The laboratory measurement is most commonly carried out in an apparatus known as a divided bar (Birch 1950). The measurement is based on a comparison principle in which a known quantity of heat is conducted through two materials—a standard of known conductivity (usually fused silica) and a rock sample of unknown conductivity. The temperature drops across each are proportional to their respective conductivities, and with the one known the other can then be calculated. Samples are water saturated prior to measurement in order to make the conductivity determination in an environment that is as similar to the natural environment as possible. The measurement is also carried out at a temperature appropriate to the in situ temperature of the rock.

In the drilling of some boreholes, particularly for petroleum and water, rock fragments or chips, rather than solid cores, are obtained. These fragments are amenable to conductivity measurements (Sass et al 1971) in the same manner as discs of core, by filling a disc-shaped container with both chips and water and determining the conductivity of the loaded container as if it were a rock disc. Knowing the fraction of the container volume occupied by the rock chips enables the calculation of the intrinsic rock conductivity.

Transient methods of determining thermal conductivity also are utilized. They employ a line source of heat within the body of a sample, with the thermal conductivity emerging from the asymptotic value of the rate of change of temperature with the logarithm of time. The transient method is particularly suited for use in soft sediments, where a heating needle is inserted into the sample. The method is also employed (with some modification) to solid materials with planar surfaces, which sandwich the line source of heat.

The experimental uncertainties in the measurement of temperature gradients and thermal conductivities seldom exceed 5%. Experimental errors, however, are not the major source of uncertainty in a heat flow determination. The variability of conductivity within a visually homogeneous length of core can easily exceed the measurement error and introduces a sampling uncertainty. Local geological structures, with attendant distributions of conductivity contrasts, can distort the heat flow lines and isothermal surfaces sufficiently to yield local variations in heat flow of 20–30% about a regional mean. Similarly, slow ground water circulation and the evolution of topography by uplift and erosion or subsidence and deposition can have large effects on the near-surface heat flow distribution. Thus it is the effects of less than adequately known subsurface structure, hydrologic patterns, and geologic, climatic, and geomorphic evolution of a terrane that are the principal uncertainties associated with heat flow determination.

THE CONTINENTAL HEAT FLOW DATA SET

It has been known from antiquity that the interior of the Earth is a great reservoir of heat. Many references to and measurements of the increase of temperature with depth appear in the scientific literature, dating back at least to Robert Boyle (1671). However, it was not until 1882 that the first determinations of both the geothermal gradient and thermal conductivity were combined by William Thomson (Lord Kelvin) to yield an estimate of the heat flow in Great Britain (British Association 1883). Kelvin utilized both published and personal measurements of temperatures in boreholes and mines throughout Britain to obtain a mean gradient, which when combined with determinations of the thermal conductivity of representative rocks led to a heat flow value of 68 mW m^{-2}.

The motivation for Kelvin's determination of the heat flow was related to his position in the nineteenth century debate over the age of the Earth and Sun. He believed that the Earth was cooling by conduction from a hot primordial condition, and therefore the heat loss from the planet would diminish with time. A measurement of the heat flow would determine how far along in the cooling history the Earth had progressed. Subsequent discoveries have rendered untenable Kelvin's approach to determining the age of the earth. The first nail in the coffin was the discovery of radioactivity in the late nineteenth century, and the quick recognition of its significance as a heat source that replenished to some degree the escaping primordial heat of the Earth.[1] A second difficulty arises from the more recent realization (Tozer 1965, 1972) that temperature-dependent solid-state creep may be a very significant process within the Earth's mantle that leads to heat transfer principally by convection, rather than by conduction as Kelvin had assumed.

A hiatus of interest in geothermal measurements set in following the laying to rest of both Kelvin and his hypothesis, until the late 1930s when Edward Bullard initiated the modern systematic investigtion of heat flow with a series of measurements in South Africa. In North America, Francis Birch recognized early the significance of heat flow to the tectonic and petrologic evolution of

[1]It is interesting to note that the conductive cooling of the oceanic lithosphere following its magmatic emplacement at oceanic ridges does yield an age dependence of heat flow of the same form that Kelvin derived for the entire Earth. Indeed the mean age of the oceanic lithosphere is very similar to Kelvin's estimate of the Earth's age.

the Earth's crust, and established a geothermal laboratory that was for two decades one of the principal centers for geothermal research in the world. Birch's students and research associates, and a generation of scientists subsequently trained by them, now carry on geothermal studies in more than a score of institutions.

In the first review of heat flow measurements, prepared by Birch in 1954, the total number of determinations on the continents was 43. Subsequently the data set has grown substantially, until in 1981 the number of published continental measurements approaches 3000; a large body of unpublished data exists in the national laboratories of several countries. Significant periodic reviews of the global heat flow data document the dramatic increase in awareness of the significance of the Earth's heat loss, and accordingly in the importance of heat flow measurement (Table 1).

Heat flow measurements have been made in at least modest numbers on all the continents except Antarctica (although a few exist there as well). However, the number and distribution of measurements on the continents remain very uneven (Figure 1). Not surprisingly the greatest concentration of data occurs in the northern continents. Of the total data set, approximately 50% is from Europe and western USSR, 30% from North America, 10% from Asia, and 10% from Australia, Africa, South America, and Antarctica combined. Of the total area represented by continents, about 30% has been sampled by heat flow measurements. Significant national reviews of heat flow data include Australia (Sass & Lachenbruch 1978), the European countries and western USSR (Cermak & Rybach 1979), Japan (Uyeda 1972), and the United States (Sass et al 1980). The data set clearly has a geographical bias; it also has more subtle geologic and tectonic biases as well. For example, in the United States roughly 75% of the heat flow measurements have been made in states from the Rocky Mountains westward because that region exhibits above average heat flow and has been a principal focus in geothermal energy exploration. Because of such biases, simple statisitics, such as the mean or median of all observations, are of limited use; they tend to overestimate significantly the heat flow from the continents as a whole. An areally weighted data set yields improved estimates, but is still hampered by the fact that less than half of the continental area has been sampled with measurements.

Table 1 Numbers of published heat flow measurements

Year of compilation	Continental	Oceanic	Reference
1954	43	20	Birch (1954a)
1965	131	913	Lee & Uyeda (1965)
1970	597	2530	Lee (1970)
1976	1699	3718	Jessop et al (1976)
1979	2808	4409	Chapman & Pollack (1980)

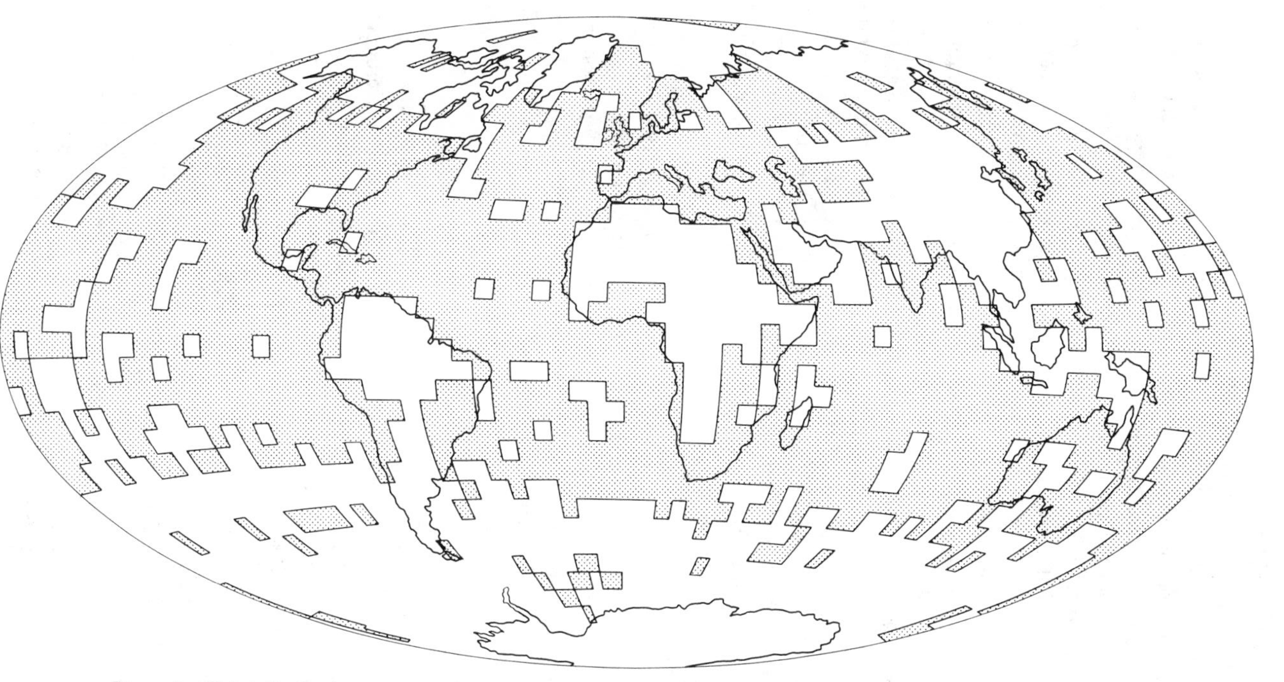

Figure 1 Global distribution of heat flow data in 5°×5° geographic grid. Shaded areas contain one or more observations.

Because temperature gradients are usually determined at depths no greater than a few hundred meters, the possibility exists that long term climatic variations, such as those characterizing the glacial and interglacial intervals of the Pleistocene and Holocene, may have perturbed subsurface temperatures in the first kilometer or so of depth, thus introducing a transient into the heat flow determination (Birch 1948). Inasmuch as the climatic variations in the Pleistocene were not confined to high latitudes but were global, Beck (1977) has argued that there exists the possibility of systematic error within the entire continental heat flow data set. The demonstration of such a bias must come from measurements in very deep boreholes, which would reveal a variation in heat flow with depth; unfortunately very few deep holes have been temperature logged in adequate detail to resolve this question.

Comparable perturbations must also be considered in tectonic terranes undergoing uplift, because the temperature at the surface will diminish with increasing elevation due to the adiabatic lapse rate in the atmosphere, thus introducing a transient into the surface heat flow. A kilometer of uplift over a million years (not uncommon in orogenic belts) would be accompanied by some 5°C of surface cooling, clearly similar in magnitude to climatic perturbations over similar time intervals.

Erosion likewise can introduce a transient into the surface heat flow by exposing deeper warmer rocks to surface conditions (Birch 1950, Jaeger 1965). When erosion rates are sufficiently high so as to remove a given thickness of rock in less time than is required for a surface temperature perturbation to propagate to that depth, the erosional transient can be a significant fraction of the observed heat flow.

VARIATION OF HEAT FLOW WITH AGE

As soon as a small number of heat flow observations from different tectonic settings began to accumulate, it became apparent that there were differences in the thermal characteristics of various tectonic elements. Kraskovski (1961) noted that the heat flux from Precambrian shields generally was less than that from younger terranes. Lee & Uyeda (1965) assembled 131 continental measurements into broad age groups, which showed the heat flow in Cenozoic volcanic terranes to be, on average, more than twice that from the shields. Polyak & Smirnov (1968), in a detailed and systematic analysis of 446 measurements, demonstrated a general decrease of heat flow with tectonic age. With increasing numbers of observations, analyses of data subsets for North America (Sclater & Francheteau 1970) and Europe (Cermak & Rybach 1979) established separate but similar patterns for those two well-studied continents. Recent analyses of large global data sets (Chapman & Furlong 1977, 1699 continental observations; Sclater et al 1980, 1411 continental observations) differ in detail but confirm the general decrease of heat flow with age (Table 2). As can be seen in both compilations in Table 2, the scatter of the observations is greatest in the youngest age group, probably due in part to the effects of hydrothermal circulation driven by the steep temperature gradients in young terranes (Lachenbruch & Sass 1977, Blackwell 1978).

In all such analyses, the definition of age is important; usually it is the age of the last tectonothermal mobilization of the terrane in which the measurement is made. Measurements in undeformed platform sediments carry the age of stabilization of the platform basement, measurements in igneous bodies carry the radiometric age of the intrustion or flow, a fold belt carries the youngest age of deformation, and a metamorphic terrane carries the age of the latest thermal metamorphic episode. Obviously the assignment of age is somewhat subjective, particularly in partially or weakly remobilized terranes, and this subjectivity contributes to some of the scatter about the age-group heat flow means. Moreover, there are certain geologic and tectonic settings where the regional heat flow may depart significantly from the appropriate age-group mean. Examples would include the low heat flow of Mesozoic or Cenozoic continental margins situated above ongoing or recent subduction, as observed by Lachenbruch (1968) in the Sierra Nevada of California, by Blackwell et al (1978) on the western margin of Oregon, and by Henry (1981) in the coastal region of Peru. Another example is the elevated heat flow in Precambrian terranes of Africa undergoing or in a stage antecedent to rifting (Morgan & Swanberg 1978, Chapman & Pollack 1977).

Anyone familiar with the heat flow literature can point to other departures from the general pattern of decreasing heat flow with increasing age, and indeed some critics question the existence of this empirical relationship. Critics notwithstanding, I believe the empiricism to be well established, although why such a generality should emerge from such a variety of geologic and

Table 2 Variation of heat flow with age of most recent tectonothermal event

Chapman & Furlong (1977)				Sclater et al (1980)			
Age group	Mean heat flow (mW m^{-2})	Standard deviation	N	Age group (m.y.)	Mean heat flow (mW m^{-2})	Standard deviation	N
Archean	41	11	136				
Early Proterozoic	51	21	78	>1700	46	16	375
Late Proterozoic	54	20	265	800–1700	50	10	138
Early Paleozoic	52	17	88	250–800	63	21	500
Late Paleozoic	61	18	514				
Mesozoic	73	29	85				
Cenozoic	71	37	587	0–250	76	53	398
		Total	1753			Total	1411

tectonic circumstances is not well understood. Specific tectonic and thermal models have been proposed for an extensional setting, such as the Basin and Range province of western North America (Lachenbruch 1978), and for magmatic accretion to the crust in convergence zones (Wells 1980). A generalized thermal model (Vitorello & Pollack 1980) linked directly to the observed variation of heat flow with age is discussed in more detail below.

One of the uses for the heat flow–age relationship is the estimation of heat flow in unsurveyed areas on the basis of the tectonothermal age of the terrane. Chapman & Pollack (1975) supplemented the existing heat flow observations with such estimates to produce a global data set and the first global heat flow map. A similar analysis by Sclater et al (1980), incorporating additional data and with adjustments for the heat lost to ocean water circulating through the young oceanic crust, has established a mean heat flow of 57 mW m^{-2} for the continents (including marine shelves) and 99 mW m^{-2} for the oceans; the global weighted average is 82 mW m^{-2}. The notion, firmly rooted in the literature for more than two decades, that oceanic and continental heat flow are approximately equal, is no longer tenable.

RADIOGENIC HEAT

Since the discovery of radioactivity by Becquerel in 1896 and the identification of radioisotopes in rocks in the early part of this century, it has been recognized that the energy liberated by radioactive decay ultimately is dissipated as heat and comprises a significant component of the heat flow from the continents. The principal heat producing isotopes are ^{232}Th, ^{238}U, ^{40}K, and ^{235}U with respective half-lives of 14.0, 4.47, 1.25, and .70 billion years. Other radioactive isotopes do not presently contribute significantly to terrestrial heat, either because their decay chains are not sufficiently energetic, their abundances are insignificant, or their half-lives are too short. However, certain short-lived isotopes, such as ^{26}Al or ^{129}I, may have been substantial contributors to the thermal budget in the early history of the Earth.

Accordingly, an important adjunct to heat flow investigations has been the measurement of isotopic abundances in rocks and the determination of the heat production therefrom (Birch 1954b, Adams & Gasparini 1970). The concentrations of uranium and thorium in crustal rocks are generally in trace amounts measured in parts per million, while potassium is considerably more abundant, with concentrations of a few percent, of which a small but well-known fraction is ^{40}K. The abundances of those isotopes are commonly obtained using a multichannel gamma ray spectrometer, which separates and counts gamma ray emissions on the basis of energy. Certain steps in the decay pattern of each isotope involve gamma radiation with characteristic energies and thus are indicative of the individual isotopic abundances in the sample.

The abundances of heat producing isotopes in rocks are highly variable, as can be seen in Table 3. There is almost an order of magnitude decrease in concentrations of U, Th, and K from granites to gabbros, and another very substantial decrease from mafic to ultramafic rocks. However, in all these rock types the ratios of Th/U and K/U are much less variable than the actual abundances. In a recent analysis, Taylor & McLennan (1981) estimate 3.8 and 1.0×10^4 as characteristic values for Th/U and K/U, respectively, in the crust. In terms of heat production within the crust and upper mantle, the data of Table 3 imply a marked upward concentration of the Earth's heat-producing isotopes, particularly in the continents. The processes by which this segregation has occurred are not well understood, but clearly it is closely associated with the magmatic and metamorphic evolution of the continents as a whole. These isotopes represent elements with relatively large ionic radii in comparison to silicon, aluminum, magnesium, calcium, iron, and oxygen, which comprise the bulk of the Earth's mantle as oxide minerals. The larger ions fit less readily into the denser crystal lattices of the mantle oxides; in magmatic and metamorphic events they are more easily mobilized and tend to accompany the magmatic derivatives and metasomatic volatiles upward where they are incorporated into the more open crystal structure of the crust.

The contribution to the surface heat flow of the continents by crustal radioactivity and its attendant heat production is substantial. Indeed, a crust comprised completely of granodiorite could generate the entire average continental heat flow, with no flux from the mantle required. The continental crust, of course, is not granodiorite throughout, although the upper several kilometers in many areas may be approximately that composition. The middle and lower crust is thought to comprise principally metamorphic amphibolites and granulites with lesser heat production. Petrologically and geophysically realistic models of the heat source distribution (Smithson & Decker 1974, Smithson & Brown 1977, Allis 1979) indicate that about 25 mW m^{-2}—some 40% of the average continental heat flow—arises radiogenically within the continental crust. When weighted by the area of the continents, this crustal radiogenic heat represents 12% of the global heat loss.

Table 3 Heat production of common rocks (after Rybach 1973, 1976) and of the continental crust (after Taylor & McLennan 1981)

Igneous rock type	U (ppm)	Th (ppm)	K (%)	Th/U	K/U	Density (g cm^{-3})	Heat production 10^{-6} W m^{-3}
Granite/Rhyolite	3.9	16.0	3.6	4.1	0.9×10^4	2.67	2.5
Granodiorite/Dacite	2.3	9.0	2.6	3.9	1.1×10^4	2.72	1.5
Diorite/Andesite	1.7	7.0	1.1	4.1	0.7×10^4	2.82	1.1
Gabbro/Basalt	0.5	1.6	0.4	3.2	0.8×10^4	2.98	0.3
Peridotite	0.02	0.06	0.006	3.0	0.3×10^4	3.23	0.01
Dunite	0.003	0.01	0.0009	3.3	0.3×10^4	3.28	0.002
Continental crust	1.25	4.8	1.25	3.8	1.0×10^4	—	0.8

The continental crust also exhibits lateral heterogeneity, probably at all levels. Roy et al (1968) observed that the variability of heat flow in some regions is simply related to the variable heat production of the surface rocks. The empiricism is expressed as $q_0 = q_r + bA_0$, where q_0 is the surface heatflow, A_0 is the volumetric heat production of the surface rocks, q_r is the "reduced" heat flow (i.e. the heat flow that would be observed in the absence of any upper crustal heat production), and b is a parameter with dimension of depth that characterizes the vertical distribution of heat sources within the crust. The relationship in effect separates a variable shallow contribution from a uniform deeper contribution to the surface heat flow of an area. Roy et al (1968) define a heat flow province as a geographic area in which the heat flow and heat production are linearly related.

In the years following the initial observation of this linear relationship some seventeen heat flow provinces have been identified; their parameters are tabulated by Vitorello & Pollack (1980) and their distribution is shown in Figure 2. The provinces range in age from Archean to Cenozoic; some provinces comprise terranes of diverse ages. The relationship is sometimes obscured in young terranes by the effect of hydrothermal circulation, but careful winnowing of the observations can demonstrate its existence (Blackwell 1978). Each province has a characteristic reduced heat flow and source distribution parameter. From province to province the reduced heat flow varies from about 10 to 70 mW m^{-2}, while the source distribution parameter is in the range of 4 to 16 km. In the subsequent discussion, one should keep in perspective the relative state of knowledge of the reduced heat flow. While there are a few thousand direct measurements of surface heat flow, and several hundred suites of rocks for which heat production has been determined, there are less than twenty published estimates of the reduced heat flow derived from joint heat flow-heat production investigations.

Roy et al (1968) interpreted the linear heat flow-heat production relationship with a simple model in which different elements of a heat flow province are represented by discrete areas of equal thickness but each with a different heat production, $A_0\ (x,y)$. The parameter b then represents the present common thickness of the blocks, and $bA_0\ (x,y)$ is the regionally variable upper crustal increment to q_r, the regionally uniform reduced heat flow from below. In this model b would decrease with time as erosion removed heat sources from the surface, provided the erosion acted uniformly over the entire surface of the province.

Lachenbruch (1970) presented a thorough analysis and interpretation of the linear heat flow-heat production relationship. He demonstrated that several radiogenic source distributions can satisfy the linear relationship, including an exponential source distribution of the form $A_0 \exp(-z/b)$. In such a model the variability of the surface heat production arises from erosion to various

Figure 2 Geographic distribution of seventeen heat flow provinces where the relationship between measured heat flow and radiogenic heat production from near-surface rocks has been empirically determined: SN denotes Sierra Nevada; SP, Superior Province; EUS, eastern United States; SEA, southeastern Appalachians; Bz, Brazilian coastal shield; Ba, Baltic shield; EW, England and Wales; BM, Bohemian Massif; U, Ukrainian shield; N, Niger; Z, Zambia; I_1, late Proterozoic province of India; I_2, Archean shield of India; WA, western Australia; CA, central Australia; EA, eastern Australia; and BR, Basin and Range (Reprinted by permission from I. Vitorello and H. N. Pollack, *J. Geophys. Res.* 85:(B2):983–95. Copyright © 1980 by the American Geophysical Union).

depths in the source distribution, while b (the logarithmic decrement or vertical scale length of the distribution) remains unchanged during the erosional evolution of the province.

Another empiricism first proposed by Pollack & Chapman (1977) and later elaborated by Vitorello & Pollack (1980) relates the reduced heat flow of a province to the average heat flow therein via a simple proportionality: $q_r = 0.6q$. Conceptually the empiricism is reasonable; it asserts that in provinces of higher average heat flow, the reduced heat flow is also proportionally higher, i.e. a greater heat flux at the surface is in part due to an increased flux from the mantle. The complement of this relationship is that crustal radiogenic heat comprises about 0.4 of the mean heat flow of a province, with the implication that higher heat flow provinces display proportionally greater crustal radioisotopic enrichment. This implies a linkage between thermal mobilization of a magmatic or metamorphic province, accompanied by a higher reduced heat flow, and the concomitant radioisotopic enrichment of the upper crust.

It is widely accepted that heat-producing isotopes are redistributed upward by magmatic and metamorphic processes, but the details of the fractionation, transfer, and stabilization at upper crustal levels remain less clear (Lambert & Heier 1967, Albarede 1975, Heier 1978, Jaupart et al 1981). While U, Th, and K are geochemically coherent in magmatic fractionation, they diverge somewhat during crystallization and have rather different recycling characteristics in the presence of meteoric or juvenile thermal waters or other volatiles. Subsequent to the magmatic and/or metamorphic peak, the mobilized terrane undergoes conductive cooling, accompanied by a decrease in the reduced heat flow with time. The corresponding decrease in the crustal radiogenic heat, which preserves the empirical proportionality, apparently is accomplished by erosion and removal of radioelements from surface rocks.

The surface heat flow, surface heat production, source distribution parameter, and reduced heat flow provide strong constraints on temperatures in the continental crust. Crustal temperatures are strongly dependent on the reduced heat flow, and thus differences in the thermal structure between heat flow provinces arise principally from variations in the subcrustal flux. Temperature versus depth curves ("geotherms") characterizing the thermal regime of the crust have been calculated for a variety of heat flow settings by Lachenbruch & Sass (1977). Pollack & Chapman (1977) present a general family of geotherms, each corresponding to a different surface heat flow and extended to upper mantle depths.

THE THERMAL EVOLUTION OF CONTINENTS

The heat lost at the surface of the Earth is the principal observational constraint on models of the internal dynamics and thermal evolution of the planet. As noted in the introduction, the greater part—nearly three fourths of the total—is exhausted through the creation and subsequent cooling of new oceanic lithosphere at oceanic ridges. The plates of oceanic lithosphere serve as the cooling fins of the Earth's heat engine. The heat flow from the continents, while representing only sligthly more than one fourth of the planetary heat loss, is closely associated with the petrology and trace element chemistry of the continental crust, and therefore must be an important component of any model of the thermal, petrologic, and tectonic evolution of the continents.

The aspect of continental heat flow most central to evolutionary models has been the age dependence. Models divide roughly into two types. The first and more common type (Crough & Thompson 1976, Vitorello & Pollack 1980) interprets the decline of heat flow with age in terms of deep-seated thermal and petrologic processes intimately associated with the development and evolution of the continental lithosphere. The second type of model (England & Richardson 1980) interprets the age dependence of the heat flow principally in terms of processes within and erosion of the continental crust, with little requirement for the involvement of the continental upper mantle and with little implication for the thermal evolution of the subcrustal lithosphere.

England & Richardson place considerable weight on the effects of deep erosion on the heat flow in continental mobile belts, emphasizing the temporary augmentation of the surface heat flow by the progressive uncovering of deeper and warmer crustal rocks. They argue that, in comparison to the typical crustal thickness of shields and stable platforms, the excessive crustal thicknesses observed in Cenozoic convergence zones involving continents represents an unconsummated erosion that will eventually remove 20–40 km of the crust. Such erosion on a suitable time scale can account for the observed decay of surface heat flow without any need of augmentation by magmatic activity or deeper heat flow.

The England & Richardson model, while perhaps appropriate to the Alps, is lacking in generality. The higher heat flow of Cenozoic terranes is observed not only in continental convergence zones, but also in several other tectonic settings, such as the Rhinegraben, Massif Central and Pannonian Basin of Europe, and the Basin and Range province of western North America, for which the deep erosional arguments are less persuasive. None of these areas exhibit erosion to deep crustal levels and all exhibit relatively thin crust. Nonmagmatic thickening of continental crust may perhaps be a tenable process in a continent-continent collision, as in the Alps or Himalayas, but it is less credible as an explanation of the Andean root, where the subduction is oceanic and the thick crustal root is centered on the zone of Pleistocene and Holocene volcanism. Indeed, the evolution of the entire western Cordillera of both North and South America is marked by extensive magmatism over long periods of time. While nonmagmatic processes may occasionally provide a mode of crustal thickening, it seems unlikely that this has been the characteristic mode of the Mesozoic and Cenozoic.

The contrasting model presented by Vitorello & Pollack interprets the age dependence of continental heat flow in terms of three components (see Figure 3): (I) a radiogenic component arising from the zone of radioelement enrichment within the crust, (II) a contribution derived from the cooling of a thermal perturbation associated with the tectonothermal mobilization that defines the "thermal age" of the crust, and (III) a background heat flow, probably of deep origin, with no significant time variation and contributing equally to terranes of all ages. All three components are approximately equal in young terranes, while in ancient terranes only the crustal radiogenic and background components remain, the former reduced by half by erosion into the zone of crustal heat sources. Because a significant part of the variation of

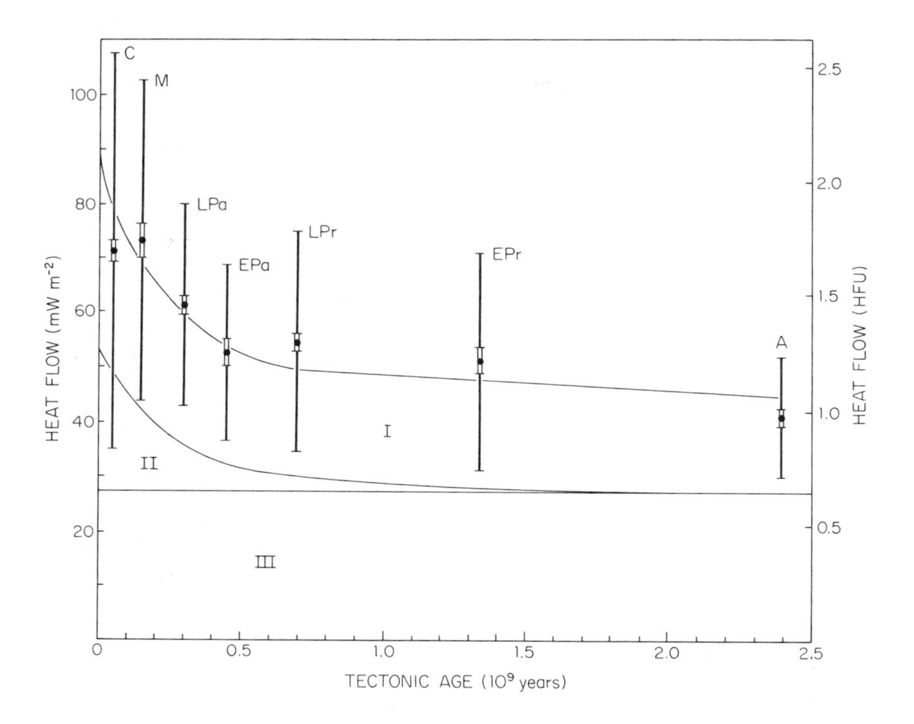

Figure 3 Decrease of continental heat flow with age and its three principal components; component I is radiogenic heat from the crust, component II is heat from the transient thermal perturbation associated with tectonogenesis, and component III is the background heat flow from deeper sources (after Vitorello & Pollack 1980). The data points are from Chapman & Furlong (1977). C denotes Cenozoic; M, Mesozoic; LPa, late Paleozoic; EPa, early Paleozoic; LPr, late Proterozoic; EPr, early Proterozoic; and A, Archean. Points are plotted at the mean age of the respective age ranges. Double bars represent the standard error of the mean; single bars the standard deviation. The upper curve corresponds to a visually fitted curve through the data points; the middle curve corresponds to 60% of the upper curve; the lower curve represents the background heat flow from deeper sources. (Reprinted by permission from I. Vitorello and H. N. Pollack, *J. Geophys. Res.* 85(B2):983–95. Copyright © 1980 by the American Geophysical Union.)

heat flow with age in this model arises from the decay of the thermal perturbation, the pace and extent of the requisite erosion is much less than in England & Richardson's model, and therefore the heat flow transient introduced by the erosion is insignificant.

In contrast to the oceanic thermal regime, where the cooling of lithosphere from an initial high temperature yields a simple $(\text{age})^{-1/2}$ dependence for the heat flow, the continental flux has a longer and more complex age dependence governed by the time scales of two different processes: crustal erosion and lithospheric cooling. In the Vitorello & Pollack model, the time scale of the erosion is fixed by the requirement that the crustal radiogenic heat must diminish in proportion to the surface heat flow; the cooling time scale is thereby fixed, as the cooling of the thermal perturbation must provide the remaining time dependence of the heat flow.

The cooling and background components of the Vitorello & Pollack model together comprise a "reduced" heat flow that diminishes with time, and this decay can be compared to the observed variation of reduced heat flowwith age. Sclater et al (1980) compile and display such data and note that the reduced heat flow apparently decays in 200–400 m.y. to a "background" level, somewhat faster than the 300–500 m.y. decay of reduced" heat flow of the Vitorello & Pollack model.

Vitorello & Pollack present models of the magnitude and configuration of the thermal perturbation that in cooling will yield component II of the heat flow. A perturbed zone some 300–500 km thick, with a maximum temperature disturbance of 750–850°C occurring at depths of 80–100 km, provides a good fit to component II (see Figure 4). The inferred depth extent of the perturbed zone is of major significance; it implies that the conducting boundary layer beneath the shields and stable platforms of the continents is some 2–3 times thicker than that beneath oceans, and that it has remained as an entity at least over the time interval since the last major tectonic/magmatic event within it. Even if the thermal perturbation decayed more rapidly, as suggested by the age dependence of the reduced heat flow, the requirement would still exist for a relatively thick conductive boundary layer beneath the stable continental nuclei.

The acquisition of this long-term stability is a complex process intimately linked to the petrological development of the continents. Three types of stability characterize the cratonic lithosphere: thermal, mechanical, and buoyant. Substantial devolatilization of the upper mantle during metamorphic and magmatic events imparts to the lithosphere a stability against later remelting by elevating the solidus to a more refractory state and depressing the eventual equilibrium geotherm by redistributing the heat-producing isotopes upward. Mechanical stability, manifest as a resistance to deformation and dismemberment, is acquired concomitantly with thermal stability; it derives from the

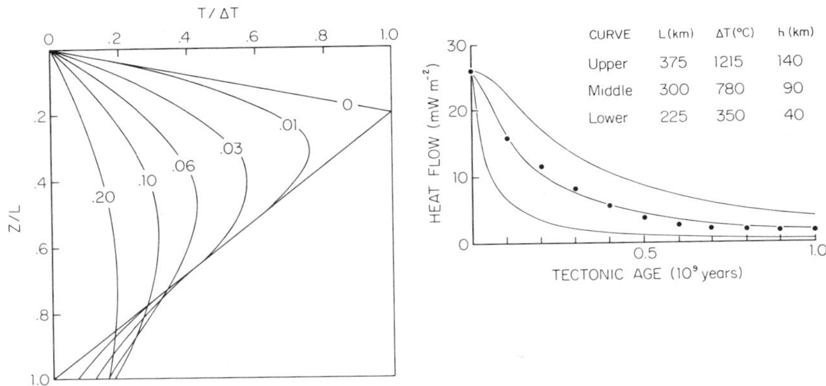

Figure 4 (*left*) Typical temperature versus depth curves for the cooling of a thermal perturbation within a lithosphere of thickness L; the maximum temperature disturbance occurs at a variable depth h. Cooling curves are shown for several values of the dimensionless time kt/L^2, where t is the time since cooling began and k is the thermal diffusivity. (*right*) The decay of the surface heat flow from the thermal perturbation shown above. The three curves are obtained by varying the layer thickness L, the maximum temperature disturbance T, and the depth h at which the maximum occurs. Circles are points taken at 100 m.y. intervals from the curve representing component II in Figure 3 (after Vitorello & Pollack 1980).

strong dependence of strength and viscosity on both temperature and volatile content. Buoyant stability (the resistance of continental lithosphere to later subduction) is acquired by differentiation during partial melting. Both melt product and residuum may be less dense than the parent mantle, leading to upward migration of the melt in penetrative magmatism followed by an underplate of the refractory residuum. The most complete development of the geophysical and petrological aspects of this thermal, chemical, and mechanical boundary layer can be found in a series of papers by Jordan (1975, 1978, 1981).

Lithospheric stability, therefore, is an acquired property, the result of a thermal and magmatic history that includes an equilibration period on the order of a few hundred million years following a tectonothermal event. During the equilibration period, the affected lithosphere is in a weakened state and is vulnerable to recurrent tectonism and magmatism. In this context it seems not extraordinary that the Atlantic Ocean opened almost exclusively along Paleozoic or latest Precambrian orogenic belts, several of which were at the time of opening recent sutures welding components of Pangea together. Similarly, the occurrences of Cenozoic volcanism in Africa are confined almost exclusively to the Pan-African terranes (Thorpe & Smith 1974), last remobilized in late Precambrian and early Paleozoic. Because the characteristic time for thermal equilibration (300–500 m.y.) exceeds the characteristic time of major reorganizations of the global plate system (100–200 m.y.), there will be zones of lingering weakness within the lithosphere vulnerable to the redistribution of intraplate stress accompanying plate reorganization. Thus it is not surprising to find that persistent zones of weakness and tectonic reactivation of previously mobilized terranes are common geologic phenomena.

If a terrane safely passes through the period of peril and reaches a stable cratonic condition, it is considerably more difficult to remobilize; to do so the processes leading to stabilization must be reversed. A thick, stiff refractory lithosphere can be thinned and weakened by a reinfusion of heat and volatiles from below, a thermal and metasomatic process for which increasing evidence is accumulating (Lloyd & Bailey 1975, Boettcher et al 1979, Menzies & Murthy 1980). It seems unlikely, however, that the continental buoyancy can be easily altered or reversed.

Gass et al (1978) and Pollack et al (1981) discuss the parameters that determine whether sublithospheric thermal disturbances penetrate the lithosphere and reach the surface as mid-plate magmatism. They quantitatively examine the interrelationship of plate thickness and velocity, and conclude that thick lithosphere moving rapidly over sublithospheric thermal perturbations is less vulnerable to penetrative magmatism than are thin slow-moving plates. Evidence for this relationship can be seen by the nearly complete absence of Cenozoic volcanism on the thick continental cratons ($>$ 1000 m.y. age). Because of the durability of the cratons, lithospheric perturbations may not develop fully to the stage of widespread surface volcanism. Crough (1981) assembles geologic evidence of a hot-spot track across eastern North America, more subtle in character than the obvious Hawaiian-Emperor volcanic track across the Pacific. Perturbations of sufficient magnitude and longevity may of course penetrate to the continental surface and leave volcanic tracks; the Snake River volcanic plain culminating at the Yellowstone rhyolite pile is perhaps the clearest modern example. The major Mesozoic flood basalts in the Parana and Karroo Basins and on the Deccan Plateau likely developed above major hot spots of their day.

What can be said of the heat flow earlier in geologic history? Clearly the radiogenic heat production of past times was greater because of the isotopic decay. If the K/U ratio throughout the Earth is the same as in the crust, then the heat production 3000 m.y. ago was some 2.75 times greater than the present (Wasserburg et al 1964). However, it is unlikely that the heat flow over the entire surface was greater by that factor; rather an increased heat loss would probably be concentrated in the ocean basins, where the additional heat can be readily exhausted by an increased rate of production of oceanic lithosphere (Bickle 1978).

The radioisotopes actually locked in the continental crust yielded greater heat in past times, of course, but crustal radiogenic heat comprises less than half of the continental heat flow. Moreover, because the increase in heat flow occurred principally in the higher levels of the crust, the increment to lower crustal and upper mantle temperatures was not great. The oft-repeated notion that temperature gradients through the Archean protocontinents were substantially higher than present-day gradients is probably untrue. Careful application of metamorphic geothermometry and geobarometry indicates that the range of crustal conditions inferred for Archean terranes are represented in present-day tectonic settings. In particular the conditions for high-grade metamorphism of the lower continental crust exist in the modern Basin and Range province of western North America (Lachenbruch & Sass 1977).

CONCLUDING REMARKS

The widespread measurement of terrestrial heat flow has been an endeavor essentially of the last two decades, and is still far from complete in terms of global coverage. However, the recognition of its variability in different settings, both oceanic and continental, has forged an undeniable link between the loss of the Earth's internal heat and tectonic processes within and at the surface of the Earth. On the continents in particular, these processes are intimately associated with the petrological evolution of the continental lithosphere, and with the establishment of those very properties that make the continents stand out: their low density and long-term durability. If the inadequacies of past interpretations from both geophysicists and petrologists can be attributed to an attempt to isolate thermal, rheologic, and petrologic parameters from each other as uncoupled independent variables, then the promise of the future lies in the recognition of the inseparability of these aspects of continental evolution and in the integration of them into a geological equivalent of the "grand unification" theories of physics.

ACKNOWLEDGMENTS

I am grateful to Francis Birch for stimulating my interest in geothermal studies, and to my late colleague James T. Wilson for his encouragement and support over two decades. It is also a pleasure to acknowledge my collaborations with David Chapman, Icaro Vitorello, and Steven Henry; together we have taken the Earth's temperature in many places, and tried to decide whether the patient was feverish or had a chill. The US National Science Foundation has supported geothermal research at the University of Michigan through Grants GA-36360, DES75-17065, EAR78-09131, and INT80-16941.

Literature Cited

Adams, J. A. S., Gasparini, P. 1970. *Gamma-ray Spectrometry of Rocks*. New York: Elsevier. 295 pp.

Albarede, F. 1975. The heat flow/heat generation relationship: an interaction mode of fluids with cooling intrusions. *Earth Planet. Sci. Lett.* 27:73–78

Allis, R. G. 1979. A heat production model for

the stable continental crust. *Tectonophysics* 57:151–65

Beck, A. E. 1965. Techniques of measuring heat flow on land. In *Terrestrial Heat Flow,* ed. W. H. K. Lee, Geophys. Monogr. 8:24–57. Washington DC: Am. Geophys. Union. 276 pp.

Beck, A. E. 1977. Climatically perturbed temperature gradients and their effect on regional and continental heat flow means. *Tectonophysics* 41:17–39

Bickle, M. J. 1978. Heat loss from the Earth: a constraint on Archean tectonics from the relation between geothermal gradients and the rate of plate production. *Earth Planet. Sci. Lett.* 40:301–15

Birch, F. 1948. The effects of Pleistocene climatic variations upon geothermal gradients. *Am. J. Sci.* 246:729–60

Birch, F. 1950. Flow of heat in the Front Range, Colorado. *Bull. Geol. Soc. Am.* 61:567–630

Birch, F. 1954a. The present state of geothermal investigations. *Geophysics* 9:645–59

Birch, F. 1954b. Heat from radioactivity. In *Nuclear Geology,* ed. H. Faul, pp. 148–75. New York: Wiley.

Blackwell, D. D. 1978. Heat flow and energy loss in the western United States. In *Cenozoic Tectonics and Regional Geophysics of the Western Cordillera,* ed. R. B. Smith, G. P. Eaton, *Geol. Soc. Am. Mem.* 152:175–208

Blackwell, D. D., Hull, D. A., Bowen, R. R. 1978. Heat flow in Oregon. *Oregon Dep. Geol. Min. Ind. Spec. Pap. 4.* 42 pp.

Blackwell, D. D., Steele, J. L., Brott, C. A. 1980. The terrain effect on terrestrial heat flow. *J. Geophys. Res.* 85:4757–72

Boettcher, A. L., O'Neil, J. R., Windom, K. E., Stewart, D. C., Wilshire, H. G. 1979. Metasomatism of the upper mantle and the genesis of kimberlites and alkali basalt. In *The Mantle Sample: Inclusions in Kimberlites and Other Volcanics,* ed. F. R. Boyd, H. D. A. Meyer, pp. 173–83. Washington D.C: Am. Geophys. Union. 423 pp.

Boyle, R. 1671. Of the temperature of the subterraneal regions as to heat and cold. In *Robert Boyle, The Works* 1966, ed. T. Birch. Hildesheim: G. Ohlms

British Association. 1883. Rep. 52nd Meet., pp. 72–90. London: John Murray

Cermak, V., Rybach, L. 1979. *Terrestrial Heat Flow in Europe*. New York: Springer. 362 pp.

Chapman, D. S., Furlong, K. 1977. Continental heat flow-age relationships. *EOS, Trans. Am. Geophys. Union* 58:1240

Chapman, D. S., Pollack, H. N. 1975. Global heat flow: a new look. *Earth Planet. Sci. Lett.* 28:23–32

Chapman, D. S., Pollack, H. N. 1977. Heat flow and heat production in Zambia: evidence for lithospheric thinning in central Africa. *Tectonophysics* 41:79–100

Chapman, D. S., Pollack, H. N. 1980. Global heat flow: sperical harmonic representation. *EOS, Trans. Am. Geophys. Union* 61:383

Crough, S. T. 1981. Mesozoic hotspot epeirogeny in eastern North America. *Geology* 9:2–6

Crough, S. T., Thompson, G. A. 1976. Thermal model of continental lithosphere. *J. Geophys. Res.* 81:4857–62

Davies, G. F. 1980. Review of oceanic and global heat flow estimates. *Rev. Geophys. Space Phys.* 18:718–22

Degens, E. T., Von Herzen, R. P., Wong, H. 1971. Lake Tanganyika—water chemistry, sediments, geological structure. *Naturwissenschaften* 58:229–40

England, P. C., Richardson, S. 1980. Erosion and the age-dependence of continental heat flow. *Geophys. J. R. Astron. Soc.* 62: 421–38

Gass, I. G., Chapman, D. S., Pollack, H. N., Thorpe, R. S. 1978. Geological and geophysical parameters of mid-plate volcanism. *Philos. Trans. R. Soc. London Ser. A* 288:581–97

Heier, K. S. 1978. The distribution and redistribution of heat-producing elements in the continents. *Philos. Trans. R. Soc. London Ser. A.* 288:393–400

Henry, S. G. 1981. *Terrestrial heat flow overlying the Andean subduction zone*. PhD thesis. Univ. Mich., Ann Arbor. 207 pp.

Jaeger, J. C. 1965. Application of the theory of heat conduction to geothermal measurements. In *Terrestrial Heat Flow,* ed. W. H. K. Lee, Geophys. Monogr. 8:7–23. Washington, D.C: Am. Geophys. Union

Jaupart, C.,. Sclater, J. G., Simmons, G. 1981. Heat flow studies: constraints on the distribution of uranium, thorium and potassium in the continental crust. *Earth Planet. Sci. Lett.* 52:328–44

Jessop, A. M., Hobart, M. A., Sclater, J. G. 1976. The world heat flow data collection—1975. *Geothermal Ser.* 5, Energy Mines Resour., Earth Phys. Branch, Ottawa

Jordan, T. H. 1975. The continental tectosphere. *Rev. Geophys. Space Phys.* 13: 1–12

Jordan, T. H. 1978. Composition and development of the continental tectosphere. *Nature* 274:544–48

Jordan, T. H. 1981. Continents as a chemical boundary layer. *Philos. Trans. R. Soc. London Ser. A* 301:359–73

Kraskovski, S. A. 1961. Thermal heat in shields. *Izv. Akad. Nauk SSSR, ser. geofiz.* 3:274–80

Lachenbruch, A. H. 1968. Preliminary geothermal model of the Sierra Nevada. *J. Geophys. Res.* 73:6977–90

Lachenbruch, A. H. 1970. Crustal temperature

and heat production: implication of the linear heat flow relation. *J. Geophys. Res.* 75:3291–3300

Lachenbruch, A. H. 1978. Models of an extending lithosphere and heat flow in the Basin and Range province. In *Cenozoic Tectonics and Regional Geophysics of the Western Cordillera,* ed. R. B. Smith, G. P. Eaton, *Geol. Soc. Am. Mem.* 152:209–50

Lachenbruch, A. H., Sass, J. H. 1977. Heatflow in the United States and the thermal regime of the crust. In *The Earth's Crust,* ed. J. G. Heacock, Geophys. Monogr. 20:626–75. Washington D.C: Am. Geophys. Union

Lambert, I. B., Heier, K. S. 1967. The vertical distribution of uranium, thorium and potassium in the continental crust. *Geochim. Cosmochim. Acta* 31:377–90

Lee, W. H. K. 1970. On the global variations of terrestrial heat-flow. *Phys. Earth. Planet. Inter.* 2:332–41

Lee, W. H. K., Uyeda, S. 1965. Review of heat flow data. In *Terrestrial Heat Flow,* ed. W. H. K. Lee, Geophys. Monogr. 8: 87–100. Washington, D. C: Am. Geophys. Union. 276 pp.

Lloyd, F. E., Bailey, D. K. 1975. Light element metasomatism of the continental mantle: the evidence and the consequences. *Phys. Chem. Earth* 9:389–416

Menzies, M., Murthy, V. R. 1980. Enriched mantle: Nd and Sr isotopes in diopsides from kimberlite nodules. *Nature* 283:634–36

Morgan, P., Swanberg, C. A. 1978. Heat flow and the geothermal potential of Egypt. *Pure Appl. Geophys.* 117:213–26

Pollack, H. N. 1980. The heat flow from the earth: a review. In *Mechanisms of Continental Drift and Plate Tectonics,* ed. P. A. Davies, S. K. Runcorn, pp. 183–92. London: Academic. 364 pp.

Pollack, H. N., Chapman, D. S. 1977. On the regional variation of heat flow, geotherms, and the thickness of the lithosphere. *Tectonophysics* 38:279–96

Pollack, H. N., Gass, I. G., Thorpe, R. S., Chapman, D. S. 1981. On the vulnerability of lithospheric plates to mid-plate volcanism: reply to comments by P. R. Vogt. *J. Geophys. Res.* 86:961–66

Polyak, B. G., Smirnov, Y. A. 1968. Relationship between terrestrial heat flow and the tectonics of the continents. *Geotectonics* 4:205–13

Roy, R. F., Blackwell, D., Birch, F. 1968. Heat generation of plutonic rocks and continental heat flow provinces. *Earth Planet. Sci. Lett.* 5:1–12

Rybach, L. 1973. Warmeproduktionsbestimmungen an Gesteinen der Schweizer Alpen. *Beitr. Geol. Schweiz,* Geotechn. Ser. 5l. Bern: Kummerly & Frei

Rybach, L. 1976. Die Gesteinsradioaktivitat und ihr Einfluss auf das Temperaturfeld in der Kontinentalen Kruste. *J. Geophys.* 42: 93–101

Sass, J. H., Blackwell, D. D., Chapman, D. S., Costain, J. K., Decker, E. R., Lawver, L. A., Swanberg, C. A. 1980. Heat flow from the crust of the United States. In *Physical Properties of Rocks and Minerals,* ed. Y. S. Touloukian, W. R. Judd, R. F. Roy, Ch. 13. St. Louis: McGraw-Hill

Sass, J. H., Lachenbruch, A. H. 1978. Thermal regime of the Australian continental crust. In *The Earth, Its Origin, Structure and Evolution,* ed. M. W. McElhinny, pp. 301–51. New York: Academic

Sass, J. H., Lachenbruch, A. H., Munroe, R. J. 1971. Thermal conductivity of rocks from measurements on fragments and its application to heat flow determinations. *J. Geophys. Res.* 76:3391–3401

Sclater, J. G., Francheteau, J. 1970. The implications of terrestrial heat flow observations on current tectonic and geochemical models of the crust and upper mantle of the earth. *Geophys. J. R. Astron. Soc.* 20: 509–42

Sclater, J. G., Jaupart, C., Galson, D. 1980. The heat flow through oceanic and continental crust and the heat loss from the Earth. *Rev. Geophys. Space Phys.* 18:269–311

Sclater, J. G., Vacquier, V., Rohrhirsch, J. H. 1970. Terrestrial heat flow measurements on Lake Titicaca, Peru. *Earth Planet. Sci. Lett.* 8:45–54

Smithson, S. B., Brown, S. K. 1977. A model for the lower continental crust. *Earth Planet. Sci. Lett.* 35:134–44

Smithson, S. B., Decker, E. R. 1974. A continental crustal model and its geothermal implications. *Earth Planet. Sci. Lett.* 22: 215–25

Swanberg, C. A., Morgan, P. 1978. The linear relation between temperatures based on the silica content of groundwater and regional heat flow: a new heat flow map of the United States. *Pure Appl. Geophys.* 117:227–41

Taylor, S. R., McLennan, S. M. 1981. The composition and evolution of the continental crust: rare earth element evidence from sedimentary rocks. *Philos. Trans. R. Soc. London Ser. A* 301:381–99

Thorpe, R. S., Smith, K. 1974. Distribution of Cenozoic volcanism in Africa. *Earth Planet. Sci. Lett.* 22:91–95

Tozer, D. C. 1965. Heat transfer and convection currents. *Philos. Trans. R. Soc. London Ser. A* 258:252–71

Tozer, D. C. 1972. The present thermal state of the terrestrial planets. *Phys. Earth Planet. Inter.* 6:182–97

Uyeda, S. 1972. Heat flow. In *Crust and Upper Mantle of the Japanese Area,* ed. S.

Miyamura, S. Uyeda, pp. 97–105. Earthquake Res. Inst., Univ. Tokyo
Vitorello, I., Pollack, H. N. 1980. On the variation of continental heat flow with age and the thermal evolution of continents. *J. Geophys. Res.* 85:983–95
Von Herzen, R. P., Vacquier, V. 1967. Terrestrial heat flow in Lake Malawi, Africa. *J. Geophys. Res.* 72:4221–26
Wasserburg, G. J., MacDonald, G. J. F., Hoyle, F., Fowler, W. A. 1964. Relative contributions of uranium, thorium, and potassium to heat production in the Earth. *Science* 143:465–67
Wells, P. R. A. 1980. Thermal models for the magmatic accretion and subsequent metamorphism of continental crust. *Earth Planet. Sci. Lett.* 46:253–65

Ann. Rev. Earth Planet. Sci. 1982. 10:483-526

APPLICATIONS OF THE ION MICROPROBE TO GEOCHEMISTRY AND COSMOCHEMISTRY

N. Shimizu and S. R. Hart

Center for Geoalchemy, Department of Earth & Planetary Sciences,
Massachusetts Institute of Technology, Cambridge, Massachusetts 02139

1. INTRODUCTION

Material is ejected from solid surfaces under bombardment of energetic ions in a process known as sputtering. A part of the sputtered material is ionized and these secondary ions can be analyzed with a mass spectrometer in a technique known as secondary ion mass spectrometry (SIMS). The ion microprobe uses a finely focused primary beam in order to perform SIMS analysis of selected areas on the surface of a solid sample. In contrast to an electron probe, which utilizes an electron beam to bombard a solid sample and analyzes intensities of characteristic X-rays emitted from the sample, an ion-probe obtains mass spectra of the secondary ions ejected from the sample. An ion probe can provide not only a chemical and isotopic analysis of the sample, but can also determine variations of chemical and isotopic compositions as a function of depth into the sample, as the primary ion beam continuously erodes the sample.

These characteristics of an ion-probe attracted the attention of geochemists immediately after the instrument first became commercially available in the late sixties. The subsequent years have seen continued effort by geochemists in exploring possible applications, in finding systematic relationships between secondary ion intensities and chemical compositions in search of a general scheme for quantitative analysis, and in understanding the fundamental physical processes involved. In the same period, the ion probe has proven to be an

0084-6597/82/0515-0483$2.00

extremely powerful tool in electronic engineering and materials science for three-dimensional material characterization.

In this article, we do not attempt a historical review of ion microprobe analysis; the reader is referred to early review articles such as Evans (1972), Liebl (1974), Morrison & Slodzian (1975), Colby (1975), and Lovering (1975). Nor do we attempt to describe the technical details of instrumental operation, or make comparisons between various existant machines. For a comprehensive review of these aspects of ion probe technology, we refer the reader to the papers of Werner (1978, 1980). For a review of the technical aspects of secondary ion production by ion bombardment, the papers of Blaise & Nourtier (1979) and Wittmaack (1980) should be consulted. For extensive bibliographies on the subject of secondary ion mass spectrometry (SIMS), see Wittry (1980) and Geiss (1981). This paper is intended to describe the present status of geochemical and cosmochemical applications of the ion microprobe; it is not a review, in the sense that we highlight numerous ion probe studies in these areas without being necessarily comprehensive. Nor is it a historical review, in the sense that we do not discuss most of the early development work. Instead, we concentrate on the more recent, state-of-the-art work, especially that which appears to have made successful use of ion probe technology within the present limitations. In general, we stress the applications from a problem-oriented point of view, and we refer the reader to the referenced papers for particular details of how various analytical problems have been documented and overcome.

The chemical complexity of geologic samples results in complex secondary ion mass spectra, a major obstacle for routine applications of SIMS in geochemistry. If, for instance, a secondary ion mass spectrum of a silicate mineral is observed, then it must be made certain that interference-free signals are obtained for the isotopes of interest. The abundance of molecular ion species (oxides, hydroxides, dimers, etc) produced in the sputtering process and the resulting isobaric mass interferences on a monatomic ion species are an overwhelming difficulty. The methods to resolve this need to be evaluated. Suppose that we also intend to determine the chemical composition of the sample based on the secondary ion intensities of representative isotopes for individual elements. A simple calculation reveals that the secondary ion population has a different chemical composition from the sample. The extent of the non-stoichiometry and the systematics within a matrix and among various matrices also should be studied.

Although only systematic relationships between intensity (in many cases intensity ratio) and concentration are needed for practical purposes (i.e. working curves), the observations made on complex systems should contain the information required for more generalized modeling of the sputtering/ ionization process.

In the following sections, we discuss some of the aspects involved in the sputtering/ionization process, and the problems arising from molecular interferences. We follow this with a discussion of the relationship between isotopic and elemental ratios observed in the secondary ion spectra compared to those in the bulk target sample. This provides the basic understanding necessary for developing quantitative analysis schemes; the last section is then devoted to presenting selected examples of applications of quantitative ion probe analysis to geochemical and cosmochemical problems.

2. A BRIEF DESCRIPTION OF THE SPUTTERING EVENT

It is useful at this point to visualize the succession of events which results in emission of secondary ions. Primary ions with kinetic energy in the keV range bombard the surface and produce energetic recoil atoms which, in turn, produce multiple collisions (collision cascade). During the collision cascade, some atoms acquire momentum that has a significant vector directed back to the surface. These atoms can transfer sufficient energy to a surface atom in a subsequent collision to result in the ejection of the surface atom. Since the efficiency of energy transfer in the "backward" collision cascade is low, and since the surface atoms have to overcome the surface binding energy, the ejected atoms leave the surface with relatively low kinetic energy (ranging up to a few hundreds of eV) compared with the keV energy of the primary ions.

Figure 1 is a simplified reproduction from Williams (1979), based on a computer simulation of the sputtering event (Harrison et al 1978), illustrating the movements of atoms during sputtering and the final state of the surface. It is important to note that a surface atom (Number 3 in Figure 1) is ejected by a collision with another surface atom (Number 2 in Figure 1), not with the primary ion, indicating that subsequent excitation and ionization is primarily controlled by the properties of the surface and surface atoms. It should also be noted that the time scale involved in the single event leading to the ion emission is on the order of 10^{-14} to 10^{-12} seconds. This suggests that under the normal operating conditions of an ion microprobe, a sputtering event caused by an impinging primary ion is completely finished before the next ion bombards the surface. Thus, the sputtering process can be considered as a succession of individual events. In addition, the surface state during the sputtering event is highly disordered to such an extent that the electronic structure of the surface may be different from the bulk crystal (Williams 1979). Thus, models of emission of ions and excited atoms based on the band structure of the crystalline bulk should be questioned.

Understanding of the dynamic aspects of sputtering involves evaluating how many atoms are sputtered per incoming ion (sputtering yield) and the kinetic

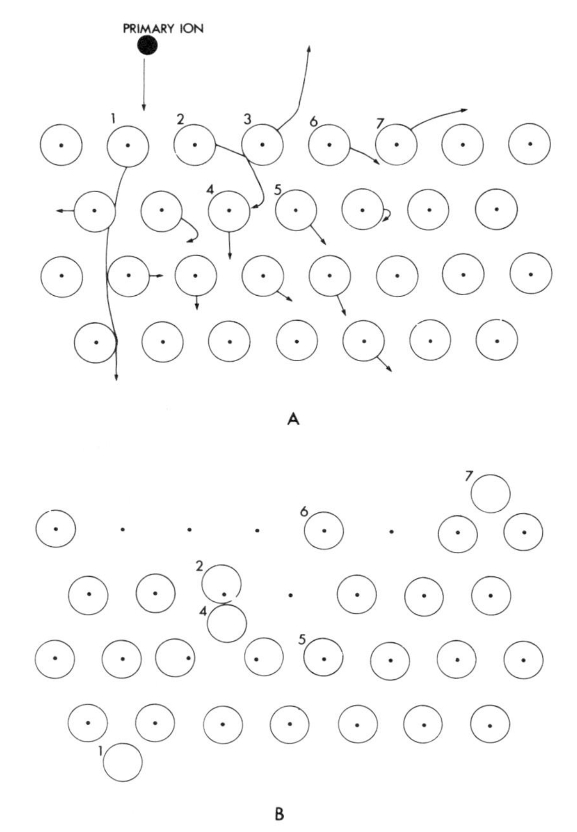

Figure 1 A simplified representation of atomic collisions during sputtering (from Williams 1979). (*A*) Bombardment by a primary ion (solid circle) causes collisions of atoms whose future trajectories are shown by arrows. (*B*) Final state of the surface after a sputtering event (10^{-10} seconds after *A*). Atom Number 1 is knocked into depth, Number 4 is in an interstitial position, and Number 3 is sputtered away.

energy level of sputtered atoms (energy distribution). The pioneering work by Thompson (1968) and Sigmund (1969) concentrated on formulating the sputtering yield and the energy distribution of the sputtered atoms on the basis of a random collision cascade model using a Boltzmann transport equation.

There is still much controversy as to where and when ionization occurs and how many ions are produced per sputtered atom, and no generally accepted model exists. Although there is a negative correlation between secondary ion yield and ionization potential (i.e. the lower the ionization potential, the more ions are produced), there are lines of evidence against the model of Andersen & Hinthorne (1973), which assumes that the sputtering region resembles a dense plasma in local thermal equilibrium (LTE model). Specifically, it appears that ionization occurs when a sputtered atom interacts with the surface rather than in a "cloud" of neutral atoms outside the surface, and the energy distribution of secondary ions may be different from that of the sputtered atoms because the probablility of ionization may be energy dependent (Sroubek 1974, for instance). A detailed account of ionization models is beyond the scope of this article and the reader is referred to Williams (1979).

3. MOLECULAR ION INTERFERENCES

It has been stated (e.g. Lovering 1975, Meyer et al 1974) that the mass spectra of geologic samples are overwhelmingly complicated due to the presence of molecular ion species. An important aspect of this complexity is that the measured isotope ratios are different from the values expected from the natural abundances. An example has been given by Shimizu et al (1978). They reported that even the major elements show significant molecular ion interferences judging from the isotope ratios.

Shimizu et al (1978) extensively explored energy filtering (originally suggested by Herzog et al 1973) as a practical way to eliminate molecular ion interferences. Energy filtering is based on the fact that the major types of molecular ions (oxides, dimers) have a distinctly lower high energy component than monatomic species, so that they can be practically eliminated by shifting the energy bandpass of the secondary ion optics to accommodate only high energy ions. However, there may be instrumental limitations, since the energy spectrum should be obtained before a specific bandpass is selected, and certain designs of double-focusing mass spectrometers cannot produce an energy spectrum. For instance, the Mattauch-Herzog design (utilized in ARL and AEL ion-probes) forms parallel rays between an electrostatic sector and a magnetic sector (i.e. focusing point at infinity) and therefore the energy spectrum, which is obtained by the electrostatic sector, cannot be observed. In contrast, the Nier design forms a crossover of rays between the electrostatic and magnetic sectors, thereby providing an energy spectrum for ions with a given m/e. This type of design is utilized in the Cameca IMS 3f and in the instrument designed and constructed at the Australian National University (Clement et al 1977). Vertical extraction of the secondary ions in the Cameca instrument (and the ANU instrument as well) makes it easier to select a specific part of the energy spectrum by adjusting the energy slit for a given width of bandpass, or by reducing the secondary ion accelerating voltage in a way similar to the retarding potential method utilized by Jurela (1973) in his determination of secondary ion energy spectra.

The data presented by Shimizu et al (1978) on the measured isotope ratios of various trace elements as a function of secondary ion energy (obtained with a Cameca IMS 300 instrument) demonstrated that the interfering molecular ion species could be essentially eliminated at a 150 eV level, where the isotope ratios approached the correct values. This has been confirmed on a Cameca IMS 3f instrument (see Figure 2).

An alternative method is to use a sufficiently high mass-resolving power of the mass spectrometer to resolve interfering molecular ions from monatomic ions. Steele et al (1976) recognized $^{44}Ca^{28}Si^{16}O$ and $^{28}Si_2^{16}O_2$ (among others) interfering with ^{88}Sr in a feldspar. With a mass resolution of 2300, $^{28}Si_2^{16}O_2$ can be separated from ^{88}Sr, whereas a mass resolution of 4050 is required for separating $^{44}Ca^{28}Si^{16}O$. Hinton & Long (1979) were successful in separating HfSi and HfO_2 species from Pb in zircon samples with a mass resolution of 3200. Figure 3 illustrates a mass spectrum at (resolution 7500) nominal mass number 29 on pure Si metal, obtained with a Cameca IMS 3f.

Energy filtering works at the expense of intensity, since the ion intensity drops strongly with energy (see Figure 10) in both monatomic and polyatomic species. The measured ion intensity drops also with increasing mass resolution due to decreasing transmission. Thus, the two methods should be compared on the basis of intensity loss (with required mass resolution versus required energy filtering) to resolve a given intereference. The intensity loss as a function of mass resolution is an instrument characteristic and Reed et al

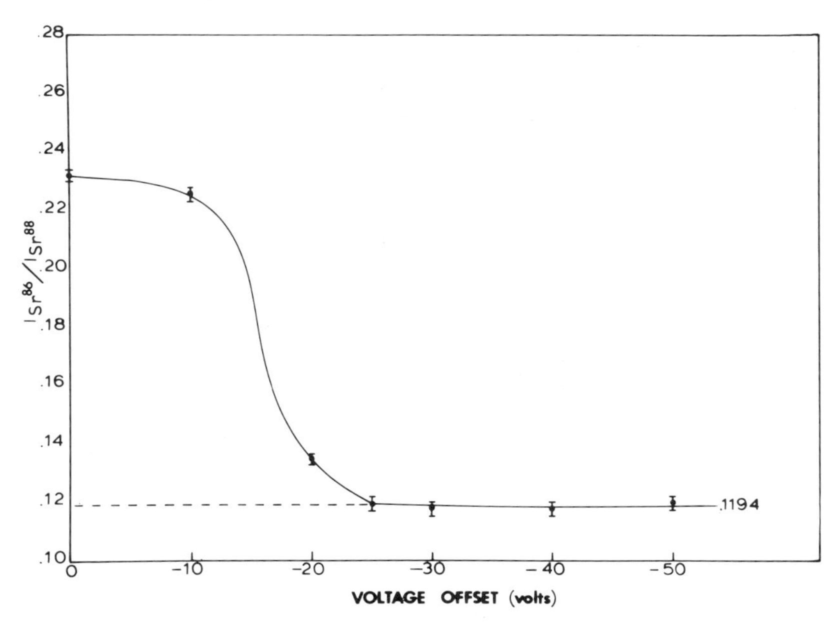

Figure 2 Variation of $^{86}Sr/^{88}Sr$ as a function of secondary ion energy, measured in a silicate glass standard containing 500 ppm Sr (from Ray 1980).

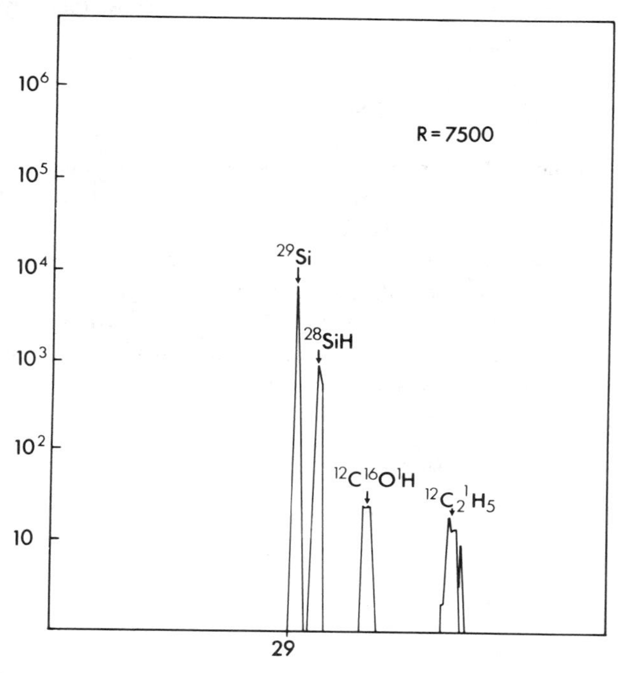

Figure 3 Mass spectrum of pure Si (NBS SRM 990) in the vicinity of mass number 29 taken with a mass resolution of 7500.

(1976) presented an example (seen in Figure 4) with an AEI instrument. Figure 4 was obtained with a Cameca IMS 3f representing typical operational conditions (not necessarily the best performance of the instrument). Also shown in the figure are relative intensities with various secondary ion voltage offsets. As Ray (1980) showed, an offset of 80 volts with an energy bandpass of $\pm$ 25 volts is sufficient for eliminating major interferences in analyzing trace elements (Ti, Sc, Sr, Sm) in diopside and silicate melts. The cross on the curve corresponds to the intensity loss at 55 volts (80-25), representing the edge of the energy spectrum selected. This corresponds to the intensity loss at a mass resolution of approximately 4500. If a mass resolution greater than 4500 is required to separate a specific interference, then energy filtering is preferred because of better sensitivity, and vice versa. Figure 5 provides an overview of the required mass resolution for various types of molecular ions as a function of mass. It is clear from the figure that a mass resolution greater than 4500 is required to resolve monoxide ions for mass numbers greater than 70. Comparing Figures 4 and 5, we conclude that energy filtering is favored in resolving molecular ion interferences for elements heavier than 70, a list which includes many trace elements. Figures 4 and 5 also show that for the major element mass range, high mass resolution is preferred.

4. ISOTOPIC FRACTIONATION

We can eliminate molecular ion intereferences either with energy filtering or high mass resolution. In the following sections, we therefore assume that all secondary ion intensities are interference free.

Suppose that we analyze isotope ratios of an element in a sample. Generally, the measured ratios are different from what we expect, i.e. isotopes are fractionated during the sputtering/ionization process. For practical purposes, analysis of a standard sample to determine a fractionation factor is sufficient if the standard is identical with the sample and if the analytical conditions are

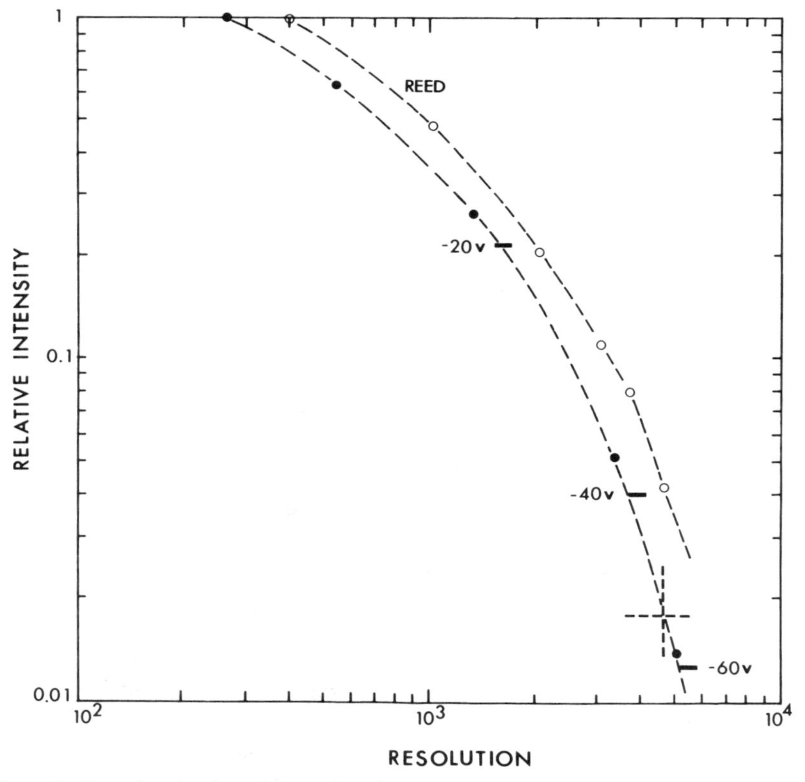

Figure 4 Secondary ion intensity as a function of mass resolution. Solid circles: Cameca IMS 3f; open circles: AEI, from Reed et al (1976). Relative intensities corresponding to 20, 40, and 60 eV levels of the energy distribution curve (Al used as an example) are also shown.

the same. However, we consider isotopic fractionation as one of the basic features of the sputtering/ionization process, because transport of energy and momentum from primary ions to the sample is the major part of the process and thus must involve mass-related effects. The mass-dependent term(s) in the relative sputtering-yield formula would be best determined by measuring different isotopes of the same element, because in isotopic systems chemical

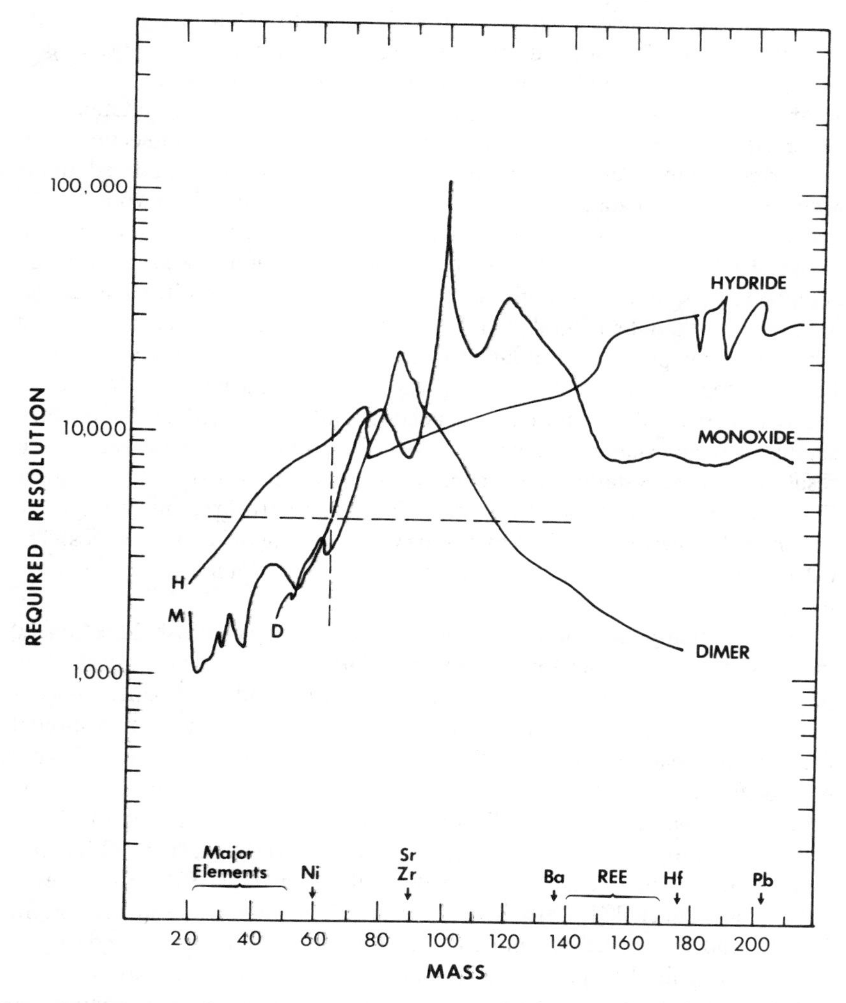

Figure 5 Required mass resolution as a function of mass for monoxide, hydride, and dimer. The dashed horizontal line represents required resolution of 4500 taken from Figure 4, as the crossover point of energy filtering and high mass resolution.

differences can be neglected. Conversely, any acceptable sputtering/ionization model must explain the observed isotopic fractionation.

Important questions to be answered regarding isotopic fractionation include the following: *(a)* Is isotopic fractionation related to the energy spectrum of secondary ions? *(b)* Is it related to the matrix? *(c)* What are the overall systematics of fractionation over the entire mass range and can the systematics be modeled by a simple mathematical formula? There have been very few systematic studies made on this question despite its fundamental importance. Russell et al (1980) studied fractionation of Ca isotopes in fluorite, plagioclase, and apatite under bombardment with high energy N^+ and N_2^+ ions, in an attempt to lay an experimental basis for the Ca isotopic fractionation observed in lunar soil specimens (Russell et al 1977) in connection with sputtering of lunar surface materials by the solar wind. The sputtered atoms were collected in a stainless steel "catcher cylinder," rinsed off with HNO_3, and analyzed by a mass spectrometer using a ^{42}Ca-^{48}Ca double spike technique. Their results show that with a 130 keV N^+ ion beam, the first Ca fraction to be sputtered is significantly light ($^{40}Ca/^{44}Ca$ in fluorite samples was 1.3% greater than the natural abundance ratio). This preferential sputtering of the lighter isotopes results in an enrichment of the sample's surface layer in heavy isotopes. The isotope ratio of the sputtered Ca becomes heavier as bombardment continues until it approaches the unfractionated ratio of the bulk sample as steady state is reached. This sequence is very well observed in their results on a polycrystalline fluorite (chip-A). A theoretical explanation of these observations was attempted by Watson & Haff (1980), in terms of the dissipation of the energy deposited by primary ions among different isotopes. The calculations yielded an initial isotopic fractionation of Ca in reasonable agreement with the data of Russell et al (1980).

The isotopic fractionation we observe in the secondary ions shuld be treated in terms of ion production during sputtering rather than during energy sharing, provided that data are collected under steady-state conditions, since the conservation of matter dictates that, at a steady state, the isotopic composition of the sputtered material should be the same as the bulk specimen. Recent work by Slodzian et al (1980) is one of the first attempts in this respect, although previous ion probe analyses of isotopic compositions (Mg, Li, etc) reported significant isotopic fractionation in the secondary ions (Lorin et al 1977, Steele et al 1976, Bradley et al 1978, Macdougall & Phinney 1979, Klossa et al 1981). Slodzian et al (1980) analyzed the isotopic compositions of Li, Mg, Si, K, Ca, and Zr in various minerals and observed *(a)* that secondary ion production of the lighter isotope was always enhanced relative to the heavy isotope, *(b)* that the magnitude of the isotopic fractionation was proportional to the mass difference, and *(c)* that the degree of fractionation was a function of the secondary ion energy. They also noted that Ca showed smaller isotopic fractionation in feldspar than in calcite, which was associated with a greater secondary ion yield in the feldspar.

A qualitative model proposed by Slodzian et al (1980) considers positive ion emission to be a result of bond-breaking, caused by collision cascades, of a cationic element from anionic groups existing in the lattice. The probability of ionization is formulated on the basis of the Landau-Zener theory of dissociation of diatomic gas molecules. With the use of a hypothetical potential energy diagram, Slodzian et al (1980) suggest that the magnitude of isotopic fractionation can be expressed as

$$\Delta_{ij} = \frac{aK}{V_c}\frac{M_{ij}}{M_j},$$

where $\Delta_{ij} = (R_{ij}/R_{ij}^{\circ} - 1)$, with measured (R_{ij}) and standard (R_{ij}°) isotope ratios

$$\frac{\delta M_{ij}}{M_j} = \frac{M_i}{M_j} - 1 \textit{ with } M_i > M_j,$$

a is a parameter related to the chemical bond between a cation M and the anionic group in the lattice, K is a function of mass and energy of the secondary ions and V_c is the relative velocity of M and of the anionic group. Although it is in general difficult to formulate a quantitative bond-breaking model for a solid (Williams 1979), Slodzian et al argue that the above formula provides a qualitative explanation of the data, in that K/V_c increases with increasing energy of the secondary ion, thereby increasing the fractionation, and that for a similar V_c, smaller values of a (associated with high ionization probability, i.e. high ion yield) result in smaller fractionation.

An independent systematic study of the isotopic fractionation of secondary ions was made by Shimizu & Hart (1981), who analyzed the isotopic compositions of B, Mg, Si, Ti, Cr, Fe, Ni, Cu, Ge, Mo, Ag, Sb, Re, and Pb in pure metal specimens with a O^- primary ion beam at 8.7 keV energy. These samples represent the simplest possible matrix for individual elements, ranging in mass from 10 (B) to 208 (Pb) and ranging in ionization potential from 6.77 eV (Cr) to 8.30 eV (B). Since the same results were obtained using two different detection systems (faraday cup and electron multiplier), the observed isotopic fractionation was indeed due to the ion production process, and not due to mass discrimination of the electron multiplier used in the pulse-counting mode. The possibility of transient isotopic effects can be ruled out because, for instance, the isotope ratios of Mo (92/100, 94/100) stayed constant (fractionated to 1.1% per mass unit) for more than 2 hours after the initiation of primary ion bombardment.

Shimizu & Hart (1981) observed that secondary ion production of the light isotope is always enhanced relative to the heavy isotope, an observation consistent with the work of Slodzian et al (1980). Figure 6 demonstrates that the magnitude of observed isotopic fractionation is linear with mass difference, also consistent with Slodzian et al (1980). Shimizu & Hart also found that the magnitude of isotopic fractionation is a function of secondary ion energy, with individual elements showing their own characteristic curves; these curves are not as simple as Slodzian et al (1980) suggested. For instance, Figure 7 illustrates the measured isotope ratios (note that ratios are always taken as light isotope/heavy isotope) as a function of secondary ion energy. In each case, an energy bandpass of 2 ~ 3 eV was used to obtain a sufficient resolution with respect to the energy. Typically, light elements show a maximum isotope ratio at 0 V, while heavy elements tend to have a plateau extending toward higher energy, suggesting that the energy dependence of isotopic fractionation, by itself, shows overall mass dependence. It was also observed that isotopic fractionation was variable as a function of position in a given primary spot due to heterogeneous spatial distribution of secondary ion

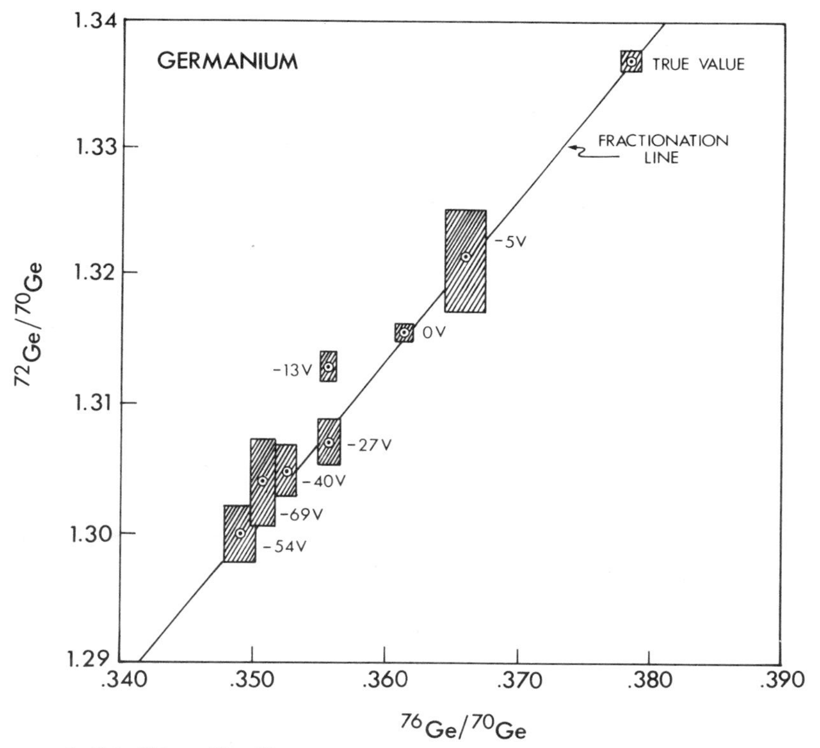

Figure 6 $^{72}Ge/^{70}Ge$ vs $^{76}Ge/^{70}Ge$ showing linearity of isotopic fractionation with mass difference. Data points represent different secondary high voltage offset values.

energy (see Figure 1 of Shimizu & Hart 1981). It is clear from the observation that attainment of accurate isotope ratios using ion microprobe techniques will require careful attention to the relative positioning of the primary ion beam and the secondary optical axis, as well as the position of any downstream field apertures. Figure 8 shows the systematics of isotopic fractionation as a function of mass based on the maximum value of fractionation obtained from the energy dependence curves (Figure 7). It is clear that the observed magnitude of isotopic fractionation is much greater than the square root of mass ratio and is closer to a simple mass ratio, although the data points in the low mass region are below (and in the high mass region, above) the curve representing a simple mass ratio dependence (Figure 8).

Shimizu & Hart (1981) suggested that the first-order features of the results are explained by the quantum mechanical ionization model proposed by Schroeer et al (1973). The model formulates the probability of ionization as that of the transition of the wavefunction of an electron initally in the conduction band to that of an electron in the ground state of a free atom when the quantum mechanical transition occurs as a sputtered atom leaves the surface. The probability of ionization modified according to the mass and mean energy of the sputtered atom is

$$R^{+} = \frac{A^2}{(I - \Phi)^{n+2}} \left(\frac{h}{a}\right)^{n} \left(\frac{2\bar{E}}{m}\right)^{n/2},$$

where A is the binding energy of the surface, a is the thickness of the surface, I is the ionization potential, Φ is the work function of the surface, $\bar{E}$ is the mean energy, m is the mass of the sputtered atom, h is a constant, and n is a fitting parameter. Assuming that A, I, Φ, and a are independent of mass, the ratio of the ionization probabilities of two isotopes of an element provides the factor by which the measured isotope ratio is fractionated from the true abundance ratio:

$$\frac{R_{\mathrm{L}}^{+}}{R_{\mathrm{H}}^{+}} = \left(\frac{M_{\mathrm{H}}}{M_{\mathrm{L}}} \cdot \frac{\bar{E}_{\mathrm{L}}}{\bar{E}_{\mathrm{H}}}\right)^{n/2},$$

where subscripts L and H denote light and heavy isotopes, respectively. Using the arguments of Gries (1975), $\bar{E}$ is written:

$$\bar{E} = A\,[2\ln(1 + E^{*}/A) - 3]$$

where E^{*} is the maximum energy that a sputtered atom can possess and is written using the energy (E_{p}) and mass (m_{p}) of the primary ion (if $m > m_{\mathrm{p}}$) as

$$E^{*} = \frac{4m\, m_{\mathrm{p}}\,(m - m_{\mathrm{p}})}{(m + m_{\mathrm{p}})^{3}} \cdot E_{\mathrm{p}} - A\,.$$

Curve III of Figure 8 was obtained from $R_{\mathrm{L}}^{+}/R_{\mathrm{H}}^{+}$ calculated for the elements

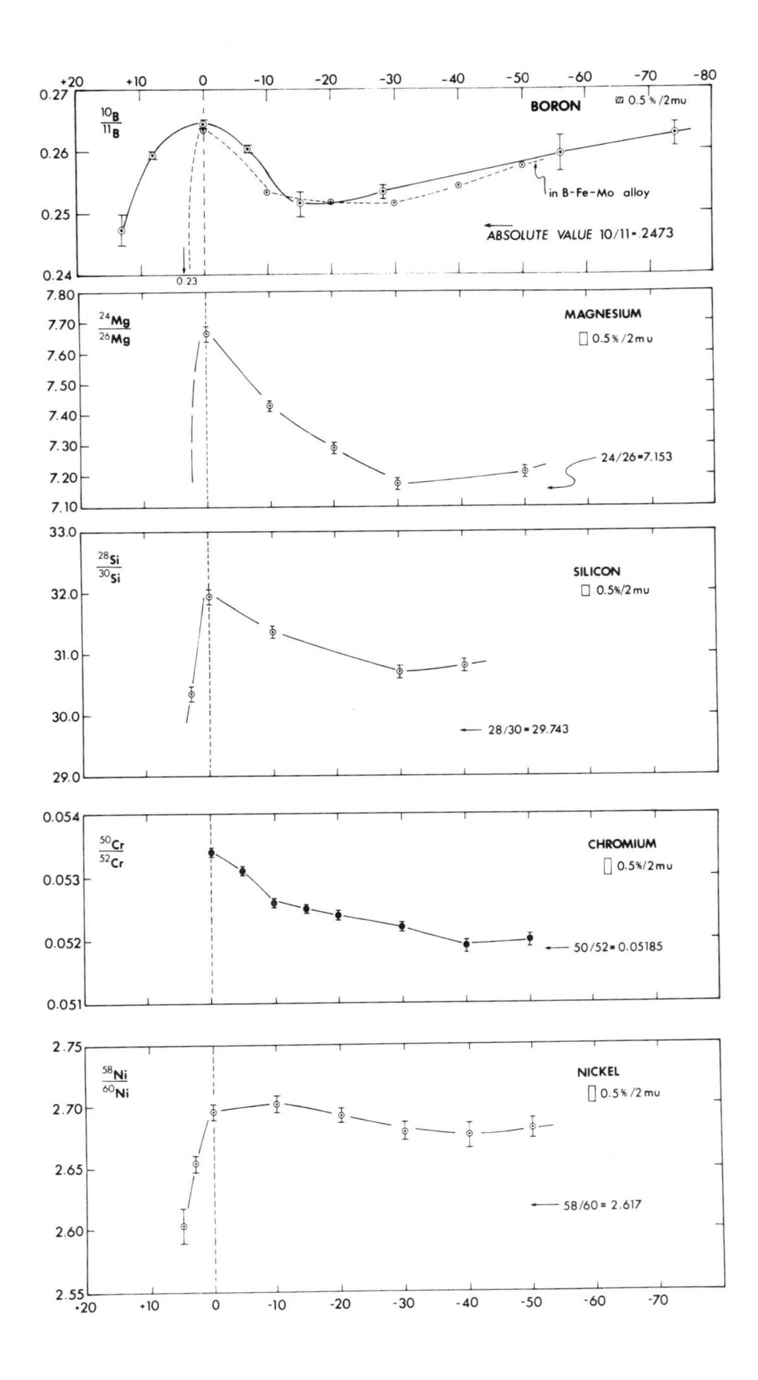
BORON
0.5 % /2mu
in B-Fe-Mo alloy
ABSOLUTE VALUE 10/11=.2473
0.23
MAGNESIUM
0.5 % /2mu
24/26=7.153
SILICON
0.5%/2mu
28/30=29.743
CHROMIUM
0.5%/2mu
50/52=0.05185
NICKEL
0.5% /2mu
58/60=2.617

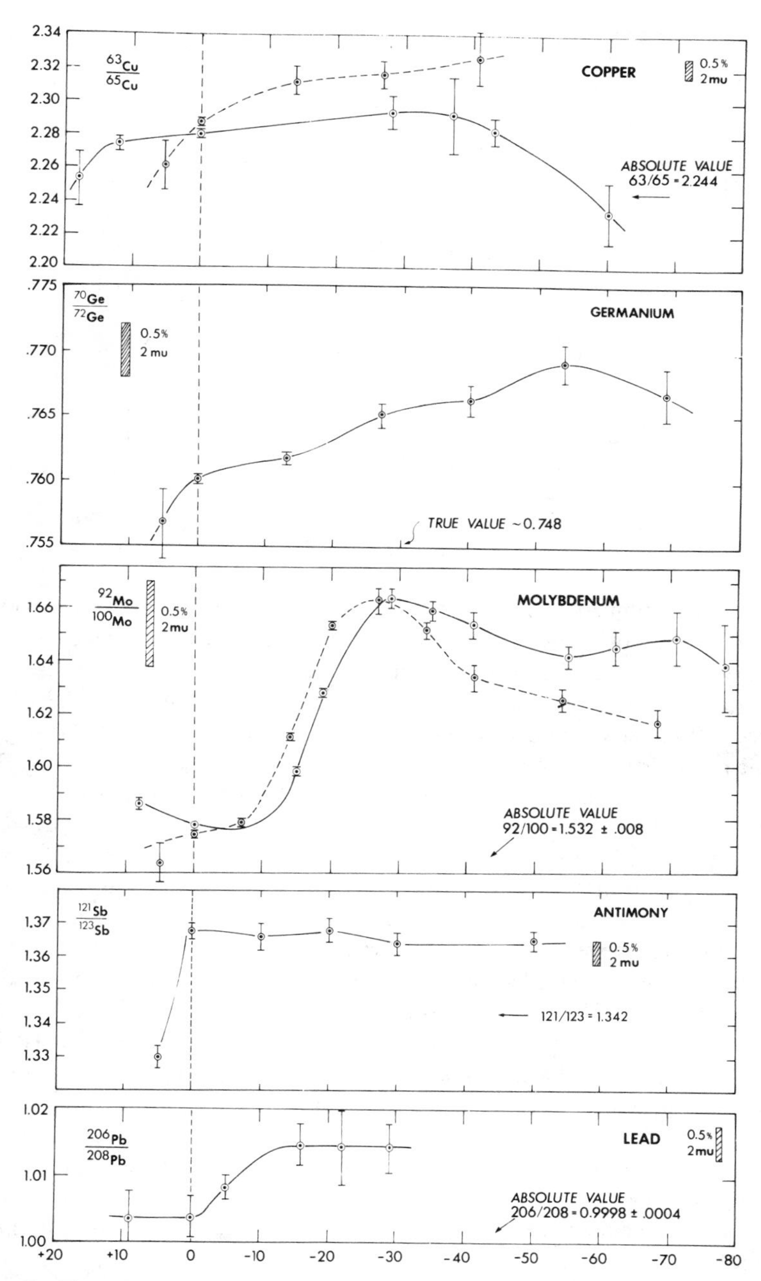

Figure 7 (above and facing) Variations of isotope ratios as a function of secondary ion energy. Data are on pure metal samples (from Shimizu & Hart 1981).

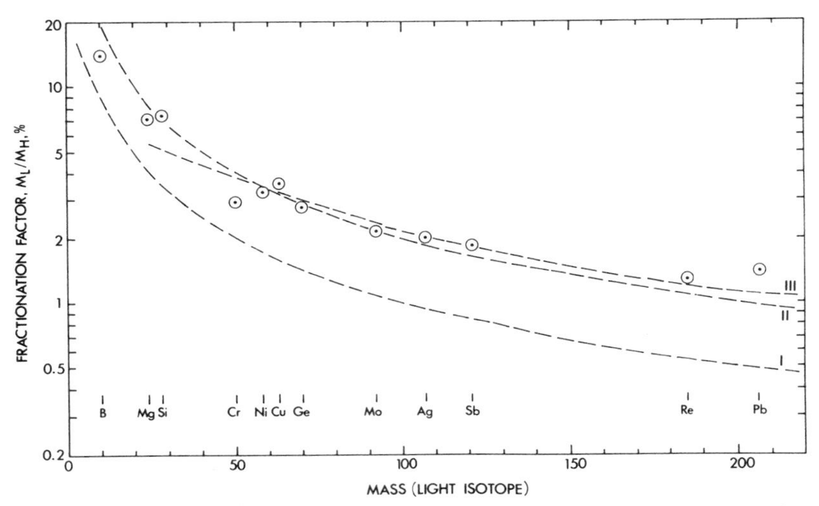

Figure 8 Isotopic fractionation factor as a function of mass. Each point represents the maximum fractionation observed. Curve I: $(M_L/M_H)^{1/2}$; curve II: M_L/M_H; curve III: R_L^+/R_H^+ with $n=2$.

studied by Shimizu & Hart (1981). Since Curve III is based on the mean kinetic energy of sputtered atoms and since the energy dependence curves of isotopic fractionation have a maximum at 0 V for Mg and Si, the discrepancy between Curve III and the Mg and Si data points could be minimized if the fractionation factor at the mean energy is plotted. It should be noted that in the high mass region, Curve III fits the data points better than Curve II. This model, however, is only applicable to metals for which the postulated electronic transition is reasonable.

As mentioned earlier, isotopic fractionation is the simplest example of the sputtering/ionization process in the polycomponent system and the work by Slodzian et al (1980) and Shimizu & Hart (1981) should be regarded as a new step toward its better understanding. For analytical purposes, it is advisable to choose well-documented standards of the same mineral type as the unknown. Thus, the study of Shimizu & Hart (1981) explored the various factors leading to large isotopic fractionation effects; systematic studies of this type also lead to identification of those conditions under which isotopic fractionation is minimal and most reproducible, so that these conditions can be employed during actual analysis. For example, in the study of Mg isotope anomalies reported by Lorin et al (1977), terrestrial plagioclase with a normal Mg isotopic composition was used as a standard and fractionation effects were minimized by collecting the data at a − 40 eV level, where $^{26}Mg/^{24}Mg$ in the standard plagioclase was found to be normal.

5. SECONDARY ION INTENSITIES IN POLYCOMPONENT MATERIALS

Given that the isotopic composition of secondary ion populations is different from the true value due to significant isotope effects during the ion production process, it is not difficult to imagine that the secondary ion population formed on the surface of an augite sample by O^- bombardment will have a chemical composition different from its bulk chemical composition. The problem is complex for polycomponent materials. Recent review articles by Werner (1980) and Wittmaack (1980) should be consulted for technical aspects. For example, differing ionization potentials, work functions, and binding energies of different elements complicate the interelement ratios of ionization probabilities and thus interelement intensity ratios. The dynamics of sputtering in polycomponent systems are also complicated by the complex energy sharing among atoms of different size, mass, and binding energy. Due to different sputtering yields, some elements are sputtered more easily than others (preferential sputtering) and as a result, it is generally observed that the surface composition changes as sputtering proceeds. Recent theoretical and experimental studies (e.g. Sigmund 1979, 1980, Kelly 1978, 1980, Okutani et al 1980, Betz 1980) show that in some cases a lower mass component is preferentially sputtered, whereas in others a component with a weaker bond to neighboring atoms is removed more efficiently. The change in surface chemical composition with time is depicted in Figure 9. The component that is enriched in the sputtered atoms is designated as L, and H is the component less preferentially sputtered and thus enriched in the residue. As the process goes on, the abundance of the L component in the sputtered population decreases due to the finite rate of mixing/diffusion replenishment of the component in the boundary layer (Figure 9*B*). Finally, at time t_s, a steady state is reached in which the sputtered population has the same chemical composition as the undisturbed interior of the sample. The same principle applies to the isotopic systems previously mentioned. The boundary layer thickness is considered to be similar to the range of the primary ions. In the case of 3 keV Ar^+ bombardment of Cu-Ni alloy, the thickness is approximately 40 Å (Okutani et al 1980). A similar thickness was suggested for Ca and Si in feldspar under bombardment of NO_2^- with 9 kV energy (Zinner 1980). Since secondary ion measurements in quantitative analysis and isotope analysis are made after the steady state is reached, the effect of preferential sputtering can be neglected in these cases. However, in depth-profiling, the possible effect of preferential sputtering may make it difficult to interpret the very-near-surface part of the profile.

At steady state, the sputtered particles have the same chemical composition

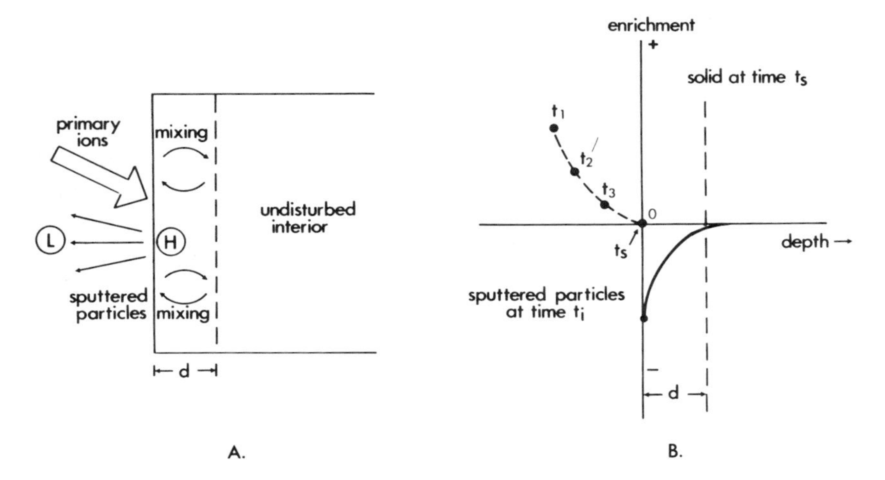

Figure 9 Schematic diagram showing the change in the surface chemical composition with time during transient sputtering. (*A*) Preferential sputtering results in enrichment of the L component in the sputtered particles and the residual solid is thus enriched in the H component. Mixing occurs over the depth range of the primary beam. (*B*) As the sputtering continues, enrichment of the L component in the sputtered particles decreases from t_1 to t_s as a result of the finite mixing rate. At a steady state, the sputtered particles have the same chemical composition as the undisturbed interior and the distribution of the L component in the solid at steady state is shown as a curve.

as the bulk solid. The fact that the secondary ion population has a different composition from the sample should therefore be attributed to the ionization aspect of the process.

As with isotopic systems, we will first examine the energy dependence of the secondary ion population because it seems to have an important bearing on the ionization process. Figure 10 illustrates energy distribution curves for ions (some major elements only) emitted from an augite from Kakanui, New Zealand. It is clear that Na shows a narrower energy distribution than the other elements, while Si is characterized by a greater high energy tail than any of the other major elements. If the random collision cascade model of Sigmund (1969) and Thompson (1968) applies to silicates as it does to pure metals and halides (Szymonski et al 1978), the energy distribution of neutral atoms is expected to be the same for all elements. (At an energy level sufficiently higher than the binding energy, the energy distribution is well approximated by E^{-2}.) It is therefore suggested that the variable energy distributions observed among secondary ions in the augite is a result of the different energy dependence of individual ionization probabilities of the elements. From his surface excitation model, Williams (1979) predicted that the ionization probability should decrease with increasing energy for elements with low ionization potential, such as Na.

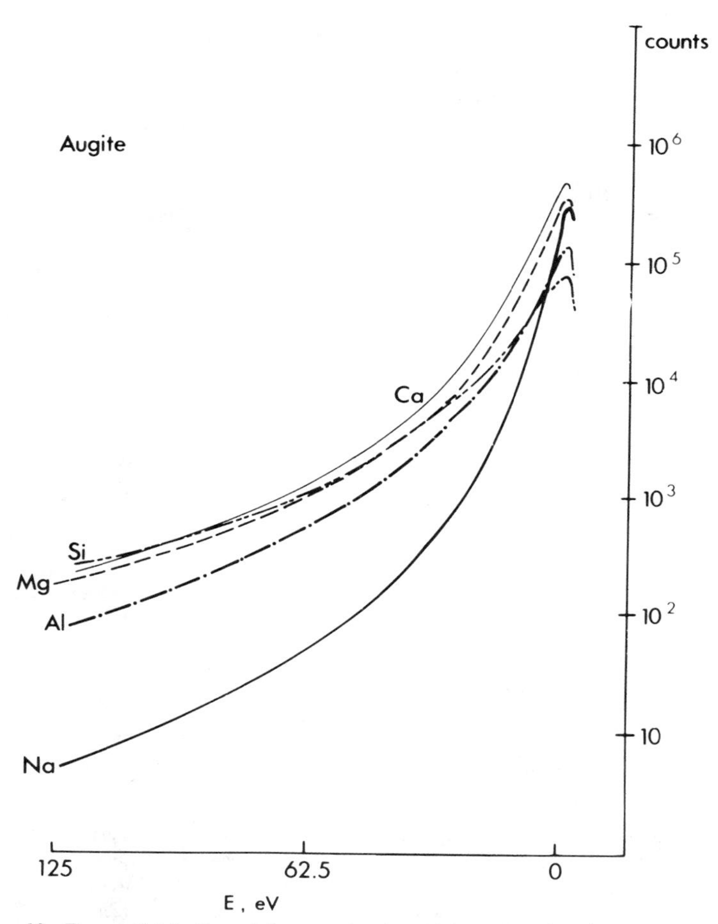

Figure 10 Energy distributions of the secondary ions Na^+, Mg^+, Al^+, Si^+, and Ca^+ in an augite.

Because of the variable energy distribution curves shown in Figure 10, we suggest that the composition of the secondary ion population is different as a function of energy. A low energy population must contain a high abundance of Na, while a high energy population is characterized by high Si abundance. Figure 11 compares the chemical compositions of ion populations at low (0 V) and high (90 ± 20 V) energy levels with the true atomic abundances of elements in the augite. To avoid the effect of molecular ions, the low energy ionic abundances were obtained using a mass resolution of 3600 (where $^{24}Mg^{16}O^+$ and $^{40}Ca^{16}O^+$ are clearly separated from $^{40}Ca^+$ and $^{56}Fe^+$, respectively). It can be seen that the ionic abundances in the high energy population are closer to the atomic abundance relative to the low energy

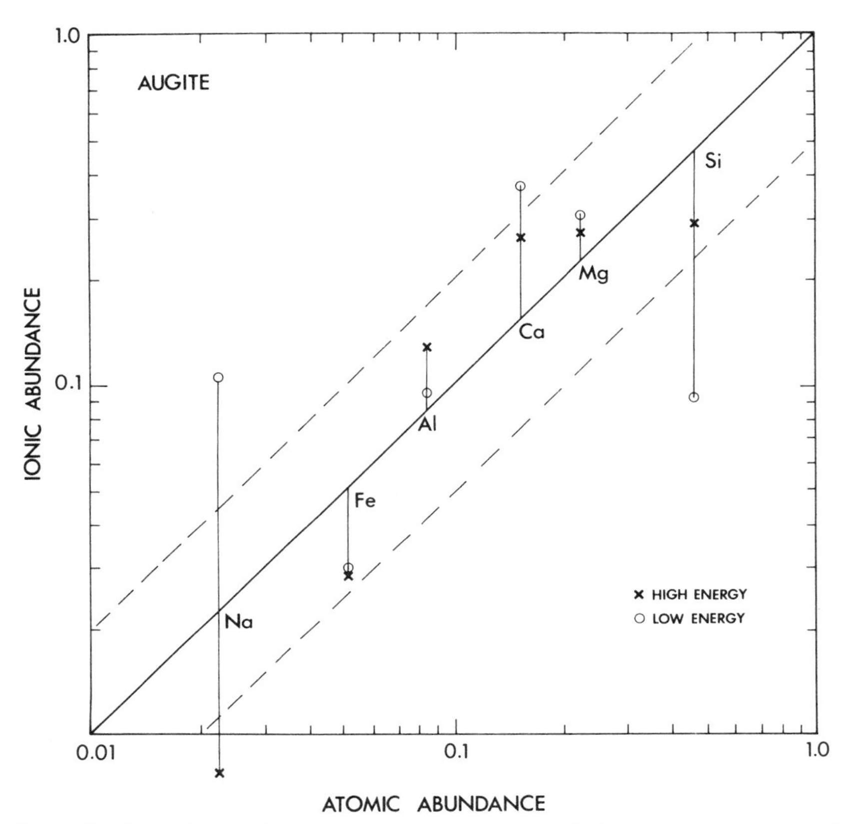

Figure 11 Comparison of atomic abundances of elements and the ionic abundance determined directly as fractional abundances of secondary ion intensities. The low energy ionic abundance was obtained with a mass resolution of 3600 and the high energy abundance was measured at the 90 ± 20 eV level. Note that the high energy ionic abundances are within a factor of two of the atomic abundances.

population (except for Na), suggesting that the high energy ion population is chemically less fractionated. It may be that at high energy, differences in ionization probability among elements become much less than the difference in ionization potentials.

With regard to high energy ions, Figure 11 shows some general characteristics of elements in various silicate matrices. For instance, Na is also much lower than atomic abundances in feldspar, indicating that the energy distribution of secondary Na^+ ions is similar to the Figure 11 distribution, regardless of mineral type. In contrast, Mg, Al, and Ca are always enriched in the high energy population relative to their atomic abundances in pyroxenes, feldspar, livine, garnet, and amphibole. Unfortunately, there is no model directly applicable to silicates that explains the energy dependence of the ionization probabilities of elements. The energy filtering technique discussed earlier not only eliminates molecular ion interference but also provides an opportunity to study energy-dependent ionic abundances in detail.

Attempts at developing a scheme for quantitative analysis with the ion probe have been hindered by another important feature: the so-called "matrix effect." The secondary ion intensity of an element in a mineral is a function not only of its concentration but also of the concentration of other element(s). This adds another dimension to the physics of secondary ion production, because the ionization probability of an isotope or an element that has been treated individually may have to include another term involving "interaction" among components. The bond-breaking model of Slodzian et al (1980) considers different ionization probabilities due to different interactions between a given cation and different anion groups, but a matrix effect is in fact observed within a given mineral. Shimizu et al (1978) noted that ionization of Ca was enhanced as a function of Fe in Ca-pyroxenes on the join diopside-hedenbergite. They also noted that in olivine, Mg ionization is enhanced as a function of Fe content. Subsequently, Reed et al (1979) observed that the secondary ion yield of Ni in olivine was also a function of Fe content, and Steele et al (1981) reported in detail of Mg-Fe relationships in olivine and low-Ca pyroxene.

By analogy to isotopic fractionation effects, metal systems may represent clear examples of polycomponent ionization processes. Two samples of binary Cu-Ni alloy ($Cu_{80}Ni_{20}$ and $Cu_{60}Ni_{40}$), together with pure Cu and pure Ni, were studied for systematics of secondary ion intensities. With an O^- primary ion beam of 8.7 keV energy, the secondary ion intensities were measured after 15 minutes of sputtering to ensure steady state. Assuming that the intensities of singly charged positive ions can also be treated as a binary between Cu and Ni, the intensity fraction I_x was calculated as $I_x = I_{Ni}/(I_{Ni}+I_{Cu})$ and plotted against atomic fraction X_{Ni} [$\equiv$Ni/(Ni+Cu)] in Figure 12. The data points are close to a curve with $K = 0.502$, where K is defined as

$$\frac{1}{1-X}\cdot\frac{1-I_x}{I_x} = K.$$

If we write

$$I_a = S_a \cdot R_a^+,$$

$$I_b = S_b \cdot R_b^+,$$

where I_a and I_b are the number of ions (secondary ion intensities) of components a and b of the binary system, S_a and S_b are the number of sputtered

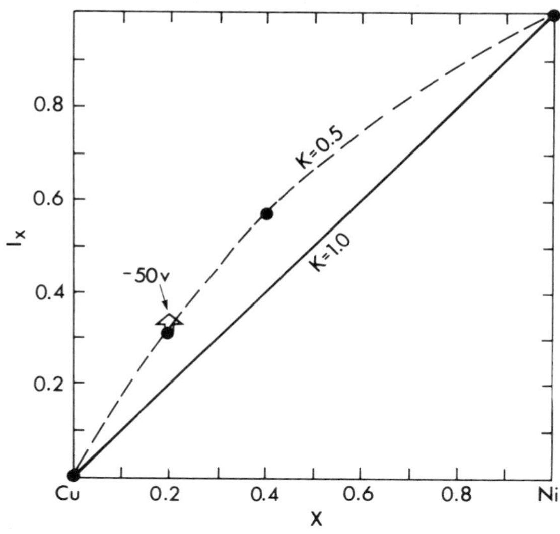

Figure 12 Relationship between atomic fraction and the intensity fraction in a system Cu-Ni. See text for explanation. The point at − 50 eV is to show that the high energy ions have the same composition as the low energy ones.

atoms of a and b, and R_a^+ and R_b^+ are the probabilities of ionization for a and b. Defining $I_x = I_a/(I_a + I_b)$, we have

$$I_x = \frac{I_a}{I_a + I_b} = \frac{S_a \cdot R_a^+}{S_a R_a^+ + S_a R_b^+},$$

$$\frac{1 - I_x}{I_x} = \frac{I_b/(I_a + I_b)}{I_a/(I_a + I_b)} = \frac{S_b R_b^+}{S_a R_b^+}.$$

At steady state, sputtered particles have the same chemical composition as the bulk sample. Therefore, $X = \dfrac{S_a}{S_a + S_b}$ and we can write

$$\frac{1 - I_x}{I_x} = \frac{S_b R_b^+}{S_a R_a^+} = \frac{S_b/(S_a + S_b)}{S_a/(S_a + S_b)} \cdot \frac{R_b^+}{R_a^+} = \frac{1 - X}{X} \cdot \frac{R_b^+}{R_a^+}, \text{ and}$$

$$\frac{1 - I_x}{I_x} \cdot \frac{X}{1 - X} = \frac{R_b^+}{R_a^+} (\equiv K)$$

Thus the secondary ion intensities data shown in Figure 12 in the Cu-Ni binary system may be interpreted with the above equation, with the ratio of the ionization probabilities being K. Using the model of Schroeer et al (1973), $R_{Cu}^+/R_{Ni}^+ = 0.39$ compared with $K = 0.502$. The discrepancy could be a result of the binding energies of Cu and Ni alloy being different from those of pure materials, thereby changing R_{Cu}^+ and R_{Ni}^+ from pure materials.

Steele et al (1981) reported that secondary ion intensities of Mg and Fe in olivines can be treated in the same way, although their data showed enhanced Mg ionization associated with suppressed ionization of Si. Our analyses of olivines at a mass resolution 4400 and at 0 eV energy confirm their results in that secondary Mg and Fe ions behave as a binary system. At a high energy level (90 ± 20 eV), the same behavior was observed with a slightly greater value of K. Our results differ from Steele et al (1981), however, in that the ionization of Si is not suppressed, thereby producing a linear relationship between I_{Fe}/I_{Si} and Fe/Si atomic ratios. Figure 13 illustrates the difference between our Cameca IMS 3f and the AEI instrument used by Steele et al.The effective secondary ion yield of Si in the AEI instrument seems much lower than the Cameca, a result which may be related to the complex secondary extraction geometry of the AEI instrument, in which the secondary ion intensities may be sensitive to sample surface conditions. The simple binary system behavior of Mg and Fe in olivine can be understood in the same way as the Cu-Ni system mentioned above. The observed K value (0.42 according to Steele et al (1981)) is the ratio of the ionization probability of Fe and Mg in the olivine solid solution. For high energy ions, $K = 0.63$, indicating that R^+_{Mg} and R^+_{Fe} are energy dependent, as discussed in the previous section.

A key issue on the interpretation of secondary ion intensities of silicates is the theoretical formulation of R^+_M in a given matrix as a function of energy. It seems clear from the above observations that R^+_M involves matrix effects, as

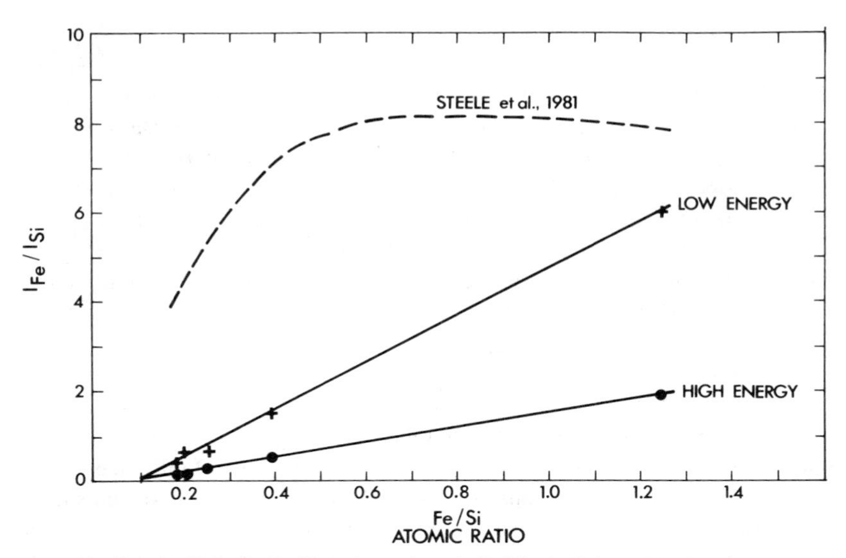

Figure 13 Relative intensity I_{Fe}/I_{Si} and atomic ratio Fe/Si of olivines. The dashed curve was obtained from Figure 4 of Steele et al (1981).

the ion yield of some elements are enhanced as a function of chemical composition. If an energy-related term of R_M^+ in polycomponent materials can be treated in the same was as in Gries' (1975) arguments used in the isotope fractionation discussion (p. 495), then the maximum energy may be rewritten to include the various collisions involved. For instance, consider a primary oxygen ion that is scattered by a Mg atom and then collides head-on with another Mg atom. Energy transfer efficiency in this series of collisions can be approximated by

$$\gamma_t = \frac{M_{Mg} - M_O}{M_{Mg} + M_O} \cdot \frac{4M_{Mg} \cdot M_O}{(M_{Mg} + M_O)^2} = 0.19.$$

If the atom involved in the first collision is Fe, $\gamma_t = 0.53$. As the abundance of Fe varies in the sample, the significance of the second type of collision varies, thereby changing γ_t, which in turn changes the energy term of R_{Mg}^+.

Despite these fundamental problems, an empirical aproach can be sufficiently accurate and convenient in determining the composition of minerals. For instance, forsterite content can be determined using the binary Mg-Fe curve; in addition, the linear relationship shown in Figure 14 can be used for the same purpose. Shimizu (1978) showed that the anorthite content can be obtained from the relationship between Al/Si intensity ratio and atomic ratio. This approach is particularly effective for trace element analyses and is discussed below.

6. TRACE ELEMENT ANALYSIS

Secondary ion intensities of trace elements can be, in some cases, modeled in a simple way relative to major elements, because only the collision between the matrix atom and trace element atom results in ionization of trace elements and the work function of the system can be approximated by that of the pure matrix elements. An example of such an attempt is Gries & Rüdenauer (1975), who combined Sigmund's formulation of sputtering yield (Sigmund 1969) and the ionization model of Schroeer et al (1973) and obtained the total yield of a singly charged trace element ion as

$$S_{tr}^+ = K \cdot C_{tr} \cdot \frac{B_{tr}^{3/2}}{(I_{tr} - \Phi)^3} \cdot \frac{M_m . M_{tr}}{(M_m + M_{tr})^2},$$

where C_{tr} is the concentration, B_{tr} the binding energy, I_{tr} the ionization potential, M_{tr} the mass of trace element, Φ the work function, M_m the mass of the major element, and K is a constant that includes the thickness of the surface and the nuclear stopping-power (approximated by the surface thickness and nuclear stopping-power of the pure major element system). The formula suggests that for a given trace element, the secondary ion intensity is proportional to the concentration.

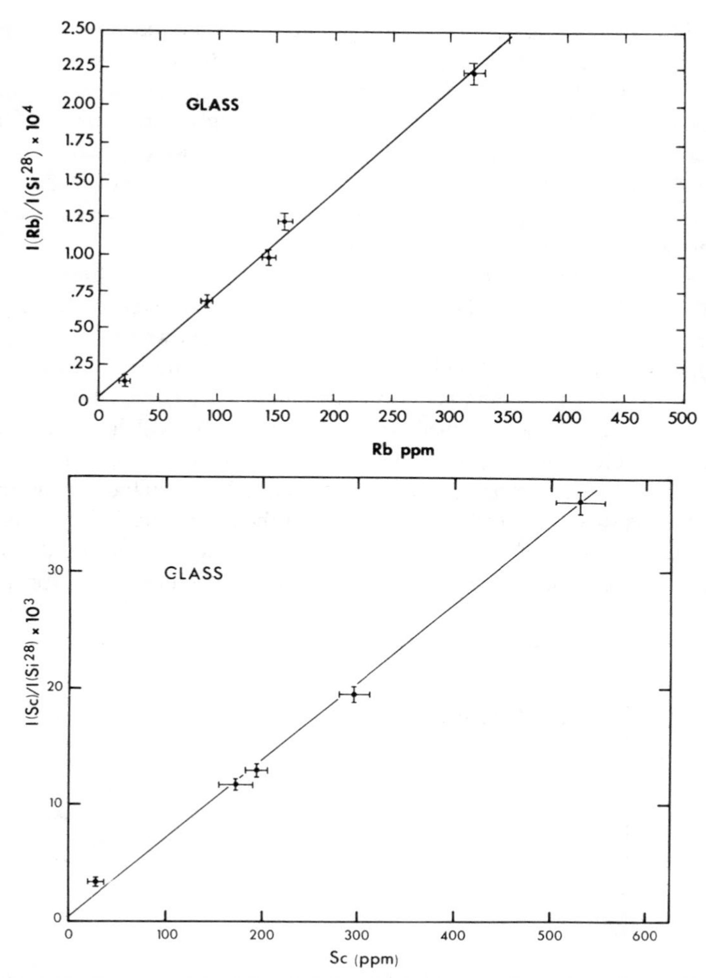

Figure 14 "Working curves" for Rb and Sc in silicate glass standards (from Ray 1980).

Empirical relationships between the concentration of an element and the relative intensity (intensity relative to Si) have been obtained for a number of trace elements in silicate matrices. Ray (1980) reported the "working curves" for Rb, Sr, Ba, Ti, Cr, Zr, and Sc in synthetic silicate glass standards with a major element composition within the diopside-albite-anorthite system. In addition to normalizing trace element intensities to that of Si, Ray (1980) further normalized the ratio to a constant Si content of $SiO_2 = 55.0$ wt %. For example, as shown in Figure 14, good linearity is obtained for Rb and Sc (correlation coefficients of $0.995 \sim 0.996$); it is significant that the regression lines pass through the origin within the analytical uncertainties involved. This is an additional assurance for the energy filtering technique, since any persistent molecular ions would result in the positive y-intercept. The slope of each line was obtained to within 5–10% precision, which serves as the limiting analytical precision encountered in this particular study. Since the slope uncertainty involves uncertainties in intensity measurements (counting statistics) and in the documentation of concentrations by other analytical techniques, improvement of the analytical precision of the "working curve approach" will require better documentation of standards.

Intensity vs concentration relationships were also obtained for Sr (Shimizu et al 1978, Ray 1980) and Ti (Ray 1980) in Ca-rich pyroxene, and they have been extended to include Sc, V, and Cr. Figure 15 shows the working curve of V in Ca-rich pyroxene. Steele et al (1981) reported similar relationships for Ca, Ni, Mn, Al, Cr, Ti, and Na in olivine and low-Ca pyroxene. Since linear relationships have been obtained for natural minerals, which cover a considerable major element compositional range, it is concluded that in general the matrix effect on trace element intensity is minimal. A notable exception is Ni in olivine, as Reed et al (1979) observed that the secondary ion yield of Ni in olivine is a function of Fe content. Steele et al (1981) confirmed this matrix effect, although they obtained a significantly different slope for the re-

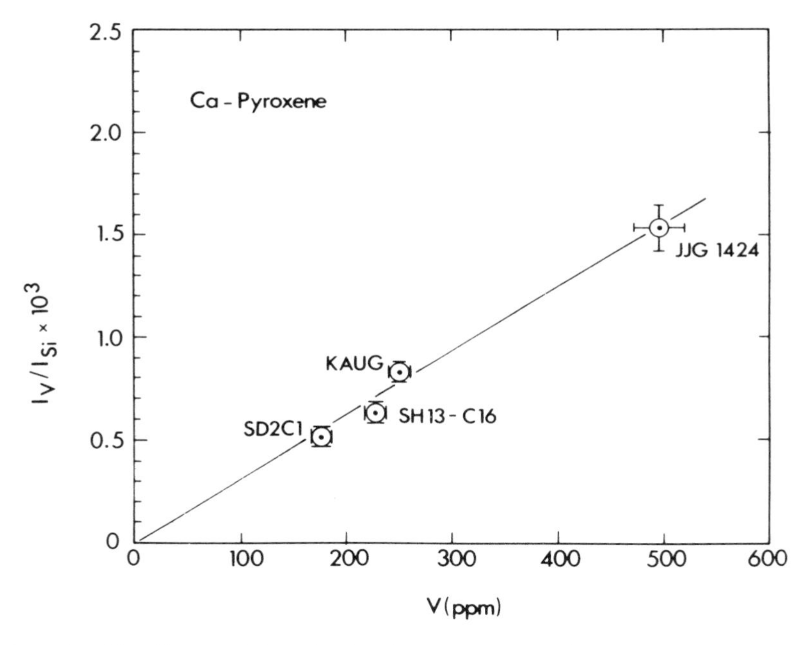

Figure 15 "Working curve" for V in Ca-rich pyroxene. V data for SD2C1 and SH13-C16 are by neutron activation (Shimizu, unpublished data), for KAUG are also by neutron activation (Mason & Allen 1973), and for JJG1424 are by XRF (le Roex, personal communication).

lationship between Ni/Fe and Fa content from that of Reed et al (1979). The fact that a trace element shows different slopes in different mineral types, as shown by Ray (1980) and Steele et al (1981), suggests that separate sets of standards will be required for each group of minerals.

7. APPLICATIONS

Distribution of Trace Elements in Minerals

Geochemical applications of the ion microprobe are based on its advantages over other analytical techniques including high sensitivity, low background, and the capability of in situ analysis of isotopic composition. This section reviews examples of successful use of the ion microprobe in researches in geochemistry from a problem-oriented point of view. Therefore, results and geochemical interpretations are highlighted rather than technical problems and limitations characteristic of the individual cases, for which the reader is referred to the cited references. The instrument's high sensitivity makes it possible to study partitioning of trace elements at concentration levels as low as the natural abundances, thereby circumventing possible complications due to the Henry's Law limit. These complications are often encountered in experimental systems using elevated trace element contents.

Ray (1980) studied the partitioning of Sr, Sc, Sm, and Ti between diopside and liquid in the system diopside-albite-anorthite at 1250°C, 1300°C, and 1345°C. The elements were selected to cover varieties ofgeochemical characteristics: compatible (Sc) vs incompatible elements (Sr, Sm, Ti); divalent (Sr) vs tetravalent (Ti); and possible inferences for clinopyroxene fractionation on Rb/Sr and Sm/Nd systematics. The major element compositions were selected to study the effects of composition on the partitioning. Using energy filtering to eliminate molecular ion interferences, Ray (1980) demonstrated that not only these trace elements but also major elements in both diopside and glasses showed linear intensity vs concentration relationships. From this observation, he determined trace element concentrations with a precision and accuracy of approximately 5 to 10%. The partition coefficients as well as the major element compositions of phases obtained for runs with different durations (ranging from 0.25 to 8 days), demonstrated that equilibrium was closely approached within approximately 4 days. The experiments made on a single major element composition yielded partition coefficients for Sr, Ti, Sm, and Sc; these coefficients were independent of trace element concentrations ranging, for example, from 23 to 517 ppm Sr in diopside. This covers a significant part of the natural concentration range, thereby indicating that Henry's Law is obeyed in the natural concentration ranges of these elements in clinopyroxene. Based on a series of isothermal experiments with different major element compositions, run at three different temperatures, Ray (1980) was able to calculate the enthalpy and entropy changes of exchange reactions involving trace elements. This was done using well-constrained linear relationships between the reciprocal of temperature and the natural logarithm of the equilibrium constant for specific exchange reactions. His results suggested that the Ti and Sr partition relationships can be useful as geothermometers, since errors involved in ln K vs $1/T$ calculations showed a precision in temperature to within $\pm$ 10°C. In terms of simple partition coefficients, his results agreed with previous attempts along the same line of approach.

Another example where use of the ion microprobe has clarified conflicting data from classical methods is in the study of nickel partitioning between diopside and melt by Steele & Lindstrom (1981). Experimental partitioning runs were made on samples spiked at natural and subnatural levels with a variety of Ni isotopes. Ion microprobe analysis of the charges not only documented Henry's Law behavior for Ni at low concentration levels (as opposed to previous studies using β-track mapping which argued for a failure of Henry's Law), but also revealed evidence for vapor transport of Ni between separate experimental charges run concurrently in the same furnace (leading to potentially serious errors in partitioning data determined with this type of experimental setup).

In contrast to the experimental studies in which one can demonstrate that equilibrium is closely approached, crystallization of phenocrysts from magmas can proceed under conditions of gross disequilibrium, thus producing chemically zoned crystals. If removal of such crystals from a magma drives igneous differentiation processes, it is important to describe how phenocrysts are zoned with respect to trace elements and to model the process of crystallization and trace element partition under disequilibrium conditions. Ion-microprobes have been used in in situ trace element analysis since the early studies of Meyer et al (1974), who described zoning of K, Sr, and Ba in a plagioclase crystal from lunar basalt 15555, and Shimizu (1978), who showed K and Sr distributions in plagioclase using samples from different magmatic environments.

The spatial resolution of such studies was much improved in recent work by Shimizu (1981), using a Cameca IMS 3f ion microprobe with a primary beam spot of approximately 5 ~ 8 μm in diameter as opposed to the minimum spot size of 20 μm used in the early work. He described distributions of major and trace elements (Sc, Ti, V, Cr, Mn, Co, Sr, and Zr) in a sector-zoned augite phenocryst in alkali olivine basalt, and used the results to examine the effects of kinetic parameters (such as the rate of crystal growth and the rate of diffusive transport of trace elements in the melt) on trace element partitioning. Traverses of the crystal with closely spaced points showed that the individual sectors were internally homogeneous from core to rim for all elements except Cr, which decreased from core to rim. The sectors were quite different, however, in chemical compositions. Figure 16 is an example of a traverse

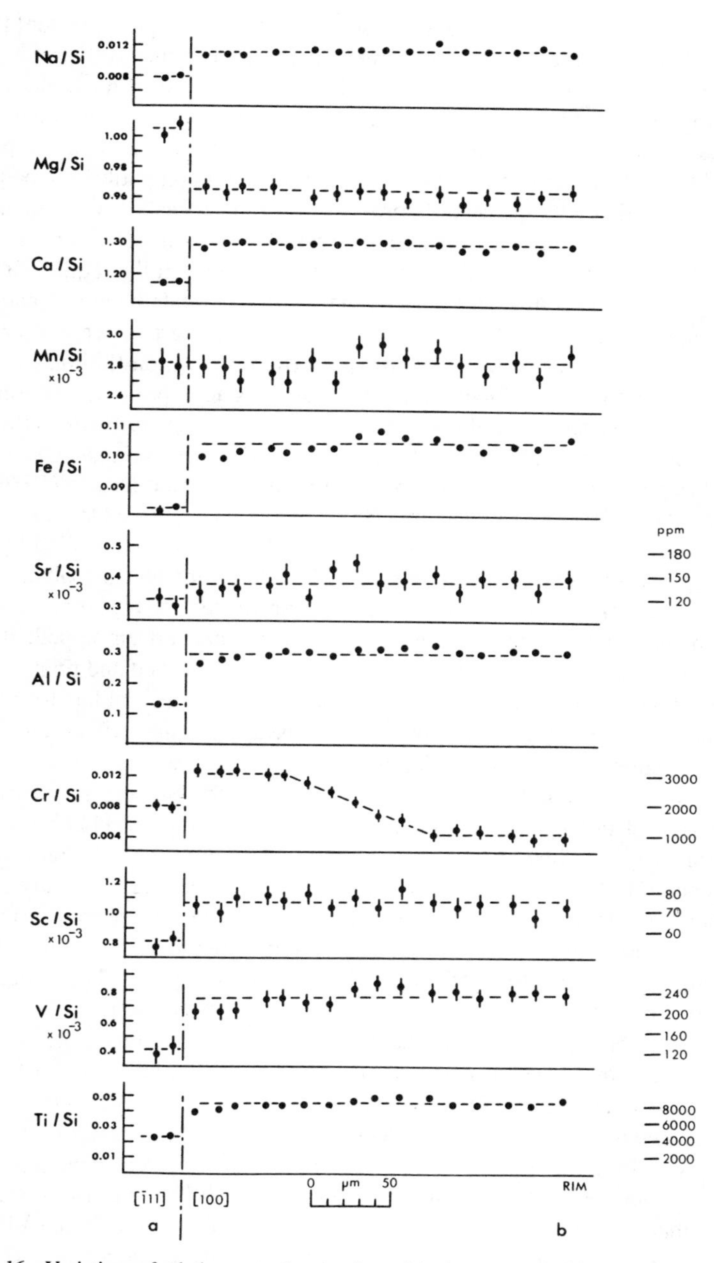

Figure 16 Variations of relative secondary ion intensities in a traverse of a sector-zoned augite, showing the difference between the [$\bar{1}$11] and [100] sectors and core-to-rim zonation in the [100] sector (from Shimizu 1981).

across the boundary between the basal sector [$\bar{1}$11] and the prism sector [100], primarily showing the core-to-rim element distribution in the [100] sector. The figure also shows that the prism sector [100] is enriched in most elements, including incompatible elements, such as Ti and V, and compatible elements, such as Sc and Cr. Since the basal sector [$\bar{1}$11] grew faster than the prism sector [100], the enrichment of both compatible and incompatible elements in the [100] together with the lack of core-to-rim zoning poses a difficult question as to applicability of conventional kinetic crystallization models. For instance, the model of Smith et al (1955), based on the assumption that equilibrium is attained at the crystal/melt interface, requires that crystals be zoned and that the apparent partition coefficient be closer to unity for greater rate of crystal growth; this is totally inconsistent with the above observation. Shimizu (1981) considered that interface kinetic processes, such as adsorption/desorption and reaction of melt species, could be the rate-limiting process, rather than the rate of removal of latent heat in crystallization of silicates from magma. The results were interpreted using the models of Nakamura (1973) and Dowty (1976) for the formation of sector-zoned augite. Shimizu (1981) suggested that the incorporation of trace elements into a growing augite crystal is controlled by two kinetic processes: one is the attachment of SiO_3 chains and the other is the adsorption/desorption of cations in surface protosites. If the attachment of SiO_3 chains is rapid, the adsorbed trace elements are left entrapped; if it is slow, however, the adsorbed atoms have time to be desorbed and finally reach an equilibrium concentration. The fact that the [100] direction has four times as many protosites (only 3/6 and 4/6 types are considered) as the [$\bar{1}$11] direction, coupled with the Coulomb interaction-type mechanism controlling the strength of adsorption of elements in protosites, results in an overall enrichment of elements in the prism sector [100] relative to [$\bar{1}$11], with the enrichment factor showing a strong positive correlation with the ratio of the ionic charge to the ionic radius squared. The significance of this study is that it presents a case where crystallization models based on surface equilibrium do not apply, and it suggests that the kinetics of interface processes are important. Mathematical formulation of trace element zoning patterns in interface-controlled crystallization is given by Shimizu (in preparation).

Trace element zoning patterns can also provide information on the nature of the magma body in which phenocrysts grow. A preliminary study of a plagioclase phenocryst from Terceira, Azores (Shimizu 1978), showed a sudden increase in Mg associated with a decrease in Fe and K, suggesting that the crystal was brought into contact with liquids with different chemical composition. The analysis of augite phenocrysts in alkali basalts from Terceira shows that they have concentric growth zones of different trace element compositions, with individual zones being internally homogeneous (Figure 17). It is clear that the crystal in Figure 17 is homogeneous with respect to Ca, Mg, and Fe (not shown), but multiply zoned with respect to minor and trace

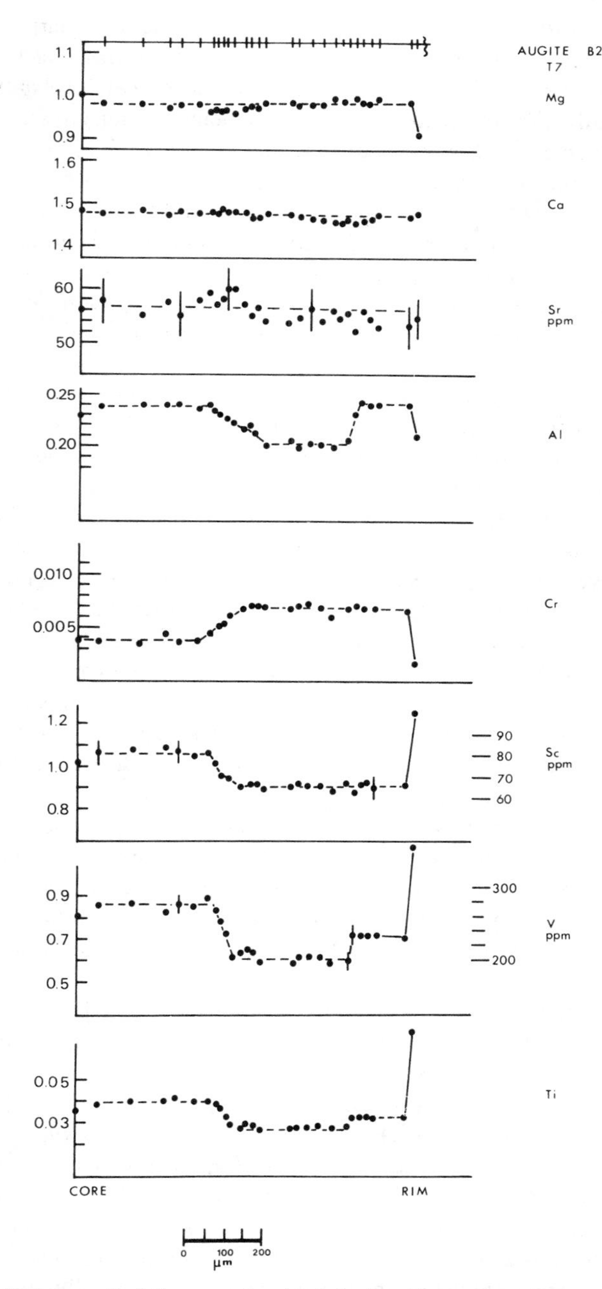

Figure 17 Variations of relative secondary ion intensities in a traverse of an augite phenocryst in alkali olivine basalt (T7) from Terceira, Azores (Shimizu, unpublished data).

elements. Transition from one zone to another is generally sharp within the spatial resolution of the analysis (5 ~ 8 μm), except for the transition occurring near the center of the crystal which is gradational, probably due to subsequent diffusion redistribution of the elements during growth. The two compatible elements, Cr and Sc, display antithetic variations from one zone to another, despite their similarity in geochemical behavior. Since the partition coefficients suggest that both of the elements should be depleted in the melt boundary layer adjacent to the crystal, crystallization itself is not the cause of the trace element variations from one zone to another. The results imply that the crystal was exposed to different liquids during its growth. The fact that some phenocrysts show repeated changes in Sc and Cr further suggests that the process is repeated many times during crystal growth. This observation is not consistent with the notion that a static magma chamber exists beneath a volcano, in which phenocrysts grow and sink, thereby driving the crystallization differentiation process. Instead, it suggests that the sudden changes of trace elements recorded in the augite phenocrysts represent changes of liquid composition due probably to batches of liquids successively introduced into the magma body. If this interpretation is correct, the trace element variations observed in bulk rock samples of lavas erupted from the same vent are probably the result of mixing of various melts, rather than fractional crystallization of a parental liquid, as is usually considered in trace element modeling. This observation also suggests that the repeated step-wise zoning, similar to that described above, is a common feature in augite phenocrysts in alkali olivine basalts from oceanic islands. The implication is that conventional trace element modeling based on bulk rock data should be reconsidered.

Inhomogeneity of minerals, particularly gradual changes in concentration of an element as a function of position, can be interpreted as a diffusion gradient, which in turn can provide information on the thermal history of a mineral. The observations made by Reed & Enright (1981) on the distribution of Ni in olivines in pallasites and of Ga and Ni in iron meteorites clearly are a start in this direction.

Water is an important minor constituent of minerals and silicate glasses that is difficult to analyze accurately. The ion microprobe's ability to analyze hydrogen is useful for quantitative analysis of water in geologic samples. Delaney & Karsten (1981) obtained significantly different linear relationships between the intensity ratio of $^{1}H^{+}/^{16}O^{+}$(corrected for wt % oxygen and water content) in basalt glasses, synthetic glasses of albite composition with different water content, and rhyolite obsidian samples, indicating a significant "matrix effect." They then applied the working curve approach to quantitatively map the water content in obsidian samples run in a series of hydration experiments, in order to determine the diffusivity of water in rhyolite melt. For runs with durations of 16 min, 1 hr, and 2.5 hr at 850°C and 700 bars, they obtained concentration profiles that suggested that the diffusion of water is dependent upon water concentration. Delaney & Karsten concluded that under these conditions the diffusion coefficient of water in the rhyolite melt may vary from 8×10^{-9} cm^2/sec at 0.2% H_2O to 1.2×10^{-6} cm^2/sec at 3.7% H_2O.

Analysis of Isotopic Compositions

Isotope anomalies The capability of an ion microprobe to analyze the isotopic composition of elements in situ provides a unique opportunity to study the isotopic inhomogeneity within a mineral. In addition, the ion microprobe is useful in studying isotopic compositions in a minor phase, particularly in cases where limited quantities of specimen are available, making laboratory contamination intolerably high. It is not surprising, therefore, that ion microprobes have been used in the studies of isotope anomalies in meteoritic samples. Since the discovery by Lee et al (1976) that ^{26}Al existed in the early history of solar system materials and is now observed as an exess of ^{26}Mg, studies have been made on Mg isotopes found in minerals in Ca-Al-rich inclusions in carbonaceous chondrite. An excess of ^{26}Mg due to in situ decay of ^{26}Al should be manifest in mineral phases poor in Mg and rich in Al, such as anorthite and hibonite. Lorin et al (1977) reported as much as a 13% excess of ^{26}Mg in anorthite grains in the Leoville meteorite, and Hutcheon et al (1977) observed up to 13.5% excess ^{26}Mg in anorthite from the Allende inclusions. They also observed variable ^{26}Mg excess in several anorthite grains positively correlated with $^{27}Al/^{24}Mg$, forming an isochron from which they obtained $(^{26}Al/^{27}Al)_{initial} \sim 4 \times 10^{-5}$. This value is slightly lower than that of Lee et al (1976). Other studies of the Allende inclusions all seem to confirm $(^{26}Al/^{27}Al)_{initial}$ ratios close to 5×10^{-5} (e.g. Bradley et al 1978, Phinney et al 1979). Discovery of the FUN (fractionation and unknown nuclear) anomaly by Wasserburg et al (1977) added another dimension to the studies of isotope anomalies, since both Mg and O in a single inclusion (Allende EKI-4-1) showed anomalies. Spinel and fassaite in the inclusion showed excess ^{25}Mg and ^{26}Mg of + 1.9–2.1% and + 3.4–3.9%, respectively. Clayton & Mayeda (1977) showed that the oxygen isotopic composition of inclusion density fractions formed an array in a $\delta^{17}O$ vs $\delta^{18}O$ plot, which is different from the mixing line between their "normal" solar system oxygen and an "extraordinary" component. Another Allende inclusion (Cl) showed an even more pronounced fractionation of Mg isotopes (up to + 3.2% and + 6.4% excess in ^{25}Mg and ^{26}Mg, respectively), whereas B29 inclusion showed depletion in both ^{25}Mg and ^{26}Mg. Since the available data suggest that the isotopic fractionation of Mg occurred during the formation of some of the Ca-Al-rich inclusions, it is important to verify if other phases (Mg-poor and Al-rich) in these inclusions have excess ^{26}Mg due to in situ decay of ^{26}Al. The ion probe data of Bradley et al (1978) of Mg isotopes in spinel from Cl are consistent with fractionated Mg isotopes. Macdougall & Phinney (1979) analyzed Ca-Al-rich inclusions in the Murchison meteorite (C2 chondrite) for Mg isotopes, and reported that hibonite in inclusion MH8 contains a large excess of ^{25}Mg ($8 \sim 10\%$) and ^{26}Mg ($16 \sim 21\%$).

A recent study by Huneke et al (1981) with improved spatial and mass resolution added ^{41}Ca to the list of extinct nuclides. Huneke et al found a small but clear excess of ^{41}K in pyroxene and anorthite in the Allende WA inclusion, which is correlated with Ca but not with K. Since the WA inclusion is known to contain excess ^{26}Mg due to ^{26}Al (Bradley et al 1978) in anorthite, the results suggest that both ^{41}Ca and ^{26}Al existed when the inclusion was formed.

Ion microprobe searches for isotopic anomalies of other elements include reports by Phinney et al (1979) and Klossa et al (1981). Neither group observed significant anomalies for Li in Allende meteorite inclusions.

Isotope zoning An example of isotopic inhomogeneity within a crystal was described by Cannon et al (1963), who analyzed different subsamples of a single galena crystal for Pb isotopes and showed that the ore solution that deposited the crystal became progressively more radiogenic with time. In view of the controversies regarding genesis of the Mississippi Valley Pb-Zn ores, it is important to know the isotopic variations of ore solutions in time and space as recorded by isotopic zoning of crystals; from this one could construct an "ore-fluid stratigraphy." The first attempts to use an ion microprobe for this problem were made by Brevart et al (1978) and Shimizu et al (1978), who analyzed the same crystal that Cannon et al (1963) described and found that an oscillatory isotopic variation was superimposed on the general trend reported by Cannon et al.

With the much improved spatial resolution of the Cameca IMS-3f instrument, Hart et al (1981) studied a galena crystal of octahedral morphology, collected from the Buick Mine, southeast Missouri. Based on repeated analyses of Pb isotopic standards (NBS 981 and 982), a galena standard from the Broken Hill Mine, Australia, and a direct comparison with the Pb analyses carried out by conventional mass spectrometry, they demonstrated that Pb isotope abundances in galena can be measured by an ion microprobe to accuracies of at least $\pm 0.1\%$ for ^{206}Pb, ^{207}Pb, and ^{208}Pb; and $\pm 0.2\%$ for ^{204}Pb. Figure 18 is a $^{208}Pb/^{206}Pb$ contour "map" clearly showing that the crystal is concentrically zoned with respect to $^{208}Pb/^{206}Pb$. Figure 19 shows that within analytical uncertainties, the data define a linear trend for $^{208}Pb/^{206}Pb$ vs $^{207}Pb/^{206}Pb$, consistent with the idea that the trend represents a simple two-component mixing relationship, i.e. the ore-forming fluid changed its isotopic composition with time depending on the relative contributions of two end-

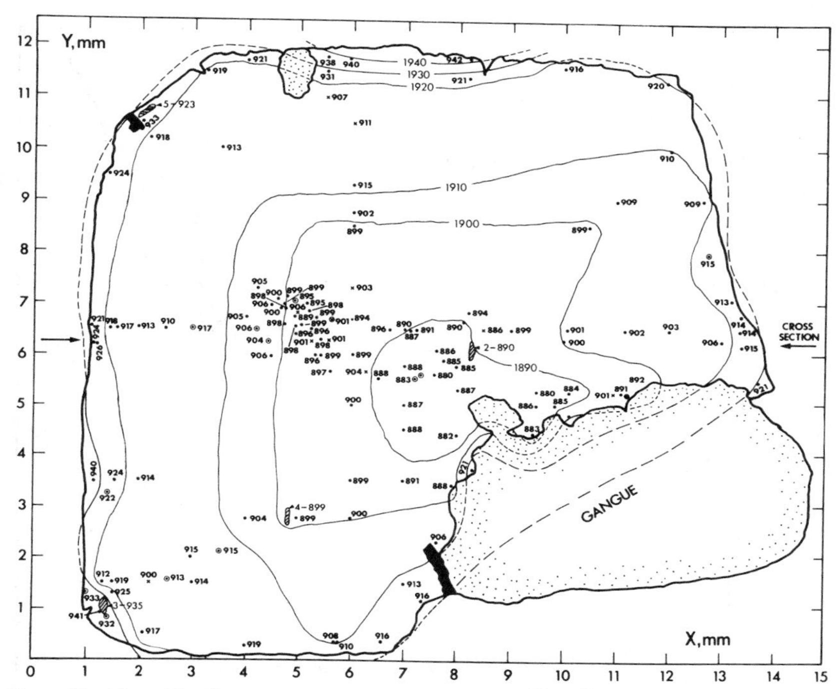

Figure 18 Map of [100] galena section showing contours of $^{208}Pb/^{206}Pb$ ratios. The numbers are postdecimal figures (913 means 1.913). Note concentric pattern originating from the dolomite gangue at lower right corner (from Hart et al 1981).

member sources of distinct Pb isotopic composition. The range of the isotopic composition found in a single crystal exceeds that of the entire mine (Sverjensky et al 1979). It is suggested that the octahedral stage occurred more or less simultaneously throughout the mine and involved substantially the same ore solution. The figure also shows that the Pb isotopic composition of galenas of cubic morphology, which postdate the octahedral galenas (Sverjensky et al 1979), is not co-linear with the octahedral galenas. Furthermore, it is evident that the later ore solution responsible for the cubic galenas is not simply further evolved from the solution that deposited the octahedral galenas, but must represent a new batch of solution. Its source must be more radiogenic than any of the solutions of the octahedral stage, and must be significantly different in Th/U ratio. Detailed studies of this type on individual galena crystals from a single mine and mining district could establish a Pb isotopic chrono-stratigraphic framework, and could then constrain temporal and spatial models for the circulation patterns of ore-forming solutions in the district.

In situ isotopic analysis of Pb has also been carried out in small (typically

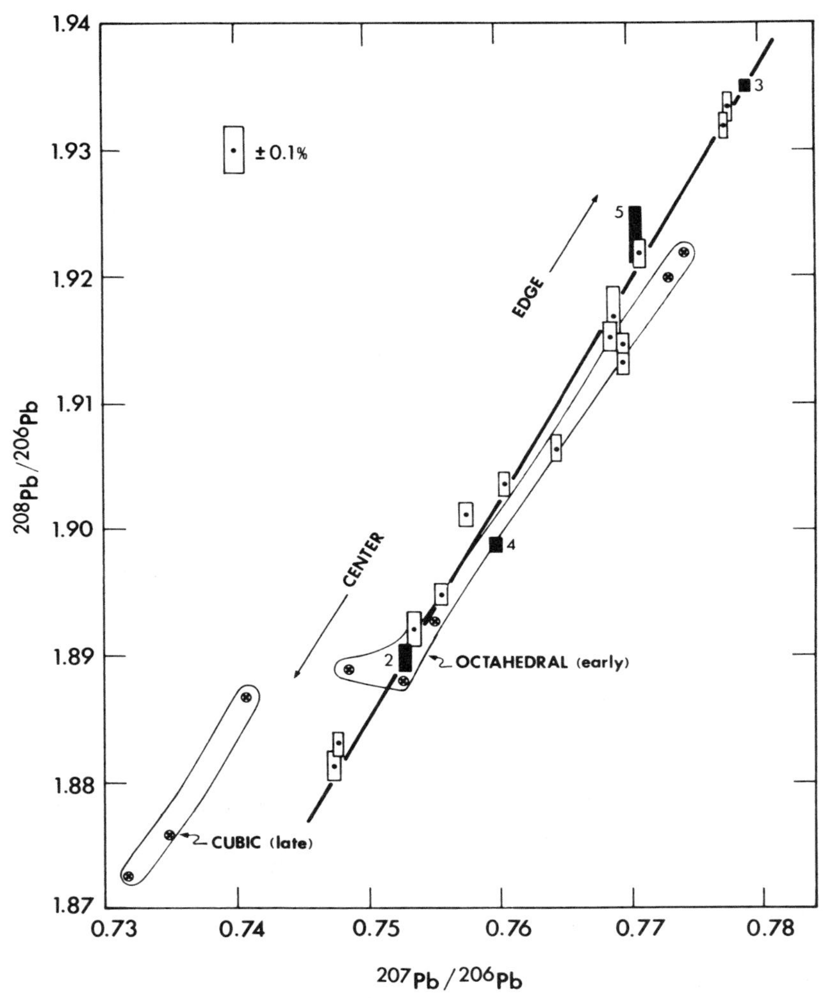

Figure 19 Plot of $^{208}Pb/^{206}Pb$ vs $^{207}Pb/^{206}Pb$ isotope ratios in Buick Mine galena sample. Open rectangles: ion probe data; solid rectangles: data obtained by conventional mass spectrometry; circled crosses: bulk galena samples by Sverjensky et al (1979). From Hart et al (1981).

10 ~ 20 μm across) blebs and veinlets of galena found in high grade uraninite ore from the New Quirke Mine, Elliot Lake, Ontario (Meddaugh et al 1981). If the galenas were formed during radiogenic Pb-loss episodes subsequent to uraninite formation, then the systematics of Pb isotopes in the galenas could provide constraints on the age of the uraninite ores. Because of the size of the galena and the low abundances of ^{204}Pb, ^{207}Pb, and ^{208}Pb, Meddaugh et al

obtained a precision somewhat lower than that of Hart et al (1981): 0.5 ~ 1% for $^{207}Pb/^{206}Pb$ and 2 ~ 5% for $^{204}Pb/^{206}Pb$. The data suggest that the large galena grains contain less radiogenic lead than blebs or small veinlets, and show a strong positive linear correlation between the $^{204}Pb/^{206}Pb$ and $^{207}Pb/^{206}Pb$ ratios and between the $^{208}Pb/^{206}Pb$ and $^{207}Pb/^{206}Pb$ ratios. Meddaugh et al interpreted the linear relationships as a result of two discrete mixing processes. A complete mixing of the crustal lead and the radiogenic lead released from the uraninite at time T_1 formed one end member of the observed Pb isotopic variation. Another mixing process between this and the radiogenic Pb released from uraninite at time T_2 generated the observed linear trend, because the second mixing process was not complete on a hand specimen scale. Based on the single-stage crustal lead at 2 b.y. and the least-radiogenic lead observed in the galenas, Meddaugh et al estimated the $^{207}Pb/^{206}Pb$ ratio of the radiogenic lead released from the uraninite, which in turn places limits on the time period between T_1 and the time of uraninite formation. They suggested that the uraninites must be at least 2100 m.y. old, and if T_1 is 1700 m.y., then the uraninite formation occurred at least 2450 m.y. ago.

Geochronology of uranium-rich minerals, such as zircon and monazite, is complex due to the overprint of later geologic processes (loss of radiogenic lead during metamorphism and/or overgrowth of young-generation crystals with different uranium content, etc), and the spatial resolution of the primary ion beam (5–10 μm) can be effective in determining U-Th-Pb systematics of individual grains. No complete geochronological study has been made, mainly because U-Th-Pb abundances have not been standardized in these minerals. However, recent work by Hinton & Long (1979) on the Pb isotopic analysis of zircons found in tonalite gneiss and granite from the Easter Lac Seul region, Ontario, clearly demonstrates that many grains are inhomogeneous with respect to the $^{207}Pb/^{206}Pb$ ratio, the cores having significantly higher values than the rims. Hinton & Long conclude, on the basis of the frequency distribution of $^{207}Pb/^{206}Pb$ ratios, that for the tonalite gneiss the minimum age of formation of the zircons is 3.3 b.y., followed by two periods of lead loss, one at 2.9 b.y. and another at 2.7 b.y.

A unique example of isotope analysis with an ion microprobe was given by Luck et al (1980) in their study of ^{187}Re-^{187}Os meteoritic chronology. The authors used an ion microprobe as a sputtering source mass spectrometer and successfully overcame the difficulty of handling small quantities of Os and of measuring Os isotope ratios precisely. Os was extracted from the dissolved meteoritic iron by CrO_3 oxidation, followed by distillation, and then converted to chloride and purified by anion-exchange column. The purified Os nitrate was loaded on a pure Al disc and run in an ion microprobe. The extracted Re nitrate was loaded on a separate Al disc and then run. They obtained precision of $\pm$ 0.2% for Re and $\pm$ 0.1% for Os. Their results on various classes of iron meteorites and metal phase separated from a LL6 ordinary chondrite (St. Sevrin) unequivocally demonstrated that the iron meteorites were formed with ordinary chondrites within a short time interval, as the data points fall on a well constrained Re-Os isochron. Using Rb-Sr and U-Pb data, the age of the meteorite formation was estimated to be 4550 $\pm$ 30 m.y. This age was then used to deduce the decay constant of ^{187}Re ($1.62 \pm 0.08 \times 10^{-11}$ yr^{-1}). They also estimated the age of the Galaxy to be between 13.3 and 22.4 b.y., based on the initial $^{187}Os/^{186}Os$ of the solar system obtained by the Re-Os isochron and on the model assuming an *s* nucleosynthetic process for Os isotopes and an *r* process for Re.

Diffusion Studies and Depth Profiling

In an experimental study of diffusion, a component is allowed to diffuse in a medium, resulting in a concentration gradient when the run is quenched. In the case of slow diffusion, the distance over which the gradient is produced in a reasonable time length is of the order of a few microns or less. For instance, a diffusion coefficient of $10^{-14}cm^2/sec$ and a run duration of 10 days (8.64×10^4sec) yield a diffusion distance of a little less than one micron. In order to study the concentration gradient, an analytical technique must have a spatial resolution much better than one micron. The spatial resolution of an ion microprobe can be improved greatly in a depth-profiling mode. This mode analyzes a gradient in terms of the variation of secondary ion intensity as a function of depth from the surface as the primary ion beam continuously erodes the sample while monitoring the secondary ion intensity. The capability of depth profiling, coupled with its surface analysis capability, makes an ion microprobe a unique tool for three-dimensional characterization of materials and, in fact, this capability was emphasized in an early review by Evans (1972). The principles and problems of depth profiling are well covered in a recent review by Zinner (1980).

The application of the technique to diffusion study in a geologic system was first attempted by Hofmann et al (1974), who analyzed $^{39}K/^{41}K$ ratios in a biotite flake (which had been reacted with an alkali chloride solution containing potassium enriched in ^{41}K) as a function of position. In fact, the sample was contoured three-dimensionally with respect to the K isotope ratio. The isotopic exchange equilibrium at the flake surface and a diffusive transport into the crystal resulted in a gradient of ^{41}K (and thus $^{39}K/^{41}K$ ratio). Applying a semi-infinite diffusion model with a constant surface concentration, the authors determined the diffusion coefficient of K in biotite as $D \simeq 1 \times 10^{-17}$ cm^2/sec in the c-direction. They also observed that in the a- or b-direction, the diffusivity was greater by a factor of 100 or more. The technique used in the study, isotopic exchange and depth profiling of an isotope ratio, was subsequently used by Giletti and co-workers in a series of studies (potassium in albite: Giletti et al 1976; oxygen in feldspar: Giletti et al 1978).

Figure 20 is an example of a depth profile obtained in a diffusion study of Sr in diopside (Sneeringer et al 1981, Sneeringer, in preparation). In this study, a diffusion couple was made of a piece of synthetic pure diopside and another piece of synthetic diopside containing Sr at the ppm level in direct contact, and Sr was allowed to diffuse into the pure diopside along its crystallographic c-axis. Since the Si intensity is constant throughout the profile and since the relative intensity I_{Sr}/I_{Si} in diopside is proportional to Sr content (Shimizu et al 1978), the Sr intensity data could be used to calculate the diffusion coefficient. Care must be exercised, however, because the observed gradient contains a spurious component from the sputtering process. For instance, some surface atoms are driven into the crystal during sputtering (see Figure 1, atom Number 1). This is known as the knock-on effect. Since the

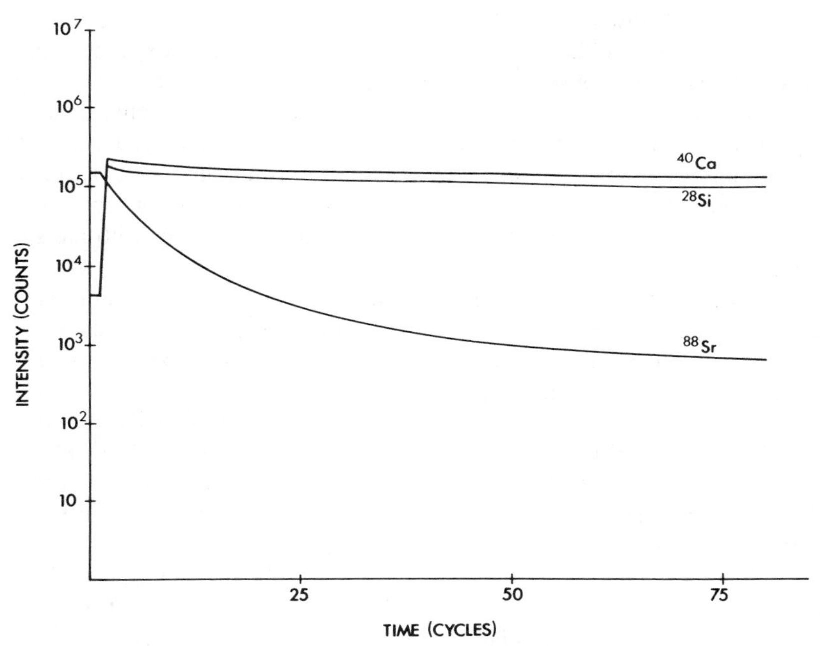

Figure 20 Depth profile of ^{28}Si, ^{40}Ca, and ^{88}Sr in diopside showing that the secondary ion intensity of ^{88}Sr decreases with depth. ^{28}Si and ^{40}Ca intensities were measured at their peak-tops for 6 seconds and ^{88}Sr intensity was measured at the peak-top for 60 seconds. One cycle of analysis consists of counting on each peak with a waiting time in between. A total of 80 cycles was obtained in approximately 4 hours, and the depth reached at the end was approximately 8000 Å. From Sneeringer (in preparation).

Sr concentration is higher near the surface, the knock-on effect broadens the diffusion gradient. Another source of uncertainty may be termed the "edge effect." As the primary beam bores into the crystal, atoms at the surface edge of the crater may be sputtered continuously and back-deposited on the crater bottom, where they are later sputtered again. Rastering the primary beam and selecting only the secondary ions originating at the center of the rastered area can reduce this effect, although quantitative evaluation is difficult. The result of knock-on and edge effects in broadening the profile can be empirically evaluated by analyzing a depth profile of Sr-free diopside with a surface film of SrO. Sneeringer (1981, personal communication) observed a Gaussian profile in this surface film due to the combined knock-on and edge effects, and this was subtracted from the observed gradient (Figure 20) in order to calculate the diffusion coefficient. Sneeringer's data shows that $D_{Sr} = 2.6 \times 10^{-15} cm^2/sec$ at 1250°C.

Other examples of the use of ion microprobe analysis in the determination of diffusion parameters are the works of Morioka (1981) on Mg diffusion in forsterite, Hallwig et al (1981) and Jaoul et al (1980) on oxygen diffusion in forsterite, and Hallwig et al (1981) on silicon diffusion in forsterite.

In addition to the effects noted above, diffusion studies of oxygen in minerals require another consideration. Since an oxygen primary beam is customarily used for minerals in order to achieve stable secondary ion emission, the oxygen atoms in the samples are mixed with those neutralized from the primary ion beam, and subsequent events ionize this mixture. As Giletti et al (1978) noted, the mixing reduces the observed $^{18}O/^{16}O$ ratio of the surface from the value expected by the isotopic exchange equilibrium with the surrounding fluid.

In contrast to the studies of slow diffusion mentioned above, fast diffusion in an experimental run product results in a gradient over a greater distance, so that the spatial resolution given by the primary beam spot size is sufficient. The gradient is traced by moving the spot laterally on the sample surface. An example of this type was given by Delaney & Karsten (1981) in their study of H_2O diffusion in a rhyolite melt. Another attempt was made by Nagy (1980) and Giletti & Nagy (1981). In these studies, the primary beam was moved along a perthite lamellae in order to determine the grain boundary diffusion coefficient of oxygen in perthitic feldspar.

Applications of depth profile techniques include the unique study of Zinner & Walker (1975, Zinner et al 1976, 1977) on the implantation of ions into lunar surface grains by the solar wind. Since the implantation is expected to be very close to the surface, where transient sputtering effects of the primary ions are significant, these authors artificially implanted various isotopes at energies similar to the solar wind so that in situ isotope dilution analysis was, in principle, achieved. Zinner et al (1977) and Zinner et al (1978) concluded that lunar plagioclase showed surface enhancement of Mg, Fe, and Ti. Although the source of the surface enhancement was ambiguous, the authors argued that the Ti/Mg ratios of the surface enhancement are, in many cases, much smaller than the bulk lunar soil, suggesting an extralunar source.

SUMMARY

Historically, the ion microprobe has fallen short of its promise in a number of areas, partly because of the difficulty of eliminating various molecular interferences in the secondary ion spectra, and partly because of the lack of a functional theory relating secondary ion intensities to the concentrations in the sample. The former problem can now be successfully overcome in most cases by the availability of instruments that can operate at high mass resolution ($\sim$ 10,000), and by the development of energy-filtering techniques. The latter problem, that of development of a quantitative theory for the sputtering/ionization process, has not yet been solved, though some advances have been made through systematic study of isotopic fractionation effects and of elemental abundances derived from simple polycomponent systems. However, many studies have conclusively shown that quantitative analysis can be achieved, even in the absence of a suitable theory, by use of well-documented standards that are close in composition to that of the samples under study. This approach can achieve accuracies of better than 5% at concentration levels of $\leq$ 10 ppm, and is limited in usefulness only by the difficulty of preparing or obtaining well-documented standards.

The ion microprobe is now unquestionably an analytical tool with a wide range of application in geochemistry and cosmochemistry. It has moved beyond the stage of being a prototype analytical tool. While its use still requires considerable care and effort, and while it cannot yet be considered a routine tool with, for example, the status of the electron microprobe, it has already provided geochemistry with significant advances into the areas of isotopic and trace element zoning on a microscale, elemental partitioning between phases, and the depth-profiling determination of diffusion parameters based on short ($< 10\mu$) profiles. It is our opinion that the ion microprobe is well on its way to revolutionizing the fields of geochemistry and cosmochemistry in much the same way that the electron microprobe revolutionized the field of petrology over the past decade.

ACKNOWLEDGMENTS

We thank K. D. Burrhus, D. S. Hall, and T. A. Miele for their professional assistance. This review was supported by NSF Grants, EAR-7922049, and EAR-8006642.

Literature Cited

Andersen, C. A., Hinthorne, J. R. 1973. Thermodynamic approach to the quantitative interpretation of sputtered ion mass spectra. *Anal. Chem.* 45:1421–38

Betz, G. 1980. Alloy sputtering. *Surf. Sci.* 92:283–309

Blaise, G., Nourtier, A. 1979. Experimental and theoretical approaches to the ionization process in secondary ion emission. *Surf. Sci.* 90:495–547

Bradley, J. G., Huneke, J. C., Wasserburg, G. J. 1978. Ion microprobe evidence for the presence of excess ^{26}Mg in an Allende anorthite crystal. *J. Geophys. Res.* 83:244–54

Brevart, O., Shimizu, N., Allegre, C. J. 1978. Intra- and inter-crystalline variation of Pb isotopic composition in galena from the Mississippi Valley type ores: An ion microprobe study. *US Geol. Surv. Open File Rep.* 78-701:49–50

Cannon, R. S. Jr., Pierce, A. P., Delevaux, M. H. 1963. Lead isotope variation with growth zoning in a galena crystal. *Science* 142:574–76

Clayton, R. N., Mayeda, T. K. 1977. Correlated oxygen and magnesium isotope anomalies in Allende inclusions, I: Oxygen. *Geophys. Res. Lett.* 4:295–98

Clement, S., Compston, W., Newstead, G. 1977. Design of a large, high resolution ion microprobe. *Int. Conf. SIMS, Munster, 1977.* 17 pp.

Colby, J. W. 1975. Ion microprobe mass analysis. In *Practical Scanning Electron Microscopy,* ed. J. I. Goldstein, H. Yakowitz, pp. 529–72. New York: Plenum

Delaney, J. R., Karsten, J. L. 1981. Ion microprobe studies of water in silicate melts: Concentration dependent water diffusion in obsidian. *Earth Planet. Sci. Lett.* 52:191–202

Dowty, E. 1976. Crystal structure and crystal growth: II. Sector zoning in minerals. *Am. Miner.* 61:460–69

Evans, C. A. Jr. 1972. Secondary ion mass analysis: A technique for three-dimensinal charcterization. *Anal. Chem.* 44:67A–80A

Geiss, R. H., ed. 1981. *A Bibliography of SIMS, 1976–1980*. San Francisco Press

Giletti, B. J., Nagy, K. L. 1981. Grain boundary diffusion of oxygen along lamellar boundaries in perthitic feldspar. *EOS* 62:428

Giletti, B. J., Semet, M. P., Kasper, R. B. 1976. Self diffusion of potassium in low albite using an ion microprobe. *Geol. Soc. Am. Abstr. with Programs* 6:754

Giletti, B. J., Semet, M. P., Yund, R. A. 1978. Studies in diffusion—III. Oxygen in feldspars, an ion microprobe determination. *Geochim. Cosmochim. Acta* 42:45–57

Gries, W. H. 1975. A formula for the secondary ion field fraction emitted through an energy window. *Int. J. Mass Spectrom. Ion Phys.* 17:77–88

Gries, W. H., Rudenauer, F. G. 1975. A quantitative model for the interpretation of secondary ion mass spectra of dilute alloys. *Int. J. Mass Spectrom. Ion Phys.* 18:111–27

Hallwig, D., Schactner, R., Sockel, H. G. 1981. In *Proc. 9th Int. Symp. React. Solids,* ed. K. Ryrek,. J. Haber, J. Nowotny. Elsevier. In press

Harrison, D. E., Kelly, P. W., Garrison, B. J., Winograd, N. 1978. Low energy ion impact phenomena on single crystal surfaces. *Surf. Sci.* 76:311–22

Hart, S. R., Shimizu, N., Sverjensky, D. A. 1981. Lead isotope zoning in galena: An ion microprobe study of a galena crystal from the Buick Mine, southeast Missouri. *Econ. Geol.* In press

Herzog, R. F. K., Poschenrieder, W. P., Satkiewicz, F. G. 1973. Observation of clusters in a sputtering ion source. *Radiat. Eff.* 18:199–205

Hinton, R. W., Long, J. V. P. 1979. High-resolution ion-microprobe measurement of lead isotopes: Variations within single zircons from Lac Seul, northwestern Ontario. *Earth Planet. Sci. Lett.* 45:309–25

Hofmann, A. W., Giletti, B. J., Hinthorne, J. R., Andersen, C. A., Comaford, D. 1974. Ion microprobe analysis of a potassium self-diffusion experiment in biotite. *Earth Planet. Sci. Lett.* 24:48–52

Huneke, J. C., Armstrong, J. T., Wasserburg, G. J. 1981. ^{41}K and ^{26}Mg in Allende inclusions and a hint of ^{41}Ca in the early solar system. *Lunar Planet. Sci. XII*:482–84

Hutcheon, I. D., Steele, I. M., Solberg, T. N., Clayton, R. N., Smith, J. V. 1977. Ion microprobe measurements of excess ^{26}Mg in Allende inclusions. *Meteoritics* 12:262 (Abstr.)

Jaoul, O., Froidevaux, C., Durham, W. B., Michaut, M. 1980. Oxygen self-diffusion in forsterite: implications for the high-temperature creep mechanism. *Earth Planet. Sci. Lett.* 47:391–97

Jurela, Z. 1973. Energy distribution of secondary ions from 15 polycrystalline targets. *Radiat. Eff.* 19:175–80

Kelly, R. 1978. An attempt to understand preferential sputtering. *Nucl. Instr. Methods* 149:553–58

Kelly, R. 1980. On the problem of whether mass or chemical bonding is more important to bombardment-induced compositional changes in alloys and oxides. *Surf. Sci.* 100:85–107

Klossa, B., Pierre, A., Minster, J. F. 1981. Mesure de la composition isotopique du lithium dans les inclusions refrectaires d'Allende. *Earth Planet. Sci. Lett.* In press

Lee, T., Papanastassiou, D. A., Wasserburg, G. J. 1976. Demonstration of ^{26}Mg in Allende and evidence for ^{26}Al. *Geophys. Res. Lett.* 3:41–44

Liebl, H. 1974. Ion microprobe analyzers: History and outlook. *Anal. Chem.* 46: 22A–30A

Lorin, J. C., Shimizu, N., Christophe-Michel Levy, M., Allegre, C. J. 1977. The Mg isotope anomaly in carbonaceous chondrites: An ion-probe study. *Meteoritics* 12:299–300

Lovering, J. G. 1975. Application of SIMS microanalysis techniques to trace element and isotopic studies in geochemistry and cosmochemistry. *NBS Spec. Publ.* 427: 135–78

Luck, J. M., Birck, J. L., Allegre, C. J. 1980. ^{187}Re-^{187}Os systematics in meteorites: Early chronology of the solar system and age of the galaxy. *Nature* 283:256–59

Macdougall, J. D., Phinney, D. 1979. Magnesium isotopic variations in hibonite from the Murchson meteorite: An ion microprobe study. *Geophys. Res. Lett.* 6:215–18

Mason, B., Allen, R. O. 1973. Minor and trace elements in augite, hornblende, and pyrope megacrysts from Kakanui, New Zealand. *N. Z. J. Geol. Geophys.* 16: 935–47

Meddaugh, W. S., Holland, H. D. Shimizu, N. 1981. The isotopic composition of lead in galenas in the uranium ores at Elliot Lake, Ontario, Canada. In *Ore Genesis '80,* Springer-Verlag. In press

Meyer, C. Jr., Anderson, D. H., Bradley, J. G. 1974. Ion microprobe mass analysis of plagioclase from "non-mare" lunar samples. *Proc. Lunar Sci. Conf. 5th,* pp. 685–706

Morioka, M. 1981. Cation diffusion in olivine—II. Ni-Mg, Mn-Mg, Mg and Ca. *Geochim. Cosmochim. Acta* 45:1573–80

Morrison, G. H., Slodzian, G. 1975. Ion microscopy. *Anal. Chem.* 47:932A–44A

Nagy, K. L. 1980. Experimental determination of grain boundary transport for oxygen along lamellar boundaries in a perthitic feldspar. MSc thesis, Brown Univ., Providence, R.I. 139 pp.

Nakamura, Y. 1973. Origin of sector-zoning of igneous clinopyroxene. *Am. Miner.* 58:986–90

Okutani, T., Shikata, M., Shimizu, R. 1980. Investigation on surface compositions of Cu-Ni alloy under Ar^+ ion bombardment by ISS and in situ AES measurements. *Surf. Sci.* 99:L410–18

Phinney, D., Whitehead, B., Anderson, D. H. 1979. Li, Be and B in minerals of a refractory-rich Allende inclusion. *Proc. Lunar Planet. Sci. Conf. 10th,* pp. 885–905

Ray, G. L. 1980. An ion microprobe study of trace element partitioning between clinopyroxene and liquid in the diopside ($CaMgSi_2O_6$)-albite ($NaAlSi_3O_8$)-anorthite ($CaAl_2Si_2O_8$) system. PhD thesis, Mass. Inst. Technol., Cambridge. 142 pp.

Reed, S. J. B., Enright, M. C. 1981. Trace element distributions in meteorites determined by ion probe analysis. *Proc. R. Soc. London Ser. A* 347:195–205

Reed, S. J. B., Long, J. V. P., Coles, J. N., Astill, D. M. 1976. Ion microprobe trace element analysis with high mass resolution. *Int. J. Mass Spectrom. Ion Phys.* 22:333–38

Reed, S. J. B., Scott, E. R. D., Long, J. V. P. 1979. Ion microprobe analysis of olivine in pallasite meteorites for nickel. *Earth Planet. Sci. Lett.* 43:5–12

Russell, W. A., Papanastassiou, D. A., Tombrello, T. A., Epstein, S. 1977. Ca isotope fractionation on the moon. *Proc. Lunar Sci. Conf. 8th,* pp. 3791–805

Russell, W. A., Papanastassiou, D. A., Tombrello, T. A. 1980. The fractionation of Ca isotopes by sputtering. *Radiat. Eff.* 52: 41–52

Schroeer, J. M., Rhodin, T. N., Bradley, R. C. 1973. A quantum-mechanical model for the ionization and excitation of atoms during sputtering. *Surf. Sci.* 34:571–80

Shimizu, N. 1978. Analysis of zoned plagioclase of different magmatic environments: A preliminary ion-microprobe study. *Earth Planet. Sci. Lett.* 39:398–406

Shimizu, N. 1981. Trace element incorporation into growing augite phenocryst. *Nature* 289:575–77

Shimizu, N., Hart, S. R. 1981. Isotope fractionation in secondary ion mass spectrometry. *J. Appl. Phys.* In press

Shimizu, N., Semet, M. P., Allegre, C. J. 1978. Geochemical applications of quantitative ion-microprobe analysis. *Geochim. Cosmochim. Acta* 42:1321–34

Sigmund, P. 1969. Theory of sputtering I. Sputtering yield of amorphous and polycrystalline targets. *Phys. Rev.* 184:383–416

Sigmund, P. 1979. Recoil implantation and ion-beam-induced composition changes in alloys and compounds. *J. Appl. Phys.* 50: 7261–63

Sigmund, P. 1980. Sputtering of single and multiple component materials. *J. Vac. Sci. Technol.* 17:396–99

Slodzian, G., Lorin, J. C., Havette, A. 1980. Isotopic effect on the ionization probabilities in secondary ion emission. *J. Phys.* 23: 555–58

Smith, V. G., Tiller, W. A., Rutter, J. W.

1955. A mathematical analysis of solute redistribution during solidification. *Can. J. Phys.* 33:723–45

Sneeringer, M., Hart, S. R., Shimizu, N. 1981. Diffusion of strontium in diopside: A comparison of ion microprobe and radiotracer analytical methods. *EOS* 62:137–38

Sroubek, Z. 1974. The theoretical and experimental study of the ionization processes during the low energy ion sputtering. *Surf. Sci.* 44:47–59

Steele, I. M., Hutcheon, I. D., Smith, J. V. 1976. Ion microprobe analysis of plagioclase feldspars. *Geol. Soc. Am. Abstr. with Programs* 8:1119

Steele, I. M., Hervig, R. L., Hutcheon, I. D., Smith, J. V. 1981. Ion microprobe techniques and analyses of olivine and low Ca pyroxene. *Am. Mineral.* 66:526–46

Steele, I. M., Lindstrom, D. J. 1981. Ni partitioning between diopside and silicate melt: a redetermination by ion microprobe and recognition of an experimental complication. *Geochim. Cosmochim. Acta* 45. In press

Sverjensky, D. A., Rye, D. M., Doe, B. R. 1979. The lead and sulfur isotopic compositions of galena from a Mississippi Valley-type deposit in the New Lead Belt, southeast Missouri. *Econ. Geol.* 74:149–53

Szymonski, M., Overeijnder, H., de Vries, A. E. 1978. The sputtering process during 6 keV Xe ion beam bombardment of halides. *Radiat. Eff.* 36:189–96

Thompson, M. W. 1968. The energy spectrum of ejected atoms during the high energy sputtering of gold. *Philos. Mag.* 18: 374–414

Wasserburg, G. J., Lee, T., Papanastassiou, D. A. 1977. Correlated O and Mg isotopic anomalies in Allende inclusions: II. Magnesium. *Geophys. Res. Lett.* 4:299–302

Watson, C. C., Haff, P. K. 1980. Sputter-induced isotopic fractionation at solid surfaces. *J. Appl. Phys.* 51:691–99

Werner, H. W. 1978. Introduction to secondary ion mass spectrometry (SIMS). In *Proc. Adv. Study Inst. Electron Ion Spectrosc. Solids*, pp. 324–441. New York: Plenum Press

Werner, H. W. 1980. Quantitative secondary ion mass spectrometry: A review. *Surf. Interf. Anal.* 2:56–74

Williams, P. 1979. The sputtering process and sputtered ion emission. *Surf. Sci.* 90:588–643

Wittmaack, K. 1980. Aspects of quantitative secondary ion mass spectrometry. *Nucl. Instr. Methods* 168:343–56

Wittry, D. B., ed. 1980. *A Bibliography of SIMS, 1958–1975*. San Francisco Press

Zinner, E. 1980. Depth profiling by secondary ion mass spectrometry. *Scanning* 3:57–78

Zinner, E., Walker, R. M. 1975. Ion-probe studies of artificially implanted ions in lunar samples. *Proc. Lunar Sci. Conf. 6th*, pp. 3601–17

Zinner, E., Walker, R. M., Chaumont, J., Dran, J. C. 1976. Ion probe analysis of artificially implanted ions in terrestrial samples and surface enhanced ions in lunar sample 76215, 77. *Proc. Lunar Sci. Conf. 7th*, pp. 953–84

Zinner, E., Walker, R. M., Chaumont, J., Dran, J. C. 1977. Ion probe surface concentration measurements of Mg and Fe and microcraters in crystals from lunar rock and soil samples. *Proc. Lunar Sci. Conf. 8th*, pp. 3859–83

Zinner, E., Dust, S., Chaumont, J., Dran, J. C. 1978. Surface concentration of Mg, Ti, Fe and surface features in individual plagioclase from lunar soil samples. *Proc. Lunar Planet. Sci. Conf. 9th*, pp. 1667–86

AUTHOR INDEX

(Names appearing in capital letters indicate authors of chapters in this volume.)

D

L

CUMULATIVE INDEXES

CONTRIBUTING AUTHORS VOLUMES 6–10

CHAPTER TITLES VOLUMES 6–10

OCEANOGRAPHY, ATMOSPHERIC SCIENCE, AND PALEOCLIMATOLOGY